Jackie Belwood

8.00
7.20

D1413509

PACIFIC FISHES
OF CANADA

Fishes with their bizarre forms and hidden ways attract artists — Canadian painter David Denbigh here portrays the mystery of lingcod lurking at the bottom. (Reproduced courtesy of Dr K. S. Ketchen)

Bulletin 180

Pacific Fishes
of Canada

J. L. Hart

St. Andrews, N.B.

FISHERIES RESEARCH BOARD

OF CANADA   *Ottawa 1973*

Bulletins of the Fisheries Research Board of Canada are designed to assess and interpret current knowledge in scientific fields pertinent to Canadian fisheries.

The Board also publishes the *Journal of the Fisheries Research Board of Canada* in annual volumes of monthly issues, an *Annual Report*, and a biennial *Review* of investigations. The *Journal* and *Bulletins* are for sale by Information Canada, Ottawa. Remittances must be in advance, payable in Canadian funds to the order of the Receiver General of Canada. Publications may be consulted at Board establishments located at Ottawa; Nanaimo, Vancouver and West Vancouver, B.C.; Winnipeg, Man.; Ste. Anne de Bellevue, Que.; St. Andrews, N.B.; Halifax and Dartmouth, N.S.; and St. John's, Nfld.

Editor and Director of Scientific Information   J. C. STEVENSON, PH.D.

Associate Editor   L. W. BILLINGSLEY, PH.D.

Assistant Editors   R. H. WIGMORE, M.SC.
J. WATSON, PH.D.

Production   R. L. MACINTYRE/MONA SMITH, B.H.SC.
C. W. SHINNERS, B.A.

Documentation   J. CAMP

Department of the Environment
Fisheries Research Board of Canada
Office of the Editor, 116 Lisgar Street
Ottawa, Canada
K1A 0H3

Contents

DESCRIPTION OF COLOUR ILLUSTRATIONS: FACING PAGE 434

Editor's Foreword

In 1946 the Fisheries Research Board of Canada published
Bulletin 68, "Fishes of the Pacific Coast of Canada," by
W. A. Clemens and G. V. Wilby. A revised version was issued
in 1949, and a second edition was published in 1961. It remained
the only authoritative work on Canadian Pacific fishes for over
25 years. Since 1961 much new information on the fish fauna
has been recorded, and more than 54 new species have been
identified.

The Fisheries Research Board asked Dr John L. Hart to prepare
a book incorporating this new knowledge and new species.
This Bulletin, "Pacific Fishes of Canada," is the result of four
years' work by Dr Hart. He started with the Board in 1929 and
gained prominence for his wide research accomplishments on
factors controlling supply and availability of commercial fish
species, and in later years, as a research administrator. He retired
as Director of the St. Andrews, New Brunswick, Biological
Station, in 1967.

During the preparation of this book, Dr Hart worked at the
Department of Zoology, The University of British Columbia. A
valuable addition to this book are the all-new drawings prepared
under the author's direct supervision, and the inclusion of specially
arranged colour photographs of selected species.

Dr Hart now lives in retirement at St. Andrews, New Brunswick.

J. C. STEVENSON, *Editor and*
Director of Scientific Information

Ottawa 1973

BACKGROUND INFORMATION

INTRODUCTION

The 1946 and 1961 editions of Fishes of the Pacific Coast of Canada by Clemens and Wilby supplied a much-needed compilation for fisheries workers on the north-central part of the west coast of North America. Partly because of its success in stimulating discovery, the second edition is now becoming out of date and further expansion and revision are indicated. Although it may appear unwise to quarrel with success, several changes in species accounts have been introduced. The careful descriptions of early recognition of each species in the region have served their purpose well and will remain available without repetition, so they have been dropped. Derivations of scientific names are included. The treatments of life history have been expanded in many cases. Ranges along the Pacific coast of North America have been revised in most cases to indicate total distributions. General landing statistics have been provided for species of commercial importance. Practically all air-brush drawings have been replaced by stipple drawings so as to promote uniformity in presentation. Fish paintings have been replaced by colour photographs of important or interesting species. A gazetteer has been added to give longitudes and latitudes of places named in the text, some of which are difficult to find. A condensed account of the pertinent oceanography of the area has been included.

ACKNOWLEDGMENTS

Preparation of this handbook has relied greatly on the goodwill and active cooperation of many individuals and organizations. However, in expressing his deep gratitude, the author is in no way sharing responsibility for errors either in fact or in judgment.

The greatest debt is to the late Dr W. A. Clemens and the late Mr G. V. Wilby, co-authors of the parent handbook, Fishes of the Pacific Coast of Canada, whose information has been freely drawn upon in many ways.

The handbook has been rewritten under an agreement with The University of British Columbia through its Department of Zoology. The author is much indebted to The University for the use of its facilities, and notably to Dr W. S. Hoar, Head of the Department, and Mr W. W. Coward, executive assistant, for their gracious support in supplying amenities essential to the work, and for the attitude engendered among the graduate students. Members of the Fisheries Institute (later the Institute of Animal Resource Ecology), Drs P. A. Larkin, J. D. McPhail, and N. J. Wilimovsky permitted free use of the fish collection and fisheries library, and on occasion supplied specialist consultation.

Dr D. E. McAllister, Curator of Fishes of the National Museum of Natural Sciences, and his associate Mr C. G. Gruchy, not only met requests for information and specimens in a most encouraging way but also volunteered help and advice on points of special interest. Dr A. E. Peden, postdoctoral fellow in the group, who had already shown helpful interest when a graduate student at the University of Texas, continued to do so after his posting to the National Museums of Canada and later still as Curator of Marine Biology at British Columbia Provincial Museum. They have also reviewed parts of the text.

The staff of the Nanaimo Station of the Fisheries Research Board of Canada has shown a heartening interest in the project. Dr R. E. Foerster (sockeye salmon), Mr C. R. Forrester (flatfish), Dr K. S. Ketchen (dogfish), and Mr S. J. Westrheim (rockfishes) have reviewed parts of the manuscript to good effect, and have helped in other ways. Mr Westrheim prepared the key for the rockfishes. Mr W. E. Barraclough shared unpublished findings and gave useful advice. Mr K. V. Aro with Mrs Nora Moffat supplied the charts on the offshore distribution of Pacific salmons. Mr R. M. Wilson supplied unique information on unusual fishes and on fishing practices. I am grateful to all of these and to the former Station Director, Mr K. R. Allen, through whose good will the help was made possible. Station alumni Dr M. Waldichuk and Mr A. J. Dodimead also helped by reviewing the section on oceanography.

Dr J. M. Anderson, Director of the Fisheries Research Board's St. Andrews Biological Station (now Director-General of Research and Development, Department of the Environment) made available essential facilities at the station. Mr. J. Beckett kindly read through accounts on tunas and made many useful suggestions.

Many professional colleagues and other friends have given help of various kinds: Reeve M. Bailey, University of Michigan, names of fishes; D. M. Cohen, advice on bathylagids and myctophids, K. W. Cox, FAO, characteristics of skate egg cases; J. E. Fitch, California State Fisheries Laboratory, identity of snipe eels; W. I. Follett, California Academy of Science, illustrations of sharks and identity of gobies; R. B. Grinols, Peninsula College, zoarcids; W. R. Hourston, Department of Fisheries and Forestry (now Environment), commercial landings statistics through Blake Campbell and live salmon through Dixon McKinnon; J. G. Hunter, Fisheries Research Board of Canada, Ste. Anne de Bellevue, Pacific salmon distribution in the arctic; Samuel J. Hutchinson, International North Pacific Fisheries Commission, translations; C. R. Hitz, U.S. Bureau of Commercial Fisheries, information on skate development and pomfrets; C. L. Hubbs, La Jolla, information on hagfishes; J. E. McInerney, University of Victoria, habitat of hagfishes; G. W. Mead, formerly of the Museum of Comparative Zoology, Harvard, information on pomfrets; M. Newman, Vancouver Public Aquarium, information on behaviour of living fishes, through G. Hewlett, A. Lamb, and V. Penfold; J. W. Nicholls, Vancouver, salmon for illustrations; N. J. Nitsos, information on flathead sole; J. W. Parsons, U.S. Fish and Wildlife Service, Ann Arbor, information on Pacific salmons in the Great Lakes; J. B. Phillips, Pacific Grove, California, uniquely annotated copies of his monograph on rockfishes; J. C. Quast, U.S. Fish and Wildlife Service, Auke Bay, advance information on *Sebastes variegatus* and lingcod; R. H. Rosenblatt of Scripps Institution of Oceanography and L.-C. Chen of San Diego State College for advance information on *Sebastes babcocki;* D. Miller of the California Department of Fish and Game and his colleagues, R. Lea, D. Gotshall, and J. Geibel for initiating a valuable exchange of information; W. B. Scott, Royal Ontario Museum, friendly advice on many subjects; B. E. Skud, and F. H. Bell, International Pacific Halibut Commission, special landings statistics; International Pacific Salmon Commission, national landings statistics on Fraser River sockeye salmon; Lee Straight, Vancouver Sun, records on sizes of sport fishes; School of Fisheries, University of Washington, special information on fishes through A. C. DeLacy, D. W. Hogan, and A. D. Welander.

Librarians in three libraries at The University of British Columbia, and librarians at the University of Toronto and at The University of New Brunswick have provided sympathetic and competent help in digging out less-evident information.

Finally acknowledgment must be made of the co-workers in the project: D. R. Harriott made the drawings of the fishes, sometimes from specimens that were far from perfect; F. T. Pletcher used his special techniques and knowledge of fishes in taking the colour photographs; Mrs W. E. Young typed much of the text from impossible writing. Mrs Milly Scott applied her special talents to reading the proof and preparing the index.

DEVELOPMENT OF ICHTHYOLOGY
IN THE REGION

Although Sir John Richardson in 1836 described a pink salmon from Observatory Inlet as a new species, *Salmo scouleri* (erroneously, as it turned out), ichthyology on the Pacific coast of Canada may be considered as starting in 1857 with the collections made from HMS *Plumper*. Between 1860 and 1874 these collections were examined by Dr Albert Günther of the British Museum who based descriptions on them of five species which still stand: *Psychrolutes paradoxus, Rhamphocottus richardsoni, Anoplagonus inermis, Eumicrotremus orbis,* and *Liparis cyclopus.* The collections also included other species described first from other localities but recognized for the first time from British Columbia waters.

However, the basic work in recognizing North Pacific Basin species to be found in Canada was carried out elsewhere. The first major contributions were made by the great German naturalist G. W. Steller of the Bering expedition who accurately perceived and described in Russian the five Pacific salmons later given binomial scientific names by Walbaum. In 1810 and 1811 accounts of explorations initiated by the Russian government included descriptions by Pallas of 11 additional species now recognized from Canadian waters. Other species that occur in the northwest Pacific were described in the same year by Tilesius.

By far the largest contribution to describing fishes in the Canadian fauna was made by ichthyologists from the United States, and a third of the species were recognized and described by David Starr Jordan and Charles H. Gilbert and their associates at the focus for ichthyological ferment at Stanford University. Its influence through second and third generations continues to this day. Stanford scientists and other United States taxonomists working more or less independently described more than two-thirds of the species to be found off the coast of western Canada. Canadian specimens were considered in 28 of these new species descriptions.

European taxonomists were early in providing descriptions and names for many of the species with worldwide distributions, and some others. Nine of the species since recorded from the Pacific coast of Canada were assigned their binomial names in 1758 by Linnaeus, and other scientists continue to describe fishes that are later encountered from off the Canadian coast.

The list of fishes has been developed as a result of a long series of collections, expeditions, and individual efforts. British America Boundary Commission naturalist J. K. Lord in 1866 gave accounts of many of the fish species he encountered in his *A naturalist in Vancouver Island and British Columbia*. In 1881 Drs Jordan and Gilbert recorded findings made on a short visit to Victoria in the previous year. In 1881 and 1882 Captain H. E. Nichols of the United States Coast and Geodetic Survey vessel *Hassler* collected inshore fishes from central and northern British Columbia. The collection included three new species and the results were recorded in 1881 and 1883 by T. H. Bean. In 1885 Dr C. M. Dawson of the Canadian Geological Survey made collections in the Queen Charlotte Sound area and the results were recorded in 1887 by J. F. Whiteaves.

The survey steamer *Albatross* of the United States Fish Commission, especially equipped for work at great depths, operated briefly off the Canadian coast in 1888 and 1890 and made many collections off southern British Columbia in 1891 and 1893. For the most part the collections made, supplemented by shore collections, were recorded in Bean (1891), Gilbert (1895), and Evermann and Goldsborough (1907).

According to Clemens and Wilby (1961), "The first extensive collections of fishes to be made by a Canadian in British Columbia waters were those of Mr Ashdown Green, a civil engineer, who collected in the vicinity of Victoria. He published his records in 1891 and 1893 in the *Proceedings of the Natural History Society of British Columbia,* the first volume of which (1891) has been out of print for many years and only a few copies are extant. Mr Green's contribution to the literature included some nine first records for the Province and in recognition of his discovering a liparid new to science Drs D. S. Jordan and E. C. Starks honoured him by naming it *Neoliparis greeni,* now known as *Polypera greeni.* Mr Green's collections were the nucleus of the fish collection of the British Columbia Provincial Museum at Victoria.

"In 1898 John Fannin, first curator of the Provincial Museum, listed the fishes in the Museum, largely collected by Mr Green, and added eight new records.

"In 1900 a considerable shore collection was made on the Queen Charlotte Islands and this was listed in 1901 by W. H. Osgood, United States Department of Agriculture, Biological Survey, on the identification of Edmund Heller.

"On September 8 and 9, 1908, and from May to August, 1909, Messrs C. H. Young and W. Spreadborough collected at Departure Bay and on Barkley Sound in the vicinity of Ucluelet, adding several new distribution records. The results of these collections and some miscellaneous ones by Dr G. M. Dawson, Messrs J. H. Keen and A. Halkett, and Professor E. E. Prince, were recorded in 1920 by B. A. Bean and A. C. Weed, and the specimens obtained are now in the United States National Museum."

Throughout the history of the Fisheries Research Board Biological Station at Nanaimo, staff members and their associates have interested themselves in the life histories and identifications of fishes encountered in the course of their work. The first two directors, The Reverend G. W. Taylor and Dr C. McLean Fraser, made collections and observations, and the spinynose sculpin, *Asemichthys taylori*, was named after its discoverer in Gilbert (1912). Professor J. R. Dymond made extensive collections in 1928, and many full-time staff members contributed early records, including: W. E. Barraclough, J. L. Hart, A. L. Pritchard, and H. C. Williamson. Since 1961 new additions to the fauna have been noted by: W. E. Barraclough, N. F. Bourne, C. R. Forrester, K. S. Ketchen, F. H. C. Taylor, S. J. Westrheim, and R. M. Wilson.

To study the early life history of halibut the International Pacific Halibut Commission made many townet hauls off the west coast of Vancouver Island and the Queen Charlotte Islands. Unusual bathypelagic and pelagic fishes in the catches were described in 1939 and 1940 by W. M. Chapman. Several new species were described, but some of them have been relegated to synonymy as they have been identified with earlier-described species of the Atlantic or elsewhere.

Two series of collections were instigated by Dr W. A. Clemens to supplement information on the British Columbia fish fauna. In 1933 and 1934 G. V. Wilby collected extensively in the vicinity of Nanaimo, English Bay, and Burrard Inlet, working chiefly from commercial trawlers. In 1934 arrangements were made to have Mr E. C. Hart accommodated as a collector of fishes aboard the hydrographic survey vessel *Wm. J. Stewart*. Working with dredges and with shore collecting along the west coast of Vancouver Island, eight new species were added to the known Canadian fauna, and several ranges were extended. In 1935 collections were made in the Queen Charlotte Islands area from the *Wm. J. Stewart* under the supervision of Dr C. McLean Fraser.

In 1946, the Fisheries Research Board of Canada published *Fishes of the Pacific Coast of Canada* by Clemens and Wilby. It included records of 20 species recorded for the first time from waters of the Canadian Pacific coast. For them and each of 225 other species it provided brief descriptions, range along the North American Pacific coast, and information on its first scientific recording in the reference area. In so doing the compilation provided a stimulating reference point for recording additional knowledge. The number of published references to this work suggests a significant impact on the ichthyology of the region. However, sure appraisal of its effects is difficult because of other stimulating factors. Commitments to the International North Pacific Fisheries Commission led to cruises to study the high seas biology of salmons by Canadian and United States vessels thus providing opportunity for studies of offshore fishes. Various fishery surveys expanded information. The exercise of taxonomic interest at the Institute of Fisheries at The University of British Columbia provided an informed base for study, and the enlistment of interest among officers and crew of Department of Transport weather ships at Station "Papa" (50 N, 145 W) yielded new records and understanding. These factors in combination with the 1946 publication led to the availability of 29 additional species for inclusion in the 1961 edition of the Bulletin by Clemens and Wilby.

Since 1961 the same factors promoting increase in knowledge proved effective. They have been supplemented by the informed energy of an active fish group at the National Museum of Natural Sciences including Dr D. E. McAllister and C. G. Gruchy, and Dr A. E. Peden who has made contributions through the Institute of Fisheries as well. Workers in Canada have for the first time described new species from the Canadian Pacific Coast (C. G. Gruchy, J. D. McPhail, A. E. Peden, and S. J. Westrheim and H. Tsuyuki). The last named applied successfully new methods of species recognition and discrimination. Further contributions to the fish taxonomy of the region have been made by United States systematists. As a net result the number of species now listed for the area is about 329. It seems fitting that a new species of gunnel described by Rosenblatt in 1964 should have been named *Pholis clemensi*.

More details on some aspects of the ichthyology of the region are available in Clemens and Wilby (1961), Dymond (1964), Hubbs (1964), and Jordan (1931).

OCEANOGRAPHY

Distribution of fishes on the Pacific Coast of Canada is determined by movements and properties of the waters of the North Pacific Ocean. Many fishes are considered to be subject to passive transfer by currents during some periods of their life cycles. All have specific tolerances of temperature, salinity, oxygen, etc., which affect or limit their efficiency to compete or to survive. Because relationships among fishes and between fish and environment are complex, and because conditions within the environment are by no means simple or stable, the influence of environment on fish distribution is usually difficult to evaluate. Relationships are, however, important enough to be continually examined. Some of the general oceanographic features of the Pacific waters most affecting Canadian fishes are described below.

Two ocean *regions*[8] of the north Pacific most concern Canadian fishes: (1) A "Subtropical Region" south of latitude 42 N in which the salinity is a maximum at the surface and decreases to a distinct minimum below 500 meters depth. The stability of the water column depends upon the temperature structure. It includes along its northern boundary the strong, warm-flowing Kuroshio and the warm eastward-flowing North Pacific Current. It is the characteristic home of the tunas. (2) More closely related to Canadian fishes is a "Subarctic Region," bounded about by 42 N in the central Pacific and extending south to 40 N near the Asian coast and rather farther south near the American coast. The region is characterized by a relatively marked salinity gradient (halocline) between about 100 and 200 meters depth, above which the thermocline, which develops in summer,

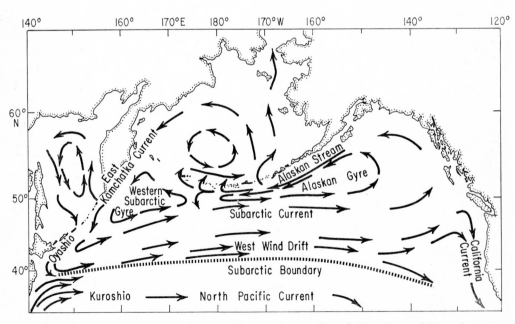

Surface currents in the North Pacific Ocean (after Dodimead, Favorite, and Hirano).

contributes to the stability of the water column. In winter, the thermocline is absent, and the stability of the water column is entirely dependent upon the halocline. An isohaline structure denoted by the 34‰ isohaline is considered to be the boundary between the two distinct regions.[8]

The Subarctic Region is considered to include the marine ranges of the Pacific salmons and steelhead trout. Within it salmon respond to seasonal and annual changes in water temperatures by making north and south migrations so that each species of salmon may remain within its own limits of preference during both marine summer and winter. Similarly the Pacific pomfret occurs farther south in winter than in summer.[15]

Within the Subarctic Region *domains* may be recognized. These have more or less consistent properties of structure, flow, depth, and locality but show quantitative variations from year to year and with season.[8]

The *Western Subarctic Domain* is found in the western Bering Sea and west of 180 longitude in the Pacific. It includes three anticlockwise "gyres" or eddies in the Bering and Okhotsk seas and in the western Pacific Ocean, and the southward-flowing cold Kamchatka Current and the Oyashio. The domain is characterized by water temperatures less than 3.5 C at the bottom of the upper zone (defined as the isohaline, isothermal surface layer formed in winter as a result of cooling and turnover[8]).

The *Transitional Domain* is immediately north of the Subarctic boundary, with its northern limit characterized by the 7 C isotherm at the bottom of the upper zone. It is dominated by the "West Wind Drift," a zonal flow toward the east arising as a partial confluence of Oyashio and Kuroshio off the Asian coast. The surface waters are warmer than 15 C in summer and 7 C in winter, and rather highly saline. Both temperatures and salinities tend to be lower toward North America. About 300 miles (480 km) off the American coast the West Wind Drift divides, part turns northward into the Gulf of Alaska, the remainder turns south forming the California Current.[8,17] The position of the division into northern and southern branches changes, which fact combining with variations in runoff, winds, and tides, keeps conditions in coastal waters continually and rapidly changing.[14]

The *Central Subarctic Domain* lies north of the transitional domain and east of the western subarctic domain. It includes the trans-Pacific Subarctic Current stemming from the Oyashio in the western subarctic domain, and the counterclockwise Alaskan gyre.

The *Alaskan Stream Domain* is characterized by relatively warm low-salinity water and is dominated by the fast-flowing Alaskan Stream moving westward along the south side of the Aleutian Islands.

The *Coastal Domain* lines the perimeter of the North Pacific Basin. Its waters show a wide variety of properties and are much subject to effects of wind, tide, and runoff.

The California Current runs slowly southward at speeds less than a kilometer per hour, the surface waters becoming further warmed by the sun and by mixing with warm waters to the westward as it flows southward. Eventually it swings west to join the North Equatorial Current. Below it, deeper than 200 meters, the warm, saline California Counter Current runs northwest from Baja California to somewhere north of Cape Mendocino.[17] Sometimes the counter current forms at the surface in winter, well on the inshore side of the main stream, and extends north of Point Conception. At various places along the Oregon and California coasts cool, deep ocean water upwells to the surface and moves offshore as a result of wind action.[17,21] Along the southern part of Vancouver Island the movement is generally northwest.[9,17,20] Mechanisms for passive transport of fishes between British Columbia and California and back seem to exist if conditions in the moving water masses allow survival.

Fresh turbid water from the *Fraser River* mixes with sea water in the Strait of Georgia. In summer when runoff and insolation are at a peak, a great labile brackish lake, rich in nutrients, becomes strongly established in the southern strait, sometimes extending to Vancouver Island and Hornby Island.[13] There is a general seaward movement of the discharged water through the passes among the San Juan Islands and the Canadian Gulf Islands, where strong tidal turbulence leads to thorough mixing. Beyond the mixing area, the diluted sea water moves on the surface through Juan de Fuca Strait entraining more saline water from below in its passage to the open ocean. The more saline water which is thus carried out of the strait is replaced by the action of a deep counter current.[12] The lake of mixed water in southern Strait of Georgia supports abundant plankton growth, which in turn supports a wide variety of fishes.[1,2,3,4,18,19] In addition, the currents in and out of the Strait of Georgia provide passive transport for migrating species.[5] Similar but less demonstrable systems occur at the outlets of other rivers.

Many of the *deep inlets* of the British Columbia coast are fiords characterized by deep basins behind relatively shallow sills.[7] Where there are ample sources of fresh water at the heads of such inlets, oxygen saturations at depth become only moderately reduced and minima may occur either at the bottom or at intermediate depths.[10,16] However, in the few places where freshwater sources are inadequate, modification of the circulation inside the sill may lead to accumulation of stagnant water containing hydrogen sulphide and little or no oxygen at the bottom.[5,11] In such cases long inlets and fiords may tend to isolate populations at their heads by impeding or inhibiting movements of bottom fishes.

References   1, 2, 3, Barraclough 1967a, b, c; 4 Barraclough and Fulton 1967; 5 Barraclough and Waldichuk 1954; 6 Birman 1960; 7 Carter 1932; 8 Dodimead, Favorite, and Hirano 1963; 9 Doe 1955; 10 Gilmartin 1962; 11 Herlinveaux 1961; 12 Herlinveaux and Tully 1961; 13 Hutchinson, Lucas, and McPhail 1929; 14 Lane 1962; 15 Neave and Hanavan 1960; 16 Pickard 1961; 17 Reid, Roden, and Wyllie 1958; 18, 19 Robinson, Barraclough, and Fulton 1968a, b; 20 Tully 1942; 21 Wickett 1967.

CANADIAN MANAGEMENT OF PACIFIC FISH RESOURCES

The management and development of fish resources in Canada is the primary responsibility of the federal Department of the Environment, formerly the Department of Fisheries and Forestry, and earlier still the Department of Fisheries. Pacific coast headquarters for conservation and protection, resource development, inspection, and processing statistics is situated in Vancouver, B.C., and officers are stationed throughout western Canada. Some aspects of the Department's work have been assigned to other agencies.

Responsibilities for research functions in general are assigned to the Fisheries Research Board of Canada which maintains a biological station at Nanaimo operating research vessels and field stations, a laboratory for fish biochemistry, bacteriology, and technology in Vancouver, and a pollution and ecology laboratory in West Vancouver.

Fisheries of the Canadian Pacific region are concerns for three international commissions. The oldest, dealing with research and management of halibut, is the International Pacific Halibut Commission established by an agreement between Canada and the United States. The headquarters for the Commission is at the University of Washington in Seattle.

The fisheries for sockeye and pink salmon of the Fraser River are investigated and managed by the International Pacific Salmon Fisheries Commission with its headquarters in New Westminster, B.C. The convention establishing the Commission is between Canada and the United States. Because salmon are anadromous and have a long inshore migration route to the Fraser River either party to the agreement could over-fish the resources. Accordingly, an important responsibility of the Commission is to recommend regulation which will equalize catches on a national basis without imposing unreasonable economic hardships on the fisheries.

The International North Pacific Fisheries Commission involving Canada, Japan, and the United States has its headquarters in Vancouver, B.C. Its work is directed to promoting scientific study useful in maintaining high sustained productivity in fisheries of common concern to the contracting parties. Much of the interest is at present directed to salmons and the ranges of various stocks in their high seas migrations.

SCOPE OF COVERAGE

This book includes the fishes found in salt water off the Canadian coast. A few freshwater fishes observed as larvae in estuaries were omitted, but carp is included since individuals clearly recognizable by resemblance to adults were taken far from likely sources in fresh water. The seaward limits of inclusion are only vaguely defined and probably inconsistently observed. Fishes likely to be taken by Canadian vessels and those included in Clemens and Wilby (1961) have been admitted. In general this book follows the policy of Clemens and Wilby in not attempting to anticipate published records. However, there are exceptions. *Bryozoichthys marjorius* has been taken only north of the boundary with Alaska, and *Amphistichus koelzi* only south of the international boundary with the State of Washington. The occurrences of *Xenomystax atrarius*, *Squatina californica*, and *Acantholiparis opercularis* are anticipated in the keys but no species accounts are provided. The most recent records from off the Canadian coast of *Bathyraja trachura*, *Bothrocara pusillum*, *Embryx crotalina*, *Stellerina xyosterna*, *Xeneretmus leiops*, and *Xenomystax atrarius*, are mentioned only in footnotes to the keys of their respective families, etc. In addition to the species mentioned above others have been recorded from waters both north and south of British Columbia, viz., *Raja rosispinis*, *Zesticelus profundorum*, *Careproctus cypselurus*, *Paraliparis dactylosus*, *Paraliparis ulochir*, *Rhinoliparis attenuatus*, *Rhinoliparis barbulifer*. It seems probable that several or most of these demersal fishes will eventually be taken off the Canadian coast. Several additional bathypelagic species have been recorded from well off the Canadian coast: *Hierops crockeri*, *Lampanyctus jordani*, and *Gonostoma gracile*. They were not included by Clemens and Wilby nor are they included in this compilation.

9

This book provides descriptions of 325 kinds of fishes. Of these, 271 were included in Clemens and Wilby (1961). The brook trout (*Salvelinus fontinalis*) of Clemens and Wilby has been dropped as no convincing saltwater record could be found. The Atlantic salmon is retained on the basis of one questionably identified old saltwater specimen. It is the one figured in the text where it will be an affront to Maritimes idolaters of a noble species. The 54 new kinds of fishes described in this book are: *Eptatretus deani*, black hagfish; *Carcharodon carcharias*, white shark; *Serrivomer jesperseni*, crossthroat sawpalate; *Avocettina infans*, closespine snipe eel; *Macdonaldia challengeri*, longnose tapirfish; *Allosmerus elongatus*, whitebait smelt; *Spirinchus starksi*, night smelt; *Nansenia candida*, bluethroat argentine; *Bathylagus ochotensis*, eared blacksmelt; *Dolichopteryx* sp., winged spookfish; *Sagamichthys abei*, shining tubeshoulder; *Scopelosaurus harryi*, scaly wearyfish; *Cyprinus carpio*, carp; *Chaenophryne parviconus*, smooth dreamer; *Oneirodes acanthias*, spiny dreamer; *Bothrocara brunneum*, twoline eelpout; *Bothrocara remigerum*, longsnout eelpout; *Lycenchelys jordani*, shortjaw eelpout; *Lycodapus grossidens*, bigtooth eelpout; *Melanostigma pammelas*, Pacific softpout; *Coryphaenoides liocephalus*, bearded rattail; *Coryphaenoides pectoralis*, pectoral rattail; *Atherinops affinis affinis*, topsmelt; *Roccus saxatilis*, striped bass; *Caulolatilus princeps*, ocean whitefish; *Amphistichus koelzi*, calico surfperch; *Hyperprosopon ellipticum*, silver surfperch; *Anoplarchus insignis*, slender cockscomb; *Bryozoichthys marjorius*, pearly prickleback; *Lumpenus maculatus*, daubed shanny; *Pholis clemensi*, longfin gunnel; *Pholis schultzi*, red gunnel; *Sebastes aurora*, aurora rockfish; *Sebastes babcocki*, redbanded rockfish; *Sebastes borealis*, shortraker rockfish; *Sebastes ciliatus*, dusky rockfish; *Sebastes emphaeus*, Puget Sound rockfish; *Sebastes entomelas*, widow rockfish; *Sebastes goodei*, chilipepper; *Sebastes helvomaculatus*, rosethorn rockfish; *Sebastes jordani*, shortbelly rockfish; *Sebastes reedi*, yellowmouth rockfish; *Sebastes variegatus*, harlequin rockfish; *Sebastolobus altivelis*, longspine thornyhead; *Artedius meanyi*, Puget Sound sculpin; *Icelinus burchami*, dusky sculpin; *Icelinus oculatus*, frogmouth sculpin; *Icelus spiniger*, thorny sculpin; *Nautichthys robustus*, smallsail sculpin; *Paricelinus hopliticus*, thornback sculpin; *Radulinus boleoides*, darter sculpin; *Occella impi*, pixie poacher; *Liparis mucosus*, slimy snailfish; and *Reinhardtius hippoglossoides*, Greenland halibut or turbot.

Seven of the additional species have been described since 1961: *Bryozoichthys marjorius* McPhail, 1970; *Pholis clemensi* Rosenblatt, 1964; *Sebastes borealis* Barsukov, 1970; *Sebastes reedi* Westrheim and Tsuyuki, 1967; *Sebastes variegatus* Quast, 1971; *Nautichthys robustus* Peden, 1970; and *Occella impi* Gruchy, 1970. Also recorded is a suspected new species of *Dolichopteryx* still to be described.

The arrangement of species follows that proposed by Greenwood et al. (1966) as interpreted by Bailey et al. (1970). Common names recommended by the latter authors were used when available. Otherwise names were based on describers' recommendations or informal usage, or when necessary, they were coined in the Bailey et al. style.

Of the 325 species considered in the book, 68 had ranges terminating off the Pacific coast of Canada, with the northern limit off Canada in 53 cases, and the southern limit in 13. Two additional species, *Asemichthys taylori* and *Allolumpenus hypochromus*, have their whole known range in British Columbia. Four other species are known from only one specimen or from two or three specimens taken together off the west coast of Canada: *Coryphaenoides cyclolepis*, *Coryphaenoides filifera*, *Occella impi*, and *Careproctus ovigerum*. Each of the remaining species was found both north and south of the reference area off British Columbia, or the distribution could not be assessed because data were scarce. Some species occur around the North Pacific basin or in more than one ocean.

10

DESCRIPTION OF A SPECIES

Each species account is headed by the common name followed by the scientific name and comments on the derivations of names and their previous use in Clemens and Wilby's two publications. Scientific names are changed for two main reasons. Continual study of fishes leads systematists to discover new relations among fish kinds that are reflected in scientific naming — usually in generic names. To avoid utter chaos there is a rule that the species name first properly assigned to a kind of fish is the only valid one, and that others even when applied in another locality must give way to it. Careful research has often indicated that kinds of fishes recognized in the eastern Pacific were described earlier, and accordingly, the species names have to be changed. Common names for European and other Atlantic fishes have frequently been applied to Pacific species that were more or less similar, thus leading to possible confusion. The American Fisheries Society Committee on Common and Scientific Names of Fishes is developing and applying new names in order to reduce continuing ambiguities. It is hoped that the comments on Canadian species will forestall some irritating confusion.

A general section of description deals with shape and other miscellaneous characters that help in conveying the appearance of the fish or to distinguish it from other species. Most measurements and counts are based on the definitions in Hubbs and Lagler (1958). The characters are mentioned in the glossary, and the positions of the spines and cirri are shown in the illustration. Except where ascribed to a reference, measurements and counts should not be used for critical comparisons.

Observations on head spines, fins, and counts of gill rakers and vertebrae (without hypural) when given, are set off in separate paragraphs. Features of the integument such as scales, cirri, barbels, photophores, and pores are dealt with in a separate paragraph, as are descriptions of colour.

Size records the largest individual of a species encountered — usually with a statement of greatest total length, but sometimes the greatest weight. When available information suggests that record size may be misleading, additional information on usual sizes or sizes in various localities is included. Information taken from Clemens and Wilby is based on total length measurements with the tail in normal position rather than with the tail compressed from above and below as recommended by Hubbs and Lagler.

A section on recognition can be used in making quick identifications, although the results of its use must be subject to confirmation.

Comments on life history are given in very condensed form for some of the species that have been much studied; for others the section gives an indication of the scarcity of knowledge.

Total range and distribution in British Columbia are presented in one section, and utilization in industry and/or economic significance in another.

In order to avoid breaks in the text disturbing to nontechnical readers, references are indicated by index numbers that in turn are identified with authors' names and dates at the end of each species account. Authors' names, dates, titles, and journals are listed alphabetically in the References at the end of the book.

Much of the information in this compilation has been taken from Fishes of the Pacific Coast of Canada by Clemens and Wilby. Information from this source has not been acknowledged unless interpretations have differed or there were other special circumstances. As references to sources of information and interpretations in Clemens and Wilby (1961) are not always clear, the bibliography of those authors is alphabetized with new references and entries marked with an asterisk when not referred to in the current text. References to Canadian records are included in the reference list even when trivial.

KEYS

Analytical keys to help in recognizing species are provided at three levels. The first key on page 15 allows the assignment of a fish to a major category: Class or Subclass. Keys to each of the subclasses carry the identification to family — in many cases these keys employ relatively unimportant characters suitable for separating the fishes in the local fauna, and as a result they should be used with caution in other regions or with species new to the fauna. When, as is often the case, only one species of the family is recognized in the book, the identification is completed by reference to the family. In other cases, keys to the family are provided and they carry the identification to species. In arranging family keys, fishes of the same genus were arranged in a group and the generic name shown in the key.

In all the keys the user is presented with a series of numbered alternatives. When a decision is made on which alternative applies to the fish in question, the user may follow the directions along the right hand margin to turn to the appropriate page or to the next step in the key.

IDENTIFICATION AND CLASSIFICATION OF FISHES

All species of the animal kingdom that resemble each other in important features are assigned to large separate groups called Phyla (singular Phylum). An important phylum is the Chordata whose members share in common at some stage of their existence a firm rod called the notochord, which supports the longitudinal axis of the body. In some Chordata the notochord remains unmodified or becomes inconspicuous in older individuals. In others it becomes modified by the association of cartilaginous or bony segments called vertebrae, which support the notochord and frequently replace it. These latter animals, the so-called higher Chordata, are grouped together under the name Vertebrata, and include such "Classes" as jawless fishes, cartilaginous fishes, bony fishes, amphibians, reptiles, birds, and mammals. This account deals with the classes of vertebrates that characteristically live in water and use the gas dissolved in water to meet their needs for oxygen, i.e. the first three named above.

SPECIES ACCOUNTS

KEY TO CLASSES
AND SUBCLASSES

1   Mouth without jaws; one median nostril; body more or less cylindrical; no paired fins or scales; gill openings porelike; gill openings 1 to 14 .... Class Agnatha, p. 16

or   1   Jaws present; nostrils paired; paired pelvic and/or pectoral fins present; gill openings usually as slits, or covered by a flaplike operculum; body in a wide variety of shapes, with or without scales 2

2   Gill openings 5 to 7, on sides or undersurface; body without overlapping scales, frequently with rough denticles .... Class Chondrichthyes, Subclass Elasmobranchii, p. 24

or   2   One gill opening on each side of head, covered by an operculum 3

3   Operculum without bones; dorsal fin with a long sharp spine; teeth fused to form a grinding plate; mouth inferior; caudal fin continuing to a point .... Class Chondrichthyes, Subclass Holocephali, p. 65

or   3   Operculum a bony flap; fins supported by rays that are usually joined by membranes, erectile, and flexible .... Class Osteichthyes, p. 68

CLASS AGNATHA
(Cyclostomata, Marsipobranchii)

Elongate cylindrical animals, without jaws, ribs, or paired fins and girdles. Teeth are horny. The skeleton is cartilaginous, without centra, an unsegmented notochord, and with an incompletely developed cranium. There are six to 14 pairs of gill pouches, supported by a more-or-less developed cartilaginous branchial basket; the inner openings may be direct into the pharynx or into a common tube joining the mouth below the gullet, the pouches opening either direct to the side of the fish or through a single aperture near the midventral line. There are no scales. There is a single nostril. There is no cloaca, so the genital opening is separate. The group is oviparous and some are morphologically but not functionally hermaphroditic. They are scavengers, parasites, or predators on larger fishes. **Hagfishes** and **lampreys.**

KEY TO THE CLASS AGNATHA

	1	Gill pores on each side of body 10 to 14; eyes covered with skin; 8 barbels around mouth and nostril; mouth a fleshy funnel ...... Order Myxiniformes 2
or	1	Gill pores on each side of body 7; eyes not covered with skin; no barbels around mouth; mouth a toothed sucking disc .... Order Petromyzoniformes 3
	2	Distance from snout to first gill opening 3.6 to 4.5 into total length; prebranchial slime pores 10 to 16; colour tan; eye spot indistinct .... *Eptatretus stouti,* Pacific hagfish, p 18
or	2	Distance from snout to first gill opening 5.4 to 6.6 into total length; prebranchial slime pores 4 to 10; colour black; eye spot conspicuous .... *Eptatretus deani,* Black hagfish, p. 17
	3	Supraoral bar with 3 cusps; lateral horny plates in mouth in 4 pairs (see figure on page 20) .... *Lampetra tridentatus,* Pacific lamprey, p. 20
or	3	Supraoral bar with 2 cusps; lateral horny plates in mouth in 3 pairs (see figure on page 22) .... *Lampetra ayresi,* River lamprey, p. 22

ORDER MYXINIFORMES
(Hyperotreta)

Primitive or degenerate marine animals with six to 15 gill pouches with individual openings or a common opening to the outside, barbels on nostrils and mouth, a single nostril opening through to the mouth, which is not funnel-like and has an evertible tongue with two rows of teeth. The eyes are rudimentary. There is a single fin around the posterior profile. There is a well-marked series of mucous pores along the side. Eggs are few and large. The young do not go through a metamorphosis. **Hagfishes.**

BLACK HAGFISH

Eptatretus deani (Evermann and Goldsborough 1907)

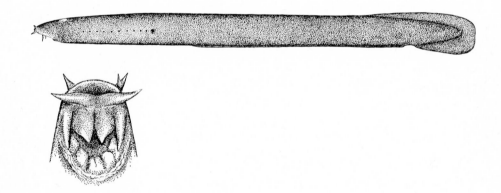

Scientific names from the Greek roots *(h)epta* (seven) and *tretos* (apertures); and from Bashford Dean, U.S. ichthyologist and bibliographer.

Description Body very elongate, cylindrical, compressed posteriorly, depth about 14 into total length. Head short. Snout pointed, depressed. Mouth a fleshy funnel, 4 horny plates inside, 2 above with 12 or 13 teeth, 2 below with 10 or 11 teeth. One dorsal median tooth. Nostril single, large, slitlike, median, terminal, opening into phar-ynx. Barbels around mouth 4, around nostril 4. (Sometimes one barbel branched.) Eyes not evident but positions well marked by large whitish areas with lengths about 2 percent of total length (with pink veins in life). Gill apertures (10)11(12), without sharply contrasting rings. The last aperture may be greatly expanded. Distance from tip of snout to first gill pore 5.4 to 6.6 into total length. Length of branchial region from first to last gill pore 6.1 to 7.6 into total length. Anus large, near posterior end of body.

Fins   No true fins. Dorsal finfold (1), far back, median, very low, continuous with caudal. Caudal moderately broad and round with raylike markings. Ventral finfold very low, origin somewhat posterior to last gill aperture, extending to anus.

Skin   Thin, smooth, loose. Mucous sacs numerous, about 79 in single series along each side of body.

Colour   Prune coloured, becoming black on preservation in alcohol, rarely tan. Frequently piebald with light spots. The very edges of caudal and ventral finfolds may be light coloured.

Size   Total length to 25 inches (63.5 cm).

Recognition   No visible eyes, paired fins, jaws, or toothed sucking disc. Flat pointed snout bearing eight barbels, small fleshy sucking disc, 11 or 12 gill pores on each side, large anus remote from head. Distance from tip of snout to first gill opening 5.4 to 6.6 into total length.[4]

Distribution   Recorded from southern California to southeastern Alaska at depths of 85 fathoms (156 m)[2] in Washington to 585 fathoms (1070 m) or deeper in California.[3,6] Canadian records at 90 fathoms (165 m) in Queen Charlotte Sound. (51.47 N, 129.58 W)[1] and 373 meters off the west coast of Vancouver Island (48.53 N, 126.40 W).[5] Recorded from mid-depths over deep water off Canada and California.

References   1 Bourne and McAllister 1969; 2 Evermann and Goldsborough 1907; 3 Grinols 1965a; 4 Hubbs personal communication; 5 McAllister personal communication; 6 Phillips 1935.

PACIFIC HAGFISH

Eptatretus stouti (Lockington 1878)

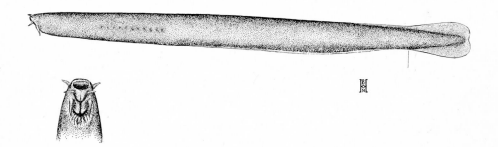

Scientific names from the Greek roots *(h)epta* (seven) and *tretos* (apertures); and from Dr Stout, corresponding secretary of the California Academy of Science.

This species was recorded as *Polistotrema stoutii* in Clemens and Wilby 1961.

Description   Body elongate, cylindrical, compressed posteriorly. Depth about 13 into length. Head short. Snout pointed, depressed. Mouth a fleshy funnel. Horny plates with cusps on roof of mouth and on tongue. Nostril single, large, median, terminal, opening into pharynx. Barbels, around mouth 4, around nostril 4. Eyes not visible but position often marked with small light areas with lengths about one percent of total length. Gill apertures (11)12(13), evident as white rings. Distance from tip of snout to first gill pore 3.6 to 4.5 into total length.[6] Length of branchial region from first to last gill pore about 7.8 into total length.[3] Anus large, near posterior end of body.

Fins   No true fins. Dorsal finfold (1), far back, median, very low, continuous with caudal. Caudal broad, rounded. Ventral finfold very low, origin somewhat posterior to last gill pore, extending to anus. No paired fins.

Skin   Thin, smooth, loose. Mucous sacs numerous in a single series on either side of the body.

Colour   Dark brown, tan, gray, or brownish red, often tinted with blue or purple, never black, lighter ventrally, rarely with large patches of white. Light brown in preservation.

Size   Length to 25 inches (63.5 cm).

Recognition   No visible eyes, paired fins, jaws, or toothed sucking disc. Flat pointed snout bearing eight barbels, small fleshy sucking disc, 10 to 14 gill pores on each side. Large anus remote from head. Distance from tip of snout to first gill opening 3.6 to 4.5 into total length.

Life History   The life history is not well known. Each egg is enclosed in a transparent horny capsule about 1.3 inches (33 mm) long and 0.4 inch (10 mm) wide. Tufts of short hooked spines at the ends of the egg cases serve for attachment to sea-weeds and to each other.[2] When disturbed Pacific hagfish produce an incredible amount of mucilaginous slime. Evidently it makes poor use of the food it ingests.[8] Pacific hagfish were caught in traps in some numbers in Mayne Bay, Barkley Sound, in October, on bottom, in about 20 fathoms (37 m). The bottom was fine silt and clay with small quantities of sand. At 30 meters temperatures were between 10.4 and 10.6 C, salinities between 31.1 and 31.7‰, and dissolved oxygen between 2.7 and 3.4‰.[7] Hagfish live on the viscera and muscles of larger fishes, such as cod, dogfish, blackcod, lingcod, perch, flounders, and salmon.[8] It enters by the mouth or anus, eating away the body of the fish while protected by its skin. As many as four hagfish have been found in a dogfish skin.[1]

Distribution   Recorded from southern California to southeastern Alaska, at depths from 516 fathoms (944 m) off Washington to 43 fathoms (79 m) off Oregon, and 10 to 456 fathoms (18–835 m) in California.[5] In British Columbia it is recorded off and in Barkley Sound and is probably quite generally distributed.[1,4] Alaska records have not been confirmed in recent reviews.

Place in Economy   By destroying large commercial fishes caught in various fixed gears, Pacific hagfish are a serious nuisance to fishing operations. At Monterey, California, losses of up to 41 percent of lingcod caught in trammel nets and 19 to 28 percent of other species such as salmon are reported.[8] Success of hagfish in attacking fishes not restrained by gear is unknown. Hagfish have a primitive metabolism[7] and for that reason are sought for biochemical and physiological research.

References   1 Barraclough 1948a; 2 Cox 1963; 3 Evermann and Goldsborough 1907; 4 Fannin 1898; 5 Grinols 1965a; 6 McAllister 1960; 7 McInerney and Evans 1970; 8 Phillips 1935.

Relatively unspecialized freshwater or anadromous animals with seven gill pouches opening separately to the exterior, and internally opening to a common respiratory tube connected anteriorly to the mouth. There are no barbels and the nostril is blind. The mouth is a disclike funnel with a fringed lip and armed with horny teeth. The dorsal finfold is separated from the caudal fin. There is no row of prominent mucous pores along the side and the eyes have both lenses and irises. The young have a long larval period before going through metamorphosis. Eggs are small and numerous. **Lampreys.**

PACIFIC LAMPREY

Lampetra tridentatus (Gairdner *in* Richardson 1836)

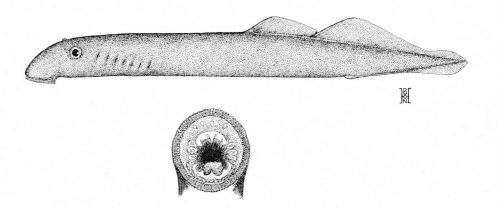

Scientific names from the Latin *lambere* (to suck), and *petra* (stone); and *tridentatus* (three-toothed).

Description   Body very elongate, depth about 10 or more into standard length, cylindrical anteriorly, somewhat compressed in posterior half. Head vaguely delimited, without jaws. Mouth a funnel-like disc, directed downward, with a margin of leaflike lamillae. The interior surface of the funnel is lined with horny so-called teeth arranged as follows: marginal series around disc with very small cusps, several supraoral teeth with small cusps on dorsal part of funnel, supraoral bar with 3 large cusps above gullet opening and continued around disc as an irregular suboral series of small single cusped teeth; laterals, 4 well-developed teeth with 1,2,2, and 1 cusp on each side of gullet; infraoral bar below gullet with about 5 well-developed cusps. There are also small rasping cusps on the tongue and the floor of the mouth, the linguals. Eye small, its diameter about 40 into total length, about 10 or

11 percent length from snout in downcurved position. No eyelids. Behind each eye a series of 7 slits opening into gill pouches, arranged in a downward sloping row starting about midway down side. The gill pouches contain filaments that are irrigated either in the usual way of passing new water over them from a respiratory duct opening from the mouth, or when the mouth is being used as a sucker, water is alternately admitted and expelled through the slitlike pore. Slightly in advance of the eyes and between them, the nasal aperture opens in a small protuberance. Behind the eyes and median is a low cavity, the so-called pineal eye. Anus posterior to point below origin of second anal finfold.

Fins There are no true fins. Two dorsal finfolds, the first begins about midlength and extends for less than a fifth of the length of the animal, rather low, abruptly passing into the second that in turn is continuous with the caudal finfold. The separation between dorsal finfolds is highly variable in both shape and extent. The caudal finfold is most prominent below the body. The finfolds have cartilaginous raylike supports. A barely discernible anal finfold extends from the vent to merge with the caudal. Pectoral and pelvic fins are not represented.

Skin There are no scales, but the skin is protected by slime produced by unicellular glands. There is a small urinogenital papilla.

Colour Dark bluish gray; red, dark brown, or gray on spawning grounds.

Size Length to 27 inches (69 cm).

Recognition Recognized by absence of jaws; seven gill pores; sucking disc with supraoral bar with three cusps, infraoral bar with five cusps, and four pairs of lateral teeth.

Life History The Pacific lamprey is anadromous. Maturing individuals enter streams from the salt water from July to October but they do not spawn until the following spring. They make their way upstream by swimming briefly against the current and then resting, sucking to rocks with their mouths. Both sexes share in nest construction by moving rocks, and by digging with rapid vibrations of the tail. The position of the nest shifts as nest construction continues between the numerous spawning acts. The elliptical eggs hatch in 2 to 4 weeks, depending on temperature (19 days at 15 C). When 2 or 3 weeks old larvae leave their nests and are carried downstream where they bury themselves in mud at the bottom of pools. They spend at least 5 years as larvae, moving from place to place, and eating diatoms, desmids, etc. They may reach a length of 110 millimeters by these steps: 0 year, 18; 1 year, 39; 2 years, 52; 3 years, 67; 4 years, 78; and 5 years 97. At about this stage (there is some uncertainty) the toothless larvae begin to transform to the adult condition. Transformation is complete at about 137 millimeters. Lampreys migrate downstream during spring and start parasitic life soon thereafter. The length of parasitic life is uncertain. Males and females take on different appearances during breeding. Males are reddish and the tail bends downward. In females the tail bends up, the finfold develops posterior to the vent and often becomes bruised during nest building; the anterior end of the second dorsal finfold becomes marked with a transparent oedema or is sometimes filled with blood, the anterior edge of the vent may become swollen, and the body wall becomes distended with spawn. Females produce between 10,000 and 106,000 eggs with an average around 34,000. Pacific lampreys die after spawning.[7]

Distribution Baja California, north of Cedros Island about 29 N, 115.25 W, in cool, upwelling water,[4] southern California[4] to Aleutian Islands[9] and Bering Sea[3,8] and Hokkaido, Japan.[5] Abundant off entire coast of British Columbia, 20 miles (32 km) off Barkley Sound.[2] Identified at various points along coast by scars on fishes, etc.[1,6]

Place in Economy The European lamprey is highly regarded as food but the

Pacific lamprey is only occasionally taken as migrants congregate at waterfalls or in canyons. They are then used fresh or are smoked by native Indians or recent arrivals from Europe.

Commercial species of marine fishes are frequently found with lamprey scars. They also parasitize freshwater fishes in Cowichan and Elsie lakes on Vancouver Island. Damage to the growth of fish and the quality of the flesh must be significant but is unassessed. There is no known estimate of the numbers of fish that are attacked and, as a result, do not survive to be captured and examined. These fish are a direct loss but the effect on sustaining the resource is less certain. However, marked fluctuations in spawning populations of fish that pass through narrow canyons of the Fraser and Bulkley rivers have been reported.[7] Lampreys and sperm whales feed on each other.[4]

References   1 Bell and Kask 1936; 2 Clemens and Wilby 1961; 3 Evermann and Goldsborough 1907; 4 Hubbs 1967; 5 Matsubara 1955; 6 Pike 1953; 7 Pletcher 1963; 8, 9 Wilimovsky 1954, 1964. Additional information can be found in Breland 1943, Eng 1949, Hubbs and Potter 1971, Seer 1937.

RIVER LAMPREY

Lampetra ayresi (Günther 1870)

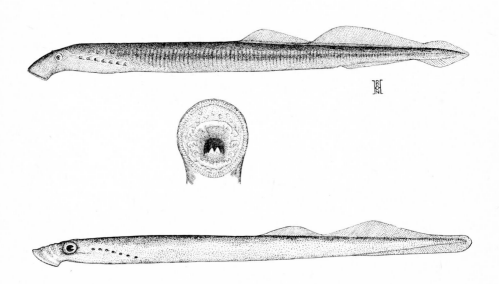

Scientific names from the Latin *lambere* (to suck) and *petra* (stone); and W. O. Ayres, U.S. ichthyologist who was first to recognize the species.

Description Body drawn out, its depth about 15 into standard length, cylindrical forward, somewhat compressed in posterior part. Head uncertainly delimited, without jaws. Mouth a funnel-like disc, directed downward, its rim lined with a row of small tubercles. The inner surface of the disc bears horny so-called teeth as follows: a marginal series is reported as continuous around inner margin of oral disc but is not easily seen in small specimens; several supraoral teeth with small cusps dorsal to the gullet; supraoral bar above gullet with large teeth on either side of gullet opening; laterals, 3 pair with teeth having 2 or 3 cusps on either side of the gullet; infraoral bar with about 8 strongly developed cusps. There are also rasping teeth on the tongue with some large cusps. Eye small, about 31 (23–43)[8] into standard length, anterior margin of orbit about 6 percent of length from end of snout in downcurved position. No eyelids. Behind each eye and slightly below, starts a series of 7 pairs of slits or gill pores arranged in a downward sloping row. Slightly anterior to the eyes and slightly raised is a single median nostril. Anus below point posterior to origin of second dorsal finfold. There are no scales.

Fins There are no true fins. The first dorsal finfold originates about midlength and extends for rather less than a fifth of the standard length, moderately high. Second dorsal finfold higher, sometimes confluent with first and with caudal. Space between dorsal finfolds highly variable. Caudal finfold barely rounded. Ventral finfold very low barely continuous with caudal. Pectoral and pelvic fins not present.

Colour Metallic blue black on dorsal surface with the colour extending on caudal finfold but not reaching margin. Pale to silver on the lower parts of sides and on ventral surface. Yellowish on finfolds.

Size Length to 12 inches (30.5 cm).

Recognition No jaws and seven gill pores. Supraoral bar with two cusps and infraoral bar with six or more cusps. Three pairs of lateral teeth.

Life History Little is known about the freshwater life of the river lamprey. It may be presumed from comparison with other species that spawning takes place in riffles and that young spend several years moving from site to site where they bury themselves in mud and live on small drifting animals and plants. Individuals 93 to 267 millimeters total length occur commonly within the freshwater influence off the mouth of the Fraser River and in Saanich Inlet.[1,2,3,4,6,7] In some samples about 20 percent of young salmon show characteristic injuries.[9] The extent of total damage to salmon stocks is uncertain. The fate of injured fish is unknown and their incidence in catches may show only the proportion of individuals in the stock that have survived attacks.

Distribution From San Francisco, California, to the Taku River and Lynn Canal in southeast Alaska, including Oregon, Washington, and British Columbia.[8] British Columbia records include Discovery Island, Porlier Pass, mouth of the Fraser River, Skeena River, and Skidegate Lake, Queen Charlotte Islands.[5]

References 1, 2 Barraclough 1967b, c; 3 Barraclough and Fulton 1967; 4 Barraclough, Robinson, and Fulton 1968; 5 Carl, Clemens, and Lindsey 1959; 6, 7 Robinson, Barraclough, and Fulton 1968a, b; 8 Vladykov and Follett 1958; 9 Withler 1955.

CLASS CHONDRICHTHYES (or SELACHII)
Cartilaginous Fishes

Highly diverse forms with cartilaginous skeletons, sometimes partly calcified, with hard teeth, and well-developed jaws placed ventrally, the upper jaw not rigidly attached to the cranium. Vertical and paired fins both present and supported by cartilaginous unjointed rays. Paired fins attached to simple girdles. Nostrils are paired and ventral; the olfactory sacs blind. Gill openings are elongate, the pouches supported by cartilaginous arches. Scales are toothlike in structure, placoid, may be absent. There is no gasbladder. **Sharks, rays, chimaeras** (ratfishes).

SUBCLASS ELASMOBRANCHII
(or EUSELACHII)

Diverse forms with five to seven pairs of gill clefts directly connecting pharynx to exterior. Teeth are numerous. A cloaca receives both anus and urogenital canal. The subclass falls into two natural divisions: the sharks with lateral gill clefts, and the skates and rays with gill clefts wholly ventral and no free eyelids. **Sharks** and **rays.**

KEY TO THE ELASMOBRANCHII
PLEUROTREMATA

	1	Gill openings wholly or in part on sides of body; pectoral fins not attached to sides of head (**Pleurotremata**)	2
or	1	Gill openings entirely on lower surface of body; pectoral fins attached to sides of head (**Hypotremata** or **Rajiformes**)	p. 48
	2	Gill openings 6 or 7; dorsal fin, 1 (Hexanchiformes)	3
or	2	Gill openings 5; dorsal fins, 2	4

25

12   Body rounded; gill openings evident on sides of body, dorsal fin in anterior half of total length ....

.... *Somniosus pacificus,* Pacific sleeper shark, p. 43

or   12   Body flattened with pectoral and pelvic fins expanded laterally but pectoral not fused to head; gill openings crowded in a deep notch behind head; dorsal fins both far back on body. This species has not been recorded from off the Canadian coast but is known from southeast Alaska as well as from the Californian coast where it is not uncommon.

Squatinidae
Squatina californica
Pacific angel shark

ORDER HEXANCHIFORMES
(Notidanoidea)

Sharks with six or seven gill openings, upper and lower teeth unlike at centre of mouth, the first gill openings widely interrupted at the throat, and an anal fin present.

FAMILY HEXANCHIDAE   COW SHARKS

In the cow sharks the dorsal fin is placed far back on the body posterior to the pelvics; there are no keels or precaudal pits on the caudal peduncle; and the caudal fin is elongate. Primitive sharks well represented in fossil records, six or seven living species recognized. Sixgill and sevengill sharks.

SIXGILL SHARK

Hexanchus griseus (Bonnaterre 1788)

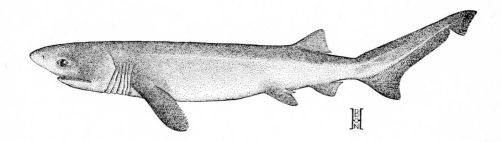

Scientific names from the Greek roots *(h)ex* (six) and *ankos* (bend or sinus — gills); and the Latin *griseus* (gray).

Clemens and Wilby in 1961 referred to this species as *Hexanchus corinum* Jordan and Gilbert 1880 and in 1946 the name *Hexanchus griseus*, the mud shark, was used.

Description   Body elongate, depth at pectoral fins 7 or 8 into length to origin of caudal fin, compressed posteriorly. Head large, depressed, its length about 5 into total length. Mouth inferior, very large, extending through most of the length of the head, directed forward. Snout broadly rounded and short. Upper lip overlying posterior part of lower jaw. Teeth in 2 or 3 functional series of moderate-sized teeth in upper jaw, one series of larger teeth in lower jaw, a median tooth in lower jaw. Interorbital space wide. Eyes large, oval. Six gill openings, all long, the first longest, well separated on ventral surface from opening on opposite side. Small spiracle behind eye, nearer first gill opening than eye. Caudal peduncle rather stout without precaudal pits.[1]

Fins   Dorsal (1) weakly convex on upper margin with a free rear tip. Caudal about one-third total length with marked subterminal notch. Anal about as long in base as dorsal, free margin almost straight. Pectorals large and broad with nearly straight free edge. Pelvics abdominal with nearly straight margins and rounded corners.

Scales   Placoid, minute, each with 3 ridges, the middle ridge largest, scales largest and smooth on the upper margin of the caudal fin where they form a ridge.

Colour   Dark brown or dark gray above, nearly black in some specimens, somewhat paler below. At least some individuals with a pale streak along side.

Size   Largest Pacific specimen 15 feet (4.5 m).[2] Largest reported 26 feet 5 inches (8 m).

Recognition   Distinguished by the six gill slits well separated at the lower ends, and by having the upper and lower teeth differing markedly.

Life History   A wide variety of fishes and crustaceans are taken as food. From the fact that sixgill sharks are taken in purse seines and other fishing gear in British Columbia, it may be deduced that they associate with and eat commercial species.

27

Sixgill sharks have been used to produce oil and meal. Throughout its range the species is noted for its sluggish habits and for the great depths at which it is encountered. The species is viviparous and prolific, 108 embryos being reported unofficially as having been taken from a 4.5 meter female.

Distribution   In temperate oceans of the world including the southern Indian Ocean. Off the west coasts of the United States and Canada and in the Gulf of Alaska, off Cuba, Europe from the Mediterranean to the Shetland Islands and Iceland, South Africa, Chile, Japan, and Australia.

References   1 Bigelow and Schroeder 1948; 2 Herald 1968. See also Miller and Greenfield 1965.

SEVENGILL SHARK

Notorynchus maculatus Ayres 1855

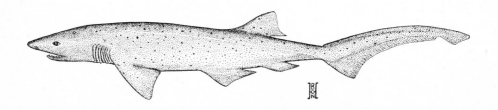

Scientific names from the Greek roots *noto* (back) and *r(h)ynchos* (snout); and the Latin *maculatus* (spotted).

Clemens and Wilby 1946 listed this species as spotted cow shark, *Notorynchus cepedianus* (Péron 1807).

Description   Body elongate, the depth at the pelvic fins about 8 into length to base of caudal fin, rounded. Head depressed and broadly rounded as seen from above, its length to the first gill slit about 5 into length to caudal base. Mouth inferior, large, opening extending across most of undersurface of head, directed down and forward. Snout low and blunt. Upper lip overlying posterior part of lower jaw. Teeth in only one complete functional series in each jaw. Dentition of jaws quite different. In upper jaw many but not all teeth with a dominating cusp curved inward. In lower jaw each tooth with a series of cusps, the largest median, in a row at an angle to main direction of jaw, trending out and back. Interorbital space very wide, raised. Eye oval, moderate in size, length less than distance between nostrils, on side of head. Seven gill openings, all long, all anterior to pectoral fins, the first longest and the last shortest, all well separated from those on other side along the ventral surface. Spiracle small but clearly evident, nearer to eye than to first gill opening. Caudal peduncle stout, its least depth about 17 into length to base of caudal fin, moderate dorsal precaudal pit.

28

Fins   Dorsal (1), placed far back on body, free margin gently concave, a small free posterior tip. Caudal heterocercal, directed mostly backward, long, upper lobe 3 or less into total length, subterminal notch. Anal small with almost straight edges. Pectorals with slightly curved free edges rounded to posterior and anterior edges. Pelvics abdominal.

Scales   Placoid, minute; to touch, the skin has texture but no real roughness.

Colour   Sandy gray to reddish brown with scattered round black spots, paler ventrally. A semi-albino with a pale ground colour has been reported.[3]

Size   Length to 8 feet 6 inches (2.62 m)[1] and a weight of 235 pounds (107 kg).[3]

Recognition   Distinguished by having seven gill slits on each side of body, upper and lower teeth that differ markedly, and dark spots scattered over upper part of body.

Life History   The sevengill shark is primitive and unspecialized in its anatomy although fossil records are all comparatively recent.[2] Some are mature at 6 feet 5 inches (197 cm) and 76 pounds (34.5 kg), but others have not reached maturity at 106.5 pounds (48.4 kg). A 2.62-meter female carried 86 developing eggs.[3] In captivity the sevengill shark swims constantly seldom resting on bottom. It responded to disturbance and molestation by fighting back, and may attack unprovoked.[4] Small sharks are included in the food.

Distribution   Southern California,[5,6] through Washington,[1] to northern British Columbia off Butedale and Bonilla Island in 20 to 25 fathoms (37–46 m). Occurs in deeper water in southern part of its range.[5]

References   1 Bonham 1942; 2 Daniel 1916; 3, 4 Herald 1953, 1968; 5 Roedel and Ripley 1950; 6 Schultz and De-Lacy 1936. See also Daniel 1934.

ORDER SQUALIFORMES

The higher sharks with five gill clefts, and two dorsal fins. Includes the great majority of the living species of sharks.

FAMILY ALOPIIDAE   THRESHER SHARKS

Sharks with extremely long tails, about half total length. There is a well-marked dorsal precaudal pit, the ventral pit may be present or absent, and the caudal peduncle is compressed. Gill openings are short, posterior one or more over pectoral fins. There are two dorsal fins, the second much smaller than the first.

THRESHER SHARK

Alopias vulpinus (Bonnaterre 1788)

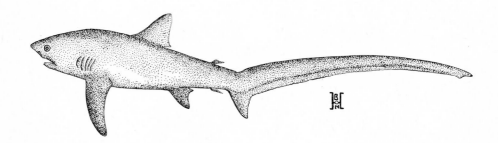

Scientific names both mean fox, Greek *alopos* and Latin *vulpes*.

The French name is *renard marin*.

Description   Body elongate, its greatest depth at the pectoral fin and about 4.5 into length to base of caudal (at dorsal precaudal furrow or pit), somewhat compressed; dorsal profile convex. Head conical, its length 3 to 4 into length to precaudal pit. Mouth inferior, moderate in size, directed forward, broadly rounded. Snout short, rounded at tip. Teeth moderate in size, subtriangular, with a single sharp pointed cusp with smooth edges, similar in both jaws, 1 or 2 functional rows. Interorbital space wide. Eyes circular, only moderately large, diameter one-third to one-half of snout in front of mouth, anterior edge ahead of mouth. Five gill openings, rather short, about equal in size, rather high, lower ends of fourth and fifth close together over pectoral fin. Spiracle porelike behind centre of eye, about over corner of mouth. Caudal peduncle stout, compressed without lateral ridges, dorsal precaudal pit but none ventral.

Fins   Dorsal (2), the first with its leading edge convex, the tip rounded, and the free rear end relatively small. Second dorsal very small with relatively long free tip at posterior free angle. Caudal very long, a little more than half of total length of fish, scythelike in shape with a subterminal prominence but no subterminal notch, the lower lobe a moderate-sized triangle a little smaller than the first dorsal. Anal very small, behind second dorsal but resembling it in shape. Pectorals with leading edge convex and apex rounded, posterior edge concave. Pelvics abdominal, about the same area as the first dorsal, anterior margin concave, tip rounded, free edge concave, and a rounded posterior corner.[1]

Vertebrae   Number very variable from 282 to 419 with about 300 caudal. Caudal vertebrae continue to form through life.[5]

Scales   Placoid, minute, closely overlapping with 3 or 5 low keels ending in marginal teeth.

Colour   On back brown or gray to black shading to white below except that lower anterior surface of snout and lower surfaces of pectorals may be similar in colour to back.

Size   Length to 25 feet (7.6 m).[2] Sizes of 13 to 16 feet (3.9–4.9 m) common.

Recognition   Immediately distinguished by the enormously long tail.

Life History   Maturity is probably not reached at a length of less than 14 feet

(4.2 m) but is apparently reached at about that length. Embryos of 155 centimeters and about 134 centimeters have been observed. However, a small free living specimen without an umbilical scar was taken at 144 centimeters. Evidently only two to four young are produced at a birth. Feeding is on smaller schooling fishes, such as herring, anchovy, or pilchard, that are herded together in a tight school in preparation for a direct attack. On occasion the tail is used to disable prey. The species is not known to attack man although in some areas it causes damage to fishing gear.

Distribution   Pelagic in warm temperate and subtropical seas. In the east Pacific off Chile and Panama, southern California and Oregon to Johnstone Strait, British Columbia. In the Atlantic from off the Cape of Good Hope to off Lofoten, Norway and from northern Argentina to Nova Scotia and the Gulf of St. Lawrence. A similar shark in the western Pacific and Indian oceans may be the same species.[1,4]

In British Columbia from Saanich Inlet and Sooke to Johnstone Strait and Goose Bay (between Smith Inlet and Fitz Hugh Sound).[2,3]

References   1 Bigelow and Schroeder 1948; 2 Clemens and Wilby 1961; 3 Cowan 1938; 4 Leim and Scott 1966; 5 Springer and Garrick 1964.

FAMILY LAMNIDAE   MACKEREL SHARKS

Large streamlined sharks (like mackerel) with two dorsal fins, lunate caudal fins, prominent keel or keels on sides of caudal peduncle, precaudal pits well developed, teeth large and relatively few, or with a remarkable complement of long horny gill rakers, and the last gill slit in front of the origin of the pectoral fin. Pelagic, widely migrating sharks, some plankton feeders but others highly aggressive with sharp teeth and dangerous. Basking, salmon, and white sharks.

WHITE SHARK

Carcharodon carcharias (Linnaeus 1758)

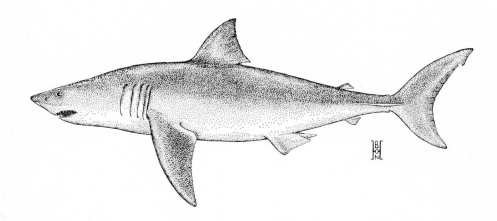

Scientific names from the Greek roots *karkaros* (rough) and *odon* (tooth); and from the old Greek name *karcharios* for man-eater sharks.

The French name is *requin blanc*.

Description   Body elongate, fusiform, its depth about 4 to 4.5 into length to base of caudal fin, greatest depth under anterior part of dorsal fin. Head large, its length to last gill slit 3 or less into snout-to-caudal-base length. Snout bluntly pointed, its length about 3 times diameter of eye. Mouth rather large, inferior. Teeth nearly triangular, all but median teeth with slightly concave sides, coarsely and regularly serrate, uppers about as high as broad, lowers narrower, central teeth largest in both jaws, a young specimen showed cusps on either side of bases of teeth in lower jaw.[4] Interorbital space wide. Eye moderate in size, nearly round. Five moderately sized gill openings, the fifth at the origin of the pelvic fins, and the longest; the first shortest but little difference. Spiracle absent or porelike, behind eye by a distance about half length of snout in front of mouth. Caudal peduncle depressed with lateral keels extending from anal insertion well on to caudal, precaudal pits as transverse furrows.

Fins   Dorsal (2), first moderate in size with convex leading edge, concave trailing edge, and a free tip about one quarter as long as base; second dorsal small with rounded apex. Caudal lunate posteriorly with upper and lower margins moderately convex, well-marked subterminal notch on dorsal limb. Anal similar in size and shape to second dorsal, originating behind its insertion. Pectorals moderately large. Pelvics abdominal with anterior margin nearly half as long as first dorsal leading edge, distal margin concave and corners rounded, much larger than anal.[1]

Scales   Placoid, minute, each with 3 ridges so flat that the skin is barely rough to touch.

Colour   Slaty brown or gray to almost black above, passing more or less abruptly to dirty white below, a black spot near axil of pectoral fin on smaller individuals. A white area may be present too. May show black marks on rear edges of dorsal and caudal fins, and on tips and anterior edges, and elsewhere, on pectorals. Large specimens may be lighter above.

Size   Length (in Australia) to 36.5 feet (11.2 m). A 16.5-foot (5.1-m) California specimen weighed 2820 pounds (1280 kg). The weight of the Australian specimen may be estimated as approaching 14 tons (13 metric tons).[1]

Recognition   Noteworthy for the lunate caudal, the triangular serrate teeth, and the posterior position of the anal fin.

Life History   Information on life history is scant. Maturity is probably reached at around 14 feet (4.2 m). Young are born alive; the smallest free-living specimen recorded is about 5 feet (1.5 m); the largest embryo 61.6 centimeters (2 ft).[1] These are savage animals, really attacking human swimmers,[3] sharks, sea otters,[4] seals, and other large animals, and small boats, as well as smaller fishes, such as salmon, hake, rockfishes, and crabs.[5] Because of its size it is destructive of line fishing gear and catches. It appears to be essentially a fish of the upper layers but may have been taken as deep as 700 fathoms (1280 m).[1]

Distribution   Oceanic in tropical and subtropical seas of the world.[1] Straying in the northeastern Pacific to Willapa Harbour[2] to the east coast of the Queen Charlotte Islands, and in the same year (1961) to near Craig, Alaska (55.28 N, 133.08 W). In that year many others were seen off the west coast of Prince of Wales Island.[6,7]

References   1 Bigelow and Schroeder 1948; 2 Bonham 1942; 3 Collier 1964; 4 Follett 1966; 5 LeMier 1951; 6 Pike 1962; 7 Royce 1963.

BASKING SHARK

Cetorhinurs maximus (Gunnerus 1765)

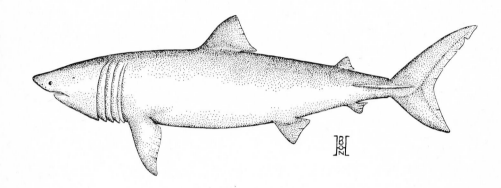

Scientific names from the Greek roots *ketos* (whale) and *rhina* (shark — from the rough skin); and the Latin *maximus* (largest).

The French name is *pèlerin*.

Description Body elongate, depth at pectoral fin from 5 to 5.5 into length to base of caudal fin, fusiform, depressed posteriorly. Head large, its length to last gill slit about 5 into total length, slightly compressed. Mouth inferior, large, directed forward. Snout short and nearly conical with rounded tip. Teeth very small and numerous, mostly conical, in 4 to 7 functional rows in each jaw. Interorbital space wide. Eyes nearly circular, small, about 8 into interorbital space. Five gill openings, extremely long, from the upper part of side to the base of the throat, the first longest, the fifth in front of pectoral fin. Gill rakers long and horny united in a joined series at their bases. Spiracles very small, circular, behind eye and posterior to angle of mouth. Caudal peduncle stout, depressed, with a stout keel-like expansion on the sides from anal to caudal fins, a transverse furrow or precaudal pit above and below base of caudal fin.

Fins Dorsal (2), the first roughly an equilateral triangle with slightly convex anterior margin and slightly concave posterior margin. The second dorsal much smaller and similar in shape. Caudal eccentrically lunate; the upper lobe larger with a definite subterminal notch. Anal resembles second dorsal and is placed posterior to it. Pectorals rather small, with blunt tips and rounded inner corners. Pelvics abdominal, about two-thirds size of first dorsal.

Vertebrae About 110.[6] Gill rakers around 1260 on one gill.[2] Gill rakers may be shed seasonally occasionally, associated with a demersal nonfeeding stage.[3]

Scales Placoid, generally small but of variable size and arranged in strips on body, erect, spiny, and abrasive.[2]

Colour Grayish brown to slaty gray to black above. The back colour may be continued below or shade variably into white.

Size The largest shark of temperate seas. Dependable measurements are not available for the largest that are probably

34

around 40 or even 45 feet (12.2 or 13.7 m). The largest measured was 36 feet (10.9 m) — all for Atlantic specimens. A 30-foot (9.2-m) Monterey specimen weighed 8600 pounds (3900 kg).[2]

Recognition   The basking shark can be identified by the very long gill slits, the combs of horny gill rakers, the small numerous teeth, and the strong keel on the caudal peduncle.

Life History   Little is known with certainty on the biology of the basking shark. There are indications that young are born at about 5 or 6 feet (1.5 or 1.8 m) in length and that maturity is reached at about 15 feet (4.6 m) or rather more. The food consists of small crustaceans screened from the water by the highly developed gill raker system. The basking shark is rather sluggish and gets its name from its habit of lying tranquilly on the surface, often with the dorsal fin exposed. It quite frequently becomes stranded and is responsible for many of the stories of dead sea serpents. The vertebrae are partly calcified giving the appearance of bone (unlike other sharks with cartilaginous skeletons), and in a decaying carcass the resistant gill rakers can be interpreted as the mane of an unfamiliar monster.

Distribution   In the temperate and boreal parts of the world's oceans. In the Pacific, from Baja California (head of the Gulf of California[1]) to the Gulf of Alaska; off Peru and Ecuador; off Japan and China; off southern Australia and New Zealand. In the Atlantic, from the Mediterranean and Madeira to Iceland and southern Norway; off South Africa; off Argentina and the Falkland Islands. Off the United States and Canada from North Carolina to Newfoundland. Only evident in summer in the northern parts of its range.[2,5] In British Columbia from southern Strait of Georgia (Hammond Bay), Queen Charlotte Sound,[4] Prince Rupert area. Common enough on occasion to be a nuisance to net fishermen in Barkley Sound.

Utilization   Not regular enough in occurrence to be of commercial importance. Oil from the large liver formerly used for lamps but it has no valuable vitamin content.

References   1 Baldwin 1961; 2 Bigelow and Schroeder 1948; 3 Bonham 1942; 4 Green 1891b; 5 Leim and Scott 1966; 6 Springer and Garrick 1964. See also Chapman 1942.

SALMON SHARK

Lamna ditropis Hubbs and Follett 1947

Scientific names from the Greek *lamna* (a shark or horrifying monster); and *di* (two) and *tropis* (keel).

Clemens and Wilby 1946 recorded this shark as *Isurus nasus* (Bonnaterre 1788), the mackerel shark.

Description   Body elongate, its greatest depth at origin of dorsal, about 4.3 into length to base of caudal fin. Head large, about 3 into snout to caudal base length. Snout rounded, blunt, and short, its length about twice diameter of eye. Mouth rather large. Teeth awl-like with smooth sides and a small point on either shoulder, in 1 or possibly 2 functional series. Interorbital space wide. Eyes moderate in size, almost round, placed high on head. Five moderately sized gill openings, the fifth at the origin of the pelvic fins and bent so as to be closer to the fourth at the bottom than through the rest of its length, all about the same length. Spiracle minute, partly covered by a fleshy flap, behind the eye and above the angle of the mouth. Caudal peduncle much depressed, with lateral keels extending from ahead of second dorsal well onto caudal, and with a second keel below it on the base of the caudal, precaudal pits as transverse furrows.[5,9]

Fins   Dorsal (2), the first moderate in size with leading edge convex passing into a rounded apex, free edge slightly concave, ending in a small projecting free tip, placed well back. Second dorsal small. Caudal lunate with upper limb expanded notably above subterminal lobe. Anal small, resembling but behind second dorsal. Pectorals rather small with curving outline. Pelvics small, abdominal, with sides almost straight.

Scales   Placoid, minute. Body almost smooth to touch.

Colour   Dark bluish gray on upper surface, abruptly white on ventral surface; in adults ventral surface coarsely blotched with dark gray or black.

Size   Length to about 10 feet (3 m).

Recognition   Noteworthy for the small anal and second dorsal fins, the black blotching on the ventral surface of adults, the secondary keel on the base of the caudal fin below the main keel, and the awl-like teeth with small sharp denticles on each shoulder of the main point.

Life History   One observer records four young to be produced at a birth.[7] It is pelagic, swift swimming, reported to be the most voracious of the northern sharks, and regarded as an important destroyer of commercial fish and gear. In Alaska food was found to be three species of salmon, a sculpin, and tomcod.[1] It has been sought by sports fishermen in the Mistaken Island area of the Strait of Georgia, and the first published Canadian record is of a specimen taken off Hippa Island (northwest of Queen Charlotte Islands) on a salmon spoon, identified as *Lamna cornubica* (Gmelin).[11]

Distribution   Pelagic and apparently coastwise in the temperate and subarctic Pacific.[4] From San Diego[4] through southern and central California,[2] the Pacific Northwest[3] to Alaska,[10] the Bering Sea and Japan (Hokkaido, Tokahu, and Chyoshi).[4,6,8] Occurs in all the Gulf of Alaska throughout the year.[7] In British Columbia common and generally distributed in the Strait of Georgia and offshore.

References   1 Bright 1960; 2 Croker 1942; 3 DeLacy, Dryfoos, and Miller 1963; 4 Hubbs and Follett 1947; 5 Jordan and Evermann 1900; 6 Matsubara 1955; 7 Neave and Hanavan 1960; 8 Okada 1955; 9 Roedel and Ripley 1950; 10 Wilimovsky 1954; 11 Williamson 1930.

FAMILY SCYLIORHINIDAE   CAT SHARKS

Small soft sharks with (nearly always) two dorsal fins, and a caudal fin confluent with the body, having neither precaudal pits or lateral keels on the caudal peduncle. The first dorsal originates behind the pelvic insertion, and the last one or two gill slits are over the pectoral fin. Mostly tropical species of deep or shoal water.

BROWN CAT SHARK

Apristurus brunneus (Gilbert 1891)

Scientific names from the Greek *a* (without), *pristis* (file), and *(d)urus* (hard); and the Latin *brunneus* (brown).

Clemens and Wilby 1946 called this species brown shark.

Description   Body elongate, depth at pectoral fins 11 into total length, compressed posteriorly. Head depressed, its length to first gill slit about 4 into total length. Mouth inferior, moderate in size, directed forward and down. Snout low and flat. Teeth in 3 rows, small, fine pointed, well spaced, in both jaws, a median gap at symphysis. Interorbital space wide, slightly concave medially. Eye small, lenticular. Five short gill openings on side, second longest, fifth shortest but all about the same length, directed down and forward, last 1 or 2 over pectoral fin base. Spiracles behind and a little below eyes. Caudal peduncle very short, compressed, no transverse furrow at base of fin.

Fins   Dorsal (2), both small with first smaller and placed far back on body, both rounded and directed backward. Caudal entirely below general posterior dorsal contour, small terminal lobe and anterior to it a ventral blade, extending anteriorly to second dorsal insertion, both with fringed edges. Anal largest of the unpaired fins, rounded, originating under posterior part of first dorsal. Pectorals moderate in size, broadly based, free ends blunt with rounded angles. Pelvics abdominal, moderate in size, anterior and free edges rounded.

Scales   Placoid, very fine, body scarcely rough to touch.

Colour   Rich light or medium brown uniformly on body, dark margins on fins.

Size   Length to 26.8 inches (68 cm).

Recognition   Recognized by the posterior position of the first dorsal fin over the pelvic fin, the large anal fin, and the caudal axis in line with the body.

Life History   Brown cat sharks are oviparous. Eggs are released in transparent oblong egg cases slightly over 2 inches (5 cm) long, with a long tendril at each corner.[2] A 3.13-inch specimen was taken on September 1 in English Bay. Taken not infrequently on longline gear and in deep trawling operations. A soft fish of no significant commercial value.

Distribution   Southern California to southern British Columbia, Oregon, Washington.[1,3] Most British Columbia records are from the Strait of Georgia. Uncommon and from deep water down to 520 fathoms (970 m) in the southern part of the range. Taken at 75 to 196 fathoms (137–360 m) in British Columbia.

References   1 Grinols 1965a; 2 Roedel and Ripley 1950; 3 Schultz and De-Lacy 1936. Additional information is contained in Anon 1941c, Roedel 1951.

FAMILY CARCHARHINIDAE   REQUIEM SHARKS

A very large family of sharks. There are two dorsal fins, the first placed well forward, the second well back. Caudal not lunate or keeled but with ventral lobe expanded and with well-developed subterminal notch, and with precaudal pits present or absent. The last gill opening is over or behind the insertion of the pectoral fin. Pelagic, active, voracious sharks of tropical and warm temperate seas, some making summer migrations into temperate areas. The only known freshwater shark from Lake Nicaragua, *Carcharhinus nicaraguensis,* is of this family. So-called requiem sharks as they are likely to occur in fair restful weather.

SOUPFIN SHARK

Galeorhinus zyopterus Jordan and Gilbert 1883

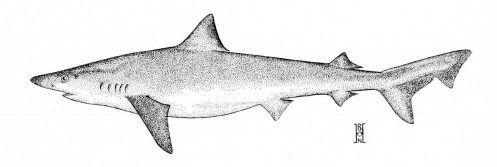

Scientific names from the Greek *galeos* (a kind of shark), *rhinos* (nose or snout); and *zuon*, (animal) and *pteron* (fin — large pectoral fin).

The species was recorded in Clemens and Wilby 1946 as *Galeorhinus galeus* (Linnaeus 1758).

39

Description   Body elongate, its greatest depth below origin of dorsal fin, about 5 into length to beginning of caudal fin, fusiform, with dorsal profile nearly straight. Head about 3.5 into snout-to-caudal-origin length or 4.5 into total length. Mouth inferior, moderate in size, directed forward and down. Snout rather flattened, long, pointed. Teeth sharp, in several rows, notched on outer edges below points, lower part of notches divided into 2 to 5 points. Interorbital space wide, raised, and flattened. Eye almost round. Five rather short gill openings, the last over the pectoral fin. Spiracle small, directly behind eye. Caudal peduncle without a keel.

Fins   Dorsal (2), first with slightly convex leading edge, slightly concave free edge, and a moderate free tip; second, generally similar in shape, but much smaller and lower. Caudal almost one-quarter total length, subterminal notch and terminal lobe exceptionally well developed, lower lobe also large but fin not lunate. Anal directly below and about same size and shape as second dorsal, slightly smaller. Pectoral length less than twice height of first dorsal, rounded. Pelvics abdominal, about same size as second dorsal.

Vertebrae   136 to 160.[6]

Scales   Placoid, small.

Colour   Dark bluish to dusky gray on dorsal surface, paler ventrally. Black on anterior edges of dorsal fins, tip of caudal fin, and most of pectoral fin.

Size   Length to slightly more than 6 feet (about 2 m).

Recognition   Recognized by the enlarged dorsal lobe of the caudal fin beyond the subterminal notch; the second dorsal fin is similar to the anal and directly above it; the fins are dark; the fifth gill slit is of moderate length over the pectoral fin, and there is no keel on the side of the caudal peduncle.

Life History   The soupfin shark bears its young alive. Males are smaller than females, they start to mature at about 140 centimeter length and all are mature at 170 centimeters. Females start to mature about 155 centimeters, 65 percent are mature at 160 centimeters, and at 190 centimeters all are mature. From 6 to 52 young are born in a brood, with an average about 35. At birth young are about 35 centimeters long. The gestation period appears to be about one year. These facts were determined in California.[4] There appear to be extensive movements without recognizable patterns[2,5] up to 35 miles (56 km) per day and sustained speeds of 10 miles (16 km) per day for 1000 miles (1600 km).[3] There seems to be a northern movement in summer extending as far as Hecate Strait where a summer fishery was pursued.[1] Soupfin sharks are general feeders both at the bottom, and mid-depths and surface. Pilchard, anchovy, salmon, rockfishes, viviparous perches, and squid are reported as foods in northern waters. In California mackerel and barracuda are significant items, and midshipman, flatfishes, and sculpins give evidence that soupfin shark seek food near bottom.

Distribution   From Cedros Island, Baja California, to northern British Columbia.

Utilization   The soupfin is the most acceptable of the sharks for food purposes and in California there is a long-established if casual fishery for fresh fillets and dried fins. Around 1940 an intense fishery developed along the coast from California to British Columbia to take soupfin shark for their vitamin A-rich livers. In British Columbia the main fishery was with sunken gillnets off the west coast of Vancouver Island and in Hecate Strait. The fishery reached its peak in 1944. By 1946 demand for vitamin A liver oils had dropped and the stock had been cut down enough to reduce catches, with the result that the fishery declined to incidental captures.

References   1 Barraclough 1948b; 2 Foerster 1945; 3 Herald and Ripley 1951; 4, 5 Ripley 1946a, b; 6 Springer and Garrick 1964.

BLUE SHARK

Prionace glauca (Linnaeus 1758)

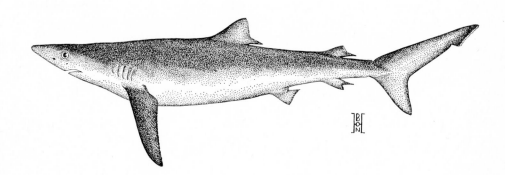

Scientific names from the Greek roots *prion* (saw) and *akis* (point); and the Latin *glauca* (blue).

The French name is *requin bleu*.

Description   Body elongate, its greatest depth at first dorsal, about 6.5 into length to precaudal notch, in undistorted specimens. Dorsal profile little arched. Head 4.5 to 5 into total length. Mouth inferior, moderate in size, directed forward. Snout conical with slightly rounded tip, long. Teeth acutely subtriangular, lateral margins strongly convex, median margins concave, edges serrate, teeth so closely placed that the bases overlap, tooth at symphysis of lower jaw sometimes reduced, in 1 to 3 functional rows. Interorbital space wide. Eyes almost circular, the mid-point above the centre of the mouth. Five gill openings, moderate in size, the middle one largest, and the last 2 over the pectoral fin. Spiracle small, close behind eye, or absent. Caudal peduncle slightly compressed, without keels on sides but tending to be rhomboid in cross section. Precaudal pits almost rectangular.[1]

Fins   Dorsal (2). Leading edge of first dorsal straight rounding into a concave free edge terminating in a moderate free tip. Second dorsal similar in shape, about one-quarter area. Caudal about one-quarter of total length, subterminal notch well developed. Anal about same size as second dorsal, its free edge very concave leaving the posterior angle acutely pointed. Pectorals very long, about as long as head, narrow, and sabre-shaped. Pelvics abdominal, small, anterior margin somewhat convex, posterior margin slightly concave.

Vertebrae   About 240.[7]

Scales   Placoid, minute, with weak ridges and scalloped edges usually overlapping. The skin not really rough to touch.

Colour   Dark indigo blue on back shading through clear bright blue on sides to white below. Tips of pectorals and anal dusky. Colour lost in preservation.

Size   Largest authenticated size 12 feet 7 inches (3.8 m). Reputed to reach 25 feet (7.6 m).[2]

Recognition   Notable for the long sabrelike pectoral fin, well-developed snout, slender form, and striking colour in living specimens.

41

Life History   Maturity is not reached at lengths of less than about 7 or 8 feet (2.1 or 2.4 m). Young are born at lengths between 18 (46 cm) and 21 inches (53 cm). Up to 30[2] or 60[5] young are born at a time. The food is a wide variety of pelagic and demersal species. In the Gulf of Alaska stomachs contained salmon, lanternfishes, daggertooth, pomfret, saury, and squid.[4] It seems to be sluggish except when feeding. It is commonly taken by salmon trollers off the west coast of Vancouver Island[8] and used to be of common occurrence around pilchard seines. It is regarded as a nuisance by fishermen.

Distribution   In the warm temperate, subtropical, and tropical oceans of the world, including the Mediterranean Sea. In mid-Pacific and inshore north to the Gulf of Alaska and Japan,[6] in the Atlantic north to southern Norway and Newfoundland and the Gulf of St. Lawrence. Chile south to Australia, New Zealand and South Africa, Hawaii, and Brazil. In British Columbia common off the west coast of Vancouver Island in summer, and off the Queen Charlotte Islands.[1,3] Experimental fishing indicated northward movement of the population from May to September and catches were made only at water temperatures between 11 and 17 C.[5]

References   1 Bigelow and Schroeder 1948; 2 Clemens and Wilby 1961; 3 Fowler 1941; 4 LeBrasseur 1964b; 5 Neave and Hanavan 1960; 6 Okada 1955; 7 Springer and Garrick 1964; 8 Williamson 1930.

FAMILY SQUALIDAE   DOGFISH SHARKS

These sharks have no anal fin and two dorsal fins. The dorsal fins may or may not be preceded by prominent spines. There are no keels or precaudal pits on caudal peduncle. All five gill openings are anterior to the pectoral fin insertion. Dogfish and sleeper sharks.

PACIFIC SLEEPER SHARK

Somniosus pacificus Bigelow and Schroeder 1944

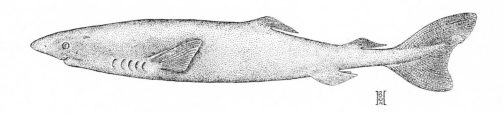

Scientific names from the Latin *somniosus* (sleepy) and *Pacific* (Ocean).

Clemens and Wilby 1946 called this species sleeper shark, *Somniosus microcephalus* (Schneider 1801).

Description   Body elongate, depth at tips of pectorals about 6 into length to origin of caudal fin. Head large, depressed, its length about 5 into total length. Mouth inferior, large, nearly as wide as snout length, a deep straight groove at each end, labial palps well developed. Teeth all with smooth edges; in upper jaw pointed, in several functional series, about 70 rows; lower teeth broader, triangular, directed inward, in about 54 rows. Snout rounded. Nostril closer to end of snout than to eyes. Interorbital space wide and arched. Eyes small, diameter about 5 into length of snout. Five gill openings, all about same size, short, the upper ends in line with top of pectoral fin. Spiracle medium in size, above and behind eye. Caudal peduncle rather short.

Fins   Dorsal (2), both small, about the same size, short based, and without spines, the first placed well back with the posterior end of its insertion behind the midpoint of total length, second origin above posterior end of pelvic insertion, the fin flabby. A low dermal ridge in front of first dorsal. Caudal rather large, broad, asymmetrically forked with convex margins above and below. Anal absent. Pectorals small with rounded angles, extending about half way to dorsal origin. Pelvics larger than dorsals, placed well back on body, anterior angle rounded, posterior angle acutely rounded.

Scales   Placoid, minute, bluntly pointed, with fluted cross sections.

Colour   Blackish brown throughout[1,2,5] or slate green with darker streaklike mottling.

Size   Length to 25 feet (7.6 m).

Recognition   Recognized by the absence of an anal fin, and absence of spines at the insertions of dorsal fins.

Life History   A 12-foot (3.7-m) individual contained 300 large eggs[6] but conditions of fertilization and development are unknown; there was no evidence of shell or egg case. The species is a voracious and versatile feeder; a 12-foot (3.7-m) female contained 300 pounds (136 kg) of fish, mostly rex and dover soles, but also including three chinook salmon and a halibut.[6] Other foods include hair seal (3 in one stomach), octopus, squids, crabs, triton,[3] short spine rockfish,[8] and carrion.

Distribution   Southern California,[8] through Washington[4] and British Columbia to the Gulf of Alaska[3] and Bering Sea.[9] On the Asian coast off Sagami Bay and south of Shikoku Island, Japan.[7] In British Columbia recorded at Victoria and Comox. A bottom fish to at least 245 fathoms (448 m) occasionally coming to surface.

References 1, 2 Bigelow and Schroeder 1948; 3 Bright 1959; 4 DeLacy, Dryfoos, and Miller 1963; 5 Garman 1913; 6 Gotshall and Jow 1965; 7 Matsubara 1955; 8 Phillips 1953a; 9 Wilimovsky 1954.

SPINY DOGFISH

Squalus acanthias Linnaeus 1758

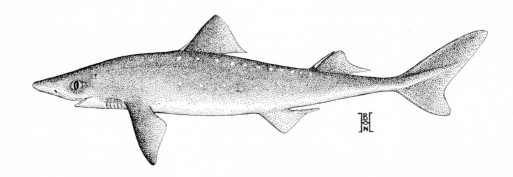

Scientific names from the Latin *squalus* (shark); and the Greek *akanthias* (an old name for the species referring to the spines).

The French name is *aiguillat commun.*

Clemens and Wilby 1946 and 1961 refer to this species as Pacific dogfish, *Squalus suckleyi* (Girard 1854). Significant morphological characters have not been found to separate *Squalus suckleyi* from *Squalus acanthias* of the Atlantic or from *Squalus lebruni* from off the southern coast of Chile. Stocks from these two areas can be separated on the basis of vertebral number and it seems probable that they could be regarded as distinct at the subspecies level.[17] However, pending a critical study this account considers all under the oldest name.[6]

Description Body slender, its greatest depth at front of first dorsal, about 7 in length to origin of caudal. Head about 4 into length to base of caudal, moderately flattened above. Mouth inferior, rather small and straight, directed forward and down. Snout rounded. Teeth moderate in size with single cusps directed outward so that their inner edges form a continuous cutting edge across the mouth, in 1 or 2 (or 3) functional series. Interorbital space wide. Eyes, oval moderate in size. Five short gill slits, low on body, ahead of pectoral fin, the last may be longest. Spiracle close behind eye and a little above. The nostril is approximately transverse with its anterior margin a simple subtriangular lobe (unlike related species with complicated margins). Caudal peduncle rather slender, flattened below but rounded

44

above. There is a low rounded longitudinal dermal ridge below midlevel of the caudal peduncle, extending from below second dorsal to anterior part of caudal. Subcaudal pit of irregular occurrence.[6]

Fins   Dorsal (2), each preceded by a stout spine. First dorsal rather small, with a straight leading edge curving into a concave free edge, which in turn concludes in a moderate free tip. The second dorsal has nearly, but not quite, as large outside dimensions as the first but its area is cut down by the greater concavity of the free edge. Caudal about 5 into total length with the axis only a little turned up and no subterminal notch. No anal. Pectorals moderate in size, leading edge gently convex, free edge concave, and inner corner broadly rounded. Pelvics small with almost straight margins.[6]

Vertebrae   105 (96–118).[28]

Scales   Placoid, small, usually with three ridges, but variable, and irregularly spaced on body.

Colour   Slate gray or brown above, shading into white or dirty white below. A row or two of light spots on backs of young, disappearing with age.

Size   Length to 5 feet 3 inches (160 cm),[11] not confirmed, or 4 feet 3 inches (130 cm).[7,19,21] Weight to 20 pounds (9.1 kg).[6]

Recognition   Recognizable by the spines at the origins of the first and second dorsal fins and the absence of an anal fin.

Life History   Females mature between 78.5 and 105.5 centimeters[7] or 76 and 112 centimeters with 50 percent mature at about 93.5 cm.[20] In the Atlantic maturity is reported to occur between 70 and 100 centimeters.[6] The 50 percent maturity length for males is about 72 centimeters.[7] The gestation period appears to be between 22 and 24 months,[7,14,19] although somewhat shorter periods have been proposed.[2,12,22] The number of developing

young carried by a female is from 2 to 20.[2,14,21] There is evidence that the lower figure is the result of abortion or miscarriage, and that the "natural" average minimum is four.[19] The number of developing young is related quite regularly to the size of the female, with eight or nine the common size of a litter. The large ovarian eggs pass from the ovary into the shell gland where they are fertilized before receiving a covering membrane or 'candle' in which they develop in the uterus until the membrane breaks, leaving the young dogfish free in the uterus. There is nothing corresponding to a placenta and chemical exchanges to the foetus must be through folds in the uterine wall.[2,6] At birth young are between 24 and 30 centimeters in length.[19] Growth may be fairly rapid at first but is relatively slow later, of the order of an inch or less a year.[3,7,16,19] Many dogfish encountered in fishing operations are old (up to 40 years) and the population structure is correspondingly unusual.[19] An intensive fishery with gillnets and other methods for mature females cut down their abundance drastically between 1943 or before, and 1946.[4]

Dogfish are adaptable in their feeding habits. Young have been observed living planktonically[5] and adults have been observed at the surface eating euphausiids. Stressed dogfish may be able to adjust buoyancy by quickly changing the ratios in the liver of the lipoids diacyl glyceryl ethers to higher density triglycerides.[23] They congregate in packs where fishing is good as determined by smell.[26] They bite their prey, sometimes in two[27] or cut chunks out of larger fish or invertebrates. The diet covers a wide range of species and varies geographically, seasonally, and with depth. The principal food items appear to be herring, hake, sand lance, smelts, and euphausiids. However, dogfish are known to eat at least 27 other species of fish (eight at least of commercial value), and 13 varieties of invertebrates (including commercial crabs and shrimps, and octopus).[8] At the mouth of the Fraser River they concentrate to prey on eulachon and their eggs and thus provided a recognizable fishery when the market was favourable.[9] They also appear to concentrate among the southern Gulf of Georgia islands in the autumn when herring are moving into the Strait of Georgia, and they prey heavily on runs of spawning capelin such as in Departure Bay and Hammond Bay near Nanaimo. In western Hecate Strait they feed heavily on commercial crabs during their soft-shell stage. There is little evidence from numerous sampling expeditions to indicate that dogfish are serious predators of salmon although it is possible that salmon injured by fishing operations would be ready prey for the opportunistic activities of dogfish.[19]

The movements and migrations of spiny dogfish present a confusing pattern. General congregations of dogfish come and go on individual fishing grounds. In Dixon Entrance and Hecate Strait old mature dogfish are available only during the summer months but it is uncertain whether their movements are mainly horizontal or in depth. However, immature dogfish are available throughout the year in British Columbia waters and at least part of the adult population remains over winter. In Puget Sound and Strait of Georgia about three-quarters of the tags recovered from dogfish came from the area of release and suggested an indigenous population in Puget Sound.[16] Similar conclusions are to be reached from tagging conducted in Canadian waters of the Strait of Georgia. There seems to be little movement outside the Strait or mixing with dogfish in Puget Sound.[19] However, tagging also makes it clear that local movements take place; in six months from Gabriola Bluffs to White Rock,[10] and Cherry Point to Scotch Fir Point in 10 years.[17] Washington tagging experiments suggested indigenous inshore populations and offshore migrating ones.[16] A California tagging experiment indicated general moving around, a resident population, and extensive seasonal migrations.[15] Some quite spectacular movements have been demonstrated: Fife Point, Queen Charlotte Islands, to Santa Cruz, California,[24] from Washington waters to Rose Spit, Queen Charlotte Islands, and to San Martin Island, Baja California,[16] and from Willapa Bay, Washington, to the northeast end of Honshu Island, Japan, 4000 miles (7200 km) in 7 years.[18]

Distribution   In the eastern north Pacific *Squalus acanthias* occurs from Baja California to the Bering Sea[30,1] but is most abundant between northern California and northern British Columbia. It also occurs off Chile. The same and/or related species are found in the western Pacific from the coast of China northward to Korea[13,25] and Hawaii. Spiny dogfish are found at depths from the surface to 400 fathoms (730 m). In the Atlantic Ocean and Mediterranean and Black seas; from Florida and Cuba rarely, more commonly from South Carolina to southern Labrador and southwest Greenland. On the European side from Senegal to Norway and the Murman Coast. Very similar species occur in the southern hemisphere and may be identical. They are recorded from Australia, New Zealand, South Africa, the south Indian Ocean, Magellan Strait, Uruguay, and northern Argentina.[6,21]

Utilization   The economic status of dogfish has shown wide fluctuations. Its use started with a small longline fishery to take fish whose livers were rendered to produce oil for mine lamps in the Nanaimo area, for lighthouse lamps, for other commercial and domestic lighting purposes, and for lubricating machinery. This was followed by the establishment of several reduction plants, but for technical reasons dogfish had to be dealt with in a batch system less efficient than the continuous process used for other fishes, with the result that reduction operations proved marginal or unprofitable. The vitamin A content of dogfish liver oil was reported in 1927 but it was not until the late 1930's that the commercial potential of exploiting the vitamin A potency of dogfish liver oils was appreciated. This was followed by an expanded fishery and the fitting out of many small vessels that marketed livers only and discarded carcasses. An intense and profitable fishery grew, complicated by the facts that (old) large dogfish livers are richer in vitamin A than smaller ones,[2,29] that fishermen had major control over the sizes of fish they captured, and that some buyers purchased livers by the pound whereas others kept deliveries separate for assay and paid by vitamin A units. Around 1945 declining abundance of dogfish, especially older ones,[4] and markets weakened by renewed competition from Atlantic sources of vitamin A oils, led to a decline in the fishery, which about 1950 approached collapse with the importation of vitamin A oils from Japan and the introduction of synthetic products. Later, as dogfish stocks recovered they again became a serious nuisance on fishing grounds, eating captured fish and destroying gear, and they were suspected of competing successfully with food species. Government subsidies for dogfish fishing at various intervals between 1959 and 1962 increased captures to some extent but not nearly to 1940–45 levels. The recent production from the fishery is given in the following tabulation showing catches in thousands of pounds (454 kg). The production figures differ significantly from those previously published,[20] presumably mainly because of a higher (9:1) liver-to-whole-fish conversion factor used in calculating the catches given here.

Production reached a sharp peak in 1944 with a coastwise total of 123,540 thousand pounds (56,000 metric tons), and after 1949 never reached a seventh of that amount. In all years but 1946 Canadian production was more than half of the coastwise production. In 1946 it was 47 percent.

In Europe fresh dogfish is sold for food and is found acceptable on some markets, but the practice has not found favour in North America.

Average catch dogfish in thousands of pounds (454 kg):

| | British Columbia | | Pacific Coast Oregon to Alaska |
Years	Liver	Estimated whole fish	Estimated whole fish
1917–21	–	3770	3700
1922–26	–	6300	6300
1927–31	–	16230	16230
1932–36	–	8350	8350
1937–41	1310	17670	23820
1942–46	4960	46950	79020
1947–51	2470	22440	34730
1952–56	620	5640	7270
1957–61	990	9370	10790
1962	101	920	1460
1963	55	500	1060
1964	–	0	–
1965	–	0	–
1966	–	900[a]	–
1967	–[b]	1000[a]	–[b]
1968	–[b]	623	–[b]
1969	–[b]	2	–[b]
1970	–[b]	305	–[b]

[a]From Department of Fisheries.

[b]No data available.

References   1 Alverson, Pruter, and Ronholt 1964; 2 Alverson and Stansby 1963; 3 Anon 1952; 4 Barraclough 1948c; 5 Barraclough, Robinson, and Fulton 1968; 6 Bigelow and Schroeder 1948; 7 Bonham, Sanford, Clegg, and Bucher 1949; 8 Brocklesby 1927; 9 Chatwin and Forrester 1953; 10 Clemens 1932; 11 Clemens and Wilby 1946, 1961; 12 Ford 1921; 13 Grinols 1965a; 14 Hart 1942a; 15 Herald and Ripley 1951; 16 Holland 1957; 17 Kato, Springer, and Wagner 1967; 18 Kauffman 1955; 19 Ketchen 1970; 20 Larkin and Ricker 1964; 21 Leim and Scott 1966; 22 Lucas 1930; 23 Malins and Barone 1970; 24 Manzer 1946a; 25 Matsubara 1955; 26 Parker 1915; 27 Shippen and Alton 1967; 28 Springer and Garrick 1964; 29 Swain 1947; 30 Wilimovsky 1954. Additional information is contained in Bonham 1954, Metten 1939.

ORDER RAJIFORMES
(Hypotremata, Batoidei)

Elasmobranchs conspicuously flattened by having a very long-based pectoral fin attached to the side of the head and continuously with the body. The mouth and five pairs of gill clefts are wholly ventral. There is a marked spiracle. Dorsal fins are placed well back on the body, and like the caudal fin are usually but not always reduced in size. There is no anal fin. Teeth are bluntly pointed or flat in many rows forming rasping plates on the jaws. Swimming is by undulating movements of the large pectoral fins. **Skates** and **other rays** in western Canadian waters, elsewhere: **sawfishes, guitarfishes, mantas,** and related species.

KEY TO THE HYPOTREMATA
(RAJIFORMES, BATOIDEI)

1   Dorsal fins 2, both quite small 2

or   1   Dorsal fins absent; tail fin absent; stout spine on slender tail ....
.... Dasyatidae, *Dasyatis* sp., Stingray, p. 63

2   Skin extremely smooth, caudal fin moderately developed ....
.... Torpedinidae, *Torpedo californica*, Pacific electric ray, p. 50

or   2   Skin more or less rough with scattered spines; tail fin absent or reduced to
an inconspicuous fold .... Rajidae, Skates 3

Raja (Bathyraja) trachura, the roughtail skate, was recently reported informally from off the British Columbia coast (A. E. Peden).

3   Straight line from tip of snout to outer edge of pectoral fin passes at least
partly outside outline of body edge 4

or   3   Straight line from tip of snout to outer edge of pectoral fin passes entirely
inside edge of body outline 5

4   Pelvic fins shallowly concave in their lateral margins (illustration on left);
snout firm, back at base of pectorals with a
large eye spot surrounded by a ring of light
spots; ventral colour nearly white ....
.... *Raja binoculata*, Big skate, p. 56

or   4   Pelvic fins deeply concave in their lateral margins (illustration on right); snout sharply
pointed and very flexible; simple ring of
darker pigment on back at base of pectoral
fins; ventral surface muddy blue ....
.... *Raja rhina*, Longnose skate, p. 59

5   No spine on shoulder girdle in older individuals; a break in line of spines along mid-dorsal line anterior to notch behind pectoral fin .... *Raja abyssicola*, Deepsea skate, p. 54

or   5   Shoulder girdle with 1 or more prominent spines 6

6   No spines at inner margins of orbits; white patches on either side of posterior part of body .... *Raja kincaidi*, Black skate, p. 58

or   6   Spines on inner edges of orbits; back with indistinct "eye spots" at base of pectoral fins .... *Raja stellulata*, Starry skate, p. 61

FAMILY TORPEDINIDAE   ELECTRIC RAYS

The electric rays have rounded outlines and the disc comprised of body and pectoral fins is rather thick. Dorsal and caudal fins are quite well developed, and the body moderately stout. There are no scales. Well-developed internal electric organs are situated on either side of the head. Young are born free living. Fishes of the warmer seas.

PACIFIC ELECTRIC RAY

Torpedo californica Ayres 1855

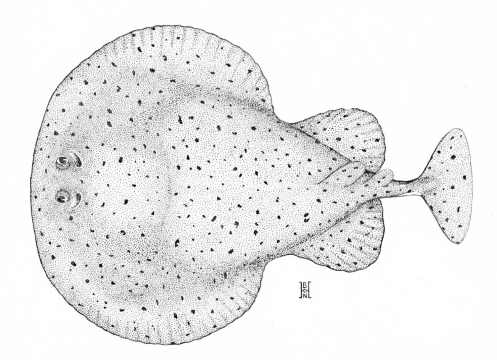

Scientific names from the Latin *torpedo* (numbness — from electric shock); and (State of) California.

This species was recorded in Clemens and Wilby 1946 as electric ray, *Tetranarce californica* (Ayres 1855).

Description   Body very depressed, its depth about 11 into total length, and its width about 1.3 into total length, head not distinguishable from rest of body as head, pectoral fins, and body are fused to make a smoothly rounded disc, flattened anteriorly, its width about 1.4 times its length. Mouth inferior, moderate in size, directed downward, palps on either side of upper jaw. Teeth in 4 or 5 rows in each jaw, the tooth bases fitting together to make a pavement, each tooth with a moderately raised cusp. Interorbital space almost flat and rather narrow. Eyes small and round. Five gill slits opening on ventral surface of body. Spiracle large, crescent shaped, immediately behind eyes. Caudal peduncle readily recognizable, lateral keel-like projections, a ventral ridge under the vertebral column, and rounded dorsally.

Fins   Dorsal (2), small, the anterior larger, and placed posterior to the outline of the body disc, both rounded. Caudal barely rounded, almost symmetrical with dorsal part slightly larger, fin vertical (twisted in illustration to show shape). Anal absent. Pelvics abdominal, confluent with main body disc.

Scales   Absent. Skin completely smooth.

Colour   Dorsally, dark blue or brown gray with numerous dark spots of various sizes up to nearly 1 percent of body length scattered on disc, body, and caudal fin. Dirty white on ventral surfaces.

Size   Length to 3 feet (91 cm) and 50 pounds (23 kg).

Recognition   Recognized by its depressed rounded form, the smooth skin, and well-developed caudal and dorsal fins.

Life History   Bears living young, ovoviviparous. Remarkable for the specialized muscle tissue on either side of the head which generates and stores electric potential capable of giving a strong electric shock to any person or animal making contact with the fish at two points. In British Columbia herring have been observed in the food.

Distribution   San Diego, southern California[5] to northern British Columbia about 5 miles (8 km) off Wiah Point in Dixon Entrance.[2] Locally abundant in California, and sporadically common in British Columbia. In the winter of 1940–41 Pacific electric rays were frequently encountered in herring catches in Barkley Sound and Kyuquot Sound.[1] Observed at Nootka,[5] off Cape St. James[3] and in the southern part of the Strait of Georgia[2] and Nanoose Bay. Taken as deep as 150 fathoms (275 m) but most commonly encountered in shallower water.[4]

References   1 Anon 1941b; 2 Clemens and Wilby 1961; 3 Crawford 1927a; 4 Grinols 1965a; 5 Schultz and DeLacy 1936.

FAMILY RAJIDAE   SKATES

These rays have slender tails with lateral keels, two small dorsal fins, and no significant caudal fin. Scales are distributed irregularly, and may be quite spinelike. Body approaches rhomboid shape. Fertilization is internal and the eggs are deposited for incubation in characteristic horny cases.

Egg cases in the Rajidae containing one to five or more developing eggs, are frequently encountered on beaches or in fishing operations. They are basically rectangular in shape with prominent horns of various shapes and sizes at the corners; they are flat or slightly convex on the ventral surface and arched dorsally. Egg cases produced by different species of skates differ in size and shape and can be distinguished with reasonable assurance by applying the following key and descriptions. Among Canadian fishes deposited eggs are also enclosed in egg cases by Pacific hagfish, the brown cat shark, and the ratfish.

KEY TO EGG CASES OF
CANADIAN PACIFIC FISHES

(egg cases from the deepsea skate, *Raja abyssicola* not included)

1   Egg cases more or less flattened and rectangular with prominent corners or
     horns 2

or   1   Egg cases not rectangular 5

2   Egg cases more than 19 cm in "least"
     length (between the centres of the two
     ends).
     All horns are short, blunt, and flatten-
     ed; dorsal rectangular outline moder-
     ately pinched about mid-length; pos-
     terior edge of case between horns
     nearly straight, anterior edge slightly
     concave; dorsal surface highly arched; prominent ridges originating near
     middle of dorsal arch extend forward roughly parallel for about half
     length and then separate to edges of egg case and on anterior horns;
     anterior horns obscured by a flat connection between them ....
     .... *Raja binoculata*, p. 56

or   2   Egg cases less than 19 cm least length 3

3   Egg cases less than 5 cm least length.
     Horns at anterior end of case bent inward and crossing
     near tips, anterior margin of case almost a straight
     line, posterior margin strongly convex. Surface rough
     from presence of coarse longitudinal fibres. Fine at-
     tachment fibres along edges of prominent lateral keels ....
     .... *Raja kincaidi*, p. 58

or   3   Egg cases more than 6 cm least length 4

52

4   Surface of case with pronounced longitudinal stria-
     tions arising from closely packed fibres.
     Anterior horns longer than posterior ones and
     have flattened tips. Anterior margin of case al-
     most a straight line, posterior margin strongly
     convex. Attachment fibres along lateral keels
     sparse and confined to bases of anterior horns

     ....

     .... *Raja stellulata*, p. 61

or   4   Surface of case relatively smooth with longitudinal
     striations not pronounced.
     All horns slender and short, the anterior horns
     somewhat longer. Posterior edge of case almost
     straight or even convex; anterior edge moderate
     concave. Attachment fibres abundant at lateral
     edges ....

     .... *Raja rhina*, p. 59

5   Egg case slightly constricted about one-third of distance from truncated
     anterior end; posterior end rounded; a flange around margin is drawn
     out into long coiled tendrils at each corner, which may be used as hold-
     fasts or may be lost at one end. Body of case about 5.5 cm long, 2.3
     cm wide and about half as deep as wide ...... *Apristurus brunneus*, p. 38

or   5   Egg case spindle shaped or nearly cylindrical 6

6   Horny egg cases spindle shaped with one end reduced and drawn out into a
     filament; case with longitudinal radially asymmetrical ridges, some car-
     rying elaborate frills. Body of case up to 20 cm long ....
     .... *Hydrolagus colliei*, p. 61

or   6   Egg cases transparent, cylindrical with rounded ends, each end with tufts
     of adhering hooked fibres; often found in long strings. Individual cases
     about 2.5 cm long and 10 mm in diameter ...... *Eptatretus (stouti?)*, p. 18

DEEPSEA SKATE

Raja abyssicola Gilbert 1895

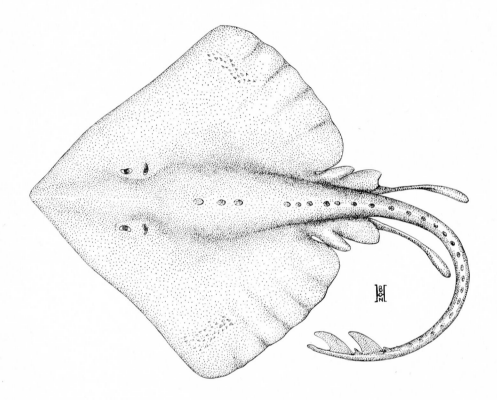

Scientific names from the Latin *raja* (skate); and the Greek *abyssos* (bottomless) and *cola* (living — at depths).

Description   Body much depressed, not clearly demarked from pectoral fins or head. Outline between tip of snout and tips of pectoral fins convex so that it lies outside a straight line between the two points. Snout pointed, the angle at its tip less than a right angle. Outer angles of pectoral fins rounded and greater than right angles. Mouth inferior, moderate in size, directed downward, its width more than half its distance from tip of snout. Teeth small in about 31 rows in each jaw. Eyes small, dorsal. Interorbital space broad and deeply concave. Five gill slits on ventral surface. Spiracles large behind eyes. Tail slender tapering, a little more than half total length.

Spines   An interrupted series of about 24 broad spines along mid-dorsal line from front of pelvic fins to first dorsal fin. Continued with 1 spine between dorsal fins and 3 spines in a row in middle of back. Pectoral hooks weakly developed in a broken band inside posterior margin of pectoral fin.

Fins   Dorsal (2), moderately high and large, separated, and both well back on tail. Anal

54

absent. Pectorals broad, attached to snout and body. Pelvics abdominal, rather small, rounded, incised. Wide lateral folds on either side of tail confluent at tip of tail with dorsal finfold.[1]

Claspers of male long, slender, and flexible.

Scales   Placoid, in form of long, close-set, bristlelike, flexible spines which give a velvetlike texture to skin; bare areas on extreme anterior margin of disc, posterior margin of disc, orbit region, most of upper part of pelvics, and basal parts of tail. A band of enlarged prickles on either side of tail.

Colour   Dark brown above and below. Said to have obscure darker brown spots with definite margins anteriorly.

Size   Length to 4.5 feet (137 cm).

Recognition   Recognizable by the gap in the row of spines along the mid-dorsal line. Adolescent and older individuals have the shoulder spine reduced to a remnant or absent.

Distribution   A rarely observed deep-sea benthic fish. Recorded from off northern Oregon at 800 to 850 fathoms (1460–1560 m), off the Queen Charlotte Islands in 1588 fathoms (2910 m),[2,3] and from the Bering Sea.[4]

References   1 Garman 1913; 2 Gilbert 1895; 3 Grinols 1965a; 4 Wilimovsky 1954.

BIG SKATE

Raja binoculata Girard 1854

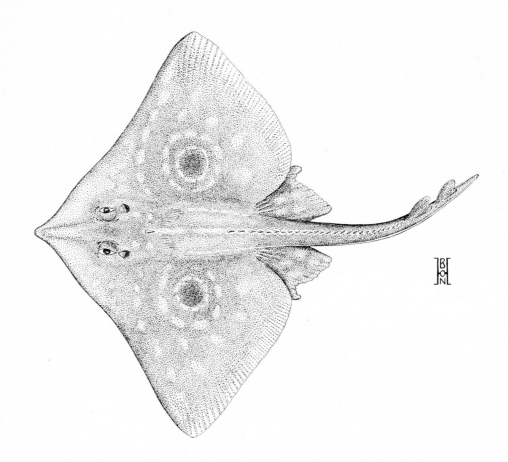

Scientific names from the Latin *raja* (skate); and *bi* (two), and *oculata* (eyed — arrangement of pigment on tops of pectoral fin bases).

Description　Body much depressed, not clearly demarked from head or pectoral fins. Outline between snout and tips of pectoral fins slightly concave so that most of it is inside a straight line joining the two points. Head depressed. Snout pointed with a blunt tip, supported by a firm cartilage. Mouth inferior, moderate in size, and directed downward. Nares deep and joined to corners of mouth by deep slits forming free palps. Teeth small with bases touching, in rows, with raised cusps. Eyes dorsal, interorbital space concave. Five gill slits on ventral surface. Spiracles large, open, immediately behind and lateral to eyes.

Spines　An irregular row of about 33 mid-dorsal spines on posterior part of body to second dorsal fin, interrupted by the first dorsal. A solitary mid-dorsal spine a little more than 1 interorbital width behind the orbits. Moderate spines median to orbits anterior and posterior to eyes, and out-

56

side orbits anterior to eyes. In males a patch of spines near margin of each pectoral fin extends from snout to beyond the fin tip.

Fins   Dorsal (2), well back on tail, small. Caudal and anal absent. Pectorals broad, attached to snout and incorporated with body. Pelvics abdominal, large, moderately concave on free margin. Posterior sides of tail with a small fleshy keel on either side.

Scales   Minute, placoid, rather sparse on body, tail, and posterior part of head.

Colour   On dorsal surface dull olive brown or gray to near black on large individuals. White on ventral surface, a large eye, or ocellus, at the base of each pectoral fin with concentric zones of light and dark, the light colour including red. Light spots on body.

Size   Length to 8 feet (2.4 m). A 6-foot (1.8-m) specimen weighed about 200 pounds (91 kg).

Recognition   Noteworthy for the prominent ocellus at the base of each pectoral fin, the moderate, broad concavity in the edge of the pelvic fin, and the posterior

start of the continuous mid-dorsal row of spines.

Life History   The big skate, like the other skates, expels its eggs in horny egg cases. In the big skate these may be up to a foot in length and contain up to seven eggs. They have been found in recognizable beds where embryos may be found at various stages of development.[2] The food includes crustaceans and fishes such as great sculpins.

Distribution   Southern California (but not common south of Point Conception)[4] to southeastern Alaska. Common throughout British Columbia at moderate depths.[1,3,5]

Utilization   Big skates are used to a limited extent by removing the pectoral fins for sale on fresh fish markets. The rest of the fish is discarded.

References   1 Grinols 1965a; 2 Hitz 1964; 3 Hubbs 1916a; 4 Roedel and Ripley 1950; 5 Wilimovsky 1954.

BLACK SKATE

Raja kincaidi Garman 1908

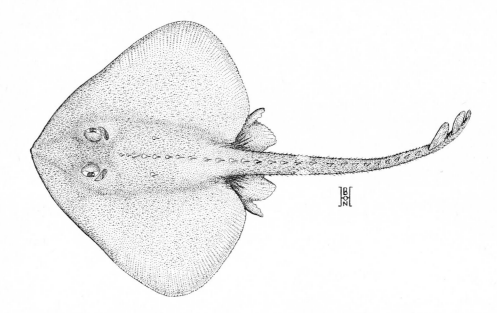

Scientific names from the Latin *raja* (skate); and Professor Trevor Kincaid, University of Washington.

Description   Body much depressed, not clearly demarked from head or pectoral fins. Outline between snout and tip of pectoral fins convex so that a straight line joining the two points is entirely within the outline. Head depressed. Snout blunt. Mouth inferior, moderate in size, and directed downward. Nares deep, joined to corners of mouth by deep slits forming free palps. Teeth small, closely placed in diagonal rows, each with a single raised ridge or point. Eyes dorsal. Interorbital space almost flat. Five gill slits on ventral surface. Spiracle large, immediately behind eyes.

Spines   A single row of 27 to 33[2] strong sharp spines along mid-dorsal line from a point

about 1 interorbital space behind the orbits to the first dorsal fin. One or 2 large spines on shoulder girdle. In males patches of large sharp spines near tips of pectoral fins and extending toward snout along margin of the fin.

Fins   Dorsal (2), far back on tail, moderately separated. Caudal much reduced. Anal absent. Pectorals broad, attached to snout and incorporated with body. Pelvics abdominal, large, deeply notched. All fins covered with scales.

Scales   Placoid, small. Sharp prickles fairly evenly spaced over dorsal part of body, fins, tail, and eyelids.

Colour   In adults slaty black on back. In juveniles a uniform grayed brown with small brown spots. White on ventral surface. White spot on either side of tail evident in small individuals.

Size   Length to 33 inches (84 cm).

58

Recognition Recognized by the continuous row of spines along the mid-dorsal line, the convex anterior margin of the pectoral fins, the absence of spines on the orbit rim, one or two spines on the shoulder girdle, and the sharp scales uniformly distributed over the dorsal surface.

Distribution From southern California to the Gulf of Alaska (Unalaska Island[3]). Commonly taken in shallow water in British Columbia. In Oregon taken to 450 fathoms (825 m) and in Alaska to 220 fathoms (400 m).[1]

References 1 Grinols 1965a; 2 Schultz 1937b; 3 Wilimovsky 1964.

LONGNOSE SKATE

Raja rhina Jordan and Gilbert 1880

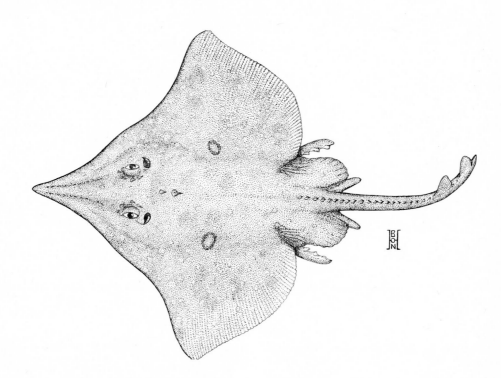

Scientific names from the Latin *raja* (skate); and the Greek root *rhino* (nose).

Description Body much depressed, not clearly demarked from pectoral fins or

59

head. Outline between snout and tip of pectoral fins definitely concave so that it lies well within a straight line between the 2 points. Head depressed. Snout pointed. Mouth inferior, moderate in size, directed downward. Nares deep and joined to corners of mouth by deep slits cutting off palps. Teeth small, in touching diagonal rows, each tooth a plate with a minute cusp. Eyes dorsal. Five gill slits on ventral surface. Spiracles large, behind eyes. Tail long and tapering.

Spines   A row of about 20 sharp mid-dorsal spines from base of tail to space between dorsal fins where there may be an additional spine. Two (or one) mid-dorsal spines immediately behind eyes. A sparse discontinuous row of spines around inner edge of orbit.

Fins   Dorsal (2), both small and well back on tail. Caudal reduced to a low ridge. Anal absent. Pectorals broad, attached to snout and incorporated with body. Pelvics abdominal, acutely and very deeply incised. A fleshy lateral ridge on each side of tail.

Scales   Placoid, very small, sparse on snout and on ventral surface along anterior edge of pectoral fin and snout.

Colour   Dorsal surface uniform brown. There is a simple dark ring at the base of each pectoral fin, and there may be a light spot poste-rior to the ring. The ventral surface is a muddy blue with small brown flecks on the anterior part.

Size   Length to 4 feet 6 inches (1.4 m).

Recognition   Noteworthy for the long, pointed, flexible snout and the concave anterior margin of the pectoral fin, the bluish ventral surface, the short row of mid-dorsal spines nearly confined to the tail, and the acutely notched pelvic fin.

Life History   The egg cases of this species are usually between 3 and 5 inches (8–12 cm) long, have tendrils, and usually contain only one egg.

Distribution   From southern California to southeastern Alaska. A common fish in trawl catches throughout British Columbia. In California taken in depths to 203 fathoms (370 m).[1,2,3]

Utilization   The pectoral fins are occasionally sold as skate wings but the species is not highly regarded.

References   1 Grinols 1965a; 2 Roedel and Ripley 1950; 3 Wilimovsky 1954.

STARRY SKATE

Raja stellulata Jordan and Gilbert 1880

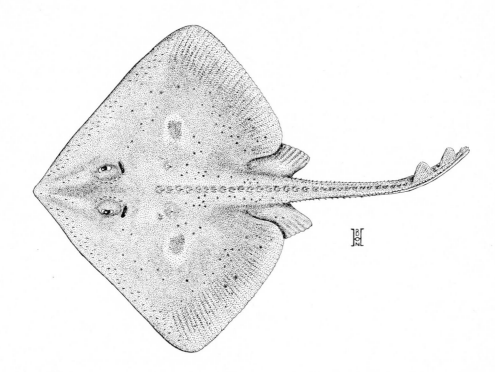

Scientific names from the Latin *raja* (skate); and *stellula* (small star — scales).

This species was called prickly skate in Clemens and Wilby 1946.

Dr Carl L. Hubbs advises that Canadian records considered here may be based on a different and undescribed species.

Description   Body much depressed, not clearly demarked from head or pectoral fins. Lines between snout and tip of pectoral fins convex so that all the lines are outside straight lines joining fin tip and snout. Head depressed. Snout bluntly pointed. Mouth inferior, moderate in size, and directed downward. Nares deep and joined to corners of the mouth by deep slits forming palps. Teeth small, each a plate with a single raised cusp, in rows. Eyes dorsal. Five gill slits on ventral surface. Spiracles large, immediately behind eyes and lateral to them.

Spines   A row of strong, sharp spines along the mid-dorsal line from a point behind the eyes by less than the interorbital width to the first dorsal fin and continued beyond it with a single spine between the 2 dorsal fins. Large spines on the shoulder girdle. A row of small spines on the inner edge of the orbit. A cluster of moderate spines along the edge of the pectoral fin from its tip to the snout, large spines in males.

Fins   Dorsal (2), both small and well back on tail. Caudal very small. Anal absent. Pectorals broad, attached to snout and incorporated with

61

body. Pelvics, abdominal, large, deeply notched. A horizontal fleshy ridge from either side of ventral surface of tail, more prominent posteriorly.

Scales   Placoid, small, stellate, scattered, becoming spinelike on tail, and dorsal surface.

Colour   Grayish brown, numerous dark spots of various sizes scattered on body, a weakly marked eye spot frequently present at base of pectoral fins.

Size   Length to 30 inches (76 cm).

Recognition   Noteworthy for the soft rounded snout, the continuous row of spines along the mid-dorsal line, the small stellate scales, and the convex anterior margin of the pectoral fins.

Life History   The eggs of starry skates, like those of other skates, are laid in horny egg cases. Two newly hatched young were taken off Ucluelet in June and July, 1909.

Distribution   From southern California to the Gulf of Alaska.[3] In British Columbia from around Vancouver Island, Port San Juan, Ucluelet, (San Juan Islands[1]), and from the Queen Charlotte Islands. In the southern part of the range to more than 200 fathoms (366 m).[1,2,3]

References   1 DeLacy, Dryfoos, and Miller 1963; 2 Grinols 1965a; 3 Wilimovsky 1964.

FAMILY DASYATIDAE   STINGRAYS

In stingrays the disc is wide and the tail very long and slender with a sharp poisonous spine about midlength. Fertilization is internal and the young are born free living. Fishes of the tropics; found in rivers there, occasionally strays into temperate waters.

STINGRAY

Dasyatis sp.

Scientific name from the Greek *dasys* (rough) and *(b)atus* (shark).

Clemens and Wilby 1946 listed this species as rat-tailed sting ray, and in 1961 used diamond stingray as the common name. The only Canadian record was identified in the field as *Dasyatis* sp., and later associated (reasonably) with the common stingray of California. The correctness of doing so now appears less certain with at least two possibilities presenting themselves:

DIAMOND STINGRAY

Dasyatis dipterura (Jordan and Gilbert 1880)

Species name from the Greek *di* (two), *pteros* (fin), and *ouro* (tail).

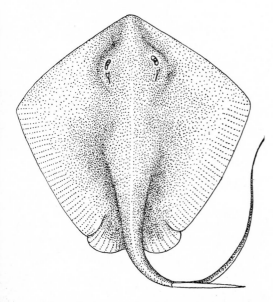

Description   Body much depressed, not clearly marked from head or pectoral fins, outline of disc shaped like a kite with the fabric torn from lower (posterior) part. A little wider than long. Anterior margin slightly convex so that the edge is a little outside a straight line from snout tip to fin tip. Moderate point at snout, no angles elsewhere in disc outline. Mouth inferior, mod-erate in size, directed downward, with 5 papillae, the outer smaller; upper jaw indented in middle. Teeth small. Eyes dorsal. Five gill slits on ventral surface. Spiracle large, open, placed immediately behind eyes. Tail less than 1.5 times length of disc.

Spines   Three rows of narrow depressed tubercles directed backward, on middle of back and base of tail, in short parallel rows on each shoulder. A strong long serrate spine arising dorsally from tail about one-third of its length from base.

Fins   No dorsal, caudal, or anal but a long fleshy fold above tail behind spine, and a larger finfold below tail. Pelvics broad, truncate, rounded.

Scales   Placoid, minute.

Colour   Bluish brown to black.

Size   Length to at least 6 feet (183 cm).[4]

Distribution   On beaches and in shallow water from Payta (Paita?), Peru, to southern California,[4] and possibly British Columbia.[5]

63

Dasyatis violacea (Bonaparte 1832)

Species name from the Latin *viola* (purple colour).

The French name is *pastenague*.

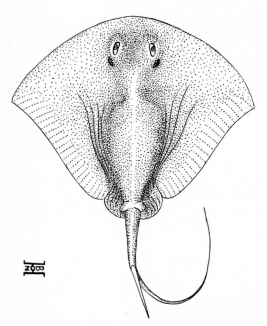

Description   Body much depressed, not clearly marked from head or pectoral fins. Disc rounded rhomboid, length of body about two-thirds width of disc. Snout blunt so that the whole anterior margin is almost a continuous curve. Mouth inferior, moderate in size, directed downward. A row of papillae behind teeth in lower jaw. Teeth small. Eyes dorsal. Five gill slits on ventral surface. Spiracles large, close behind eyes. Tail nearly round in cross section, its length about twice that of disc.

Spines   Spines on body limited to a row of tubercles along mid-dorsal line from middle of back, and a few scattered tubercles on shoulders. A long strong spine arising dorsally and directed backward arising from tail about a quarter of its length from base.

Fins   No dorsal, caudal, or anal fins but fleshy folds above tail behind spine, the larger and deeper finfold below tail. Pelvics short and rounded.[2]

Colour   Violaceous to dark brown above, light below.

Distribution   Apparently pelagic, at least at times, and sporadic. Mediterranean Sea, Japan, southern California at Santa Monica Bay, and between Malibu Beach and Point Dume,[3] and possibly British Columbia.

The Canadian record for *Dasyatis* is from off Kyuquot Sound. Several individuals were snagged on salmon trolling gear and at least one was caught by the mouth.

References   1 Follett personal communication; 2 Garman 1913; 3 Radovich 1961; 4 Roedel and Ripley 1950; 5 Williamson 1930.

SUBCLASS HOLOCEPHALI
(Chimaeriformes)

A more compact group with only a single gill opening on each side of the head covering four pairs of gills and gill clefts. There is an erectile spine ahead of the dorsal fin, the skin is naked, and the teeth are six pairs of grinding plates. Eggs are fertilized internally and expelled in chitinous cases. There is no cloaca. The subclass includes only one order, Chimaeriformes, the **chimaeras.**

FAMILY CHIMAERIDAE   CHIMAERAS

The only family in the subclass. All species have smooth skin, large heads with prominent snouts that may or may not be greatly protruding, and bodies tapered to fine tails. The lateral line is an open groove or a closed groove with pores to the surface. The family includes bizarre deepwater forms. Only one species known from waters off British Columbia.

RATFISH

Hydrolagus colliei (Lay and Bennett 1839)

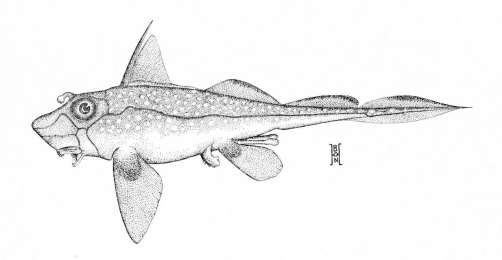

Scientific names from the Greek *(h)ydor* (water) and *lagos* (hare — prominent front teeth and hare lip); and M. Collie, naturalist on Captain Beechey's ship "Blossom."

Description Body elongate, its greatest depth at rear of dorsal fin, about 6 into length, evenly tapered to end of caudal fin, compressed. Head large, deep, compressed, its length about 5 into length. Mouth ventral, rather small, directed down and forward. Upper jaw divided anteriorly exposing prominent nares. Snout obtusely pointed in a compressed cone. Teeth in upper jaw united into a forward-directed plate. Bony plates of less obvious origin on lower jaw and roof of mouth. Interorbital space moderate, smooth, and moderately arched. Eye oval, large, its length about 4 into head length, green in life. Opercular flaps fleshy, joined together and to isthmus. Gill opening small in front of insertion of pectoral fin.

Fins Dorsal (2), I, about 10, almost triangular but extending posteriorly in a low rayless fold, the spine stout, serrate, and reputedly poisonous;[6] the second fin with a markedly undulating outline almost dividing it into 2 parts. Caudal long, low, lanceolate, barely separated from dorsal above and including anal below. Pectorals large, triangular with a well-rounded inner angle, an opaque base, and numerous fine, supporting structures. Pelvics abdominal, oval, similar in structure to pectorals.

Males have additional features. A spiny club-shaped process on the forehead fits into a depression below its base. Sharp, retractile clasping organs (that can give a nasty cut[6]) are on either side of the vent. A biramous, finely serrate clasper with expanded ends extends backward from the base of each pelvic fin.

Scales Absent and the skin smooth. A lateral line undulates (not always to the same pattern or extent) along midside to the caudal, with branches on the head extending on snout, jaws, and operculum, associated with evident pores.

Colour Basically silvery with many hues, golden, green, brown, overlaying a darker background that leaves prominent light spots. The eyes reflect an emerald green.

Size   Length to 3 feet 2 inches (97 cm).

Recognition   Notable for the large bulky snout, the forward-directed teeth, the smooth skin, and the long tapering tail. Males are further recognized by the process on the forehead and the prominent claspers.

Life History   Elaborate courtship patterns in which both sexes carry out set manoeuvres and the males undergo striking colour changes have been observed in captivity.[9] Eggs, which have a diameter of about 20 millimeters, are expelled in pairs, each with an elongated, ridged, brown case about 125 millimeters long. Extrusion is slow, lasting for 18 to 30 hours. After the capsules are completely extruded, they hang freely in the water from the female by an elastic capsular filament, which is a slender rather fragile extension of the case, for 4 to 6 days. Later, eggs are found with capsular filaments entangled in the bottom,[8] or they may be regularly planted vertically in the bottom mud as observed in the intertidal zone by Dr A. L. Pritchard.[3] Egg deposition

seems to take place throughout the year but is most active in late summer and early autumn.[4,8] Food consists mainly of clams, crustaceans such as crabs and shrimps, and fishes.[8] Ratfish seek their food by smell. Locomotion is by the large pectoral fins.[9]

Distribution   Baja California including the upper Gulf of California,[2,5] to southeastern Alaska.[10] In deeper water toward the south (as in northern California).[7] Abundant throughout Canadian waters, most abundant at 50 to 150 fathoms (92–275 m) in inside waters, but between 100 and 200 fathoms (183–366 m) outside. Taken in hauls to 499 fathoms (913 m).[1] A common visitor to shallow water where males draw attention as "fish with legs."

References   1 Alverson, Pruter, and Ronholt 1964; 2 Baldwin 1961; 3 Clemens and Wilby 1961; 4 Dean 1906; 5 Grinols 1965a; 6 Halstead and Bunker 1952; 7 Roedel and Ripley 1950; 8 Sathyanesan 1966; 9 Vancouver Public Aquarium Staff 1970; 10 Wilimovsky 1954.

CLASS OSTEICHTHYES
(Teleostomi, Pisces)

Bony Fishes

Fishes of great range in size, form, and habitat, with true bone usually present in skull, jaws, or pectoral arch, and usually with well-developed jaws. One external gill opening on each side, the two frequently united ventrally. There are usually four or five pairs of gill arches. The following statements are generally true but there are exceptions to all of them: there are two sets of paired fins; the bones supporting pectoral and pelvic fins consist of one or two series of basal elements in a parallel or fanlike arrangement, and these elements in turn support the fin rays; fin rays although appearing single have right and left halves; scales grow with the growth of the fish; anal, genital, and urinary tracts open to the exterior separately through a cloacal pouch.

KEY TO THE FAMILIES OF BONY FISHES

1   Caudal fin with dorsal lobe supported by an upward extension of the vertebral column and distinctly larger than ventral lobe; 5 well-separated rows of bony plates arranged longitudinally along body; mouth inferior, protrusible, preceded by 4 prominent barbels in a transverse row.

Acipenseridae
Sturgeons
p. 81

or 1   Caudal fin not with an obviously enlarged dorsal lobe supported by vertebral column; without 5 separated rows of bony plates along body; mouth not preceded by a row of 4 barbels 2

2   Body compressed asymmetrically with both eyes on same side of head and eyed side of body more strongly pigmented; flatfishes 3

or 2   Body shape variable but symmetrical; 1 eye on each side of head; and colour similar on both sides 4

3   Pelvic fins asymmetrically placed with fin for eyed side on ridge of abdomen, the other not on ridge; eyes and colour on left side of body ....
.... Bothidae, Lefteye flounders, p. 595

or 3   Pelvic fins symmetrically placed on sides of body; eyes and colour usually on right side of body .... Pleuronectidae, Righteye flounders, p. 599

68

4   A modified movable, jointed, protrusible organ on anterior part of head available as a fishing lure; gill opening behind pectoral fin; short black fishes.

Oneirodidae
Dreamers
p. 213

or   4   No such specialized fishing lure on anterior part of head 5

5   Body truncate, compressed, and deep; long-rayed dorsal and anal fins; no rayed caudal fin .... Molidae, Molas, p. 639

or   5   Body not so truncate, large dorsal and anal fins not excessively large 6

6   Large oval adhering disc on top of head ....
.... Echeneidae, Remoras, p. 284

or   6   No adhering disc on top of head 7

7   Pelvic fins absent or not readily discernible 8

or   7   Pelvic fins present (may be small or modified to form ventral adhering discs) 25

8   Pelvic fins represented by a single spine or scale, or by a residual base; caudal fin present 9

or   8   Pelvic fins completely absent, caudal fin present or absent 10

9   Pelvic fin reduced to a single spine or scale; caudal fin forked and directed straight backward; head flattened dorsally with lower jaw projecting; very elongate slender fishes.

Trichiuridae
Hairtails
p. 367

or   9   Pelvic fins reduced to base (buried in flesh); caudal fin with rayed dorsal lobe prolonged and extending upward; head flattened laterally, jaws about even; large elongate compressed fishes.

Trachipteridae
Ribbonfishes (adult)
p. 270

10   Body extremely elongate, its depth more than 20 into total length 11

or   10   Body moderately elongate or not elongate, its depth less than 20 into total length 14

11   Body depth more than 40 into total length; jaws strongly recurved.

Nemichthyidae
Snipe eels
p. 87

or   11   Body depth less than 40 into total length; jaws not recurved or only slightly recurved 12

12   Body encased in bony plates; head produced into a tubular snout with membranes uniting upper and lower jaws.

Syngnathidae
Pipefishes
p. 277

or   12   Body not encased in bony plates; mouth not opening at end of tubular snout 13

13   Roof of mouth with prominent double row of sharp triangular teeth giving a sawlike profile to roof of mouth.

Serrivomeridae
Sawpalates
p. 85

or   13   No sawlike profile to roof of mouth; lower jaw projecting in a fleshy flap.

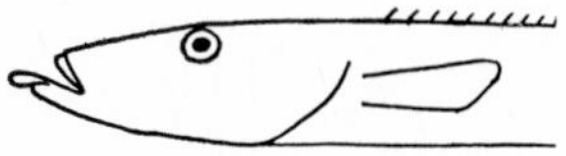

Ptilichthyidae
Quillfishes
p. 352

14   Skin in oblique folds passing down and back; scales minute; caudal forked; body little compressed or not compressed with its depth about 8 to 12 into standard length.

Ammodytidae
Sand lances
p. 360

or   14   Skin not in oblique folds; body elongate or not; caudal fin forked or not 15

15   Caudal fin forked; compressed fishes 16

or   15   Caudal fin not forked; body compressed moderately or not compressed ... 17

16   Length of pectoral fin greater than length of head; caudal fin deeply forked.

Stromateidae
Butterfishes
p. 381

or   16   Length of pectoral fin less than length of head; caudal moderately forked; body very limp; large fish.

Icosteidae
Ragfishes (adult)
p. 385

17   Large conspicuous pores on head; head blunt; mouth directed upward; smooth rounded fins; long dorsal fin.

Zaproridae
Prowfishes
p. 358

or   17   Pores on head not conspicuous; fins not smoothly rounded 18

An uncommon deepwater fish recently discovered off the coast of British Columbia fits into the key about here. It is *Xenomystax atrarius* Gilbert 1891 notable for its elongate form, absence of pelvic fins but well-developed pectorals, scaleless body and conspicuous lateral line, the wide lunate gill openings, teeth on the vomer, and the maxillaries deeply grooved throughout their lengths dividing the teeth into two series. The 70-centimeter standard length specimen, NMC 71–77 was taken by the *G. B. Reed* at 48.47.48 N, 126.32.30 W from 446 to 457 meters depth, and is recorded in A. E. Peden's paper, Redescription and distribution of the rare deep-sea eel, *Xenomystax atrarius* in the eastern Pacific Ocean (J. Fish. Res. Bd. Canada 29: 1–12). (Drawing actually based on *Xenomystax rictus* Garman 1899.)

18   Skin loose and delicate; gill openings not extending below upper 15 or 16 rays of pectoral fin.

Cyclopteridae
Lumpfishes and snailfishes
p. 568

The aberrant spinycheek liparid, *Acantholiparis opercularis* Gilbert and Burke 1912 reported from the Bering Sea and from off northern Oregon (Grinols 1966) but not from off British Columbia keys out close to here. It is unique in having at least 2 strong spines directed up and out from the anterior margin of the operculum.

or   18   Skin not loose and delicate, gill openings not restricted to level of origins of upper 15 to 16 rays of pectoral fin 19

19   Robust fishes with a hooked spine on preoperculum and a distinct caudal peduncle.

Cottidae
Sculpins, genus *Ascelichthys*
p. 472

or   19   No distinct spine on operculum, rather slender fishes 20

20   Dorsal fin composed entirely of soft rays 21

or   20   Dorsal fin composed of spines or spines and soft rays 22

21   Body deeper posteriorly than anteriorly ....
                 .... Scytalinidae, Graveldivers, p. 357

or   21   Body deeper at anterior end than posteriorly.

                                                                  Zoarcidae
                                                Eelpouts (in part)
                                                        p. 231

22   Teeth large, developed as crushing molars at back of mouth; adults with large black ocellate spots .... Anarhichadidae, Wolffishes, p. 351

or   22   Teeth small and not developed as molars; no large black spots with light borders on body 23

23   Lateral line absent .... Pholidae, Gunnels (in part), p. 344

or   23   Lateral line(s) 4 or 1, composed of faint pores 24

24   Lateral line 1; caudal fin free of anal; no crest on top of head ....
                     .... Cryptacanthodidae, Wrymouths, p. 354

or   24   Lateral line(s) 1 or 4; if 1, crest on top of head ....
                     .... Stichaeidae, Pricklebacks (in part), p. 324

25   Pelvic fins abdominal 26

or   25   Pelvic fins thoracic or jugular 49

26   Photophores or luminescent organs present 27

or   26   Photophores and luminescent organs absent .... 34—

27   Adipose fin absent 28

or   27   Adipose fin present 31

28   Teeth in jaws small 29

or   28   Teeth in jaws prominent; dorsal fin placed very far back leaving extremely short caudal peduncle 30

72

29   Several large photophores across ventral surface; tubelike projections directed posteriorly above ventral fin (less evident in large individuals) .... Searsidae, Tubeshoulders, p. 172

or   29   No photophores crossing abdomen; no tubelike shoulder organ; caudal peduncle slender .... Gonostomatidae, Lightfishes, p. 160

30   Dorsal fin with more than 19 rays; eye large, its diameter about twice caudal peduncle depth or more; a luminous bulb at the end of chin barbel.

Malacosteidae
Loosejaws
p. 168

or   30   Dorsal fin with less than 19 rays, eye rather small, no luminous bulb at end of chin barbel .... Melanostomiatidae, Scaleless dragonfishes, p. 164

31   Body very compressed; several series of enlarged, vertically elongate photophores.

Sternoptychidae
Silvery hatchetfishes
p. 162

or   31   Body moderately compressed, photophores on sides of body if present not enlarged 32

32   An iridescent patch on lower part of eyeball; small needlelike teeth.

Scopelarchidae
Pearleyes
p. 178

or   32   No iridescent patch on eyeball; teeth either very large or quite small 33

33   Teeth extremely large; dorsal fin placed far forward on body, its first ray greatly prolonged; ventral adipose fin present anterior to anal fin .... Chauliodontidae, Viperfishes, p. 170

or   33   Teeth small or moderate in size; dorsal fin about midbody; no ventral adipose fin .... Myctophidae, Lanternfishes, p. 185

34   Adipose fin absent 35

or   34   Adipose fin present 41

35   Dorsal fin reduced to a series of 30 to 35 stout spines; caudal much reduced at end of a long tapering body .... Notacanthidae, Spiny eels, p. 92

or   35   Dorsal and caudal fins not as described above 36

36   Pelvic axillary processes present 37

or   36   Pelvic axillary processes absent 38

| 37 | Pelvic fin anterior to dorsal fin; mouth very large, overhung by snout .... Engraulidae, Anchovies, p. 103 |

or | 37 | Pelvic fin below dorsal fin; mouth moderate in size at end of head .... Clupeidae, Herrings, p. 94 |

| 38 | Dorsal fins 2, well separated; cylindrical fishes .... Sphyraenidae, Barracudas, p. 313 |

or | 38 | Dorsal fins 1, with or without following finlets .... 39 |

| 39 | Dorsal fin followed by 5 or 6 finlets .... Scomberesocidae, Sauries, p. 258 |

or | 39 | No finlets following dorsal fin .... 40 |

| 40 | Dorsal fin long based and low; compressed fishes with rounded fins.

Icosteidae
Ragfishes (alternative)
p. 385 |

or | 40 | Dorsal fin with only moderately long base; sturdy fishes with large sculptured blunt heads, and large scales.

Melamphaeidae
Melamphids
p. 262 |

| 41 | Dorsal fin absent.

Anotopteridae
Daggertooths
p. 176 |

or | 41 | Dorsal fin present .... 42 |

| 42 | Dorsal fin long based and very high; teeth prominent.

Alepisauridae
Lancetfishes
p. 174 |

or | 42 | Dorsal fin moderate in both length of base and height .... 43 |

| 43 | Paired fins large and fragile; eyes telescopic or otherwise modified .... Opisthoproctidae, Spookfishes, p. 157 |

or | 43 | Paired fins not enlarged and fragile; eyes unmodified .... 44 |

| 44 | Eyes large, not otherwise modified, diameter about one-third length of head .... 45 |

or | 44 | Eyes smaller than one-third length of head .... 46 |

45   Pelvic fins under centre of dorsal fin; branchiostegals 2; fishes with large heads; deepest immediately behind head ....
.... Bathylagidae, Deepsea smelts, p. 152

or   45   Pelvic fins behind dorsal fin or below its posterior third; branchiostegals 3 or more; deepest between head and dorsal fin ....
.... Argentinidae, Argentines, p. 150

46   Pelvic fins definitely anterior to dorsal fin; anal fin relatively short based.

Scopelosauridae
Paperbones and wearyfishes
p. 183

or   46   Pelvic fins below or behind dorsal fin, or with base of anal fin longer than length of head posterior to orbit 47

47   Dorsal and pelvic fins placed well back on body; slender fishes with narrowly pointed heads.

Paralepididae
Barracudinas
p. 180

or   47   Dorsal and pelvic fins only little posterior to midpoint of body; robust or slender fishes with blunt or moderately pointed heads 48

48   Pelvic axillary processes present ...... Salmonidae, Salmon and trout, p. 106

or   48   Pelvic axillary processes absent .... Osmeridae, Smelts, p. 136

49   Rows of photophores on sides and ventral surfaces; head depressed ....
.... Batrachoididae, Toadfishes, p. 206

or   49   No photophores or luminescent organs 50

50   Fins soft rayed, sometimes not all branched, in some macrourids fusions of rays produce 1 or 2 spinelike structures in the first dorsal fin, the first one equipped with characteristic slender spinules; scales present or absent, cycloid when present, but in macrourids scales frequently bear spinules 51

or   50   Fins with one or more spines; scales when present usually ctenoid 60

51   Barbels present on lower jaw; dorsal fins 2 or 3 52

or   51   Barbels absent; dorsal fins 1 54

52   Dorsal fins 2, the second low, its even outline continuous to the posterior end of the body where it merges with caudal and anal.

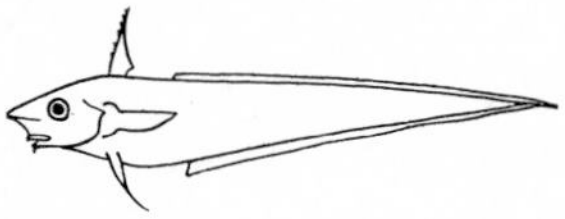

Macrouridae
Grenadiers
p. 249

or   52   Dorsal fins 3 or 2, if 2, second fin notched or strongly indented, caudal peduncle distinct 53

53   Mouth inferior under an overhanging rostrum projecting back below eye as a prominent ridge; dorsal and anal fins emarginate; first rays of first dorsal and pectoral fins elongated .... Moridae, Moras, p. 220

or   53   Mouth terminal or nearly so; snout without lateral ridges extending below eyes; dorsal and anal fins entire: first rays of dorsal and pectoral fins not elongated .... Gadidae, Codfishes, p. 221

54   Well-developed adhesive disc on anterior ventral surface 55

or   54   No sucker on ventral surface 56

55   Adhesive disc formed of recognizable anterior and posterior parts.

Gobiesocidae
Clingfishes
p. 209

or   55   Adhesive disc formed entirely by modified pelvic rays; body may be covered by spiny tubercles, otherwise smooth.

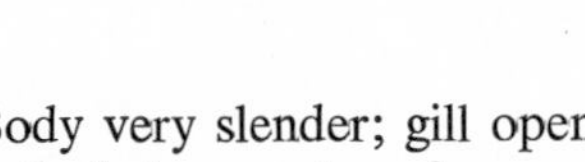

Cyclopteridae
Lumpfishes and snailfishes (in part)
p. 568

56   Vertical fins confluent with caudal fin, not clearly demarked 57

or   56   Vertical fins not confluent with caudal 58

57   Body very slender; gill opening a vertical slit in front of pectoral fin; pelvic fin below centre of eye .... Derepodichthyidae, Cuskpouts, p. 248

or   57   Body only moderately slender; gill opening extending below base of pectoral fin; pelvic fins well behind vertical from eye.

Zoarcidae
Eelpouts (in part)
p. 231

58   No well-marked caudal peduncle; anal fin reduced to a rough row of tubercles; pectoral fin (in juveniles) long and delicate; much compressed species with large eyes ....
.... Trachipteridae, Ribbonfishes (juvenile), p. 270

or 58   Caudal peduncle and anal fins both well marked; moderately compressed species 59

59   Body deep, wide lunate tail fin; anterior part of dorsal fin elevated ....
.... Lamprididae, Opahs, p. 268

or 59   Rather elongate body with small rounded tail fin; dorsal fin low and evenly contoured .... Ophidiidae, Cusk-eels and brotulas p. 229

60   First dorsal fin composed of 2 or 3 stout locking spines free of membrane; large serrate spine in pelvic fin; scales represented as oblong vertical plates
.... Gasterosteidae, Sticklebacks, p. 275

or 60   First dorsal fin, pelvic fin, and scales not specialized as above 61

61   First dorsal fin consists of about 25 small spines without intervening membranes; snout prolonged into a tube with small terminal mouth ....
.... Aulorhynchidae, Tube-snouts, p. 273

or 61   Dorsal fin and snout not modified as above 62

62   Body completely encased in touching bony plates ....
.... Agonidae, Poachers, p. 546

or 62   Body not completely encased in bony plates although rows of bony or horny plates may be present 63

63   Fishes with 1 dorsal fin 64
or 63   Fishes with 2 dorsal fins 78

64   Fishes with 1 spine only 65
or 64   Fishes with more than 1 spine 66

65   Stout compound spine (regarded as a fusion of rays) at origin of dorsal fin; stout fishes with barbels at side of mouth; only young known from salt water.

Cyprinidae
Minnows
p. 203

or 65   Only spine at insertion of pelvic fin; elongate rather compressed fishes with a long dorsal fin composed of unbranched and branched rays.

Bathymasteridae
Ronquils
p. 317

66   Scales at base of dorsal fin separated from those on rest of body by a marked furrow .... Embiotocidae, Surfperches, p. 298

or   66   No furrow along base of dorsal fin 67

67   Second and subsequent spines of dorsal fin forming a great mane extending nearly to caudal fin and capable of being recessed into a sheath along the sides of the fin; snout blunt .... Caristiidae, Manefish, p. 291

or   67   Second dorsal fin spine not elongate as part of a flexible mane 68

68   Eye very large, the diameter fewer than 3 into length of head; strongly compressed fish; juveniles with horny protuberances on sides in rows ....
.... Oreosomatidae, Oreos, p. 266

or   68   Eyes smaller than one-third of head length; no horny protuberances on sides 69

69   Preopercles with serrated edge; dorsal moderately low and even with flexible spines anteriorly and branched rays posteriorly; falcate pectoral fin; forked tail, little compressed fishes.

Branchiostegidae
Tilefishes
p. 282

or   69   No serrate edge on preoperculum; combination of other characters not found 70

70   Dorsal fin with 13 to 16 (rarely 17) stiff spines; anal fin with 3 spines, the second usually stoutest and longest; sturdy, deep-bodied fishes with spines on preopercles and opercles, and usually elsewhere on head.

Scorpaenidae
Scorpionfishes
p. 388

or   70   Fishes not with combination of characters described 71

71   Fishes with forked tails 72
or   71   Fishes with rounded or truncate tails 73

72   Tail lunate; snout blunt; dorsal fin high anteriorly ....
.... Bramidae, Pomfrets, p. 289

or   72   Tail strongly forked but not lunate; snout concave in profile, dorsal fin with irregular outline, bones of head with radiating striations ....
.... Pentacerotidae, Armorheads, p. 296

73   Dorsal fin rather long, and higher at both anterior and posterior ends than through centre part.

Clinidae
Clinids
p. 321

or   73   Dorsal fin without longer rays at both ends 74

74   Top of head with raised patch of spongy bone with a small backward extension; compressed, moderately deep fish with long low dorsal and anal fins.

Centrolophidae
Medusafish
p. 381

or   74   No mass of spongy bone on posterior part of top of head 75

75   Robust fishes or fishes moderately rounded in cross section 76

or   75   Compressed elongate fishes 77

76   Body covered with scales; occasionally more than 1 lateral line; 0 to 4 spines in anal fin; dorsal fin with 17 to 27 flexible spines; head without spines .... Hexagrammidae, Greenlings, p. 459

or   76   Scales on body when present arranged in bands, no spines in anal fin; dorsal fin with 6 to 17 spines, gill cover and head usually with spines frequently well developed .... Cottidae, Sculpins (in part), p. 472

77   Pelvic fins with 1 spine and 3 or 4 soft rays .... Stichaeidae, Pricklebacks (in part), p. 324

or   77   Pelvic fins with 1 spine and 1 soft ray .... Pholidae, Gunnels (in part), p. 344

78   Second dorsal fin followed by 1 or more finlets 79

or   78   No finlets following second dorsal fin 80

79   Second dorsal fin followed by 1 finlet; second dorsal fin long based .... Carangidae, Jacks, p. 286

or   79   Second dorsal fin followed by 5 or more finlets, base of second dorsal shorter than base of first dorsal .... Scombridae, Mackerels and tunas, p. 369

80   Two lateral keels, dorsal and ventral on caudal peduncle giving caudal peduncle a square or rhomboidal cross section.

Tetragonuridae
Squaretails
p. 384

or   80   Caudal peduncle without lateral keels arranged as above 81

81   Two pelvic fins fused to form a ventrally projecting cone free of the body.

Gobiidae
Gobies
p. 362

or   81   Pelvic fins not fused to form a projecting cone 82

82   Fringes on both lips.

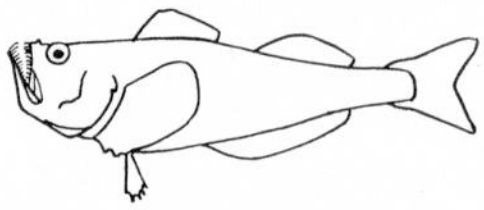

Trichodontidae
Sandfishes
p. 315

or   82   No fringes on lips 83

83   First dorsal fin small, its base less than half base of second dorsal, and separated from it by about twice first dorsal base; tail forked.

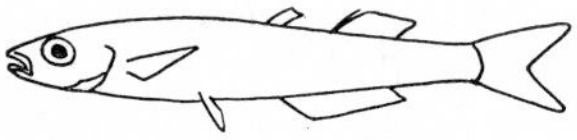

Atherinidae
Silversides
p. 260

or   83   First dorsal fin neither narrow based nor removed from second dorsal by as much as the length of its base 84

84   Accessory pelvic appendages present.

Sciaenidae
Drums
p. 293

or   84   Accessory pelvic appendages absent 85

85   Eyes on side of head; no cirri or spines on head; tail more or less forked 86

or   85   Eyes usually on top of head, usually cirri and/or spines on head; tail rounded or truncate .... Cottidae, Sculpins (in part), p. 472

86   Seven or 8 dark longitudinal stripes along side; broad spine on preoperculum; 2 blunt protuberances on posterior edge of preoperculum .... Percichthyidae, Temperate basses, p. 280

or   86   No obvious longitudinal stripes; margins of operculum and preoperculum entire .... Anoplopomatidae, Sablefishes, p. 454

ORDER ACIPENSERIFORMES

Rather large subcylindrical fishes with one dorsal fin placed well back on body, a moderately forked heterocercal tail with an upward-bending fleshy axis enclosing the notochord. Skin with minute scattered platelets and/or rows of large bony scutes that may continue on caudal axis. Teeth minute or absent. Branchiostegal rays absent. Usually snout large and flattened. Mouth ventral, protractile, with barbels. Skeleton mostly cartilaginous with ossifications in the membrane bones. Ventral fins abdominal with more fin rays than basal supports. Gasbladder present and attached to oesophagus. Freshwater or anadromous. Sometimes regarded as a separate subclass Neopterygii. Two living families, **sturgeon**, and **paddlefish.**

FAMILY ACIPENSERIDAE   STURGEONS

Body elongate and fusiform with five rows of bony shields, sharp in young, becoming blunt with age. Skin with small ossifications. Snout protruding. Mouth inferior and protractile. Teeth absent. Four barbels in transverse row between mouth and snout. Head covered by bony plates separated by sutures. Pectoral fins with first ray enlarged and ossified. Stomach with numerous pyloric appendages organized into a compact gland. Rectum with a spiral valve.

KEY TO THE ACIPENSERIDAE

1   Lateral shields 38 to 48; row of barbels on underside of snout nearer tip of snout than mouth; colour gray ....
.... *Acipenser transmontanus,* White sturgeon, p. 83

or   1   Lateral shields 23 to 30; row of barbels on underside of snout nearer to mouth than tip of snout; colour greenish ....
.... *Acipenser medirostris,* Green sturgeon, p. 82

GREEN STURGEON

Acipenser medirostris Ayres 1854

Scientific names from the Latin *acipenser* (sturgeon); and *medium* (moderate) and *rostris* (snout).

Description   Body elongate, depth about 7 into length to beginning of caudal fin, almost round in cross section. Head flattened above, its length about 3.6 into length to caudal fin. Mouth ventral, moderate in size, directed down, transverse. Snout flattened, concave in profile. Nares prominent. Lips protrusible in both jaws. No teeth. Interorbital space wide, convexly raised generally, but concave in the centre, width about 3.8 into length of head. Eye small, oval, the length about 17 into head length. Gill membranes broadly attached to isthmus. Caudal peduncle rather slender, its least depth about 25 into length to beginning of caudal fin.

Fins   Dorsal (1), 33 to 36, placed far back on body, highest anteriorly. Caudal heterocercal, dorsal rays rather rigid and short, ventral blade excentrically forked with its dorsal arm prolonged. Anal 22 to 28, narrow. Pectorals well developed and slightly pedunculate with many cartilaginous rays. Pelvics abdominal.

Scales   No real scales, body covered with small rough bony plates. Prominent sharp bony plates, each with a curved sharp spine, in 5 rows; mid-dorsal, midlateral, and ventrolateral. Rows start at the head or pectoral fin and extend to the dorsal fin, 7 to 11 plates; to central caudal axes, 22 to 30 plates; to level of pelvic insertion, 6 to 10 plates. No lateral line canal. A prominent transverse row of 4 barbels on lower surface of snout closer to mouth than to end of snout.

Colour   Olive green, olive stripes on midventral surface and on lower parts of each side.

Size   Length to 7 feet (213 cm) and weight to 300 pounds (136 kg). Although green sturgeon is not common, 75 fish weighing in all 2100 pounds (952 kg) were taken in one day off Kyuquot Sound. They were 37 to 80 inches (94–203 cm) long. They had been eating sand lance.[1]

Recognition   Identified by the 23 to 30 sharp bony plates along midside, the 4 barbels in a line closer to the mouth than to the tip of the snout, and the concave snout in profile.

Distribution   From southern California (between Newport and Huntington beaches[4]) to the Gulf of Alaska[6] and Unalaska Island[7]; Oregon, Washington.[5] On the Asian coast from the Amur River through Sakhalin, Tatar Strait, Hokkaido, Peter the Great Bay, and Korea[2,3] to Taiwan.[3] Best known from southern British Columbia and the west coast of Vancouver Island. It is not the subject of an organized fishery.

References   1 Anon 1954a; 2 Berg 1948; 3 Matsubara 1955; 5 Roedel 1941; 5 Schultz and DeLacy 1936; 6, 7 Wilimovsky 1954, 1964.

WHITE STURGEON

Acipenser transmontanus Richardson 1836

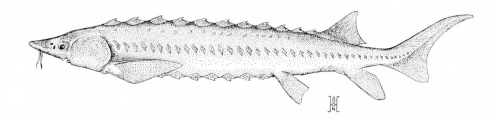

Scientific names from the Latin *acipenser* (sturgeon); *trans* (across) and *montes* (mountains).

Description Body elongate, depth about 6 into length to beginning of caudal fin, moderately compressed. Head somewhat flattened above but subconical, its length about 4 into length to caudal fin. Mouth ventral, moderate in size, directed downward, transverse. Nares prominent. Lips protrusible on both jaws. No teeth. Interorbital space wide and arched, its width about 3 into head length. Eyes small, oval, the length about 15 into head length. Operculum almost smooth with a weak focus for radiating lines. Gill membranes broadly attached to the isthmus. Caudal peduncle rather slender, its depth about 25 into length to beginning of caudal fin.

Fins Dorsal (1), 44 to 48, highest forward, rear free corner somewhat extended. Caudal heterocercal, dorsal rays rather rigid, ventral blade excentrically forked with its dorsal arm prolonged. Anal 28 to 31, narrow. Pectorals well developed and slightly pedunculate with many cartilaginous rays. Pelvics abdominal.

Scales No real scales. Small bony plates generally distributed more abundantly ventrally and forward. Prominent bony plates each with a curved sharp spine in 5 rows, mid-dorsal, mid-lateral, and ventrolateral. Rows start at the head

or pectoral fin and extend to the dorsal fin (11–14 plates); the central caudal axis (38–48 plates); and the pelvic fins (9–12 plates). In some specimens there is a noticeable row of smooth plates between the dorsal and lateral rows. No lateral line canal. Four prominent barbels in a transverse row between mouth and snout, closer to the end of the snout.

Colour Gray, lighter below.

Size Length to about 20 feet (6 m). Weight possibly to 1800 pounds (817 kg) although the largest documented record is for 1387 pounds (630 kg).

Recognition Identified by the 38 to 48 bony plates along the midside, the four barbels closer to the tip of the snout than the mouth, and the short broad snout.

Life History White sturgeon are anadromous although they may spend much or all of their lives in fresh water. They are found in various rivers from the Fraser to the Skeena. Spawning takes place in spring and early summer; it has not been studied. In the Fraser River young fish are found in sloughs in the lower reaches.[4] In the Sacramento River large fish move upstream in winter and spring and downstream in summer, and young fish are nonmigratory.[1] Migrations are also reported in the Columbia

83

River.[4] In the Fraser River both males and females are about 40 inches long (1 m) at 15 years of age, but after about 20 years females grow faster so that by age 30 males are about 57 inches (145 cm) and females 72 inches (183 cm) in fork length. Males mature at about 11 to 22 years of age and females not until 11 to 34 years. Intervals between spawnings may be 4 to 11 years or more.[3,4] Growth in the Sacramento River is much faster.[1] Growth rates make it clear that sturgeon reach a great age.

In the Fraser River spawning or spawned-out eulachon is an important food and some sturgeon migrations seem to be associated with eulachon availability. Other foods include sculpins, sticklebacks, lampreys, young sturgeon, crayfish, and molluscs.[3] Young are reported to feed on insect larvae and mysids[3] and 8-inch (20-cm) individuals in California on amphipods and mysids.[2] Observations on captive specimens showed that they did not feed on the clean bottom of an aquarium but when sand was added the mouth was protruded, the barbels trailed the bottom, and feeding began.[5]

Distribution　　From northern California to the Gulf of Alaska. Generally but sparsely distributed in the inshore waters of British Columbia.

Utilization　　The white sturgeon has long been highly regarded for the characteristic quality of its flesh, and for the ovaries which are used in production of caviar. Until the mid 1880's swimbladder linings were used in the production of isinglass. Catches in the Fraser River have been erratic as shown in the tabulated data in thousands of pounds (0.454 metric tons[4]).

Years	Average landing
1880	80
1881–1885	251
1886–1890	259
1891–1895	410
1896–1900	530
1901–1905	37
1906–1910	271
1911–1915	265
1916–1920	33
1921–1925	33
1926–1930	30
1931–1935	29
1936–1940	14
1941–1945	21
1946–1950	34
1951–1955	36
1956–1960	37
1961–1965	31
1966	26
1967	21
1968	25
1969	31
1970	40

The peak of the fishery was reached in 1897 with a landing of 1,137,700 pounds (516,000 kg) but by 1901 the Fisheries Inspector noted that the fishery was "practically extinct commercially."[4] Such a dramatic decline of the fishery is an expected result of actively exploiting a virgin stock of long-lived fish.

References　　1 Pycha 1956; 2 Schreiber 1962; 3 Semakula 1963; 4 Semakula and Larkin 1969; 5 Vancouver Public Aquarium 1969.

ORDER ANGUILLIFORMES

Fishes of this order have extremely elongate median fins supported by soft rays and continuous with a small caudal which may be reduced to a filament. There are no pelvic fins or pelvic girdle. Scales when present are cycloid and may be embedded. The upper jaw is formed by the maxillary and the premaxillary is fused with the ethmoid. Mesacoracoids and postcleithrals are absent. Opercular bones are reduced and gill openings very small. A gasbladder is present, connected by a duct to the oesophagus. There are no oviducts. Larvae are leptocephalous. **Eels** and eel-like forms, many deep-sea or bathypelagic.

FAMILY SERRIVOMERIDAE   SAWPALATES

The Serrivomeridae are slender fishes with long vertical fins having many rays. The dorsal fin originates well back from the head and behind the anal origin. Neither dorsal nor anal extends behind the caudal. The jaws are long and straight with the lower jaw more protruding. The roof of the mouth is divided longitudinally by a double row of large, laterally flattened teeth in a sawlike ridge on the vomer. There are no scales. Uncommon bathypelagic fishes of the open seas.

CROSSTHROAT SAWPALATE

Serrivomer jesperseni Bauchot-Boutin 1953

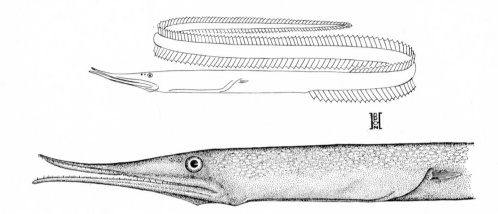

Scientific names from the Latin *serra* (saw) and *vomer* (bone); and P. Jespersen, monographer of the anguillid leptocephalids.

Description   Body drawn out, its depth about 40 into standard length, tapering to a fine caudal fin. Head elongate, slender, compressed, its length about 5.3 into standard length. Mouth terminal, large, directed forward. Upper jaw extends past posterior margin of eye, very long, straight and pointed, its length nearly half length of head, lower jaw longer than upper. Teeth, in upper jaw, along distal end on outside, small rows of minute conical teeth, a median row of large, sharp depressible teeth, and an inner row of smaller sharp teeth; on vomer a double row of very large bladelike teeth in 2 close series, decreasing in size anteriorly, but prominently entering profile of opened mouth; in lower jaw 3 rows, an outer row of small conical teeth and 2 inner rows of canine teeth, the outer of them much better developed.[4] Interorbital space narrow, concave, with 2 prominent ridges, its width about 26 into length of head. Eye diameter about 19 into length of head. Gill membranes united to isthmus. Bases of the first and fifth branchiostegal rays extend past hyoid arch, but the fourth does not, the second and third appear borderline.[1,2,3,5] Anus about 0.25 length of fish behind head. A loop of the intestine in an extension of the body cavity behind anus.

Fins   Dorsal (1), 141 to 170,[1] originating well behind anus, and continuing to be confluent with caudal, rays longer posteriorly. Caudal minute, narrow, and pointed, 6 rays. Anal 127 to 161,[1] extending from anus to caudal. Pectorals small, 6 or 7, high on side. Pelvics absent.

Vertebrae   About 150.[1]

Scales   Absent. Lateral line canal not discerned.

Colour   Dark. Mouth, lining of gill cover and peritoneum black.

Size   Length at least to 16 inches (40.6 cm).[5]

Recognition   Very long slender body, sawlike vomer dividing mouth, dorsal fin inserted well behind anus.

Distribution   Bathypelagic.[5] Across tropical Indian and Pacific oceans. Gulf of Panama.[1] One British Columbia record from off Cape St. James at 51.36 N, 131.09 W in 730 to 825 meters over depths of 2290 to 2380 meters.[5]

References   1 Bauchot 1959; 2, 3 Bauchot-Boutin 1953, 1954; 4 Garman 1899; 5 Taylor 1967b.

FAMILY NEMICHTHYIDAE   SNIPE EELS

The Nemichthyidae are extremely slender fishes with long vertical fins having many rays, with or without membranes. The dorsal fin originates close behind the head well in front of the anal origin. Neither dorsal nor anal fin extends beyond the caudal posteriorly. The jaws are very long and slender; they are recurved; the upper is slightly longer; both jaws are armed with numerous minute inward-pointing teeth. There are no scales. Bathypelagic fishes, some species occasionally taken near the surface. Threadfishes and snipe eels.

KEY TO THE NEMICHTHYIDAE

1   Anus near head, below pectoral fins; anal fin originating about 1 eye diameter behind posterior edge of gill opening; lateral line pores in 3 rows; colour darker on ventral surface ....
.... *Nemichthys scolopaceus*, Slender snipe eel, p. 90

or   1   Anus and anal fin origin about one-fifth total length from head; lateral line a single row of pores; ventral surface not darker .... Genus *Avocettina*, 2

2   Dorsal fin rays fewer than 275; anal fin rays fewer than 210; lateral line pores ferew than 160 .... *Avocettina gilli*, Spaced snipe eel, p. 88

or   2   Dorsal fin rays more than 280; anal fin rays more than 260; lateral line pores more than 160 ....
.... *Avocetina infans*, Closespine snipe eel, p. 89

SPACED SNIPE EEL

Avocettina gilli (Bean 1890)

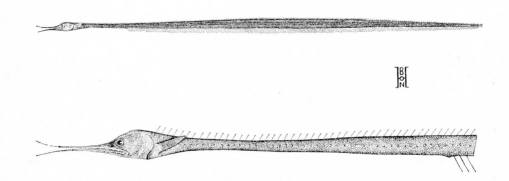

Scientific names from the Latin *avocetta* (the bird avocet with a recurved beak); and Theodore Gill, U.S. ichthyologist.

Clemens and Wilby (1946, 1961) called this species plain snipe eel.

Description   Body much drawn out, its depth about 50 into length, compressed throughout, less so anteriorly. Head small and slender, its length about 13 into the standard length. Mouth terminal, very large, directed forward. Jaws very slender, tapered toward fine ends, recurved. Upper jaw extending beyond orbit by about half an orbit diameter. Teeth minute on both jaws, directed inward, said to be on a pad at the extreme end of each jaw. Interorbital space flat from occipital to snout, the bony part very narrow, about 25 to 30 into length of head, supplemented by soft tissue. Eye about 12 into length of head. Gill membranes united to each other and the isthmus. No caudal peduncle.

Fins   Dorsal (1), about 260, extending from just behind pectoral insertion to about 2 eye-lengths from end of body, rays very flexible at ends, shorter over central part of body. Caudal

extremely small, reduced to a stiff flagellum. Anal, about 205, origin immediately behind anus, ending ahead of dorsal. Pectorals small. Pelvics absent.

Scales   Absent. Lateral line canal complete with about 156 large open pores in a single line.

Colour   Uniform black to mottled dark brown (in alcohol).

Size   Length to 19.5 inches (50 cm).

Recognition   Notable for its finely tapered recurved jaws, the anus and origin of the anal fin about a fifth of the distance from head to tail, lateral line canal pores evident in a single line. Dorsal fin rays are fewer than 275, anal fin rays fewer than 210, and lateral line canal pores less than 160.

Life History   The young are much compressed, pelagic, and like other eels (Anguilliformes) quite unlike the adults.[3]

Distribution   Washington to southeast Alaska at the east end of Prince of Wales Island.[4] Rare. Bathypelagic from 50 to 100 fathoms (91–183 m) to 1559 fathoms

(2850 m).[2] In British Columbia from the entrance to Queen Charlotte Sound,[1] and 60 miles (96 km) off Moresby Island, Queen Charlotte Islands.

References   1 Chapman 1940; 2 Grinols 1965a; 3 Orton 1964; 4 Wilimovsky 1954. See also Whitley 1931.

CLOSESPINE SNIPE EEL

Avocettina infans (Günther 1878)[1]

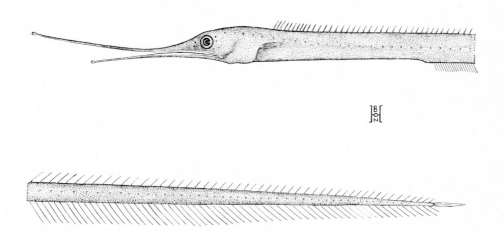

Scientific names from the Latin *avocetta* (the bird avocet with a recurved beak) and *infans* (immature).

Description   Body much drawn out, its depth about 45 into length, compressed throughout, less so anteriorly. Head small and slender, its length about 10 in total length. Mouth terminal, very large, directed forward. Jaws slender, tapering toward fine ends, each with a small knob at its tip, recurved. Upper jaw extending beyond orbit by about one-half orbit diameter. Teeth minute, pointed, directed inward. Interorbital space narrow and flat. Eye small, its diameter about 15 into length of head. Gill membranes united to each other and to the isthmus. Anus about twice as far behind pectorals as pectorals are behind posterior margin of orbit.

Fins   Dorsal (1), about 300 to 350, originating just behind pectoral insertion, rays frail, membranes much reduced through length of fin. Caudal much reduced, linear. Anal about 265 to 270 or more, originating immediately behind anus. Pectorals small. Pelvics absent.

Scales   Absent. Lateral line canal along midside of body from head to extremity of tail, with pores in a single staggered line, about 188 to 191,[3] (166 to 191[2]).

89

Colour   Uniform dusky brown, except jaws, pectoral fins, and lower abdomen which are paler.

Size   Length to 18 inches (45.7 cm)[3] off British Columbia, 23.5 inches (59.7 cm)[2] in the Atlantic Ocean.

Recognition   Notable for its finely tapered recurved jaws, the anus and origin of the anal fin being about one-fifth of the distance from head to tail, lateral line canal pores being in a single line, and for having dorsal and anal rays over 280 and 260 respectively, and over 160 lateral line canal pores.

There is uncertainty about the justification for separating *Avocettina infans* from *Avocettina gilli*.

Distribution   In the Pacific; at the Gulf of Panama; and off the Queen Charlotte Islands at Cape St. James (51.30 N, 131.03 W), and off Tasu Sound (52.11 N, 133.11 W in 510–595 m).[4] In the subtropical Atlantic, sometimes at great depths (2500 fathoms (4580 m)). Not common.

References   1, 2 Günther 1878, 1887; 3 Roule and Bertin 1929; 4 Taylor 1967b.

SLENDER SNIPE EEL

Nemichthys scolopaceus Richardson 1848

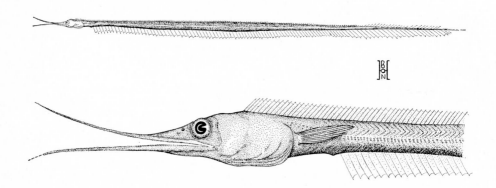

Scientific names from the Greek *nemo* (thread) and *ichthys* (fish); and the Latin *scolopax* (snipe — long bill-like jaws).

The French name is *avocette ruban.*

This fish was called threadfish *Nemichthys avocetta* Jordan and Gilbert 1880 in Clemens and Wilby 1946, 1961. As there is no evident basis for thinking there are two species the older name is used.

Description   Body greatly drawn out, depth about 65 into standard length, cylindrical behind head, posteriorly compressed through most of length. Anus underneath the head. Head compressed and shallow, its length about 8.5 into standard length. Mouth terminal, very large, directed forward. Jaws extremely long, slender, tapering toward fine ends, somewhat recurved. Upper jaw reaching point behind and below posterior edge of orbit. Teeth on both jaws numerous, fine, sharp, directed inward, and arranged in pads. Interorbital space concave between the eyes; ridges from the upper edges of the orbits extend forward to join, forming a single ridge extending out along the snout. Interorbital width about 25 into length of head. Eye diameter about 12 into length of head, entering dorsal profile. Gill membranes united and fused to the isthmus. Folds of skin from the inner sides of the opercula to the bases of the pectoral fins. No caudal peduncle.

Fins   Dorsal (1), about 330, starting at occiput and extending through full length of the body, anterior rays frail, of moderate length, and supporting fin membrane, posterior rays rather stout, sharp, directed backward, without intervening membrane. Caudal not recognizable. Anal, about 320, originating about 1 eye-diameter behind line from posterior margin of operculum and extending to the end of the body where it is much reduced. Pectorals about 10, slender. Pelvics absent.

Scales   Absent. Lateral line canal pores in a band 2 to 4 pores wide.

Colour   Usual colour pattern reversed. Dorsal surface and dorsal fin pale. Ventral surface and sides dark. Anal fin and tips of pectoral fins almost black.

Size   Length at least to 57 inches (145 cm) in the Atlantic.[2] Largest seen 34 inches (86 cm).

Recognition   Noteworthy for the greatly drawn-out body, the long recurving jaws, the anus under the head, and the lateral line canal pores in a band rather than in a single row. The ventral surface of the body is the darker.

Life History   Young (larval) threadfish are like an elongate transparent leaf quite unlike their adult form. They shrink to take on adult form at about 8 inches (20 cm). Threadfish are usually taken at great depths but are sometimes taken close to the surface by fishermen or are attracted to lights. They are known to eat crustaceans and there is one record of a 30-inch (76-cm) threadfish having been spit up by a captured rockfish.[1]

Distribution   Recorded from the main oceans of the world : Atlantic, Indian, Western and tropical mid-Pacific. In the eastern Pacific from northern Central America, Mexico, California, Oregon, Washington, British Columbia, Alaska, and Japan. Bathypelagic to 200 fathoms (366 m).[2,3] In British Columbia at 16 fathoms (30 m).

References   1 Fitch and Lavenberg 1968; 2 Grinols 1965a; 3 Leim and Scott 1966.

ORDER NOTACANTHIFORMES
(Heteromi)

Generally deep-sea fishes of elongate tapering form, with long anal fins reaching the much reduced caudal, eight to ten rays in an abdominal pelvic fin; a gasbladder is present but there are no oviducts. The larva is a leptocephalus. Spiny eels. Only one species represented in waters off the British Columbia coast.

FAMILY NOTACANTHIDAE   SPINY EELS

Spiny eels with the dorsal fin reduced to a series of isolated spines, anal fin of spines and soft rays joined by membranes, and inferior mouths.

LONGNOSE TAPIRFISH

Macdonaldia challengeri (Valliant 1888)

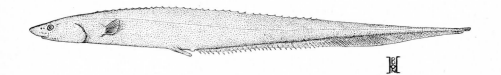

Scientific names from Colonel M. Macdonald, U.S. Commissioner of Fisheries; and H.M.S. *Challenger* of distinguished service in study of the seas.

Description   Body very elongate, its depth about 13 into standard length, compressed, greatest depth at origin of pelvic fins. Head length about 7.4 into standard length, compressed, dorsal profile nearly straight. Mouth ventral, small, directed forward. Upper jaw not reaching anterior margin of eye. A strong spine directed backward at upper posterior angle of jaw. Lower jaw shorter. Snout about 2.9 into

92

length of head, rounded. Teeth small, sharp, uniform in single rows on both jaws, and on palatines; teeth of lower jaw fitting between rows in the upper part of mouth. There is a blind pouch in the roof of the mouth, above the palatine teeth. Interorbital space raised and smooth, its width about 10 into length of head. Eye diameter about 9 into length of head. Operculum large and extended posteriorly.

Fins   Dorsal (1), XXXII to XXXV widely spaced sharp stout spines without intervening membranes. Caudal very small. Anal 161 or 162 rays altogether, 26 to 35 of them spines, long, low, confluent with caudal, deepest at about 0.8 of distance from snout to end of vertebral column. Pectorals about 12 or 13, about midside, with a fleshy base. Pelvics about I, 8, abdominal.

Gill Rakers   On first arch about 14.

Vertebrae   About 242 to 244.

Scales   Cycloid, small, overlapping. Lateral line canal arching over eye and operculum, then down midside. Rather prominent pores in rows on head.

Colour   Cream to faintly pink, possibly, with light brown markings. Black on posterior margins of anal and caudal fins. Black on posterior edge of gill cover, lining of mouth and gill chamber, and parts of peritoneum.

Size   Length to about 20.5 inches (52 cm).

Recognition   Noteworthy for its elongate compressed body, the dorsal fin limited to about 32 spines without intervening membranes, the long anal fin with spines and soft rays, and the small inferior mouth.

Distribution   Deep benthic from very deep water: off British Columbia at 50.54.5 N, 130.06 W, 2103 to 2196 m, off Triangle Island; the Bering Sea; and off Japan. Infrequently seen: as all records are from great depth the species may be more common and widely spread than so far indicated.

References   Peden 1968.

ORDER CLUPEIFORMES
(Isospondyli in part)

The Clupeiformes are rather generalized bony fishes with soft-rayed fins only, abdominal pelvic fins with more than five soft rays, and no adipose fin. The support of the homocercal tail is characteristic among other things by having its urostyle formed from the fusion of the first uroneural spine and the terminal vertebrae. There are connections between the gasbladder and the oesophagus and the inner ear. The maxillary bones are included in the gape usually comprising the upper jaw. Teeth are small or absent. Scales are cycloid. **Herring** and **anchovies** and similar freshwater and saltwater fishes.

FAMILY CLUPEIDAE   HERRINGS

These are laterally compressed species with deciduous scales, often with specially developed keeled scales along the midventral line. Scales generally large and deciduous. No lateral line canal. Dorsal fin short based. Oviducts are usually present. Usually schooling species of fresh or salt water, or anadromous. Fishes of commercial importance, such as herring and pilchards, in the reference area. Herring, pilchard, shad, and related species.

KEY TO THE CLUPEIDAE

1   No large specialized scales on sides of tail fin; no striae on operculum; no black spots on sides of body ....
.... *Clupea harengus pallasi*, Pacific herring, p. 96

or   1   Specialized scales on sides of tail fin; striae on operculum; black spots on sides of body 2

2   Body terete; keels on ventral scutes weak ....
.... *Sardinops sagax*, Pacific sardine, p. 100

or   2   Body deep and compressed; strong keels on enlarged scales (scutes) along midventral line of body .... *Alosa sapidissima*, American shad, p. 95

AMERICAN SHAD

Alosa sapidissima (Wilson 1812)

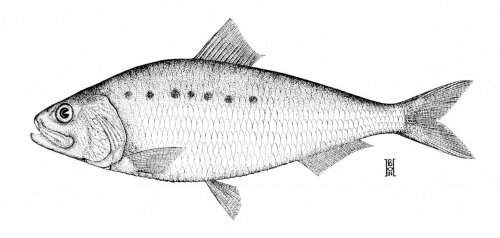

Scientific names from Saxon, European shad; and the Latin *sapidissima* (most delicious).

The French name is *alose savoureuse*. Clemens and Wilby 1946, 1961 called this species shad, which will probably continue in common usage.

Description   Body depth 3 to 4 into standard length, strongly compressed. Head compressed, around 4.0 into standard length. Mouth terminal, moderately large, directed slightly upward. Upper jaw extending to posterior part of eye. Lower jaw fitting into notch in upper jaw. Teeth absent in adults. Interorbital space flat with ridges medially and above eyes, its width about 1.2 into eye diameter and nearly 5 into length of head. Operculum with coarse downward-curving striae.

Fins   Dorsal (1), 15 to 19. Caudal forked. Anal 18 to 24. Pectorals about 16. Pelvics 9, abdominal, each with a fleshy scale above its insertion.

Vertebrae   53 to 59.[4]

Scales   Large cycloid, easily detached, about 60 rows along midline of body. On mid-ventral line of body heavy keeled scutes from head to anus, large scales above and below midside on tail fin. No lateral line canal.

Colour   Metallic blue on dorsal surface shading through white to silvery on belly. Variable row or rows of 4 or more round dark spots on side.

Size   Length to 30 inches (76 cm).

Recognition   A herringlike fish, usually large and deep, with a row of dark spots on the side decreasing in size posteriorly, and coarse curved radiating striae on the operculum.

Life History   The shad was introduced from the Atlantic to the Sacramento River, California, in the early 1870's. It spread quickly both in spawning rivers and at sea, reaching British Columbia by 1891 and Alaska by 1904.[6] Anadromous. Little is known of the life history in British Columbia. On the Atlantic coast it spawns in lower reaches of the larger rivers in late spring. After spawning shad ordinarily return to the sea. After hatching in about a week young drift down stream, reaching the estuaries by September or much sooner. They mature at a length of 18 or 19 inches (46 or 48 cm) and after age of 5 or 4 years. A large female may produce as many as 150,000 eggs. Ordinarily shad do not migrate far[3,4] but the rapid spread of the species on the Pacific coast is good evidence of substantial movement. Food at sea consists mainly of crustacean plankton but fishes are sometimes taken.

Distribution In the Pacific from Todos Santos Bay,[1] Baja California, to Cook Inlet and Kodiak Island, Alaska.[6] Off the USSR (Kamchatka).[5] A minor commercial species in California. In the Atlantic from Florida to Bonavista, Newfoundland.[4] Formerly in Lake Ontario but not recently observed there.[2] In moderate numbers in the Fraser River, less commonly in Rivers Inlet, and in catches of schooling fish away from river mouths.

References 1 Claussen 1959; 2 Dymond, Hart, and Pritchard 1929; 3 Leim 1924; 4 Leim and Scott 1966; 5 Nikol'skii 1961; 6 Welander 1940.

PACIFIC HERRING

Clupea harengus pallasi Valenciennes 1847

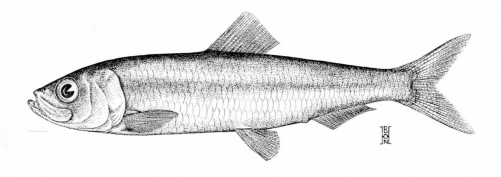

Scientific names from the Latin *clupea* (herring); Low Latin *harengus* (from the old High German, possibly associated with (das) Herr, army or multitude in reference to the formation of large schools); and Petrus Simon Pallas, great Russian naturalist and explorer.

The French name is *hareng pacifique*.

Clemens and Wilby 1961 use the name *Clupea pallasii*. It now appears that Pacific and Atlantic herring are not different enough to be given full species rank and *pallasi* is reduced to a subspecies.[52]

Description   Body elongate, depth about 4.5 into standard length, considerably and variably compressed. Head compressed, about 4.0 to 4.5 into standard length. Mouth terminal, moderate in size, and directed moderately upward, upper jaw extending to around middle of eye. Teeth, none on jaws, a patch of fine teeth on vomer. Interorbital space slightly rounded, about 1.3 into eye. Eye diameter about equal to snout and about 3.5 to 4.0 into length of head. Opercles smooth.

Fins   Dorsal (1), 15 to 21. Caudal forked. Anal 14 to 20. Pectorals about 17. Pelvics about 9, abdominal, each with a fleshy scale above its insertion.

Vertebrae   Usually 51 to 53 in British Columbia.[56] Number increases significantly with latitude, and is affected by rate of development.[19,22,24,25,26]

Scales   Large, cycloid, easily removed but less so at spawning time, in British Columbia usually in 51 to 54 rows along the midside, on midventral line modified with keels moderately developed anterior to the pelvic fins and strongly developed between pelvic fins and anus. No lateral line canal.

Colour   Bluish green to olive on dorsal surface shading to silvery on sides and belly.

Size   Greatest length in British Columbia 13 inches (33 cm).[1] Lengths in British Columbia seldom exceed 10 inches (25 cm). Reputed to reach 15 inches (38 cm) in Alaska.

Recognition   Herring can be distinguished as the silvery fish lacking special features. There are no spines or adipose fin,

no scales or striations on the head or gill cover, no spots on the sides, no modified scales or flaps on the side of the tail fin, no teeth on the jaws, although there are fine teeth on the vomer. Keeled scales along the midventral line are present but only moderately developed. Compression is moderate. (See colour illustration, Plate II.)

Life History   In British Columbia herring spawn in late winter with heaviest concentrations in March, some in February and April, and occasionally some as late as early June[5] or July.[45] Spawning temperatures in British Columbia are 4.4 to 10.7 C (40–51 F) and are 3.0 to 12.3 C (37.4–54 F) on a coastwise basis. Female herring produce about 19,000 eggs annually at 19 centimeters standard length and 29,500 at 22 centimeters,[14] but the range may extend from 9000 in second-year fish in southern British Columbia to 38,000 for eighth-year fish in central British Columbia. Large, old, northern herring produce most eggs.[30] Estimates as high as 134,000 are made for USSR herring.[20,31] In commercial catches female herring were more abundant than males on the west coast of Vancouver Island but less so on the Saltspring Island fishing grounds on the east coast of Vancouver Island.[56] Spawning may extend in British Columbia for more than 160 miles (258 km) of shoreline at depths between high tide and 36 feet (11 m).[49] Eggs are 1.2 to 1.5 millimeters (0.05–0.08 inch) diameter after exposure to sea water. They are very sticky so that sometimes they adhere in great masses to the eelgrasses, kelps, rockweed, other seaweeds, or sometimes rocks, piling, or trash.[53] When spawning is less intense eggs are arranged in rows on the substrate where females have brushed vents while swimming with tail quivering in the spawning act. Extrusion of eggs appears to be impeded unless the vent is in contact with the substrate.[46] There is no observable pairing of the sexes but the whole spawning area is white with milt from the males,[55] so that the rate of fertilization is usually high. When herring spawning is followed

97

by heavy weather the eelgrass sometimes becomes dislodged and is washed up in windrows along the shore or the eggs become loose and packed in solid masses on the beach. This leads to high mortalities.[14,33,53,55] Egg mortality can also be caused by foraging gulls and ducks. Eggs hatch in about 10 days depending upon prevailing temperatures. Newly hatched herring larvae average about 0.25 inch (7.5 mm) long, usually with a yolk sac which persists for a variable length of time, depending upon temperature but not usually exceeding 2 weeks. They are repelled by light.[48] The first food is mainly invertebrate eggs, copepods, and diatoms. Larval herring quickly become the prey of a succession of forms beginning with such filter feeders as pilchards and entrappers like ctenophores, other jelly fishes, and chaetognaths.[48,51] Within a couple of months a length of an inch or more (2.5–4.0 cm) is reached and the diet has broadened to include barnacle larvae, mollusc larvae, bryozoans, rotifers, and young fishes, but copepods still are the most important food. By this stage the young herring are beginning to bear some resemblance to adults and they are forming schools, which appear at the surface toward dusk.[2,55,64] Through summer herring continue to grow and congregate, living mainly on copepods,[54,55] and reach a length of 3 to 4 inches (7–10 cm). They disappear into deeper water in the fall.[16,17] On the west coast of Vancouver Island the limiting factor for the survival of young herring during the first half year of life is the incidence of offshore wind-induced drifts that remove the young fish from a secure environment.[51] Salinity effects on egg development seem relatively unimportant and tolerance is wide at all stages.[27,53] The relative success of a year class of fish in Barkley Sound is established by the survival during the first summer.[16] After their disappearance from shallow water in their first autumn, herring are little in evidence on usual fishing grounds for 2 or 3 years. After maturing in their second, third, or fourth years herring growth in length slows down. On the lower east coast of Vancouver Island standard lengths average 155 millimeters at the end of the second year, 187 millimeters at the end of the third year, 199 millimeters at the end of the fourth year, and 228 millimeters at the end of the eighth year.[54] Growth is a little faster on the west coast of Vancouver Island and slower in northern British Columbia. The lengths correspond to weights of 2 ounces (57 g), 3 ounces (85 g), 3.75 ounces (105 g), and 6.5 ounces (183 g).[53] Copepods remain an important food but are partly superseded by euphausiids. As the spawning condition is approaching in autumn, feeding among the herring migrating toward shore almost comes to a stop, and when it does take place causes damaging belly-burn in catches.[58] A characteristic cycle of fattening in summer, and in winter fasting and ripening sexual products at the expense of stored oil is established.[15] Larvae and post larvae are very common in the surface layers of the Strait of Georgia within the influence of the Fraser River and beyond during May and June. There the earliest stages eat ostracods, small copepods and their nauplii, small fish larvae, diatoms, etc. Larger young eat mainly crustaceans such as copepods, amphipods, cladocerans, decapod and barnacle larvae, euphausiids, etc., with some consumption of small fishes, marine worms, and larval clams. The food of adults in the area was much the same with increased preference for larger forms of Crustacea and small fishes, such as eulachons, herring, starry flounder, ronquil, sand lance, hake, marbled sculpin, rockfish.[2,3,4,6,7,8,40,41] Both herring and their eggs are subject to unexplained mortalities.[59,60] Although juvenile herring are known to be eaten by other species there is no evidence of excessive predation at that stage. Later stages however appear to be one of the major fodder animals of the sea providing food for chinook and coho salmon,[35,36,37,38,39] as well as for waterfowl,[29] dogfish, other sharks, lingcod, sea lions and whales.

Young herring from different spawning grounds tend to mingle in nearby nursery areas,[17,18] but do not always do so.[13,23,24] At later stages exchanges of individuals among larger areas, while occurring, are reduced so that an array of local populations with recognizable physical characteristics is developed[56,57,63] paralleling the situation in Alaska,[43,44] the State of Washington,[12] and beyond. The conclusion about restricted mixing is confirmed by tagging and recovery operations.[11,48,50] The annual inshore movement of herring preliminary to spawning is very variable in time, sometimes recognizable in October or September, and at other times immediately preceding active spawning on the beaches. Vertical movements toward surface in evening and down at dawn are facilitated by special features of the swimbladder mechanism.[9] Air content and oil content of herring are negatively correlated in a way that facilitates vertical movements.[10]

Distribution   In the eastern Pacific from northern Baja California (about 37.40 N)[44] and San Diego[42,47] to St. Michael Island and to Cape Bathurst in the Beaufort Sea.[45] Effective commercial use is between San Francisco and Tomales Bay,[28] and Central Alaska. On the Asian coast from Korea to the estuary of the Lena River in the Arctic Ocean[31] including waters off the north end of Honshu Island as far south as Niagata and Ibaraki Prefecture, Sea of Okhotsk,[32,47] Kamchatka,[34] and Sakhalin Island, and Bering Strait.

Utilization   The herring is a much prized and widely used article of commerce. Historically, early uses were mainly for bait and dry-salting whole for sale on oriental markets. The dry-salt market collapsed in the 1940's being replaced as the big user of herring catches by the reduction industry that processed raw fish for sale as oil and meal. During the 1940's small amounts of herring were canned to provide food that was barely acceptable and failed to find a market in free peacetime trading. Throughout the century there has been a continuous

small market for fresh and specially treated herring as pickled or kippered.

Total annual catches in millions of pounds (454 metric tons) averaged over 5-year periods are given in the following tabulation.[21]

1910/11–1914/15	55.3
1915/16–1920[a]	73.1
1921 –1925[a]	111.4
1926 –1930[a]	141.8
1931 –1935/36[a]	100.4
1935/36–1940/41	221.1
1941/42–1945/46	199.3
1946/47–1950/51	343.3
1951/52–1955/56	336.2
	(414.4)[b]
1956/57–1960/61	333.1[c]
1961/62–1965/66	467.4
1966/67	250.9
1967	117.0
1968	6.4
1969	4.4
1970	8.5

[a]Records from 1917 to 1932 are for the calendar years rather than herring seasons. Little distortion occurs in the tabulation as most fishing during that period was in the fall before the end of December.

[b]Fishing effort was very low in 1952/53 as a result of a dispute over prices. The figure in brackets is the average of catches for the 4 years when 1952/53 is excluded.

[c]Fishing effort was low in 1957/58 because of a price dispute. The total catch, mostly made by a fishermen's cooperative, represented less than half of what would ordinarily have been expected. The 5-year average is accordingly reduced.

References   1 Anon 1951; 2, 3, 4, 5 Barraclough 1967a, b, c, d; 6, 7 Barraclough and Fulton 1967, 1968; 8 Barraclough, Robinson, and Fulton 1968; 9, 10 Brawn 1964, 1969; 11 British Columbia Fisheries Department 1937–57 a series of reports on herring tagging (and on the status of the herring resource) by various combinations of the following authors : Boughton, Hart, Hourston, Jackson, Lanigan, McHugh, Outram, Stevenson, Taylor, Tester; 12 Chapman, Katz, and Erickson 1941; 13 Hart and McHugh 1938; 14 Hart and Tester 1934; 15 Hart, Tester, Beall, and Tully 1940; 16, 17, 18 Hourston 1958,

1959a, b; 19 Hubbs 1925b; 20 Katz 1948; 21 Larkin and Ricker 1964; 22, 23, 24, 25 McHugh 1940a, 1942a, b, 1954; 26 McHugh and Fitch 1951; 27 McMynn 1951; 28 Miller and Schmidtke 1956; 29 Munro and Clemens 1931; 30 Nagasaki 1958; 31 Nikol'skii 1961; 32 Okada 1955; 33 Outram 1958; 34 Popov 1933; 35, 36, 37, 38, 39 Pritchard and Tester 1939, 1941, 1942, 1943, 1944; 40, 41 Robinson, Barraclough, and Fulton 1968a, b; 42 Roedel 1953b; 43 Rounsefell 1930; 44 Rounsefell and Dahlgren 1935; 45 Scattergood, Sinderman, and Skud 1959; 46 Schaefer 1937; 47 Shmidt 1950; 48, 49, 50, 51 Stevenson 1947, 1949, 1955, 1962; 52 Svetovidov 1952; 53 Taylor 1964; 54 Taylor, Hourston, and Outram 1957; 55, 56, 57, 58, 59, 60, 61, 62 Tester 1935, 1937a, b,

1941, 1942a, b, 1945, 1955; 63 Thompson 1917b; 64 Wailes 1936.

No direct text reference was made to 1945 and 1955 papers by A. L. Tester that are included because of their importance in considering dynamics of exploited herring populations. Tester 1935 is a useful record of the fishery during the 1930's and before. The 1942 papers by J. L. McHugh call attention to the availability of their information. Taylor 1964 with its appendices provides a useful review and summary of research on the herring population in British Columbia and of the reasons for dropping quota controls of fishing during a period of rapidly increasing fishing efficiency. See also Hart and Tester 1937, Katz and Erickson 1950.

PACIFIC SARDINE

Sardinops sagax (Jenyns 1842)

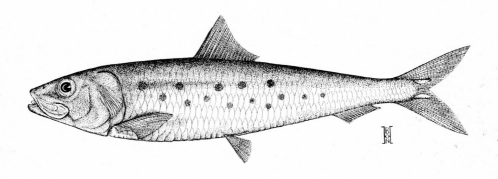

Scientific names from the Latin *sardine* (or *sardina*), and the Greek root *ops* (like); and the Latin *sagax* (of quick perception, acute, or alert).

In the northern part of its range this species is consistently referred to as pilchard.

Recorded by Clemens and Wilby 1946 as *Sardinops caerulea* (Girard) and by many earlier authors as *Sardinia caerulea*.

Description   Body elongate, depth about 4.5 to 5.5 into standard length, spindle-shaped, and only moderately compressed. Head compressed, about 4 into standard length. Mouth terminal, moderate in size, directed slightly upward. Lower jaw contained in upper with mouth closed. Upper jaw extending to point below pupil. No teeth. Interorbital space flat between low supraorbital ridges, about equal to eye, and 4.5 to 5 in head. Opercular bones with a series of about 7 gently radiating almost straight striae directed down and back. Caudal peduncle stout.

Fins   Dorsal (1), 17 to 20, posterior rays rather short and almost equal in length. Caudal deeply forked; scalelike appendages above and below midlateral line on base of tail, the upper one double. Anal 17 to 19, low. Pectorals about 17. Pelvics about 9, a fleshy scalelike appendage extending back from the insertion.

Gill Rakers   On lower limb of first arch, 45 to 110, increasing in number notably with fish size; shorter near angle of arch;[46] processes on gill rakers complex with flask-shaped bases and grooved leaflike free ends.[28]

Vertebrae   50.7 average through range north of Mexico, somewhat lower in Baja California, some differences between year classes.[12,20,22]

Scales   Cycloid; apparently variable in how firmly they are attached to the body and in seeming thickness; in 52 to 60 rows along midline of body; weakly keeled scutes along midventral line as far as anus; not in alternating rows of large and small scales overlapping. No lateral line canal.

Colour   Dark metallic blue or green on dorsal surface shading into silver on sides and belly. Much black pigment dorsally. Black spots in a wide variety of sizes and patterns on the upper part of the sides.

Size   The largest specimen recorded is BC 62-248 with a total length of 15.5 inches (39.4 cm) corresponding to a fork length of about 14.5 inches and a standard (body) length of 332 millimeters, correcting Anon 1935c.[5] This is significantly more than the calculated maximum standard lengths (about 258 mm maximum)[17] illustrating the limitations of calculations on ultimate length as applied to individual fish.[31] The weight was 486 grams. Ordinarily the largest pilchards do (did) not exceed 290 millimeters body length, corresponding to 335 millimeters total length.

Recognition   Recognizable by the spindlelike streamlined form, the fine striae on the operculum, specialized flaps on the tail fin, and by black spots on the sides of the body under the scales.

Life History   Pilchard spawning is not known to occur off the Canadian coast although in some years females with well-developed loose eggs in the ovaries have been taken early in the fishing season (June and July). The main spawning area for the pilchards that supplied the Canadian fishery was between Point Conception and San Diego, California, out to about 100 miles (160 km) offshore.[14,24,43] Some spawning apparently occurs as far north as Point Arena and there is circumstantial evidence of spawning even farther north,[13,26] and some spawn is encountered as far as 250 miles (400 km) offshore. There is another spawning area of little concern to Canadian interests off central Baja California.[2] Most spawning is in April and May but it extends from January to June. Spawning mostly occurs at temperatures between 15 and 18.3 C (59 and 65 F) and no evidence of spawning below 12.8 C (55 F) was encountered.[2,38,47] A few fish are mature at 18 centimeters, half at about 21.5 centimeters, and practically all at 24 centimeters. Each female produces several batches of 30,000 to 65,000 eggs with large individuals producing about 200,000 during a season.[10,35] Spawning takes place mainly during the first part of the night,[16] and most of the eggs

101

remain in the upper (50 m) water layer.[44] On Canadian grounds females are more abundant than males (56 percent of all sampled) with the disparity greatest among the larger sizes.[49] A newly fertilized egg is about one-sixteenth of an inch in diameter. The yolk with its single large oil globule and the embryo float freely within the shell surrounded by considerable clear space. Eggs hatch in about 3 days at usual water temperatures,[1,33] to produce larvae about one-eighth inch (3 mm) long carrying a yolk sac. The yolk sac is absorbed in about 3 weeks. By the time the young fish has reached a length of about 1 inch (2.5 cm) it bears a general resemblance to the adult.

Young fish make their way inshore where they congregate in schools near beaches. Through life female pilchards grow rather faster than males. There is a good deal of variation in growth rate but in general lengths in central California are about 115 millimeters after 1 year, 173 after 2 years, 200 after 3 years, and 215 after 4 years. In the Pacific northwest, they are 215 millimeters after 4 years, and 235 after 5 years.[38,39] Each year pilchards make northward migrations early in summer and travel back south again in autumn. With each year of life the migration becomes farther. The largest oldest fish as the culmination of the northward movement reached the west coast of Vancouver Island, with somewhat smaller sizes off Washington and Oregon. There is evidence from growth parameters and from length distributions in different fisheries that the migration is complex;[17] timing and the extent of movement were affected to some extent by oceanographic conditions; the pattern of migration produced a reasonably dependable fishery in British Columbia for about 20 years.[9,11,15,19,21,23,26,29,30]

Off the west coast of Vancouver Island small fish occurred in the run in numbers in 1936.[7] During the summers pilchards sometimes entered inlets on the west coast of Vancouver Island and occasionally became cut off in the deep water there where they survived until the following year.[6,24] In the summer of 1940 large numbers of year-old pilchards entered the Strait of Georgia[25] where they suffered high mortalities during the following winter.[18]

Food off the west coast of Vancouver Island is mainly diatoms supplemented with copepods and other animals and plants.[27] Off California copepods are the dominant food.[34,40]

Distribution   Baja California including the Gulf of California[48] to southeastern Alaska,[42] interrupted by the tropics, Peru and Chile 5 to 42 S latitude.[41]

Formerly in Canada most regularly in summer on the west coast of Vancouver Island south of the Brooks Peninsula, less frequently in or off Quatsino Sound, and infrequently in central part of the coast.

Utilization   Pilchards were fished entirely with purse seines.[19] The main use was for reduction to oil and meal with a relatively small proportion used for canning. Landings in millions of pounds (454 metric tons) of pilchards are given in the following tabulation. As the same individual fish are also involved in United States fisheries landings of California sardine are also included.[14,32]

Years	British Columbia	Washington and Oregon	All California
1916–20	5.7[a]	—[b]	112.4
1921–25	8.1	—[b]	198.3
1926–30	143.5	—[b]	441.7
1931–35	84.1	52.5[c]	781.9
1936–40	71.4	28.4	1088.3
1941–45	123.2	9.8	1011.5
1946–50	4.5[d]	4.6[e]	483.7
1951–55	—[b]	—[b]	127.0
1956–60	—[b]	—[b]	91.0
1961–65	—[b]	—[b]	16.1

[a]Average for last four years.
[b]No fishery.
[c]Average considers 1935 only.
[d]Average for only 1946 and 1947.
[e]Average for only 1946, 1947, and 1948.

Canadian fishing failures in 1933 and 1939 with landings less than 1.1 million pounds were results of fish not being found on usual grounds, presumably because of changes in migration routes. However, the decline in yield beginning in 1944 reflects a reduction in the supply of fish. Since 1939 the pilchard population has been unsuccessful in producing a really big brood of young. The 1939 and adjacent year-classes provided the main supply for the successful 1943 fishery. Thereafter the average sizes and ages of fish on Canadian grounds increased but the supply of fish fell off. The cause of lack of successful reproduction is uncertain. Changes in seawater circulation have been suggested but fail to explain all poor year broods. Reduction in spawning potential by fishing[3] may cause inadequate use of possible spawning areas. Another possibility is that the California anchovy may have preempted the ecological niche of the California sardine while the latter was under heavy exploitation, competing with it for food at all stages and feeding on its young thus making difficult the production of a strong brood.[36] All three and other causes may be involved.[8]

Fishing failures for pilchards and sardines have been observed in other parts of the world. The recurrent crises in the fisheries of western Europe may have represented changes in the pattern of fish movements.[45] However, the disappearance of the Asian form from the USSR fishery in the early 1940's is probably associated with a decline in abundance.[4,37]

As the prosperity of a Canadian fishery depends upon the presence in the eastern Pacific of stocks of large old fish, it is evident that a restoration of the Canadian fishery can only follow by several years the full restoration of the California stocks.

References 1, 2, 3 Ahlstrom 1943, 1954, 1966; 4 Andriashev 1937; 5, 6 Anon 1935c, 1941a; 7 British Columbia Fisheries Department 1937; 8 California Bureau of Marine Fisheries 1953–55; 9 Carter 1968; 10, 11, 12, 13, 14 Clark 1934, 1935, 1936, 1938, 1952; 15 Clark and Janssen 1945; 16 Farris 1963; 17 Felin 1954; 18 Foerster 1941; 19, 20, 21, 22, 23, 24, 25, 26 Hart 1933a, b, 1937a, c, 1938a, b, 1943a, e; 27 Hart and Wailes 1932; 28 Hubbs 1929; 29, 30 Janssen 1938, 1948; 31 Knight 1968; 32 Larkin and Ricker 1964; 33 Lasker 1964; 34 Lewis 1929; 35 MacGregor 1957; 36 Murphy 1966; 37 Nikol'skii 1961; 38, 39 Phillips 1948a; b; 40 Radovich 1952; 41 Regan 1916; 42 Schultz, Hart, and Gunderson 1932; 43 Scofield 1934; 44, 45 Silliman 1943, 1945; 46 Thompson 1925; 47 Tibby 1937; 48 Walker 1953; 49 Watanabe and Hart 1938.

There is extensive literature on the species. Useful sources of additional references are to be found in Anon 1940, Carter 1968, Clark 1952, Murphy 1966, Phillips 1948b, Silliman 1945, Thompson 1925, Walford and Mosher 1943a, b, and Wheeler 1931.

FAMILY ENGRAULIDAE   ANCHOVIES

The Engraulidae are slender fishes only moderately compressed with large cycloid scales and without lateral lines or adipose fins. The mouth is large and the operculum lengthened backward permitting wide opening. They are schooling fishes extremely abundant in some areas. Only one species recognized in waters off British Columbia.

NORTHERN ANCHOVY

Engraulis mordax mordax Girard 1854

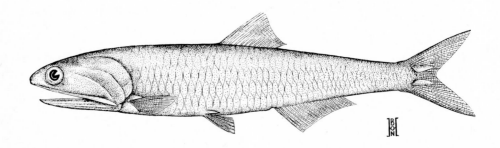

Scientific names from the Greek *engraulis* (?) (European anchovy); and the Latin *mordax* (biting).

Usually referred to as plain anchovy in Canada and elsewhere in the northern part of the range, and by Clemens and Wilby 1946, 1961. Clemens and Wilby called the species *Engraulis mordax*.[8]

Description   Body elongate, depth 5 to 6 into standard length, spindle shaped and only slightly compressed. Head long, moderately compressed, 3.5 to 4.0 into standard length. Mouth inferior, very large, directed slightly upward. Upper jaw extending back to point about 2.5 times distance from tip of snout to posterior edge of orbit. Lower jaw barely reaching beyond anterior edge of orbit. Numerous fine teeth on maxillary and mandible. Eye a little longer than snout. Interorbital space broadly rounded. Opercles much prolonged backward giving a streamlined appearance to the head, smooth.

Fins   Dorsal (1), 14 to 16. Caudal forked, scalelike appendages above and below midlateral line on fin. Anal 20 to 23, posterior part low. Pectorals about 17. Pelvics 6, abdominal, placed definitely ahead of dorsal fin, a fleshy scale above each insertion.

Vertebrae   Number in British Columbia averages 44.6.[14]

Scales   Large and cycloid in oblique rows along midside, 41 to 50. No lateral line canal.

Colour   Metallic bluish or greenish above, silvery on sides and belly.

Size   Length to 9.8 inches (24.8 cm).[4] Usually not over 7 inches (17.8 cm). Largest on record in Canada 7.8 inches (19.7 cm).

Recognition   Noteworthy for its large mouth, gill covers produced backward, and the short snout.

Life History   In British Columbia the life history is not well known and occurrence is sporadic. It was named in 1897 as an abounding potential commercial species.[13] On the west coast of Vancouver Island, adult anchovies occurred occasionally with pilchards through the 1930's or sometimes dominated schools embarrassing fishery operations by meshing in seine nets. Occasional adults are encountered in the Strait of Georgia. In 1940 many large schools mixed with young pilchards and mackerel entered the Strait of Georgia and the anchovy penetrated as far north as Port Hardy. The presence of small anchovies in Jervis Inlet and elsewhere in subsequent years suggested successful reproduction. In 1968 the capture of larval anchovies in the southern Strait of Georgia made it clear that spawning had taken place in the area.[2] Fish of the year have also been taken in Barkley Sound and spawning recorded in July and August. Fish are about 4 inches (10 cm) at the age of 1 year and 5 and 5.5 inches (12.7 and 14 cm) in standard length at 2 and 3 years. Spawning is either in inlets or offshore. In 1966 and 1967 larval anchovies about an inch long were present in July in the southern Strait of Georgia and almost certainly were produced locally.[2]

In California where the species is more important and abundant many features of the life history are known.[4] Spawning takes place between temperatures of 10 and 23.3 C and mostly between 13.0 and 17.5 C in the upper water layers and at around 10 PM.[1] Fertilization is external and nearly all eggs are fertilized. Eggs are ellipsoidal 1.23 to 1.55 millimeters in the major axis and 0.6 to 8.2 millimeters in diameter. They are pelagic, floating first with the major axes perpendicular, later horizontal with the embryo hanging below the yolk. They hatch in 2 to 4 days depending on temperature producing larvae 2.5 to 3 millimeters long. The yolk sac is absorbed in about 36 hours. By the time the young have reached an inch (25 mm) in length, they are readily recognizable by their resemblance to the adults.[5] A few reach sexual maturity at about 90 to 100 millimeters standard length at the end of the first year. About half are mature at 130 millimeters between 2 and 3 years old.[12] All are mature at 150 millimeters and 4 years.[6,7,8] Several lots of eggs are spawned each year with an annual production about 20 to 30 thousand. In winter anchovy move offshore and return in spring. They usually remain at depths often at the bottom in the daytime and come to the surface at night. The life span seems to be 7 years. Food is recorded

in British Columbia being euphausiids,[15] copepods, and decapod larvae.[3] Laboratory observations show that anchovy have two patterns for feeding — random filtering and particulate "biting." In order to meet food requirements advantage must be taken of concentrations of larger food organisms for particulate feeding.[9]

Distribution   From Cape San Lucas in Baja California to the Queen Charlotte Islands with the centre of abundance from Magdalena Bay to San Francisco.[1,10] Appears to favour water temperatures between 14.5 and 18.5 C. Eggs and larvae have been taken up to 300 miles (480 km) offshore.

Utilization   Not available abundantly or consistently enough in British Columbia to be used commercially although good canned products were developed during the period of abundance in the Strait of Georgia in the early 1940's. Fishing in California was restricted by law to bait usage from 1949 to 1955 when reduction restrictions were dropped and a 100,000 ton annual quota was established. The relaxation has had no observable effect on the stock, probably because the quota is significantly less than a tenth of the estimated stock in southern California.

In California, the anchovy tremendously increased in abundance during the last 20 years and it is probable that this is related to removal of competition and predation by pilchards, *Sardinops sagax*. It may be that now anchovies are impeding the restoration of pilchards in population abundance.[11]

References   1 Ahlstrom 1966; 2 Barraclough 1967a; 3 Barraclough, Robinson, and Fulton 1968; 4 Baxter 1967; 5 Bolin 1936a; 6 Clark and Phillips 1952; 7 Daugherty, Felin, and MacGregor 1955; 8 Hubbs 1925b; 9 Leong and O'Connell 1969; 10 McHugh and Fitch 1951; 11 Murphy 1966; 12 Pike 1951; 13 Prince 1897;

14 Taylor 1940; The California State Department of Fish and Game, Fish Bulletin 147, 1969, by J. D. Messersmith with his associates, R. A. Collins, S. J. Crooke, J. E. Hardwick, C. W. Haugen, J. D. Spratt, and R. H. Wickwire, provides an account of the recent (1965–69) anchovy research and fishery in southern California. See also Miller 1956.

ORDER SALMONIFORMES

A diverse group of families of soft-rayed fishes marked by the exclusion of the maxillary bone from the gape by the premaxillary, the consolidation of hypural bones on a terminal half-centrum, the absence of orbitosphenoid and mesocoracoid bones, and the presence of an adipose fin. Photophores are present in many families. The order includes freshwater, anadromous, marine, and deep-sea fishes.

FAMILY SALMONIDAE   SALMON AND TROUT

Robust soft-rayed fishes with cycloid scales, adipose fins, a distinct pelvic axillary scale, the last three vertebrae turned dorsally often clearly and strongly. Species in the salt water of British Columbia have large mouths with well-developed teeth on jaws, vomer, palatines, and tongue and are moderately compressed. The gasbladder is connected to the alimentary tract by a duct. Oviducts are incomplete and are replaced by a fold of peritoneum. Pyloric caeca are numerous. All are anadromous in our area although freshwater members of the family are numerous. Sexual dimorphism is strongly developed at spawning time. Very important species of commerce. Salmon, trout, chars, whitefish, and related species.

For the Pacific salmons a thoroughly analysed compilation of published scientific information has been made for the period 1900–59 (Maxfield 1967a, b) and carried over for 1960–64 including other salmonoid fishes (Holmberg and Bush 1969a, b). A researcher or other interested individual or agency can obtain all the information available on any aspect of Pacific salmon biology (or salmonoid for the later period) quickly and easily. The information is available for purchase through the United States "Clearinghouse for Federal Scientific and Technical Information, Springfield, Virginia, 22151." Its use calls for a suitably powered binocular microscope or a microfiche reader. Compilation may be continued.

KEY TO THE SALMONIDAE

1   Rays in anal fin 8 to 12 2

or   1   Rays in anal fin 13 to 19 .... Genus *Oncorhynchus* 6

2   Teeth on head of vomer only; spots on body red or yellow (spots may be faint in specimens from salt water); mouth large .... *Salvelinus malma,* Dolly Varden trout, p. 134

or   2   Teeth on both head and shaft of vomer (weak or deciduous on shaft in *Salmo salar*); large dark spots on body (which may be obscure in specimens from salt water) .... Genus *Salmo* 3

3   Dark spots on side of fish limited to above midside; few if any spots on tail, if present not in radial series; unlikely to be encountered .... *Salmo salar,* Atlantic salmon, p. 131

or   3   Dark spots on side of fish both above and below midside 4

4   Spots large (about half pupil radius) and tending to be angular; many spots surrounded by a pale halo .... *Salmo trutta,* Brown trout, p. 133

or   4   Spots usually smaller and not surrounded by a pale halo 5

5   Teeth present on back of tongue; red marks (often pale or disappearing) below and parallel to jaws .... *Salmo clarki clarki,* Coastal cutthroat trout, p. 127

or   5   No teeth on back of tongue; no red marks under jaws; red bars on sides of males at spawning .... *Salmo gairdneri,* Rainbow trout, p. 128

6   Black spots on back and caudal fin 8

or   6   No large black spots on caudal fin, fine black speckling usually present 7

7   Rakers on first gill arch 19 to 26, stout, short, smooth, and widely spaced .... *Oncorhynchus keta,* Chum salmon, p. 112

or   7   Rakers on first gill arch 30 to 39, long, slender, rough, and close set .... *Oncorhynchus nerka,* Sockeye salmon, p. 118

8   Spots on back and caudal fin large; scales small, 170 or more in first row above lateral line .... *Oncorhynchus gorbuscha,* Pink salmon, p. 108

or   8   Spots on back and caudal fin small and irregular; scales moderate in size, 155 or fewer in first row above lateral line 9

9   Black spots on caudal fin on upper lobe only; light pigment along bases of teeth; pyloric caeca fewer than 100 .... *Oncorhynchus kisutch,* Coho salmon, p. 115

or   9   Black spots on both lobes of caudal fin; black pigment along bases of teeth; pyloric caeca 120 or more .... *Oncorhynchus tshawytscha,* Chinook salmon, p. 124

PINK SALMON

Oncorhynchus gorbuscha (Walbaum 1792)

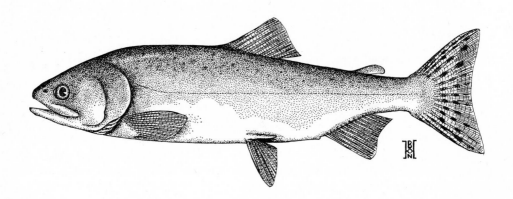

Scientific names from the Greek roots *onkos* (hook) and *rynchos* (nose); and *gorbuscha* (the Russian name for the species in Alaska).

Description   Body elongate, depth about 4 into standard length, moderately compressed. Males on spawning migration develop a high hump immediately behind the head, suggesting the common name humpback. Teeth and snout undergo disproportionate growth at the same time. Head length about 4 into standard length, conical. Mouth terminal, large, directed forward and upward. Upper jaw reaches beyond posterior margin of orbit. Snout narrowly rounded in profile. Lips fleshy. Teeth small and weak in sea-run fish becoming enlarged in breeding males. Interorbital space high, wide, convex and rounded, its width about 3.1 into length of head. Eye about 6.3 into length of head. Gill membranes free of each other and of isthmus. Branchiostegals 10 to 15. Caudal peduncle moderately compressed, its least depth about 12 into standard length. Pyloric caeca 165 to 195,[11] (100)121 to 135(195).[44]

Fins   Dorsal (1), 10 to 15. Adipose small, slender, fleshy. Caudal slightly forked. Anal 13 to 17. Pectorals about 15. Pelvics about 10, abdominal, with a free-tipped fleshy appendages above insertion.

Gill Rakers   On first gill arch 26 to 34.

Scales   Cycloid, small, in first row above lateral line canal 170 to 229, on lateral line canal 150 to 205. Lateral line canal slightly downcurved and then straight.

Colour   Metallic blue on dorsal surface, silvery on sides. Numerous large, black, oval spots on upper sides and back and all caudal fin. Mature males red to yellow on sides of body blotched with brown, dark along back. Female olive green on sides of body with dusky stripes. Flesh pink.
    Young without parr marks. Blue to greenish in colour along back, sides silvery.

Size   Length to 30 inches (76 cm). Usual weights at maturity are between 3 and 5 pounds (1.4–2.3 kg), average about 4.8 pounds (2.2 kg), 12 pounds (5.5 kg) is recorded. Maturing pink salmon vary in average size from year to year. In northern British Columbia as in southeastern Alaska fish maturing in odd-numbered years are both larger and more numerous. Average sizes in different stream runs change in the same direction from year to year. Fish were largest in 1953 and 1954.[13] In Asia fish in big runs may be smaller.[28]

Recognition Distinguished by the small scales with more than 150 on lateral line, 24 to 35 gill rakers on the first gill arch, and the large very dark oval spots on the back and over all the caudal fin. (See colour illustration, Plate IV.)

Life History Pink salmon enter spawning streams during September and October, usually on high water,[38] sometimes going well upstream but more commonly not getting far away from salt water. Males run first and are larger, and in general large fish run earlier. Fecundity is related positively to length and varies from year to year. Females usually carry between 1535 and 1900 eggs.[40] Eggs are buried in the gravel of stream bottoms, hatch in late February, and the young emerge from the gravel in (illustration below) April and May, depending on water temperatures,[11] and make an active migration downstream,[14,26,27] traveling at night, as they avoid light and prefer cover. Once they have been exposed to light and form schools, they change within 15 minutes to a preference for light.[14] The extent of survival from eggs is controlled by

Chatham Sound food is mainly copepods and *Oikopleura*.[22] During even-numbered years when young emerge from the Fraser River in great numbers many remain and grow during the summer in the less saline waters around the outlet. In April to June food is dominated by copepods but with their growth to July young pink salmon are able to supplement their diet with many other organisms like insects, *Oikopleura,* chaetognaths, amphipods, euphausiids, and such young fishes as herring, eulachon, smoothtongue, hake, pricklebacks, and gobies. In July, pink salmon off the outlet of the Fraser River were about 4 inches (102 mm) long.[3,4,5,6,7,8] During the first 40 days at sea pink salmon grow about from 3.5 to 8.4 centimeters. Thereafter until the following March (exponential growth rate declines) the fish reach a length of about 32.5 centimeters.[33] Favoured temperatures in the Gulf of Alaska were between 7 and 15 C throughout the year.[28] During the last spring and summer in the sea and through most of the spawning migration through coastwise waters growth is rapid from about 1 pound (0.45 kg) although declining as a percentage rate during the final migration through coastal waters.[20] It is accordingly sound to postpone commercial capture as long as feasible.[31,46] For one population in central British Columbia pink salmon surviving death by natural causes was around 22 percent.[32] Annulus formation on scales takes place in December and

a combination of meteorological factors and others associated with gravel conditions.[50] In the estuary salinity gradients probably play a part in directing migration [24] After leaving fresh water young pink salmon tend to remain close inshore through their first summer and move into deeper water in September.[21] During their first summer in

January in the Gulf of Alaska.[10] Food during offshore life consists mainly of euphausiids, copepods, amphipods, fish, and squid.[19] Pink salmon of Canadian origin move offshore in a region extending about 500 nautical miles from land between Prince William Sound and the outlet of the Columbia River in the subarctic region.

The return migration takes place during the second summer with extremely few exceptions.[49] The 2-year life cycle is so invariable that fish running in odd-numbered calendar years are effectively isolated from even-year fish so that there is no gene flow between them and the two cycles need separate consideration from the points of view of exploitation and conservation.[2,18] In general, odd-year runs predominate in the Fraser River and southern British Columbia, and even-year runs in northern British Columbia and the Queen Charlotte Islands. In Canada the dominance of odd- or even-year runs in any stream or river system is stable and is apparently maintained by depensatory factors.[25] Switches from odd-to even-year dominance are recorded in Asian streams to a significant extent.[25,29] There is a good body of evidence demonstrating that pink salmon show a strong tendency to return to the stream of origin.[41,42,43] However, migration routes to spawning streams may be various.[27,45] During incubation and alevin and fry life, pink salmon are eaten by a wide variety of organisms including Dolly Varden trout, cutthroat trout, coho salmon, sculpins, water ouzels (birds), muskrats, and caddisfly larvae,[35,36,37,39] but in years of plenty this is probably not critical in controlling numbers.

Distribution   Anadromous in rivers and small streams from southern California (as a stray)[15] through northern California, Oregon, Washington, British Columbia, and Alaska to the Bering Sea at Cape Dezneua and Arctic Ocean.[51] In the Aleutian,[52] Commander, and Kuril islands.[9] In the Canadian Arctic in the Mackenzie River (50 miles (80 km) south of Aklavik), at Richards Island, and in Kidluit Bay.[12,16] In the Siberian Arctic to the Lena River,[29] south along the Asian Coast through Anadyr,[1] Kamchatka,[9,17,32,33] Sea of Okhotsk,[9] Sakhalin,[9,17] Tumen River,[48] Maritime Territories,[23] Peter the Great Bay,[9] and Korea,[29] Hokkaido,[9] and Hondo Island.[29,30] Pink salmon released in Current River flowing into Thunder Bay, Lake Superior, in 1956 have survived seven generations, have spread through most of Lake Superior, have appeared in Carp River, Michigan, flowing into Lake Huron, and may be considered as established in the upper Great Lakes.[47] (J. W. Parsons personal communication.) Pink salmon may have been established on the Atlantic coast of Newfoundland, but this now (1972) seems unlikely. Eastern Atlantic introductions further to the south were not permanently established. Spawning pink salmon are found in about 700 streams in British Columbia but 75 percent of the

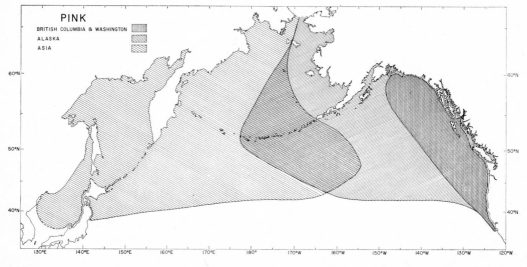

PINK

BRITISH COLUMBIA & WASHINGTON

ALASKA

ASIA

stock enters the most productive 57 rivers.[2] Usually pink salmon spawn in lower parts of rivers but occasionally they run for considerable distances upstream. The middle-river runs in the Fraser River were destroyed by a rockslide in Hells Gate Canyon but since free passage was restored the runs have to a large extent recovered.

Utilization   Pink salmon is the most abundant salmon in British Columbia. Spawning takes place in a very great number of coastal streams and in all the major rivers with the exception of those along the southeast part of Vancouver Island. The fish are caught by purse seines and gillnets offshore, in channels, and in bays as they approach their spawning streams. Most of the catch is canned but part of it is now used in the fresh and frozen trade.

Production from the fishery in millions of pounds (454 metric tons) is given in the accompanying tabulation.[18]

Years	4-year average catch
1919–22	31.2
1923–26	44.0
1927–30	50.0
1931–34	26.6
1935–38	39.8
1939–42	29.1
1943–46	35.4
1947–50	39.5
1951–54	49.6
1955–58	45.7
1959–62	48.5
1960	16.9
1961	49.6
1962	93.2
1963	59.7
1964	36.4
1965	22.7
1966	72.9
1967	49.8
1968	55.6
1969	13.8
1970	53.0

References   1 Andriashev 1937; 2 Aro and Shepard 1967; 3, 4, 5 Barraclough 1967a, b, c; 6, 7 Barraclough and Fulton 1967, 1968; 8 Barraclough, Robinson, and Fulton 1968; 9 Berg 1948; 10 Bilton and Ludwig 1966; 11 Carl, Clemens, and Lindsey 1959; 12 Dymond 1940; 13 Godfrey 1959a; 14 Hoar 1956; 15 Hubbs personal communication; 16 Hunter 1969; 17 Kaganovskii 1947; 18 Larkin and Ricker 1964; 19 LeBrasseur 1966; 20 LeBrasseur and Parker 1964; 21, 22 Manzer 1956, 1969; 23 Matsubara 1955; 24 McInerney 1964; 25, 26, 27 Neave 1952, 1955, 1964; 28 Neave and Hanavan 1960; 29 Nikol'skii 1961; 30 Okada 1955; 31, 32, 33 Parker 1963, 1964, 1968; 34 Popov 1933; 35, 36, 37, 38, 39, 40, 41, 42, 43, 44 Pritchard 1934a, b, c, 1936a, b, 1937, 1939a, b, 1944, 1945; 45 Pritchard and DeLacy 1944; 46 Ricker 1964; 47 Schumacher and Hale 1962; 48 Shmidt 1950; 49 Turner and Bilton 1968; 50 Wickett 1958; 51, 52 Wilimovsky 1954, 1964. Additional information is also contained in Anas 1959, DeLacy and Neave 1947, Pritchard 1930a, 1932.

CHUM SALMON

Oncorhynchus keta (Walbaum 1792)

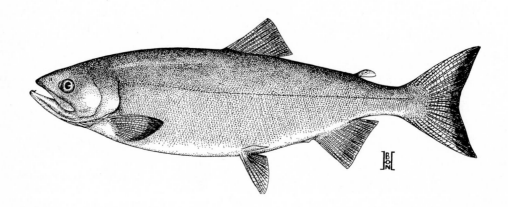

Scientific names from the Greek roots *onkos* (hook) and *rynchos* (nose); and *keta* (the vernacular name in Kamchatka).

Description   Body elongate, depth about 3.8 into standard length, deepest behind tip of pectoral fin, moderately compressed. Head length about 4.4 into standard length. Mouth terminal, large, directed forward. Upper jaw reaches about to posterior margin of orbit. Snout narrowly rounded in profile. Lips fleshy. Teeth in jaws moderate in size in sea-run fish becoming large and canine in spawning males (hence the vernacular name dog salmon); in premaxillaries, maxillaries, and palatines, and anterior part of tongue. Interorbital space high, wide, convex, rounded, its width about 2.6 into length of head. Eye diameter about 6.7 into length of head. Gill membranes free of each other and of isthmus. Branchiostegals 10 to 16. Caudal peduncle only moderately compressed, rather slender, its least depth about 14 into standard length. Pyloric caeca about 140.

Fins   Dorsal (1), 10 to 13. Adipose, small, slender, fleshy. Caudal slightly forked. Anal 13 to 17. Pectorals about 16. Pelvics about 10, abdominal, each with a free-tipped fleshy appendage above its insertion.

Gill Rakers   On first gill arch 18 to 26.

Scales   Cycloid, in row above lateral line canal 130 to 153, on lateral line canal 126 to 151. Lateral line canal slightly decurved and then straight.

Colour   Metallic blue on dorsal surfaces with occasional black speckling but no black spots. Dark tips on pectoral, anal, and caudal fins. Maturing fish in fresh water show reddish or dark streaks or bars and large pale blotches and white on tips of pelvic and anal fins. No dark spots on caudal fin. Flesh pale pink.

Young with parr marks as slender bars, scarcely extending below lateral line and with green iridescence on back.

Size   Lengths to 3 feet 4 inches (102 cm) and weights to 33 pounds (15 kg) have been recorded.

Recognition   Recognizable by the absence of large black spots from the body and fins, the slender caudal peduncle, the dark colour on the tips of all fins but the dorsal. Maturing fish have a series of dark bars across the sides, red colouring on sides, and some have great blotches of gray. (See colour illustration, Plate V.)

Life History   Chum salmon approach shore in autumn, enter streams and rivers and spawn late in the year. They move into some 800 rivers and brooks so that spawning populations are spread significantly over a great many streams. They frequently spawn quite near river outlets but occasionally go well up large rivers. This is especially the case in the Yukon River up which chum salmon travel nearly 2000 miles (3200 km) to Teslin Lake. Chum salmon are the latest of the Pacific salmons to spawn and spawning has been recorded as late as April at Deep Bay, Vancouver Island.[23] In eastern Asia summer and autumn runs differing in size, age distribution, and fecundity are recognized. Summer-run fish there have fecundities of 2000 to 3000 eggs and autumn-run fish of 3000 to 4300 eggs. Migrations can be very fast and rates of 47 kilometers per day are recorded.[17] Alevins hatch early in spring and young (illustration below) proceed to sea, sometimes in both Canada and the USSR feeding on insect larvae on the way and growing significantly.[22] Early food in salt water also

Pacific beyond 168 W and south to 54 N. After reaching a weight of about 1.5 pounds, they may be taken in the Gulf of Alaska, somewhat farther to the north during the summer.[13] In the Gulf of Alaska they appear to be concentrated in the upper 200 feet (61 m) from May through July, approaching the surface at night.[15] The principal foods are euphausiids, squids, amphipods, and crab larvae. [12,13] Scales indicate a winter check in growth in February and March.[4] Salmon return to streams to spawn after 2 to 7 (usually 3–5) years at sea, sometimes following routes paralleling the coast for great distances from as far as off Cape Spencer, Alaska, to Johnstone Strait.[19] Their growth during the offshore part of the migration is rapid so that a significant loss of product results from fishing them in early stages of their offshore migration.[20] The average sizes of maturing chum salmon vary considerably from year to year. There was a general increase in sizes from 1947 to 1952, declines in 1953, and in 1955 and 1956, with very large fish in 1954.[7]

Distribution   From off southern California about 32.5 N, 117.25 W, in many coastal streams in north California[8] and in the Sacramento River, Oregon, Washington, British Columbia, and Alaska to the Yukon River,[2] Bering Sea, Arctic Alaska,[2,25] in the Arctic Red and Peel rivers, tributary

consists largely of insects on occasion.[6] After leaving fresh water in early spring they remain inshore during the summer but start moving offshore in September.[14] Food of young in Chatham Sound was mainly copepods and *Oikopleura*.[16] A major movement to the high seas takes British Columbia chum salmon into the northeast

to the Mackenzie River and the Slave and Hay rivers flowing through Great Slave Lake. In the Anderson River entering the Arctic about 128.08 N.[5,10] Aleutian, [26] Commander, and Kuril islands.[3] In the Siberian Arctic from Providence Bay[1] to the Kolyma and Lena rivers.[3,21] Along the Asian coast at Anadyr Bay, Kamchatka,[3,18] Sea of

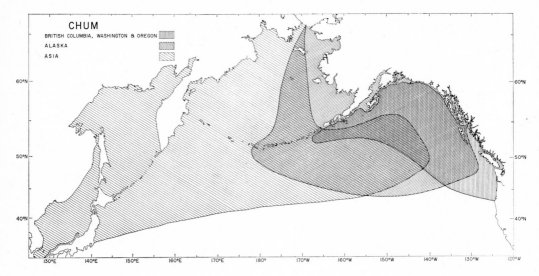

CHUM
BRITISH COLUMBIA, WASHINGTON & OREGON
ALASKA
ASIA

Okhotsk,[3] Japan in Honshu to 36 N,[17] Peter the Great Bay, and Fusan.[18,21]

Sea distribution with minor exceptions is north of latitude 46 N in the cooler waters of the subarctic region.

Utilization   Because canned chum salmon is deficient in red colour and in fat content the canned product is not highly regarded. In consequence during periods of low sales, production has been curtailed. On the other hand the breeding population is so dispersed that consistent protection of spawning migrants is not practical with the result that the extent of spawn deposits is sporadically inadequate to maintain populations well. A fish with such a short stream life might be expected not to have many compensating factors to reduce results of inadequate spawning.[24] These facts may explain fluctuations and decline in production. Total British Columbia catches, which have been subject to detailed analysis,[9,11] are given in tabular form below in thousands of pounds (0.454 metric tons).[11]

The catch was dry salted formerly but this is less common recently. Some is canned but recently most of it has been marketed fresh or frozen. Because it smokes well it is a favoured salmon for use by coast Indians.

Years	Average catch
1931–34	39,900
1934–38	49,400
1939–42	67,800
1934–46	40,200
1947–50	60,120
1951–54	56,044
1955–58	27,737
1959–62	19,017
1963	15,430
1964	23,930
1965	6,660
1966	15,360
1967	12,140
1968	36,510
1969	13,400
1970	36,970

References   1 Andriashev 1937; 2 Aro and Shepard 1967; 3 Berg 1948; 4 Bilton and Ludwig 1966; 5 Dymond 1940; 6 Foskett 1951; 7 Godfrey 1959b; 8 Hallock and Fry 1967; 9 Hoar 1951a; 10 Hunter 1969; 11 Larkin and Ricker 1964; 12 LeBrasseur 1965; 13 LeBrasseur and Doidge 1966; 14, 15, 16 Manzer 1956, 1964, 1969; 17 Nikol'skii 1961; 18 Popov 1933; 19 Pritchard 1943; 20 Ricker personal communication; 21 Shmidt 1950; 22 Sparrow 1968; 23, 24 Wickett 1958, 1964; 25, 26 Wilimovsky 1954, 1964. See also Chatwin 1953, Pritchard 1930a, 1932.

COHO SALMON

Oncorhynchus kisutch (Walbaum 1792)

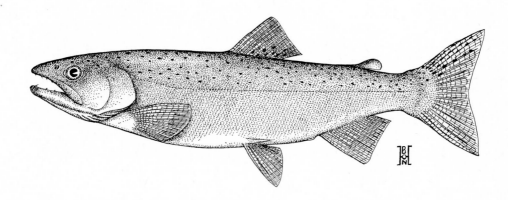

Scientific names from the Greek roots *onkos* (hook) and *rynchos* (nose); and *kisutch* (a vernacular name in Kamchatka and Alaska).

The current English name appeared as early as 1878 as co-hue and presumably descended from such similar Indian dialect names as *kwahwult* (Chilliwack and Musqueam) and *kúchuks* (Sooke and Saanich).[32]

Description   Body elongate, depth about 4.1 into standard length, deepest behind tips of pectoral fins, moderately compressed. Head length about 3.4 into standard length. Mouth terminal, large, directed forward. Upper jaw extending beyond posterior margin of orbit. Snout narrowly rounded in profile, both jaws strongly hooked inward in spawning individuals. Lips fleshy. Teeth firmly set, needlelike, enlarged and hooked inward in spawning individuals, especially males. Interorbital space high, wide, convex, rounded, its width about 3 into length of head. Eye about 6.3 into length of head. Gill membranes free of each other and of isthmus. Branchiostegals 11 to 15. Caudal peduncle compressed, relatively deep, its least depth about 11 into standard length. Pyloric caeca 45 to 83.

Fins   Dorsal (1), 9 to 13. Adipose small, slender, fleshy. Caudal only slightly indented. Anal 13 to 16. Pectorals about 15. Pelvics about 11, abdominal, each with a free-tipped fleshy appendage above its insertion.

Gill Rakers   On first gill arch 19 to 25, rough and widely spaced.

Scales   Cycloid, in rows above lateral line canal 118 to 147, on lateral line canal 121 to 140. Lateral line canal slightly decurved and then straight.

Colour   Metallic blue on dorsal surface, silvery on sides, ventral surface, and caudal peduncle. Irregular black spots on back and upper lobe of caudal fin. Maturing males in fresh water bright red on sides, bright green on back and head, often dark on belly. Females less strongly coloured. Flesh pink to red.

Young with long narrow parr marks, extending about equally above and below lateral line, the dark marks narrower than the light. White on leading edge of anal fin followed by a dark stripe. Orange tints on anal, pectoral, and pelvic fins. Anal fin with first ray elongate.[10]

115

Size Length to 38.5 inches (98 cm). The heaviest fish recorded is 31 pounds (14 kg) off Victoria in 1947.[37] Usual weights at maturity are between 6 and 12 pounds (2.7–5.4 kg). A "run" of smaller fish occurs in the Strait of Georgia. These are commonly called bluebacks locally, but the name is unfortunate as it is also applied by fishermen to the sockeye salmon in the United States.

Recognition Recognized by having black spotting confined to the back and upper lobe of caudal fin and no black along bases of teeth. The teeth are needlelike and firmly set. The 19 to 25 rough gill rakers are widely spaced. Pyloric caeca less than 85. (See colour illustration, Plate VI.)

Life History The coho salmon spawning run begins in early fall as a prelude for spawning in October and November. Spawning takes place in large rivers and their headwaters but is mainly noteworthy for occurring in some 970 small recorded streams as well as in unrecorded watercourses. A few coho reach the Shuswap system and Babine Lake of the Fraser and Skeena rivers. Fecundity ranges from 2500 for 55-centimeter fish to nearly 5000 at 70 centimeters. Eggs are buried in gravel by the parents and light is lethal to developing eggs.[11] Fry emerge from the gravel of the spawning beds around April and remain in the freshwater streams for varying periods, usually one year. At this stage they are territorial in behaviour, holding selected positions in the stream[15] and feeding on drifting insects of terrestrial origin or coming downstream from lakes.[24] Their survival and well-being depend upon maintenance of suitable stream levels, especially during the summer.[25,36,38] After a year (usually) the young coho become more active, forming schools which get into swifter currents and are carried out to sea. In salt water feeding is active and growth rapid. Young fish remain near the surface, feeding in Chatham Sound on herring larvae and sand lance.[19]

In the Strait of Georgia food during early summer is mainly such fishes as sand lance, herring, kelp greenling, rockfish, eulachon, etc.; insects of many kinds are also important; also important are various kinds of Crustacea, including copepods, amphipods, barnacle and crab larvae, and euphausiids. These crustaceans were especially important in Saanich Inlet.[4,5,6,33] Many young coho remain in the Strait of Georgia where they grow less rapidly but supply the popular blueback fishery.[22,28,29] Others migrate offshore to distances up to about a thousand miles (1600 m). At this stage principal foods are squid, euphausiids, and fish.[17,18] In schools they may become involved in feeding frenzy[13] and have been found to be eating blue lanternfish and sauries. On the return migration coho tend to move south along the coast, feeding mainly on fishes, and growing, actively as they go. They travel at rates up to 5 miles a day for considerable distances,[23] or 5 to 7 nautical miles per day (9–12 km).[1] The food is mainly fish, herring, and sand lance, supplemented by a variety of invertebrates.[20,30,31] When coho enter the spawning stream they have been observed to stem currents between 2.1 and 4.8 kilometers per hour,[12] but they are turned back by the odour of mammalian skin extracts in the water.[8]

Distribution From Baja California at Point Chamalu Bay[9,21] or near Monterey,[14] through California to northern Norton Sound and possibly to Kotzebue Sound[3] and as strays in the Sacramento River. The centre of abundance is between Oregon and southeast Alaska. Through Aleutian Islands.[39] Down the Asian coast from Anadyr,[2,5,26] Kamchatka,[20,26,27] northern Sea of Okhotsk (uncommon in south),[7,26,34] Kuril Islands,[34] Hokkaido,[20,34] northern Honshu,[34] and Korea.[20]

Anadromous in rivers and streams. Established in Michigan streams, notably the Platte River, flowing into lakes Michigan and Superior, and planted elsewhere in the Great Lakes to support put-and-take fisheries.

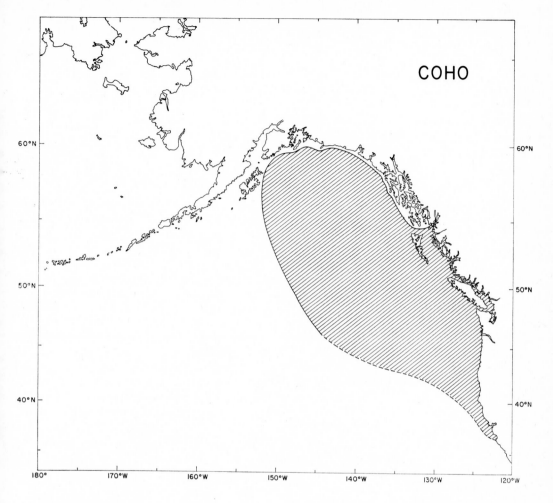

COHO

Utilization Coho salmon are caught commercially by trolling, purse seining, and gillnetting. They are also a favourite fish of sports fishermen in the Strait of Georgia and elsewhere. They are taken by hooks more readily at times when they are concentrating on a fish diet.[35] Most of the commercial fishing is carried out around Vancouver Island and north of Howe Sound. The following tabulation gives commercial landings for recent years in millions of pounds (454 metric tons):[16]

In addition to commercial landings about 0.8 million pounds of coho are caught annually by anglers. The parts of this catch and the commercial catch made early in the season represent inefficient use of the resource as the fish grow very quickly during the summer months.

Years	Average catch
1946–1950	21.2
1951–1955	22.7
1956–1960	19.4
1961–1965	26.3
1966	35.0
1967	20.4
1968	30.0
1969	15.7
1970	27.5

117

References   1 Allen 1966; 2 Andriashev 1937; 3 Aro and Shepard 1967; 4 Barraclough 1967c; 5 Barraclough and Fulton 1967; 6 Barraclough, Robinson, and Fulton 1968; 7 Berg 1948; 8 Brett and MacKinnon 1952; 9 Byres 1942; 10 Carl, Clemens, and Lindsey 1959; 11 Eisler 1957; 12 Ellis 1966; 13 Grinols and Gill 1968; 14 Hallock and Fry 1967; 15 Hoar 1951b; 16 Larkin and Ricker 1964; 17 LeBrasseur 1965; 18 LeBrasseur and Doidge 1966; 19 Manzer 1969; 20 Matsubara 1955; 21 Messersmith 1965; 22, 23 Milne 1950, 1952; 24 Mundie 1968; 25 Neave 1949; 26 Nikol'skii 1961; 27 Popov 1933; 28 Prakash 1962; 29 Prakash and Milne 1958; 30, 31 Pritchard and Tester 1943, 1944; 32 Ricker personal communication; 33 Robinson, Barraclough, and Fulton 1968; 34 Shmidt 1950; 35 Silliman 1941; 36 Smoker 1953; 37 Straight (personal communication); 38 Wickett 1958; 39 Wilimovsky 1954. Further information is contained in Brett and Groot 1963, Clemens 1930, Milne 1964, Pritchard 1934d.

SOCKEYE SALMON

Oncorhynchus nerka (Walbaum 1792)

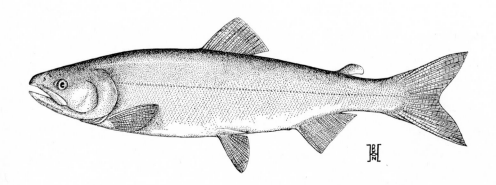

Scientific names from the Greek roots *onchos* (hook) and *rynchos* (snout); and *nerka* (Russian name for the species).

The current English name is a corruption of the name used by the Indians of southern British Columbia, originally printed as *sukkai* and appearing as recognizable variants in the various dialects of Sooke, Saanich, Snohomish, Comox, Musqueam, and Chilliwack.[26]

Description   Body elongate, depth about 4 into standard length, deepest below origin of dorsal fin, moderately compressed. Head length about 4.5 into standard length. Mouth terminal, large, directed forward. Upper jaw extends beyond posterior margin of orbit. Snout bluntly pointed. Lips fleshy. Teeth in mandibles, premaxillaries, maxillaries, palatines and anterior part of tongue small in sea-run fish, larger and jaws hook-

118

ed in breeding males. Interorbital space high, wide, and rounded, its width about 2.8 into length of head. Eye diameter about 6.6 into length of head. Gill membranes free of each other and isthmus. Branchiostegals about 10 to 15. Caudal peduncle moderately compressed, its least depth about 11 into standard length. Pyloric caeca 60 to 115.

Fins Dorsal (1), 11 to 16. Adipose small, slender, fleshy. Caudal moderately forked. Anal 13 to 18. Pectorals about 16. Pelvics about 11, abdominal, each with a free-tipped fleshy appendage above its insertion.

Gill Rakers On first gill arch 28 to 40, long, rough, slender, and closely set.

Scales Cycloid, in rows above lateral line canal, 125 to 143, on lateral line canal 125 to 145. Lateral line canal slightly decurved and then straight.

Colour Greenish blue with fine black specklings on dorsal surface, no large dark spots; called blueback in some sections of the United States. Breeding male with pale green head, dark jaws, pale below, and bright red body, fins red. Breeding female generally the same with green and yellow blotches on body in some populations, but in the upper Fraser runs usually with quite characteristically bright scarlet bodies.
Young with back uniform unmottled green, sides silver without green iridescence. Parr marks short, oval, with lengths less than diameter of eye, usually mostly above lateral line, light areas under the dark along lateral line.

Size Lengths to 33 inches (84 cm). Sockeye from different river systems have characteristic sizes.

Recognition Distinguished from other salmons by the 28 to 40 long, slender, closely spaced gill rakers on the first arch, by the few pyloric caeca, and the fine black speckling on the back. (See colour illustration, Plate VII.)

Life History In summer sockeye salmon move in over the continental shelf and approach the spawning rivers either directly or through channels among the islands. Spawning rivers are almost invariably those with lakes in their systems. Fisheries in the Fraser River and its approaches take about 67 percent of the British Columbia and Washington State landings. Rivers and Smith Inlet areas provide about 16 percent, the Skeena 8 percent, and the Nass 3 percent. All the other areas on Vancouver Island, the Queen Charlotte Islands, the smaller coastwise islands, and the mainland provide spawning areas for only about 6 percent of the sockeye.[1] Some sockeye spawn quite close to the sea, most make long migrations upstream to and through inland lakes. They can stem moderate currents at speeds up to 2 miles (3 km) per hour.[11] Long migrations are highly demanding of stored energy so that in travelling the 685 miles (1080 km) from the outlet of the Fraser to Forfar Creek beyond Stuart Lake at an altitude of 2270 feet (691 m), while ripening sexual products, salmon use 90 to 96 percent of their fat and 33 to 53 percent of their protein reserves.[16] Reserves must be greater for fish making longer migrations. In the Columbia River fish which had climbed 1500 feet (457 m) in 500 miles (800 km) were less capable of stemming currents than less-stressed fish.[23] With energy reserves so finely adjusted to needs, delays to migration from unsuitable water levels or obstructions, including dams, can be very damaging to the well-being of the fish. After migrating from the sea to the nursery lake sockeye spend periods varying both among different runs and different individuals in each run. When adult sockeye leave the lake to enter spawning streams they are nearly ready to spawn. During migration upstream and during spawning, sockeye are preyed upon by seals, bears, gulls, and human poachers, but it is doubtful if the drain on the populations by any of these is often significant in cutting down the reproductive capacity of the runs. Spawning nests or redds are prepared in

119

stream bottoms by the females. They clear away silt and fine gravel in a series of pockets. Fertilized eggs sink among the larger stones in pockets and are then covered with loose gravel, which allows a free flow of oxygenated water around the eggs. A redd is likely to have three to 10 pockets (most commonly five) each containing an average of about 750 eggs but sometimes more than 1600. Occasionally salmon spawn in spring areas along the shores of lakes. The total number of eggs found in samples of North American female sockeye ranges from under 2200 (Port John) to over 4300 (Cultus Lake) with a general average around 3720. Fecundity varies with the run, positively with size of fish, and with earlier migration history of the individual fish, shorter saltwater life being associated with higher egg counts. Incubation time depends to a large extent on temperature and may last for as little as 50 days (or less) or for more than 5 months. When the eggs hatch, the young, called alevins, remain in the gravel for 3 to 5 (?) weeks before emerging as free-swimming fry, the time to emergence again depending on temperature. Newly emerged fry avoid light by hiding among bottom stones during daylight. They emerge at night. They are thus usually subject to being swept downstream to the nursery lake, or, in rare cases, to the sea. Where spawning grounds are at lake outlets, the fry in a remarkable response to a different situation stem the current and enter the nursery lake. The stimulus producing the response is unknown. When they first enter the nursery lake sockeye fry work along the shore for a few weeks but soon move out over the deeper water in the body of the lake where they are concentrated in the top 10 or 20 meters but may be found as deep as 40 meters or more. Their food during this period is insects and their larvae (in shallow water) and later, mainly Cladocera, copepods, and amphipods. Most British Columbia sockeye spend 1 year in fresh water before migrating to sea. However, some go to sea immediately on emerging from the gravel and others may

remain in fresh water for 2 years. Farther north in the Nass River system and in Alaska 3 or 2 years of residence in fresh water is common. Some sockeye salmon never go to sea and become so-called "residuals." In addition some lakes both in North America[12] and Kamchatka and Japan[22] harbour genetic landlocked races called kokanee or kickininee. In lakes having populations of migrating sockeye these are undesirable since they provide damaging competition for food with the young of the more valuable migratory fish. However, they do provide sport for anglers and food for trout. In addition to competing with their own species young sockeye are in competition for food with other species such as threespine stickleback, and possibly other freshwater fishes. They are preyed upon by Dolly Varden, char, squawfish (*Ptychocheilus oregonensis*), rainbow trout, coho salmon, and prickly sculpin (*Cottus asper*). By the spring following hatching young sockeye have reached lengths between 6.0 and 9.5 centimeters in Canada. Some Alaskan, and second- and third-spring fish are larger. When surface water temperatures in nursery lakes approach 4 to 7 C (39–45 F) most young sockeye migrate to sea. In years of high population density when competition for food has reduced growth, larger fish tend to migrate earlier, and in addition fish that have been in the lake over a second year tend to migrate early. Migration to the sea is positive by downstream swimming in quiet reaches of rivers but passive and tail first in rapids. Speeds depend upon currents and may range from 2 to 25 miles (3–40 km) per day.[12] On reaching salt water young sockeye salmon for the early part of the summer appear to remain inshore[21] or even within the influence of the home river since individuals between 4 and 13 centimeters (1.6–5.2 inches) are taken off the outlets of the Fraser River. Food at this stage includes insects, such crustaceans as copepods, amphipods, decapods, barnacle larvae, ostracods, and euphausiids, such young fishes and larvae as sand lance, bigeye whiting, rockfishes, eulachon, starry flounder, herring, pricklebacks, and hake, and *Oikopleura*.[3,4,5,6,7,8,21,27,28] Later, growing young sockeye become scattered over the northeast Pacific Ocean, mainly near the surface[20] and mainly east of 170 E longitude. Those of Canadian origin generally remain east of the dateline and south of the Aleutian Islands. The sockeye population tends to move north during the marine summer and southward in winter. During the summer larger older fish begin to mature and start moving shoreward.[12] The food during high-seas life is mainly such crustaceans as euphausiids, amphipods, copepods, etc., with squids or young fishes occasionally an important part of the diet.[12,18,19] Annulus formation on scales during this period takes place in December and January.[10] Most sockeye from Canadian rivers spend 2 years in the ocean, others spend 3, 4, or 1. For southern British Columbia 1 + years in fresh water, 2 + years in the sea is so prevalent that the 4-year cycle of run size and character is generally applied to industry planning and resource management. Age of maturity may be partly dependent upon hereditary influences.[13] The inshore

migration takes place at a rate of about 30 miles (50 km) per day. Feeding and growth continue during early stages of migration to the spawning river. As a result best use is made of the sockeye resource by delaying capture[25] during the full growing period. By delaying capture until fish are close to the river outlet the resource can be managed so as to make best use of individual stocks as they pass through the fishing grounds.[29] There is good evidence that sockeye salmon return not only to the same river but to the part of the river system where they originated.

Distribution   Found in commercial quantities along the North American coast from the Columbia River to Bristol Bay, Alaska.[2] Reported along the coast of Oregon.[2] Reports of occurrence in and off the Klamath River[31] in northern California are not supported[2] but Hallock and Fry (1967) report spawning runs from the Sacramento River. North of Bristol Bay sockeye occur in the Yukon River[12] and Kotzebue Sound,[2] and they are reported from the Canadian Arctic at Bathurst Inlet and Holman Island.[15] Through the Aleutian Islands,[2,32]

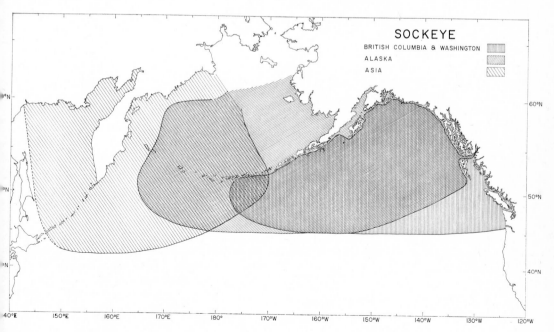

Kuril and Commander islands.[30] On the Asian coast the centre of abundance is around the Kamchatka peninsula[12,14,24] and the northern Okhotsk Sea, although the whole range extends from Anadyr[9] and Cape Chaplina[12] in the north to northern Hokkaido where it is rare.[22] Plantings of young of the landlocked kokanee have survived to form spawning runs in northern Lake Huron, but there is no evidence that the species has been established there.

Utilization   Sockeye salmon provide the most valuable of Canada's Pacific coast fisheries. Their use is of long standing. They were used by native Indians both on the coast and higher up the rivers. Now the commercial fishery is mainly by gillnets in approaches to river outlets and by purse seines in channels. Formerly large trap nets also were employed. Commercial operations in Canada began around 1870, and grew in size and expanded in area covered until around the second decade of the twentieth century when production from the Fraser River reached its peak and the stocks of the northern river systems were energetically utilized. In 1913 and 1914 rock dumping and rock slides associated with railway construction in Hells Gate Canyon of the Fraser River destroyed the big upriver run of that year. Subsequent clearing allowed passage of salmon at certain water levels but frequently at the cost of excessive fatigue to migrating fish. Finally in 1945 and 1946 an effective fishway was installed around the obstructions and runs began to build themselves up again. In 1951 in the Babine River of the Skeena system at natural rockslide blocked off much of the most important run, that to Babine Lake. This was cleared during the subsequent 2 years and the runs have been largely restored.

In the following tabulations of fisheries production the main Canadian river systems have been treated separately. For the Fraser River averages are for 4-year periods in recognition of the 4-year life cycle of the salmon there and the 1955–58 average has been adjusted to include fish headed for the Fraser River through Johnstone Strait. Approximate landings are given in thousands of pounds (0.434 metric tons).[17] Landings from 1963 are based on data on numbers of fish and average weights supplied by the International Pacific Salmon Fisheries Commission.

Fraser River

Years	Canadian catch	Total catch
1895–98	34,000	46,300
1899–1902	35,000	73,700
1903–06	23,000	46,800
1907–10	16,000	44,700
1911–14	20,000	61,500
1915–18	5,300	16,300
1919–22	3,200	8,200
1923–26	3,500	8,500
1927–30	4,600	15,800
1931–34	5,400	17,100
1935–38	9,600	15,900
1939–42	13,100	20,800
1943–46	9,500	16,500
1947–50	4,500	9,900
1951–54	15,800	31,000
1955–58	12,400	30,400
1959–62	7,100	14,600

Year	Canadian catch	Total catch	Average weight pounds
1963	3,950	11,520	5.757
1964	2,980	5,960	5.825
1965	6,030	11,960	5.792
1966	9,060	18,060	6.721
1967	10,940	23,030	5.810
1968	5,310	10,420	5.767
1969	9,570	18,580	5.697
1970	9,860	18,460	6.382

Other main river systems

Years	Rivers Inlet	Smith Inlet	Skeena River	Nass River	Smaller rivers, etc.
1906–10	5,300	–	8,800	–	–
1911–15	7,000	–	7,600	1,900	–
1916–20	4,800	–	7,600	1,700	–
1921–25	6,800	–	7,100	1,600	–
1926–30	5,500	1,700	5,900	1,100	–
1931–35	6,300	1,700	4,000	1,300	–
1936–40	4,800	1,700	5,100	1,500	–
1941–45	5,000	1,000	4,500	1,200	–
1946–50	6,300	1,700	4,300	1,100	–
1951–55	5,730	2,200	4,250	1,280	4,390
1956–60	4,280	1,400	1,720	1,400[a]	3,320
1961–65	4,600	1,390	3,135	1,020	4,770
1966	3,280	1,160	3,710	1,080	12,340
1967	4,890	1,490	6,230	2,650	16.630

[a]Excluding 1958.

Until 1967 sockeye salmon landings were ascribed to main river systems according to area of landing.[17] However, a change in fishing practices to transporting fish for long distances for processing made statistics increasingly less significant, and the compilation has not been published since 1967. The figures below are for the total British Columbia sockeye salmon landings in thousands of pounds (0.434 metric tons) as provided by the Department of Fisheries and Forestry: 1967, 36,800; 1968, 41,200; 1969, 24,000; 1970, 24,800.

The long-term trend of production is down. Some of the decline may result from inability of borderline races effectively to survive additional mortality caused by continued fishing. In both the Fraser and Skeena systems marked declines resulted from calamities in the habitat from rockslides. Remedial engineering resulting from and followed by enlightened management appears to be fostering the return of affected stocks to their production potential. It appears that production can be established at about current levels or rather better as long as (1) access to spawning grounds is maintained free from delaying or blocking obstructions, (2) the habitat is kept free of pollution by forest industry operations, industrial wastes, mining and refining effluents, deleterious agricultural practices, domestic pollution, and thermal pollution, and (3) fishing is concentrated close enough to spawning grounds (i.e., in rivers and near their estuaries) to allow resource management on the basis of individual stocks.

References   1 Aro and Shepard 1967; 2 Atkinson, Rose, and Duncan 1967; 3, 4, 5 Barraclough 1967a, b, c; 6, 7 Barraclough and Fulton 1967, 1968; 8 Barraclough, Robinson, and Fulton 1968; 9 Berg 1948; 10 Bilton and Ludwig 1966; 11 Ellis 1966; 12 Foerster 1968; 13 Godfrey 1958; 14 Hanamura 1967; 15 Hunter 1969; 16 Idler and Clemens 1959; 17 Larkin and Ricker 1964; 18 LeBrasseur 1965; 19 LeBrasseur and Doidge 1966; 20, 21 Manzer 1964, 1969; 22 Nikol'skii 1961; 23 Paulik and DeLacy 1958; 24 Popov 1933; 25, 26 Ricker 1962, personal communication; 27, 28 Robinson, Barraclough, and Fulton 1968a, b; 29 Shepard and Withler 1958; 30 Shmidt 1950; 31 Taft 1937; 32 Wilimovsky 1964.

Further references and information are to be found in the excellent monograph by R. E. Foerster 1968, in numerous papers by Clemens and Clemens in the reports of the British Columbia Department of Fisheries, in the various reports of the International Pacific Salmon Commission, and in papers by Aro and Broodhead 1950, Bolton 1930, Scattergood 1949, Scattergood, Sinderman, and Scud 1959, Withler 1945.

CHINOOK SALMON

Oncorhynchus tshawytscha (Walbaum 1792)

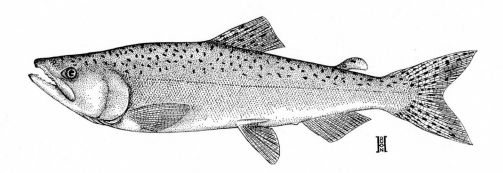

Scientific names from the Greek roots *onkos* (hook) and *rynchos* (nose); and *tshawytscha* (the vernacular name for the species in Alaska and Kamchatka).

Clemens and Wilby 1946 used the common name spring salmon for this species. Other common names, king salmon and tyee recognize the large size. Tyee is the Chinook word for large.

Description   Body elongate, depth about 4 into standard length, deepest around tip of pectoral fin, moderately compressed. Head length about 3.7 into standard length. Mouth terminal, large, directed forward. Upper jaw extends beyond posterior margin of orbit. Snout roundly pointed. Teeth in jaws movable, moderately sharp, becoming enlarged and hooked in spawning males; on mandibles, premaxillaries, maxillaries, palatines, on anterior part of tongue. Inter-orbital space high, wide, convex, rounded, its width about 2.8 into length of head. Eye diameter about 7.5 into length of head. Gill membranes free of each other and of isthmus. Branchiostegals 13 to 19. Caudal peduncle only moderately compressed, its least depth about 12 into standard length. Pyloric caeca 140 to 185.

Fins   Dorsal (1), 10 to 14. Adipose stout and fleshy. Caudal moderately forked, outer rays stiff. Anal 13 to 19. Pectorals about 14. Pelvics about 10, abdominal, each with a free-tipped fleshy appendage above its insertion.

Gill Rakers   On first gill arch 18 to 30, rough, widely spaced.

Scales   Cycloid, in rows above lateral line canal 140 to 153, on lateral line canal 130 to 165. Lateral line canal slightly decurved and then straight.

Colour   Greenish blue to black on dorsal surface. Moderately large, irregular black spots on back, upper sides, dorsal fin and both lobes of caudal fin. Black along bases of teeth. Maturing fish very dark. Flesh red or almost white, rarely pink.
Young with parr marks as long vertical bars, the longest definitely longer than the vertical diameter of eye, dark areas along lateral line equal to or greater than the light interior bars, parr marks approximately divided equally by lateral line.[13]

Size   Length to 58 inches (147 cm). Other records are for 53 inches and 126 pounds (135 cm, 57.27 kg) at Petersburg, Alaska[13] and 92 pounds (41.7 kg) by sports gear.[36] An unofficial Alaskan record is for 135 pounds (61.2 kg).[36]

Recognition   Noted for the black spotting on back, dorsal fin, and both lobes of caudal fin, black pigment along the bases of the teeth and loose conical teeth in mature individuals. Salmon over 30 pounds (14 kg) are likely to be chinooks. (See colour illustration, Plate VIII.)

Life History   Chinook salmon enter spawning rivers during most of the year,[21] in general using relatively few larger rivers.[18] They may spawn immediately above the tidal limit although some go upstream as much as 600 miles.[1,18] During their migration, chinook salmon are strongly repelled by extracts of mammalian skin.[10,11,12] Movement is active only in hour of first daylight in some areas[1] but elsewhere seems to take place through the daylight hours.[21] Eggs are buried in the gravel of the rivers bottom. The eggs are larger than those of other salmons and bright red. Females produce about 4800 eggs, depending greatly on size and, independently, the local strain of fish.[26,34] Light inhibits the survival of embryos to hatching.[15] Usually young chinook salmon go to sea soon after hatching but they may remain in fresh water for at least a year.[22] Young chinook salmon are found off the mouth of the Fraser River from April on. There they are 4 to 5 centimeters long in April, about 9 centimeters in June, and reach 13 centimeters in July. Their food at this stage is mainly such small fishes as sand lance, eulachon, herring, rockfish, and smoothtongue, and terrestrial insects. A variety of crustaceans was also found in the stomachs and included amphipods, copepods, euphausiids, and cladocerans and the larvae of crabs and barnacles.[1,3,4,5,6,7,8,32,33] Later migrations are for the most part along the coast, first northwest on a feeding migration and then returning to spawning streams.[20] Some of these migrations are very long as from Alaska (Adak Island, once) to the Columbia and from the west coast of Vancouver Island to the Columbia and even the Sacramento rivers. During this phase food off British Columbia consists mainly of such fishes as

herring, sand lance, pilchard, and rockfish.[26,27,28,29,30,31] Euphausiids were of some importance in May and June.[27] Growth continued fast along the migration and to maturity so that delaying capture increases production from the resource.[24] Apparently some chinook salmon go well out into the Pacific as far as 1000 miles (1600 km), where they tend to remain well below the surface. Most chinook salmon return to spawn in their fourth or fifth years but some return as early as the third year or as late as their eighth. Olfactory stimuli may be instrumental in guiding chinook salmon back to their spawning ground but response to other stimuli must be involved too.[10] Small third-year fish are usually males and referred to as jacks. Harbour seals damage many chinook salmon caught in gillnets in the Skeena River but it is not known whether they also destroy free fish.[16]

Distribution   Anadromous in larger rivers. From southern California at the Ventura River, important in the Sacramento River, through California, Oregon, Washington, and British Columbia to the Bering Sea as far as Unalakleet and in Norton Sound and possibly Kotzebue Sound[2] and Aleutian Islands.[37,38] Yukon River.[1,2] In the Canadian Arctic at the Coppermine River (up to 13 individuals recorded).[17] On the Asian coast from the Anadyr River,[9,35] Kamchatka,[9,23,25,35] Maritime Territories, Okhotsk Sea,[35] Hokkaido,[9,19] Amur River,[35] and Commander Islands.[9]

Introduced to New Zealand where it has become established, but rather unprofitably, and is not well regarded. It was also introduced into the Great Lakes at various times where although growth and survival to maturity were sometimes good,[14] successful reproduction has not been reported.

Utilization   The chinook salmon is the most highly prized of the Pacific salmons for the fresh fish trade. The catch is now mainly by trollers although gillnetters still make about one-third of the total

125

landings. British Columbia catches over the period of comparable good fishing statistics in millions of pounds (454 metric tons) have been:[18]

Years	Average catch
1946–50	13.6
1951–55	12.4
1956–60	11.6
1961–65	9.8
1966	13.6
1967	13.7
1968	13.6
1969	12.6
1970	13.0

Sports fishermen have taken in addition nearly a million pounds of chinook salmon annually. The chinook salmon fishery has several things reducing its productivity. Much of the Columbia River production on which the troll fishery largely depended has been cut off by power dams. Pollution of various kinds, including thermal pollution, is current or impending on the Columbia and other rivers. The troll fishery takes a high proportion of the chinook salmon at an immature stage while they are well below the maximum weight.[18,24]

References   1 Aro and Shepard 1967; 2 Atkinson, Rose, and Duncan 1967; 3, 4, 5 Barraclough 1967a, b, c; 6, 7 Barraclough and Fulton 1967, 1968; 8 Barraclough, Robinson, and Fulton 1968; 9 Berg 1948; 10 Brett and Groot 1963; 11, 12 Brett and MacKinnon 1952, 1954; 13 Carl, Clemens, and Lindsey 1959; 14 Dymond, Hart, and Pritchard 1929; 15 Eisler 1957; 16 Fisher 1952; 17 Hunter 1969; 18 Larkin and Ricker 1964; 19 Matsubara 1955; 20 Mottley 1929; 21, 22 Neave 1943, 1949; 23 Nikol'skii 1961; 24 Parker 1960; 25 Popov 1933; 26, 27 Prakash 1958, 1962; 28, 29, 30, 31 Pritchard and Tester 1939, 1941, 1942, 1944; 32, 33 Robinson, Barraclough, and Fulton 1968a, b; 34 Rounsefell 1957; 35 Shmidt 1950; 36 Straight personal communication; 37, 38 Wilimovsky 1954, 1964. See also Milne 1964, Pritchard 1934e, Rich 1925, and Williamson and Clemens 1932.

COASTAL CUTTHROAT TROUT

Salmo clarki clarki Richardson 1836

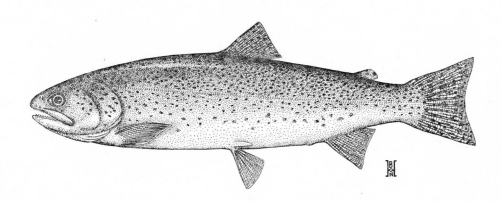

Scientific names from the Latin *salmo* (salmon); and Captain W. Clark of the Lewis and Clark expedition.

The subspecies *Salmo clarki clarki* as a coastal fish is readily recognizable in British Columbia although there is some overlapping of characters in the United States.[3]

Description   Body elongate, its depth about 4.2 into standard length, only slightly compressed. Head length about 4.3 into standard length. Mouth terminal, large, directed forward. Upper jaw extends well beyond posterior margin of eye. Jaws about even. Lips fleshy. Teeth in jaws small, strong, conical, hooked inward, on maxillaries and premaxillaries, mandibles, on head and shaft of vomer, and on back of tongue. Interorbital space smoothly convex, its width about 3.1 into length of head. Eye diameter about 6.4 into length of head. Gill membranes free from each other and isthmus. Caudal peduncle moderately compressed, its least depth about 14 into standard length.

Fins   Dorsal (1), 8 to 11. Adipose, small, fleshy, slender. Caudal shallowly forked. Anal 8 to 12. Pectorals about 13, short. Pelvics about 9, abdominal, each with a free-tipped, fleshy appendage above its insertion.

Gill Rakers   On first gill arch 15 to 22.

Scales   Cycloid, in oblique rows above lateral line canal 120 to 180. Lateral line canal very slightly decurved anteriorly and then straight to end of caudal peduncle.

Colour   Greenish blue on dorsal surfaces, silvery on sides. Angular or round black spots tending occasionally to be organized into irregular lines on back and sides and toward belly, and on vertical and pectoral fins. Red dash on lower jaw, not evident in preserved specimens and generally inclined to fade. Fresh-run fish from the sea tend to have the ground colour bluish with a silvery sheen on the sides.[1]

Size   Sea-run cutthroats range from 1.5 to 4 pounds (0.68–1.8 kg).[1] Non-migrating individuals reach 30 inches (76 cm)[2] or 17 pounds (7.8 kg).[1] The record is 41 pounds (18 kg) from Pyramid Lake, in 1925.[5]

Recognition   Known for the red or orange streaks along the inner edge of lower jaw in fresh specimens, the small teeth at the back of the tongue, and the sturdy body. (Note colour illustration, Plate II.)

Life History   Fresh water mainly and anadromous from estuaries where they move in and out with the tides. Spawning is mainly in smaller streams. Ripe individuals are found in November but most spawning is in February and March. They may go to sea when quite small and take up estuarine life for 1 or more years. They feed heavily on other fishes such as coho, sticklebacks, rockfishes, sculpins, and flatfishes, and small individuals eat Crustacea and both freshwater and terrestrial insects. Coastal

cutthroats mature usually at 3 or 4 years of age. In small streams maturity may occur at very small size.

Distribution   From northern California through Oregon, Washington,[4] and British Columbia to Prince William Sound off the Gulf of Alaska.[1] In British Columbia in the coastal area, inland as far as Ashcroft and possibly Clinton.[1]

References   1 Carl, Clemens, and Lindsey 1959; 2 Clemens and Wilby 1961; 3 Qadri 1959; 4 Schultz and DeLacy 1936; 5 Straight personal communication.

RAINBOW TROUT

Salmo gairdneri   Richardson 1836

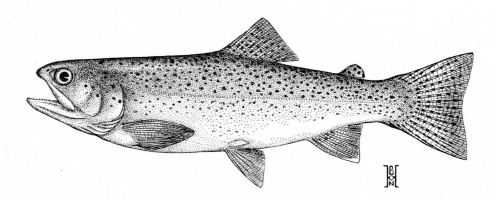

Scientific names from the Latin *salmo* (salmon); and Dr M. Gairdner, naturalist with the Hudson's Bay Company at Fort Vancouver, Washington.

Sea-run fish are usually referred to as **steelhead trout.**

The French name is *truite arc-en-ciel*.

Description   Body elongate, depth about 4 into standard length, moderately compressed. Head length about 3.8 into standard length. Mouth terminal, large, directed forward. Upper jaw extends about to posterior margin of eye. Snout blunt. Lips fleshy. Teeth on jaws small, conical, sharp, directed in, on mandibles and on premaxillaries, maxillaries, palatines, weak on head and shaft of vomer, on tongue but not on its base. Interorbital space convex and smooth, its width about 2.9 into length of head. Eye diameter about 5.2 into length of head. Gill membranes free from each other and from isthmus. Caudal peduncle compressed, its least depth about 8.5 into standard length.

Fins   Dorsal (1), 10 to 12. Adipose small-based, and fleshy. Caudal shallowly forked. Anal 8 to 12. Pectorals about 15. Pelvics about 10, abdominal, each with a free-tipped fleshy appendage above its insertion.

Gill Rakers   On first gill arch 17 to 21.

Scales   Cycloid, in oblique lines above lateral line canal, 115 to 161. Lateral line canal very slightly decurved anteriorly, and then straight to end of caudal peduncle.

Colour   Metallic blue on dorsal surface, silvery on sides, black spots on back, dorsal and caudal fins; spawning males have a pink or red band on side; no red dash below lower jaw.

Size   Length to 45 inches (114 cm).[3] The following record weights have been dependably recorded: largest sea-run, 43 pounds (19.5 kg) off Port Simpson, near Prince Rupert, netted; largest sea-run line-caught, 42 pounds (19.1 kg) near Bell Island, Alaska;[13] largest rod and reel sea-run, 36 pounds (16.3 kg) Kispiox River, B.C.;[11] largest rod and reel sea-run from Vancouver Island, 28 pounds 4 ounces (12.8 kg) Campbell River;[12] largest landlocked rainbow trout 52.5 pounds (23.9 kg) Jewel Lake, B.C.[3,13]

Recognition   Known for its short head, compressed body, absence of teeth on back of tongue, absence of a red dash below lower jaw, and for the light edges on dorsal, anal, and pelvic fins. (Note colour illustration, Plate II.)

Life History   Fresh water or anadromous. The difference in habit is accompanied by morphological differences and is hereditary.[7] Summer and winter running tendencies also appear to be inherited.[10] Freshwater fish are called rainbow trout. Adult steelhead spawn in gravel in main rivers and tributaries. Most young remain in fresh water for 2 or 3 years (1–4[15]). They return to spawn usually after 2 to 3 years (1–4[15]). Some return to spawn for second or third time.[3] Migration habits appear to be unrelated to previous history, and age composition of adults is relatively uniform from year to year.[6] Survival to spawn again however, does appear to be related to time of year for entering fresh water (up to 31 per cent of winter-run fish spawn a second time) and with latitude (decreasing from south to north).[15] Migrations at sea may be very extensive. Fish tagged in the Gulf of Alaska have been taken off Grays Harbor and in Puget Sound, Washington. Representative-appearing steelhead were taken offshore as far west as 150 W longitude, the largest fish was 88 centimeters long, most of them were in their fourth year having left fresh water in their third year, some were 7 or 6 years old after being in fresh water for 3 or 4 years, several had already spawned at least once. Their food was mainly fishes (young greenlings and a paralipid) and various crustaceans. Evidently they had been feeding near the surface.[14] In California a 7-year-old fish that had spent 4 years in fresh water was found returning to spawn.[9] Young steelhead trout occur in the less saline waters of the Strait of Georgia off the outlet of the Fraser River and in Saanich Inlet.[1,2,8] In June food consisted of insects, euphausiids, copepods, amphipods, and other crustaceans, *Sagitta*, and young fishes such as sand lance, eulachon, red devil, searcher, herring, and smooth-tongue.

Distribution   From southern California through the northwest states to the Bering Sea and Bristol Bay,[3,16] and the Aleutian Islands,[17] extending far up main

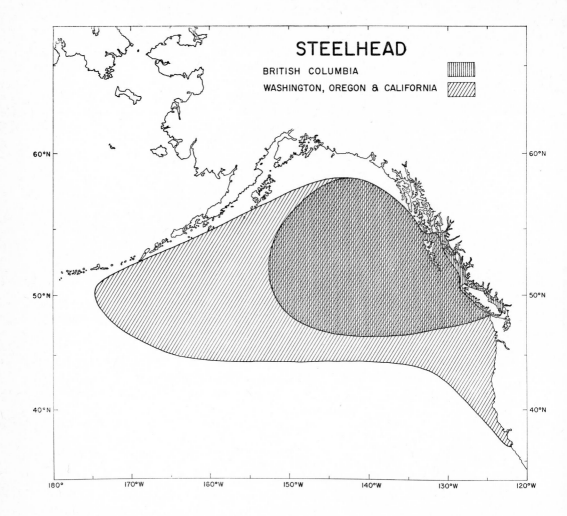

STEELHEAD

BRITISH COLUMBIA

WASHINGTON, OREGON & CALIFORNIA

rivers. Seagoing individuals are encountered as far offshore as 150 W longitude.

Introduced throughout the world. Taken in Lake Erie[4] and Prince Edward Island.

Non-migratory rainbow trout are found through the coastal area, the Fraser drainage, and the Peace River drainage, but not in the parts of the Columbia system drained by the Moyie, Elk, and parts of the Kootenay rivers.

Utilization   The steelhead trout is much sought as an angling fish in the fresh waters of the coastal area but a satisfactory

estimate of the total amount taken is not obtainable.

The commercial fishery is by gillnets, mostly in the northern part of the province. Landings in British Columbia in recent years are, in thousands of pounds (0.454 metric tons).[5]

Years	Average catch
1951–1955	437
1956–1960	203
1961–1965	195
1966	306
1967	253
1968	221
1969	142
1970	125

References   1 Barraclough 1967c; 2 Barraclough, Robinson, and Fulton 1968; 3 Carl, Clemens, and Lindsey 1959; 4 Dymond 1932a; 5 Larkin and Ricker 1964; 6 Maher and Larkin 1955; 7 Neave 1944; 8 Robinson, Barraclough, and Fulton 1968b; 9 Shapovalov and Taft 1954; 10 Smith 1960; 11, 12, 13 Straight personal communication, 1970a, b; 14 Taylor and LeBrasseur 1957; 15 Withler 1966; 16, 17 Wilimovsky 1954, 1964. See also Dymond 1932b.

ATLANTIC SALMON

Salmo salar Linnaeus 1758

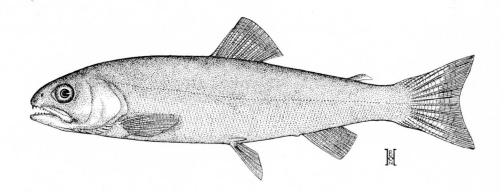

Scientific names from the Latin *salmo* (salmon) and *salio* (leap).

The French name is *saumon atlantique*.

Description   Body elongate, depth about 4.5 into standard length, moderately compressed. Head length about 4.3 (5–6) into standard length, mouth terminal, moderate in size, directed forward. Upper jaw barely extends to posterior margin of eye. Upper jaw slightly longer than lower. Teeth in jaws, small on mandibles, maxillaries, premaxillaries, and palatines, and through vomer, large on tongue. Interorbital space convex, its width about 3.2 into length of head. Eye diameter about 4.2 into length of head. Gill membranes free of each other and of isthmus. Caudal peduncle moderately compressed, its least depth about 13 into standard length.

Fins   Dorsal (1), 11 or 12. Adipose slender. Caudal moderately forked. Anal 8 to 12. Pectorals about 14. Pelvics about 10, abdominal, each with a free-tipped fleshy appendage above its insertion.

Scales   Cycloid, oblique rows along lateral line canal about 120. Lateral line canal slightly higher anteriorly and straight down midside.

Colour   Light brown on dorsal surface, silvery on sides, black spots often X-shaped, on

131

dorsal, adipose, and anal fins, may be obscured in saltwater specimens. No red or pink colour.

Size   In Atlantic reaches 60 pounds (27 kg)[2] or 48 inches (122 cm). Large specimens not recorded from British Columbia.

Recognition   Noteworthy for the sparse X-shaped dark markings, slender caudal peduncle and teeth on shaft of vomer.

Life History   The Atlantic salmon was introduced to British Columbia waters as fertilized eggs in 1905, and subsequently. In general the introduction was unsuccessful. A few individuals were taken in the Cowichan River by anglers and there is a questionable record from salt water in Clio Channel. There are no recent records and it is improbable that the species is established or will become so.[1]

Atlantic salmon are anadromous. Characteristically they spend 1 to 3 years in the stream where they hatch as alevins, fingerlings, and parr before going to sea as smolts for 1 or 2 years. Mortality in connection with spawning is high, but a significant number of recovered spawners return to spawn second or third times.

The Atlantic salmon is a valuable commercial fish. As a sports fish it is venerated by anglers through the north Atlantic region.

Distribution   Distribution in the Pacific Ocean is poorly defined. Around the North Atlantic distribution is bounded by the Connecticut River, Conn., Ungava Bay, Greenland, Iceland, northern Norway, and northern Spain.

References   1 Clemens and Wilby 1961; 2 Leim and Scott 1966.

BROWN TROUT

Salmo trutta Linnaeus 1758

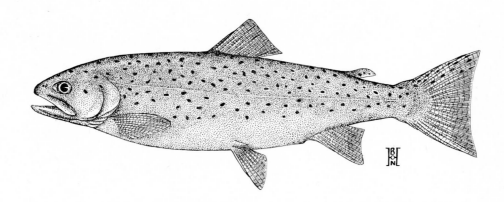

Scientific names from the Latin *salmo* (salmon) and *trutta* (trout — from truculentes, fierce, breaks gear).

The French name is *truite brune*.

Description   Body elongate, its depth about 3.5 into standard length, moderately compressed. Head about 4 into standard length, rather pointed. Mouth terminal, moderate in size, directed forward. Upper jaw extends to about posterior margin of eye. Lips fleshy. Teeth on both jaws, maxillaries, premaxillaries, palatines, mandibles, on head and shaft of vomer, large on tongue but not on its base. Interorbital space broad and convex with low longitudinal ridges, its width about 3 into length of head. Eye diameter about 5.2 into length of head. Gill membranes free from each other and from isthmus. Caudal peduncle compressed, its least depth about 10 into standard length.

Fins   Dorsal (1), 10 or 11. Adipose small, slight, fleshy. Caudal shallowly forked. Anal 9 to 12. Pectorals about 13. Pelvics about 9, abdominal, each with a free-tipped fleshy appendage above its insertion.

Gill Rakers   On first gill arch 16 to 19.

Scales   Cycloid, in oblique rows above lateral line canal 116 to 136. Lateral line canal slightly decurved anteriorly, then straight to end of caudal peduncle.

Colour   Ground colour golden brown. Large dark brown or black spots; some with orange, pink, or red halos. Fins may be edged with white. Dark spots may be continued on upper lobe of caudal fin. Adipose may have red spots.[1]

Size   Record weights with lengths; 39.5 pounds (18 kg) Loch Aire, Scotland; 27 pounds, 10 ounces (12.5 kg), 39.5 inches (100 cm) Witless Bay, Newfoundland; 8 pounds (3.6 kg), 27.5 inches (70 cm) Cowichan River, B.C. In British Columbia 5-pound (2.3-kg) or 24-inch (61-cm) fish are "large."[6]

Recognition   Recognized by the large dark spots, some surrounded by pale halos and the absence of teeth on the back of the tongue.

133

Life History   Spawning takes place mainly in November and December in tributary streams with fry emerging from the gravel in spring. Maturity is reached at 3 or 4 years but very old (14 years) individuals have been reported. Food of young in the Cowichan River consists of insects, mainly caddis larvae, and young salmonoid fishes.[3] There is sexual differentiation in anal fin shape with male fins rounded and female fins falcate.[2]

Distribution   The brown trout has been introduced from southern and north-western Europe to all the continents, and now may have filled the suitable habitat. In many regions it is confined to inland areas.[4,5] It is valued because it is believed to remain in streams through summer, and sea-going tendencies away from river outlets have not been observed in British Columbia, although there has been limited spread along the coast. Successful plantings have been made in the Cowichan and Little Qualicum rivers.

References   1 Carl, Clemens, and Lindsey 1959; 2 Gruchy and Vladykov 1968; 3 Idyll 1942; 4 Leim and Scott 1966; 5 McCrimmon and Marshall 1968; 6 Straight personal communication.

DOLLY VARDEN

Salvelinus malma (Walbaum 1792)

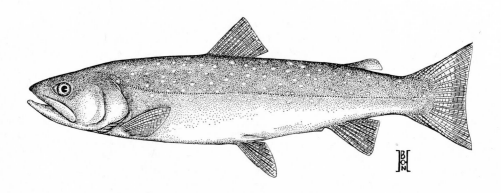

Scientific names from *salvelinus* (an old name for the European char) and *malma* (the name used for the species in Kamchatka).

The common name comes from the name of a brightly flowered sheer cloth, which in turn derives its name from a lively character in Charles Dickens' novel Barnaby Rudge whose clothes of such material were vividly described.

Although northern and southern forms of the species are recognizable they are not assigned names. It seems inadvisable to recognize here any of the numerous subspecies described.[6]

Description   Body elongate, depth about 4.3 into standard length, moderately compressed. Head length about 4.2 into standard length. Mouth terminal, large, directed forward. Upper jaw (in good-sized specimens) extending well beyond posterior margin of eye and a little beyond closed lower jaw. Lips fleshy. Teeth in jaws sharp and conical on premaxillaries and mandibles, hooked inward, on maxillaries, on head only of vomer, and on tongue. Interorbital space somewhat convex and smooth, its width about 3.4 into length of head. Eye diameter variable, 4.0 to 6.5 into length of head. Gill membranes free of each other and of isthmus. Branchiostegals 21 to 30. Caudal peduncle compressed, its least depth about 12 into standard length.

Fins   Dorsal (1), 10 or 11. Adipose, small, slender, fleshy. Caudal moderately forked. Anal about 10. Pectorals about 14, short. Pelvics about 10, abdominal, each with a free-tipped fleshy appendage above its insertion.

Gill Rakers   On first gill arch 14 to 22.

Scales   Cycloid, in oblique rows above lateral line canal 186 to 254. Pores along lateral line canal 105 to 142. Lateral line canal very slightly decurved anteriorly, then almost straight to base of caudal.

Colour   Variable, sea-run individuals silvery, others blue, olive green, or brown on dorsal surfaces, occasionally bright red on sides. Cream leading edges on pelvic and anal fins. Brightly coloured, yellow to red spots on back and sides. Sometimes dorsal surface with vermiculations.

Size   Length to 3 feet (91 cm) and 30 pounds (13.6 kg).[3] Canadian records are 40 pounds 2 ounces (18.3 kg) from the Lardeau River, and 35 pounds 7 ounces (16 kg) by rod and reel in the Duncan River in the Kootenays.[11]

Recognition   Recognizable by the pale yellow spots on the back and red to orange spots on the sides of the body, vomerine teeth restricted to the head of the vomer, slender form and unmarked dorsal fin. Except in northern British Columbia there are no vermiculate markings on back.

Life History   Anadromous, or resident in fresh water. Spawning takes place in streams in autumn. Maturity is ordinarily reached in the fifth year. In many areas regular seaward migrations take place in spring and return migrations in fall. In the Skeena River most fish spend 3 years in fresh water and 2 or 3 in the ocean, males tending to stay at sea longer. In the river 3.3 percent of females had previously spawned. Downstream migration is at about 19 centimeters.[7] Food consists of fishes, including herring, sticklebacks, and young salmon, salmon eggs, molluscs, insects, and crustaceans.

Distribution   From northern California[2,5,10] through Oregon, Washington,[10] and British Columbia and southeastern Alaska to the Aleutian Islands,[14] Bering Sea,[1,6] Bering Strait,[1] Herschel Island and Point Barrow,[6] Kamchatka,[4,9,13] Kuril Islands,[4] Japan,[12] northern Hokkaido,[4] Sakhalin,[4] Maritime Territories,[4,8] Korea,[4] and Peter the Great Bay.[5]

In British Columbia through the coastal areas, more abundant in salt water toward the north.

Utilization   The species is sought and catches reported by anglers but its fighting qualities are inferior and it is not highly regarded as a game fish.

References   1 Andriashev 1937; 2 Carl, Clemens, and Lindsey 1959; 3 Clemens and Wilby 1961; 4 Matsubara 1955; 5 McPhail 1961; 6 Morton 1970; 7 Narver 1969; 8 Nikol'skii 1961; 9 Popov 1933; 10 Schultz and DeLacy 1936; 11 Straight personal communication; 12 Tanaka 1935; 13, 14 Wilimovsky 1954, 1964. See also DeLacy and Morton 1943.

Generally frail soft-rayed fishes with cycloid scales. There are no fleshy appendages at the bases of the pelvic fins nor are the last few vertebrae turned dorsally as in the Salmonidae. Only a few (up to seven) pyloric caeca. Usually with forked tails. A lateral line canal and adipose fin are present. Colours may be silvery or dull. Sexes are differentiated at breeding time by nuptial tubercles, modified scales and anal fin, and size, but differentiation is less striking than among some Salmonidae. Small fishes, often anadromous, spawning on beaches, stream bottoms, or at sea. Of current and future potential commercial importance. Confined to the northern hemisphere.

KEY TO THE OSMERIDAE

1 Strong concentric striae on both operculum and suboperculum; gill rakers on upper part of arch 4 to 6 .... *Thaleichthys pacificus,* Eulachon, p. 148

or 1 No strong concentric striae on operculum or suboperculum; gill rakers on upper part of arch 8 to 14 2

2 Teeth on tongue medium conical to large canine, not villiform; mouth large with maxillary ending behind posterior margin of pupil 3

or 2 Teeth on tongue villiform; mouth small with maxillary ending before posterior margin of pupil 6

3 Pyloric caeca 0 to 1; orbit diameter exceeds 0.8 of caudal peduncle depth .... *Allosmerus elongatus,* Whitebait smelt, p. 138

or 3 Pyloric caeca 4 to 8; orbit diameter less than 0.8 of caudal peduncle depth 4

4 One or two large canine teeth on either side of vomer .... *Osmerus mordax dentex,* Rainbow smelt, p. 143

or 4 An arc of small pointed teeth across vomer .... Genus *Spirinchus* 5

5 Pectoral fin long, extending 83 percent or more of distance to pelvic insertion; snout blunt with premaxillary steep, forming an angle of 68 to 90 degrees with forehead; longest anal ray 1.4 to 2.2 times into head length; midlateral scales 55 to 62 .... *Spirinchus thaleichthys,* Longfin smelt, p. 146

or 5 Pectoral fin shorter, extending less than 83 percent of distance to pelvic insertion; snout rather pointed with premaxillary forming an angle of 54 to 65 degrees with forehead; longest anal ray 2.2 to 3.1 into head length; midlateral scales 62 to 66 .... *Spirinchus starksi,* Night smelt, p. 145

6 Scales large, 61 to 73 along midside; adipose fin oval, its base short, 1.2 times orbit or less .... *Hypomesus pretiosus pretiosus,* Surf smelt, p. 139

or 6 Scales very small, 170 to 220 along midside; adipose with almost straight outer margin and long base at least 1.5 times orbit diameter .... *Mallotus villosus,* Capelin, p. 141

WHITEBAIT SMELT

Allosmerus elongatus (Ayres 1854)

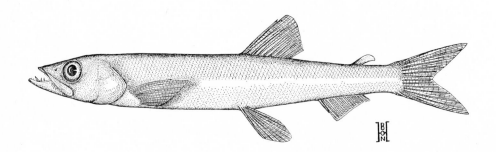

Scientific names from the Greek root *allo* (other) and *Osmerus* (smelt); and the Latin *elongatus* (elongate).

Description Body elongate, its depth 6.5 to 9 into standard length, compressed. Head length 3.5 to 4.2 into standard length. Mouth terminal, rather large, directed almost forward. Upper jaw extends just posterior to margin of eye. Snout low and pointed. Teeth fine in both jaws, a single large canine in middle of vomer sometimes flanked by 1 or 2 small and/or procumbent teeth, moderately well developed on palatines, recurved teeth on tongue, a single large tooth near end directed forward. Interorbital space broad and gently convex. Eye large, orbit diameter about 3.6 to 4.2 into length of head. Operculum smooth. Branchiostegals 6 to 7. Gill membranes free of isthmus. Caudal peduncle compressed. Pyloric caeca, 1.[3]

Fins Dorsal (1), 9 to 11, originating behind midpoint of body length. Adipose small, directed backward. Caudal forked. Anal 14 to 17. Pectorals 12 to 14, extending back by one-half to one-third distance to pelvic insertion. Pelvics 8, originating in front of dorsal, abdominal, extending about four-fifths distance to anus.

Gill Rakers On first gill arch 33 to 41; on its upper half, 10 to 13. Vertebrae 65 to 67.

Scales Cycloid, deciduous, moderate in size, between 62 and 68 along midside. Lateral line canal gently decurved anteriorly then straight along midside. Males with elongate midlateral scales, and tubercles on head, scales, and fin rays.

Colour Pale greenish, almost colourless, a sharply marked silvery stripe along side.

Size Length to 9 inches (22.9 cm).

Recognition Known for its long pointed snout, large eye, having dorsal fin placed well back on body, prominent canine tooth on vomer accompanied or not by one or two smaller canine teeth, and one or no pyloric caeca.

Life History Probably spawns in ocean. Development protracted, young remaining in translucent stage to about 3 inches (76 mm).[2]

Distribution From central California (San Francisco) to southern Vancouver Island in Juan de Fuca Strait. The only Canadian record is from Port San Juan Harbour where three individuals were taken by Dennis Guyan of the trawler *Bon Accord No. 2* in 38 fathoms (70 m) on November 2, 1969.[1]

138

References 1 Barraclough and Wilson 1971; 2 Hubbs 1925a; 3 McAllister 1963; 4 Roedel 1948b.

Utilization   Used to a minor extent as fresh fish in California, and as live bait. Reports of captures in San Diego Harbor are believed to be based on released bait.[4]

SURF SMELT

Hypomesus pretiosus pretiosus (Girard 1855)

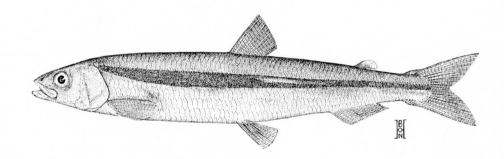

Scientific names from the Greek roots *hypo* (below) and *mesos* (middle — position of pelvic fins); and the Latin *pretiosus* (precious).

In some regions known as the silver smelt.

The North American and Asian surf smelts are usually recognizable although very similar. They do not mingle. They are accordingly regarded as subspecies of the same species. The Asian subspecies is *Hypomesus pretiosus japonicus* (Brevoort 1856). Clemens and Wilby 1946, 1961 called the species *Hypomesus pretiosus*.

Description   Body elongate, depth 4.6 to 7.3 into standard length, somewhat compressed. Head length 4.7 to 5.4 into standard length. Mouth rather small, terminal, directed only slightly upward, upper jaw extending to eye but not beyond centre of pupil. Teeth small and pointed, on dentary, maxillary, and premaxillary, none enlarged. Lower jaw somewhat protruding. Eye 4.1 to 5.9 into length of head, about same as interorbital width and snout length. Interorbital space nearly flat. Operculum smooth. Branchiostegals 7 to 8. Gill membranes free of isthmus. Caudal peduncle compressed.

Fins   Dorsal (1), (8)9 to 10, originating just above or slightly behind midpoint of body. Adipose sickle shaped, base shorter than orbit. Caudal forked. Anal (12)13 to 16, short based and small, longest ray 2.6 to 3.5 into length of head. Pectorals 14 to 16(17) small, extending less than half distance to pelvic origin. Pelvics 8, originate behind or below dorsal origin.

Gill Rakers   On first gill arch 31 to 36. Vertebrae (62, 63)64 to 68(69, 70).

139

Scales   Cycloid, along midlateral line 66 to 73, deciduous. Lateral line canal rather high and incomplete extending only about to end of pectoral fin.

There are fine tubercles on the scales and fin rays in spawning males.

Colour   Light olive green to brownish on back, sides and belly silvery and iridescent with a bright reflecting band along the side in living specimens. On preservation this band is dark from the colour of the underlying muscle. Males show more golden hues than females at spawning time.

Size   Length to 8.75 inches (22.2 cm) in British Columbia and 12 inches (30.5 cm) in California. Larger individuals encountered in Canada are around 8 inches (20.3 cm) long. (Note colour illustration, Plate III.)

Recognition   Notable for the small mouth with the maxillary not extending beyond midpoint of pupil; the pelvic fins not originating in front of dorsal, a characteristic bar down the middle of each side, reflecting in life and dark in preserved specimens, an incomplete lateral line canal, and small curved adipose fin.

Life History   Females are a little larger than males. Ages cannot be determined with certainty but some British Columbia surf smelt appear to complete at least 3 years of life. Samples taken offshore in the Strait of Georgia in April and June showed groups centering around 80 and 145 millimeters[1,2] total length, probably 1 and 2 years old. Surf smelts tend to segregate by sexes and sex ratios in samples are erratic with males predominant. Spawning occurs in most months of the year on beaches where excessive surf action or drying of the adhesive eggs buried in the sand is avoided. The sexes mate in a characteristic fashion.[8] Spawning occurs at high tide beginning as much as an hour and a half before high water. Each smelt spawns over several days with females producing between 1320 and 29,950 eggs in a batch, depend-

ing on size (10.1–15.8 cm) and population.[6] Such spawning may be repeated several times during a season with new batches of eggs being ripened,[3,8] but this is questioned.[6] Eggs deposited in summer hatch in as little as 10 or 11 days but eggs from autumn and winter spawnings take much longer. Newly hatched larvae are about one-eighth inch (3 mm) long. Subsequent life history is not known. Off the State of Washington separate populations are formed.[4,6] Examination of food in occasional offshore specimens showed the presence of a wide variety of Crustacea, copepods, amphipods, crabs, larvae, euphausiids, shrimp larvae, marine worms, insects, *Oikopleura,* combjellies, and such larval fishes as eulachon, walleye pollock, and prickleback. They in turn have been reported in the food of spring salmon.

Distribution   Known from Long Beach Harbor in southern California through Oregon, Washington, and British Columbia to Prince William Sound and Chignik Lagoon 56.20 N, 158.30 W.[7]

In British Columbia recorded most frequently from areas close to centres of population including southern Strait of Georgia, Rivers and Smith inlets, and around the mouth of the Skeena. Whether this relates to opportunities for observation or the incidence of brackish water remains to be seen. It is recorded also from Goose Island and Barkley Sound.

Utilization   The surf smelt is *the smelt* in British Columbia. It is taken by gillnets and purse seines to provide a delicacy of good appearance. Recent production is shown in the following tabulation in thousands of pounds (0.454 metric tons):[5]

Years	Average pounds
1951–55	66
1956–60	46
1961–65	102
1966	76
1967	13
1968	39
1969	19
1970	23

140

References   1, 2 Barraclough 1967a, c; 3 Hart and McHugh 1944; 4 Kilambi 1965; 5 Larkin and Ricker 1964; 6 Leong 1967; 7 Phinney and Dahlberg 1968; 8 Schaefer 1936. See also Thompson, Bell, Schultz, Dunlop, and Van Cleve 1936.

CAPELIN

Mallotus villosus (Müller 1777)

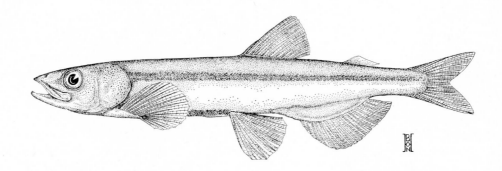

Scientific names from the Greek *mallotos* (villous or hairy); and the Latin *villosus* (hairy — rough extruded scales on spawning males).

The French name is spelled *capelan.*

Clemens and Wilby 1946 identified this fish as *Mallotus catervarius* (Pennant 1784) following Schultz (1937).[11]

Description   Body elongate, depth 4.9 to 8.3 into standard length, compressed. Head length 3.9 to 5.0 into standard length. Mouth moderately large, terminal, directed somewhat upward, upper jaw extending about to point below anterior margin of the pupil. Teeth small and pointed, on maxillary, premaxillary, and dentary, none enlarged. Snout pointed, especially in females, lower jaw somewhat protruding. Interorbital space nearly flat, moderate, about 4.5 to 5 in snout. Operculum smooth. Branchiostegals 8 to 10. Gill membranes free of isthmus. Caudal peduncle compressed.

Fins   Dorsal (1), 10 to 14, placed well behind middle of body. Adipose with long base about 1.5 times as long as the orbit or longer, outer margin only slightly curved. Caudal forked. Anal (16)17 to 22(23), long based and pronounced, especially in spawning males, and in them originating from a prominent ridge on the lower part of the body. Pectorals (16)17 to 20 extending one-third to two-thirds distance to pelvic origin. Pelvics 9 with last ray reduced and close to eighth, abdominal, insertion anterior to dorsal or under dorsal insertion.

Gill Rakers   On first gill arch 33 to 44 (48).

Vertebrae   (62–63)64 to 72(73).[2,3] In British Columbia males averaged nearly one-half a vertebra more than females, the difference apparently confined to the caudal section of the vertebral column.[2,3] There was no evidence of this in samples from the Atlantic,[7] and the situation may be reversed.[12]

Scales   Very numerous, 170 to 220 along lateral line canal. Lateral line canal almost straight.

In spawning males the scales immediately above the lateral line canal greatly elongate and overlap to form a prominent raised midlateral ridge over an expanded lateral muscle, the free ends of the scales giving a hairy appearance. Pectoral, anal, and dorsal fins are expanded and fanlike. Small conical tubercles are formed on the head and lower pectoral and caudal rays.

Colour   Olive green on dorsal surface merging into silvery on the sides and ventral surface.

Size   In southern British Columbia length to 5.3 inches (13.5 cm) for males and 5.2 inches (13.2 cm) for females.[3] In the northern Pacific 8.6 inches (21.8 cm) is cited as the greatest length. In Newfoundland 8 inches (20 cm) is reached by males[8] and 23 cm by females.[12] A female 25.2 cm in total length, 10 years of age and about to spawn for the first time was recorded from Trinity Bay, Newfoundland.[13] At Herschel Island 6.4 inches (16.3 cm).[5]

Recognition   Noteworthy for the high number of fine scales along the lateral line canal (170–200), the long adipose base and squared-off adipose fin, and the small ninth pelvic ray. Breeding males are readily distinguished by the prominently raised hairy bands on the sides.

Life History   In southern British Columbia capelin spawn in late September or early October. Spawning is on beaches with fine gravel at high tide. Water temperatures are about 10 to 12.5 C. This corresponds to beach-spawning temperatures in Newfoundland.[7] In the Atlantic spawning takes place on the Grand Bank also and at much lower temperatures (2.8 C). In some part of its range the species is spawning from April to October. Eggs are adhesive and stick to gravel, most abundantly along the sharper edges. They are about 1 millimeter (0.04 inch) in diameter. Eggs hatch in 2 to 3 weeks to produce slender larvae 4 to 5 millimeters long. The highest fecundity noted from southern British Columbia is 6670 from a 103-millimeter standard length female, and the average in a sample of smaller fish was 4600. Much higher figures up to 56,000 or 60,000 are reported from areas where fish are larger.[4,6] Little is known about their growth in British Columbia. It may be that, as has been suggested,[3] the mature fish that spawn on the beaches are completing the first year of life but this is not firmly established. Elsewhere capelin live to be 3 or more years old. Euphausiids and copepods have been observed in the food of nonspawning adults in British Columbia and similar organisms plus marine worms and small fishes elsewhere.[3,4,9,10,12] In British Columbia, while this species is not common enough to be important as food for other fishes, it is eaten by spring and coho salmon. In other areas it is eaten by cod, seals, and birds.

Distribution   In the Pacific from the Juan de Fuca Strait (Bentinck Island) through Alaska, and Arctic Alaska, Kamchatka, Sea of Okhotsk, Hokkaido, Peter the Great Bay to the Tumen River in Korea.[5,6,9] In the Atlantic from Labrador to the Penobscot River, Iceland, and Norway. Throughout the Canadian mainland Arctic, Greenland, and Norway to Novaya Zemlya,[5] but not reported from eastern Siberia.[1]

In British Columbia the capelin is not used commercially but provides diversion and excellent food for amateurs who obtain a supply during the spawning season. Elsewhere it is one of the well-known insufficiently used resources.

References   1 Andriashev 1937; 2 Hart 1937b; 3 Hart and McHugh 1944;

142

4 Leim and Scott 1966; 5 McAllister 1963; 6 Nikol'skii 1961; 7, 8 Pitt 1958a, b; 9 Popov 1933; 10 Robinson, Barraclough, and Fulton 1968a; 11 Schultz 1937a; 12 Templeman 1948; 13 Winters 1970. See also Fraser 1916b.

RAINBOW SMELT

Osmerus mordax dentex (Steindachner 1870)

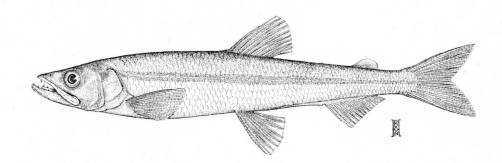

Scientific names are from the Greek *osmeros* (smelt — odorous); and the Latin *mordax* (biting) and *dentex* (toothed).

The French name for this species is *éperlan arc-en-ciel*.

Clemens and Wilby 1961 recorded this species as the toothed smelt, *Osmerus dentex*. Recent studies of skull structure and meristic characters show that European Atlantic smelts of the genus *Osmerus* are specifically distinct from those found around North America and on the Asian Pacific and Arctic, and European Arctic coasts. Although closely related, North American Atlantic stocks are distinct from Pacific and Arctic forms. The trinomial name reflects the relationships among the fish populations.

Description   Body elongate, depth 4.7 to 7.4 into standard length, compressed. Head length 3.8 to 4.4 into standard length.

Mouth rather large, terminal, directed slightly upward, upper jaw extending to posterior part of eye. Teeth well developed, canines on dentary enlarging posteriorly, small pointed teeth on premaxillary and maxillary, canines on tongue with those at anterior end enlarged, large canines on either side of vomer, strong teeth on roof of mouth. Lower jaw slightly projecting. Eye diameter about 5 into length of head or about 1.3 into snout length. Interorbital rounded, width about 1.2 into snout length. Operculum smooth. Caudal peduncle compressed.

Fins   Dorsal (1), 8 to 10(11), originating ahead of midline and the pelvics. Adipose small, sickle shaped, with base about two-thirds eye diameter. Caudal forked. Anal (12)13 to 15(16). Pectorals 11 to 13(14), tops reaching between one-half and two-thirds distance to pelvic insertions. Pelvics 8, tip reaching a little more than half distance to anal origin.

143

Gill Rakers   On first gill arch (26)27 to 36(37).

Vertebrae   (63)64 to 67(68).

Scales   Cycloid, along lateral line canal (62)63 to 69(72). Lateral line canal incomplete and almost straight, pores 14 to 28.

Colour   Olive green above, shading to silvery below, a bright clearly bounded longitudinal silvery band, becoming dark in preserved specimens; speckled with black on top of head, chin, and upper part of body, more plentifully along mid-dorsal line.

Size   Reported to reach 32.4 centimeters.[1] Specimens in Canadian latitudes rarely exceed 8 inches (20 cm).

Recognition   Noteworthy for the prominent teeth on the tongue and a large canine tooth on either side of the vomer in the roof of the mouth. The maxillary extends as far as the back of the eye, the operculum lacks striations, and the scales are moderate in size, usually 63 to 69 rows along midside.

Life History   The life history of the rainbow smelt is unknown in the region under consideration.

Distribution   From Barkley Sound through south east Alaska, Bristol Bay, Alaska, and the Chukchi Sea to Cape Bathurst in the Western Canadian Arctic. Down the Asian coast through Kamchatka, Okhotsk Sea, Hokkaido, and the Yellow Sea as far as Korea. On the Siberian coast as far as the White Sea.[2,3]

In British Columbia recorded only from Barkley Sound.

References   1 Berg 1948; 2 Kliukanov 1969; 3 McAllister 1964. See also McKenzie 1964.

144

NIGHT SMELT

Spirinchus starksi (Fisk 1913)

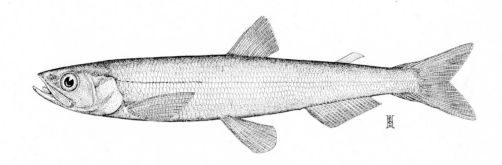

Scientific names are from the medieval Latin *spirinchus* (smelt); and E. C. Starks, U.S. ichthyologist.

Description   Body elongate, depth 5.5 to 7.2 into standard length, compressed. Head rather slender and small, its length (3.9)4.0 to 4.7 into standard length. Mouth moderate, terminal, directed only moderately upward, upper jaw of closed mouth extending to a point below posterior part of eye. Lower jaw protruding. Teeth on jaws and in a curved row on vomer, minute. Teeth on tongue moderately developed, canine. Interorbital space broad and convex. Eye moderate, diameter of orbit 4.0 to 4.8 into length of head and about the same or shorter than snout. Opercle smooth or with 3 or less longitudinal striae. Branchiostegals 7 to 8. Gill membrane free of isthmus. Caudal peduncle compressed.

Fins   Dorsal 8 to 9(10) at midpoint of body or posterior to it. Adipose fin length 1.7 times orbit or less. Caudal forked. Anal 15 to 18(19), longest ray 2.2 to 3.1 times into length of head. Pectorals 10 or 11, falling short of pelvic insertion. Pelvics 8, abdominal.

Gill Rakers   (32)33 to 34.

Vertebrae   60 to 63(64).

Scales   Cycloid, moderate in size, thin deciduous, 62 to 65 rows. Lateral line canal incomplete, pores 16 to 24.

Colour   Green with silvery sides. In preservation brownish, darker dorsally, especially on posterior margins of scales.
In males pectoral fins longer; tuberculate on head, scales, and lower fins. Lateral ridge and anal shelf not well developed.

Size   Length to 4.75 inches (12.1 cm).

Recognition   Recognized by canine teeth on tongue, maxillary extending to posterior edge of eye, absence of concentric striae on operculum, usually 62 to 65 rows of scales, mouth directed only moderately upward, anal rays not exceeding 2.5 into head length.

Life History   Probably spawning in surf at night. Mature in May at La Push, Washington.

145

Distribution   From Point Arguello, California, to southeastern Alaska, 57.08 N, 135.48 W near Sitka, and Shelikof Bay.

In Canada Hecate Strait off Graham Island, Queen Charlotte Islands, 54.30 N, 131.50 W.

References   Dryfoos 1961; McAllister 1963.

LONGFIN SMELT

Spirinchus thaleichthys (Ayres 1860)

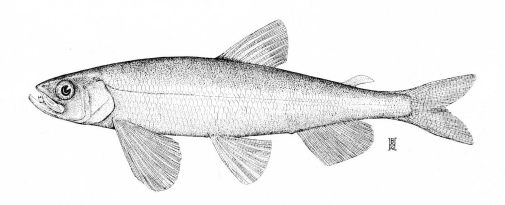

Scientific names are from the medieval Latin *spirinchus* (smelt); and the Greek roots *thaleia* (rich) and *ichthys* (fish).

Clemens and Wilby 1946, 1961, apply the name *Spirinchus dilatus* Schultz and Chapman 1934[7] to this species. It cannot now be distinguished from the older species described by Ayres in another genus.[3]

Description   Body elongate, depth 4.8 to 6.6 into standard length, compressed. Head rather slender, length 3.7 to 4.6 into standard length. Mouth moderate, terminal, directed strongly upward, closed upper jaw extending to point below posterior edge of pupil. Lower jaw protruding. Teeth on jaws; on vomer in a curved row, minute; on tongue moderately developed canine. Interorbital space broad and convex. Eye moderate, orbit 3.6 to 4.5 into length of head and about equal to snout. Operculum smooth or with 3 or less longitudinal striae. Branchiostegals 7 to 8.[6] Gill membrane free from isthmus. Caudal peduncle compressed.

Fins   Dorsal (1), 8 to 9(10), origin above or behind origin of pelvics and behind midpoint of body. Adipose small, length 1.7 orbit diameter or less. Caudal, forked. Anal (15)16 to 18(19), large with longest ray 1.4 to 2.2 into length of head. Pectorals 10 to 12, just about reaching pelvic insertion. Pelvics 8, abdominal.[6]

146

Gill Rakers   (38)39 to 47.

Vertebrae   (55)56 to 61.[6]

Scales   Cycloid, medium sized, thin, deciduous, 55 to 61 rows[6] along midside. Lateral line canal incomplete. Pores 14 to 21.

Colour   Pale olive brown dorsally, silvery white on sides and ventral surfaces.

Males at spawning period are darker on sides with profuse stippling on back and along scale margins. In addition, the first rays of paired fins and of anal and dorsal fins are enlarged and stiffened in males. In males also lateral line canal region dilated, anal base shelflike, and upper surface of paired fins and scales tuberculate.

Size   Length to 6 inches (15.2 cm). Two small specimens 22 to 23 millimeters (just under one inch) in length were taken on April 25, 1966, on the surface of the Strait of Georgia south of the mouth of the Fraser River.[1] The previous small size record for a saltwater recovery was 41 millimeters.

Recognition   Recognized by canine teeth on tongue, maxillary extending beyond the pupil, absence of concentric striae on operculum, dorsal insertion posterior to midpoint of body, pectoral fin nearly reaching pelvic insertion, premaxillary directed upward, anal fin very large (1.4 to 2.2 into length of head), midlateral scales 55 to 62.

Life History   Anadromous, but landlocked in Harrison Lake, B.C., and lakes Washington and Union, Washington. Little is known about its saltwater life history. It is taken down to 75 fathoms in shrimp trawls, mostly in winter. Spawning is reported to take place from October to December in streams near the sea at the end of the second year. Around the San Juan Islands in January adult males and females averaged 117 millimeters and 106 millimeters in standard length.

Landlocked longfin smelt in Harrison Lake are much smaller with 2-year-old males and females averaging 51 and 54 millimeters in December. At the end of 1

year fish there were about 42 millimeters long. Fecundity ranged from 535 to 1142 (2425 for a 61-mm 3-year-old).

In Lake Washington lengths are comparable to sea-run stock. At the end of a year fish are about 75 millimeters long and on the average they reach a length of about 120 millimeters. As elsewhere spawning is in winter. The sex ratio is about 1:1. Maturity is usually reached at the end of the second year with each female producing on the average 18,100 eggs (9621–23,634). Usually fish die soon after spawning with possibly a few females surviving. The eggs are adhesive, about 1.2 millimeters in diameter and hatch in about 40 days at 7 C (44.5 F). Newly hatched larvae are around 7 millimeters long. In Lake Washington the main food was crustacean zooplankton, followed by small bottom crustaceans and insect larvae. Observations at sea showed small crustaceans as the food. There is a high incidence of physical deformity in the fast-growing Lake Washington population and this may be associated with the abnormally high amount of nutrients in that urban lake.[2] The success of year broods varies considerably and is possibly related to lake conditions. Growth rate may be related to abundance and thus with competition for food within the species and with other species.

Distribution   Known from San Francisco Bay [5,6] to Prince William Sound in central Alaska. Canadian records are from the vicinity of Vancouver and the outlet of the Fraser River, Harrison Lake, and the vicinity of Prince Rupert.[1,4,6]

Utilization   Longfin smelt are reputed to be of good flavour but because of limited supply the species is not marketed by name.

References   1 Barraclough 1967b; 2 Dryfoos 1965; 3 Fisk 1913; 4 Hart and McHugh 1944; 5 Jensen 1967; 6 McAllister 1963; 7 Schultz and Chapman 1934.

EULACHON

Thaleichthys pacificus (Richardson 1836)

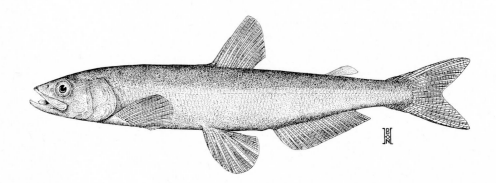

Scientific names are from the Greek roots *thaleia* (rich) and *ichthys* (fish); and Pacific (Ocean).

The vernacular name is derived from Chinook and appears in many forms. Eulachon is now a generally accepted spelling although The Oxford English Dictionary gives preference to the more phonetic spelling Oolakan while citing several variants. Also called candlefish because when dried and fitted with a wick it may be used as a candle.

Description   Body elongate, depth 5.8 to 6.8 into standard length, compressed. Head length 3.8 to 5.0 into standard length. Mouth moderately large, terminal, directed somewhat upward, upper jaw not extending to point beyond posterior margin of eye. Teeth small and pointed on both jaws, usually lost in spawning specimens. Interorbital space broad and convex. Eye rather small, orbit about 5 to 6 into length of head, about 1.5 into snout length. Operculum smooth with strong concentric striae on it and on suboperculum. Branchiostegals (6)7 to 8. Gill membranes free from isthmus. Caudal peduncle compressed.

Fins   Dorsal (1), 10 to 12(13), well behind centre of fish. Adipose sickle shaped, base less than diameter of orbit. Caudal forked. Anal 18 to 22(23) low, with a long base almost equal to head. Pectorals 10 to 12 extending two-thirds distance to pelvic insertion. Pelvics 8, abdominal, originate ahead of dorsal. In males tip may reach anus but not in females.[12]

Gill Rakers   17 to 23, only 4 to 6 on upper half of the arch, slender.

Vertebrae   65 to 72.[12]

Scales   Rather small, 70 to 78 in lateral line canal. Lateral line canal curving down anteriorly. At spawning, males with a midlateral ridge formed by a thickening of the underlying muscles, numerous tubercles on head, body, upper sides of paired fins, and anal rays.

Colour   Bluish or bluish brown on upper parts with silver white on sides and belly.

Size   Length to about 9 inches (22.9 cm).[18] Records of larger sizes must be viewed with suspicion.

Recognition   Noteworthy for having the dorsal origin behind the pelvic inser-

148

tion, the concentric striae on the gill cover, and four to six gill rakers on the upper part of the first gill arch.

Life History　In British Columbia eulachon spawn from the middle of March to the middle of May, mainly in the large mainland rivers and a few rivers of intermediate size in central British Columbia. Males are more numerous early in the spawning season but are equalled or exceeded in number in the later part of the run.[13]

Growth patterns are uncertain and may be very variable. Analysis of data on the lengths of many young and maturing eulachon taken in midwater trawls throughout British Columbia showed at the end of each year's growth to be: 1 year, 61 millimeters; 2 years, 81; 3 years, 108; and 4 years, 135, with the first onset of maturing around the end of the third year.[1] However, samples of the spawning run in the Fraser River did not show fish less than 140 millimeters standard length corresponding to about 150 millimeters or 6 inches in fork length in 1941.[9] It may be that eulachon reach ages considerably beyond four.

Fecundity is related to the size of the female. It has been observed to range from 17,300 at 145 millimeters (5.7 inches) standard length to 39,600 at 188 millimeters (7.4 inches) with an average of about 25,000.[8] The eggs have diameters between 0.03 and 0.04 inch or 0.08 and 1.0 millimeter with numerous oil globules. When deposited, they have double membranes; the outer, which has only a small attachment to the inner, ruptures quickly exposing a very sticky surface which anchors to sand grains in the river bottom.[9,14] At 4.4–7.2 C (40 to 45 F) the eggs hatch in 30 to 40 days[17] to produce larvae about a quarter of an inch (5–7 mm) long which rapidly drift out from the Fraser River to the Strait of Georgia with the current. From the outlet of the Fraser River, they are either flushed out to sea[11] where they are found in the food-rich echo-scattering layer or remain in the Strait of Georgia and the approaches to the river under the influence of the counter-

clockwise eddy in the Strait where growth seems to be less rapid. During the offshore stage when teeth are prominent, the eulachon was once regarded as a separate species.[10] Many dead spent eulachon are found in rivers during the spawning season but evidence now is that some survive. Mending spent fish are taken by trawlers off the mouth of the Fraser River and experimental gear operating in June has taken spent eulachon with food in the stomachs and (Fraser River bottom?) sand in the stomachs.[1,2]

Eulachon encountered off the mouth of the Fraser River in late spring and early summer include several stages from matures (possibly recovering spawners) to newly hatched larvae, postlarvae, and immatures. The life history is obscure as the postlarvae cannot be explained on the basis of known spawnings or recognized growth rates.[2,3,4,5,15,16]

The food of the smallest feeding eulachons found was copepod larvae. Larvae and postlarvae from about an inch (25 mm) to 2 inches (51 mm) eat phytoplankton, copepod eggs, copepods, mysids, ostracods, barnacle larvae, Cladocera and worm larvae, as well as the larvae of their own species. Juveniles and adults eat euphausiids and copepods.[2,3,4]

The eulachon populations of northern British Columbia are separate from that of the Fraser River, and finer subdivisions of the stock may exist.[9]

Distribution　The eulachon is known from Russian River, California, 38.20 N, through Oregon, Washington, and British Columbia to the eastern Bering Sea[8] and the Pribilof Islands. Pelagic. Anadromous, abundant in the larger mainland rivers and occurs in some smaller mainland streams in British Columbia.[6]

Utilization　The eulachon played an important part in the early Indian economy on the coast whom it served both as food and as a source of fat for local use or barter.

The oil is unique among fish oils in being solid at ordinary temperatures and thus is probably responsible for the unusual rigidity of the newly dead fish floating down spawning rivers. It was stored for handling in the floats of kelp after being rendered. The trail through the mountains to the lower waters of the Bella Coola River used in 1793 by Alexander Mackenzie was one of the so-called grease trails developed by the Indians to give access to supplies of eulachon oil.[9] On the Nass River at least, Indians had quite highly developed rendering stations complete with aquaducts and primitive presses.

In northern British Columbia the eulachon is protected against commercial exploitation which means that essentially it is reserved for Indian use. There is a seasonal commercial fishery on the spawning run in the lower reaches of the Fraser River. Landings from it are shown below in thousands of pounds (0.454 metric tons):[11]

Years	Average pounds
1941–45	179
1946–50	261
1951–55	447
1956–60	254
1961–65	329
1966	224
1967	191
1968	101
1969	66
1970	158

It is highly regarded as a food fish.

The eulachon plays an important part also in the economy of nature. When the fish are concentrated during the spawning run, they attract great congregations of predatory animals. Dogfish,[6] sturgeon, halibut, cod, porpoise, finback whales, killer whales, sea lions, and gulls are reported to follow the migrations.[9] At other times of year salmon and fur seals were found to be feeding on smaller eulachons off the west coast of Vancouver Island.[7] The young larvae and post-larvae contribute modestly to the food of small salmon, lingcod, etc., where they are congregated together off the mouth of the Fraser River.[2,3,4,5]

References   1, 2, 3, 4 Barraclough 1964, 1967a, b, c; 5 Barraclough and Fulton 1967; 6 Chatwin and Forrester 1953; 7 Clemens, Hart, and Wilby 1936; 8 Grinols 1965a; 9 Hart and McHugh 1944; 10 Hubbs 1925a; 11 Larkin and Ricker 1964; 12 McAllister 1964; 13, 14 McHugh 1939, 1940b; 15, 16 Robinson, Barraclough, and Fulton 1968a, b; 17 Smith and Saalfield 1955; 18 Taranetz 1933. See also Odemar 1964.

FAMILY ARGENTINIDAE   ARGENTINES

Small bathypelagic fishes with anus and pelvic fins placed well back on body, with adipose fins, and laterally directed eyes. The mouth is small, as are the maxillary and premaxillary bones, which are without teeth. The vomer is broad and thin with a long shaft and a row of fine teeth along its anterior edge. There are also teeth on the palatines and on the lower jaw. Only one species has been recognized so far from off the British Columbia coast.

150

BLUETHROAT ARGENTINE

Nansenia candida Cohen 1958

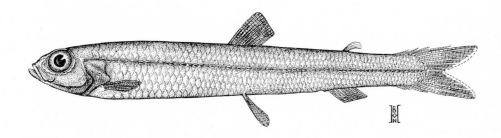

Scientific names are from the name of F. Nansen, Norwegian biologist, explorer, humanitarian, and Nobel Prize winner; and the Latin *candida* (shining white).

Description   Body elongate in large specimens, very elongate in small ones, its depth 7.3 to 9.3 into standard length, moderately compressed. Head compressed, its length 4 to 5 into standard length. Mouth terminal, small, directed upward and forward. End of maxillary extending to anterior margin of eye. Gape small. A free transparent sheath of the jugal and lachrymal bones covers the posterior two-thirds of the maxillary, extending beyond it to pupil. Snout short. Lower jaw somewhat longer than upper. Fleshy upper lip extends over upper jaw. Both jaws with papillae. Teeth in lower jaw closely spaced, long and slender, slightly larger at posterior end of jaw. Teeth in upper jaw conical and widely spaced. Interorbital space extended by clear lateral extensions of the supraorbital bones arching above and behind the eyeballs, the width of the central part about 7 into length of head. Eye very large, its diameter about 3 into length of head. Branchiostegals 3. Gill membranes joined and free of isthmus. Caudal peduncle compressed, its least depth about 17 into standard length.

Fins   Dorsal (1), 10 to 12, origin behind midpoint of standard length. Adipose small and sickle shaped. Caudal forked. Anal about 10, small, below adipose. Pectorals about 11, small. Pelvics about 10, abdominal, long and slender, inserted behind dorsal.

Gill Rakers   On first arch about 30.

Vertebrae   About 44.

Scales   Cycloid, thin, rather large, deciduous, 45 to 47 along lateral line canal. Lateral line canal almost straight, but decurved slightly anteriorly.

Colour   In preservative dark brown on body and head, lighter below, bluish on nape, preopercle, and throat, fins clear, eye silvery.

Size   Length to 8.75 inches (22.2 cm).

Recognition   Noteworthy for the small mouth, slender moderately compressed form, "picket-fence" arrangement of teeth in the lower jaw, the transparent bones arching around the upper and posterior margins of the eyes.

151

Distribution   Bathypelagic in the northern temperate Pacific.[3] Recorded off California[1,2] and Oregon, off Kyuquot and Queen Charlotte sounds[4] in Canada, and north to 52.17 N, 133.10 W off the Queen Charlotte Islands. Collected at depths of 730 to 825 meters in daytime and 100 to 330 meters in early evening over depths between 2200 and 2750 meters.[5]

References   1 Aron 1960; 2 Cohen 1958; 3 Grinols 1965a; 4 McAllister 1961; 5 Taylor 1967b.

FAMILY BATHYLAGIDAE   DEEPSEA SMELTS

Small fishes with the anus and pelvic fins placed well back on the body, with an adipose fin, with large laterally directed eyes, and a small mouth. Teeth are small and conical on vomer and lower jaw. Two branchiostegal rays. Gill membranes are united. Peritoneum and stomach black. Gasbladder absent. For the most part fishes of the deep water. Blacksmelts and deepsea smelts.

KEY TO THE BATHYLAGIDAE

| | 1 | Rays in anal fin fewer than 17 .... 2 |
| or | 1 | Rays in anal fin 18 or more .... 3 |

| | 2 | Rays in anal fin 13 or fewer; rounded radiating striations on operculum; snout flat and pointed .... *Leuroglossus stilbius schmidti,* Northern smoothtongue, p. 156 |
| or | 2 | Rays in anal fin 14 to 16; weak concentric striations on operculum; snout blunt .... *Bathylagus ochotensis,* Eared blacksmelt, p. 154 |

| | 3 | Rays in anal fin 23 to 27; pectoral rays 12 to 15; scale rows along midside 23 to 27 .... *Bathylagus milleri,* Stout blacksmelt, p. 153 |
| or | 3 | Rays in anal fin 18 to 20; pectoral rays 7 to 11; scale rows along midside 37 to 42 .... *Bathylagus pacificus,* Slender blacksmelt, p. 155 |

STOUT BLACKSMELT

Bathylagus milleri Jordan and Gilbert 1898

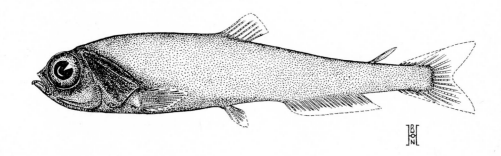

Scientific names are from the Greek *bathos* (deep) and *lagos* (hare — for the large eyes and buckteeth); and Professor Walter Miller, Stanford University.

This species was listed as big-scaled black smelt by Clemens and Wilby 1946.

Description   Body elongate, depth about 4.5 into standard length, moderately compressed, deepest forward. Head length about 3.5 into standard length, relatively deep and little compressed. Top of skull may be transparent. Mouth terminal, small, directed a little upward. Upper jaw extending to point beyond anterior margin of eye. Lips somewhat protruding. Snout sharp. Teeth fine. Interorbital space concave, its width about 5 into length of head. Eye very large, its diameter about 2.3 into length of head. Branchiostegals 2. Gill membranes united and free of isthmus. Caudal peduncle slender and compressed, its least depth about 15 into standard length.

Fins   Dorsal (1), 7 to 9, placed about mid-fish, short based and small. Adipose far back on caudal peduncle, relatively large and long. Caudal forked. Anal 23 to 27, with a long base and moderate height. Pectorals 12 to 15, mean of 36 specimens, 13.6,[2] rather small. Pelvics 3, arising from slight promontories close to the midventral line, abdominal.

Vertebrae   50 to 54, mean of 13 specimens, 51.1.

Scales   Large, thin, and deciduous in oblique rows along midside 23 to 27. Skin comes off readily. No lateral line canal.

Colour   Black to dark brown.

Size   Length to 6.5 inches (16.5 cm).

Recognition   Black colour, large eyes, body moderately robust forward, scales large, fewer than 30 along midlateral line.

Distribution   For the present this species is considered as the same as *Bathylagus alascanus* Chapman.[1,2] However, another species of the genus *Bathylagus* may be present in the reference region. The joint distribution is from southern California, through Oregon, Washington, British Columbia, Alaska, Bering Sea, and the Okhotsk Sea.[3] At depths from the surface[5] at night to 776 fathoms (1420 m).[4] Off Canada found in the Queen Charlotte Sound region.

References   1 Chapman 1939; 2 Cohen 1966; 3 Gilbert and Burke 1912; 4 Grinols 1965a; 5 Taylor 1968.

153

EARED BLACKSMELT

Bathylagus ochotensis Schmidt 1938

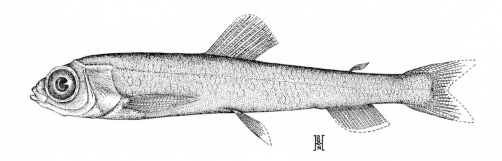

Scientific names are from the Greek *bathos* (deep) and *lagos* (hare — for the large eyes and buckteeth); and *och* (bearing) and *otos* (ears).

Description   Body elongate, depth about 6 into standard length, compressed, deepest between head and dorsal fin. Head compressed, its length about 4 into standard length. Mouth terminal, small, directed forward. Upper jaw very short, barely extending halfway to eye. Lower jaw somewhat protruding. Snout short, its length about half diameter of eye. Teeth small, in rows on jaws, palatines, and vomer. Interorbital space nearly flat with a small median ridge, its width about 4.7 into length of head, its width extended by transparent lateral extensions of possibly frontal and/or prefrontal bones. Eye large, its diameter about 3 into length of head. Opercular membranes united and free of isthmus. Operculum frail with weak striations parallel to edge. Branchiostegals 2. Caudal peduncle compressed, its least depth about 13 into standard length. Pyloric caeca 11 or 12.

Fins   Dorsal (1), 10 to 12, short based. Adipose slender, its length three-quarters diameter of eye. Caudal forked, small. Anal small, 14 to 16. Pectorals 10 to 11, slender, long, length two-thirds length of head. Pelvics 10 or 11, abdominal.

Gill Rakers   About 23 to 25 on first gill arch.

Scales   Cycloid, deciduous, large, about 46 (pockets) along lateral line canal. Lateral line canal sloping down gently.

Colour   In alcohol moderate brown. Mouth, including tongue and gill cavity, black. Peritoneum black.

Size   Length to 4.75 inches (12.1 cm).

Recognition   Distinguished by the short snout, and small mouth, projecting lower jaw, large eyes, and short dorsal fin.

Distribution   Bathypelagic offshore in the northeast Pacific. Sea of Okhotsk.[3] From northern Baja California through Oregon at 200 fathoms (400 m) and Washington to 220 fathoms[1,2] and off British Columbia from near surface to 730 to 825 meters in water from 860 to 2380 meters,[4] and about 55 N, 135 W between surface and 60 meters.[3]

References   1 Aron 1960; 2 Grinols 1965a; 3 McAllister 1960; 4 Taylor 1967b.

154

SLENDER BLACKSMELT

Bathylagus pacificus Gilbert 1890

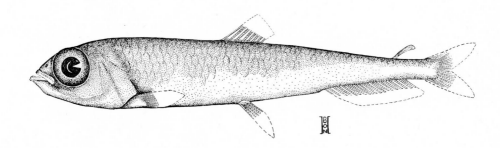

Scientific names are from the Greek *bathos* (deep) and *lagos* (hare — for the large eyes and buckteeth); and Pacific (Ocean).

Description   Body elongate, its depth about 5 into standard length, compressed. Head moderately compressed, its length about 4 into standard length. Mouth terminal, small in size, directed forward. Upper jaw extends about to anterior part of eye. Lower jaw projecting. Snout short and blunt. Teeth fine, noticeable near the anterior part of the upper jaw. Bony part of interorbital space concave between raised orbital rims, moderate in width which is about half the orbit. Eye large, nearly 3 into length of head. Opercular membranes joined anteriorly and free of isthmus. Branchiostegals 2. Caudal peduncle short, compressed, its least depth about 21 into standard length.

Fins   Dorsal (1), 8 to 10, small. Adipose slender, high with narrow base. Caudal furcate, rather small. Anal long based and moderately high, 18 to 20. Pectorals 7 to 11, mean of 47 specimens, 9.1.[3] Pelvics abdominal.

Vertebrae   44 to 48, mean of 21 specimens, 45.6.[3]

Scales   Cycloid, deciduous, large, 37 to 42 oblique rows above midside. Lateral line canal not evident.

Colour   Black or dark brown. Bluish black on head and ventral surfaces, and on peritoneum.

Size   Length to about 10 inches (25 cm).[4]

Recognition   Recognized by the black colour, large eyes, large cycloid scales, no fleshy appendages at bases of pelvic fins, long slender adipose fin, and 7 to 11 pectoral rays.

Distribution   Northern Baja California,[4] southern California,[1] or northern California[5] through Oregon, Washington, British Columbia to the Gulf of Alaska and Bering Sea (Pribilof Islands).[5] Off British Columbia taken on several occasions in the Queen Charlotte Sound region.[1,2,3,6] Occurs in depths at least to 126 fathoms (230 m) or more,[6] or more than 1000 feet (306 m).[4] Makes no diurnal migrations.[4]

References   1 Chapman 1940; 2 Clemens and Wilby 1961; 3 Cohen 1966; 4 Fitch and Lavenberg 1968; 5 Grinols 1965a; 6 Taylor 1968.

NORTHERN SMOOTHTONGUE

Leuroglossus stilbius schmidti Rass 1955

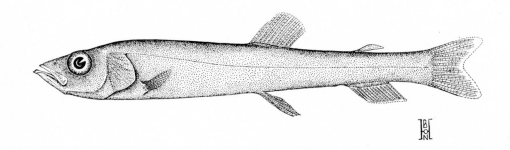

Scientific names are from the Greek roots *leuros* (smooth) and *glossa* (tongue); and the Latin *stilbius* (shining); and P. J. Schmidt, USSR ichthyologist.

The fish on which Canadian records are based were identified as *Leuroglossus stilbius* Gilbert 1890 in Clemens and Wilby 1961.

Description   Body elongate, depth about 7 into standard length, compressed. Head rather large, compressed, its length about 3 to 3.6 into standard length. Mouth terminal, moderate in size, directed somewhat upward. Lower jaw projecting and entering the dorsal profile. Upper jaw extending nearly to, but not as far as, the anterior margin of the orbit. Snout length 3 to 4 into length of head. Teeth small, absent from tongue. Interorbital space flat and narrow, its width about 1.6 into eye diameter. Eye diameter about 3.3 into length of head. Opercles with rounded radiating striations. Gill membrane joined but free of isthmus. Caudal peduncle compressed, its least depth about 2.3 into standard length.

Fins   Dorsal (1), 9 or 10, placed well back on body. Adipose long and slender, length about three-quarters diameter of eye. Caudal forked. Anal 12 or 13, rather small, more than half of base ahead of adipose. Pectorals 8 or 9. Pelvics (8)9, abdominal.[2]

Scales   Cycloid, deciduous.

Colour   Silvery. Dusky on dorsal surface and fins.

Size   Length to 6 inches (15 cm) but most individuals seen are less than 4 inches (10 cm).

Recognition   Noteworthy for its pointed head and projecting lower jaw, the weak teeth with none on the tongue, and the slender adipose fin.

Life History   A school of 2- to 4-inch (5.1–10.2-cm) northern smoothtongues was caught in the Strait of Georgia in April. They had been eating euphausiids, copepods, barnacle larvae, and fish eggs.[1] Larval and juvenile smoothtongues have been found in the food of young herring, eulachons, sand lance, and chinook salmon.

Distribution   From off Washington through British Columbia, off Alaska, Bering Sea, Okhotsk Sea, and possibly Kamchatka. Bathypelagic to about 400 fathoms (732 m).[3] Also taken at the surface. In the Strait of Georgia at the surface, and at depth off Moresby Island of the Queen Charlotte group.[4]

The related subspecies *Leuroglossus stilbius stilbius* is found from Central America through California.

References   1 Barraclough 1967b; 2 Barraclough and Butler 1961; 3 Grinols 1965a; 4 Taylor 1968. See also Borodulina 1968, Cohen 1956, Rass 1955, and Shmidt 1950.

FAMILY OPISTHOPROCTIDAE   SPOOKFISHES

These are bizarre fishes of highly variable form. Pectoral fins are usually placed high on sides of body. Position of pelvic insertion and presence of adipose is variable. Paired fins are usually well developed. The lateral line canal is nearly straight along body, not extended on caudal. Scales are cycloid, deciduous. The mouth is small. Eyes are nearly always tubular, variously directed. Interorbital space is very narrow. Light organs are sometimes present and associated with eyes. Premaxillary is reduced or absent. Branchiostegals two to four. Gasbladder may be present or absent. Rarely seen bathypelagic fishes of temperate and tropical parts of the world.

KEY TO THE OPISTHOPROCTIDAE

1   Eyes tubular, directed upward but having accessory lateral lenses; moderately slender .... *Dolichopteryx* sp., Winged spookfish, p. 158

or   1   Eyes tubular, directed upward as black-shielded tubes; deep-bodied .... *Macropinna microstoma,* Barreleye, p. 159

WINGED SPOOKFISH

Dolichopteryx sp.

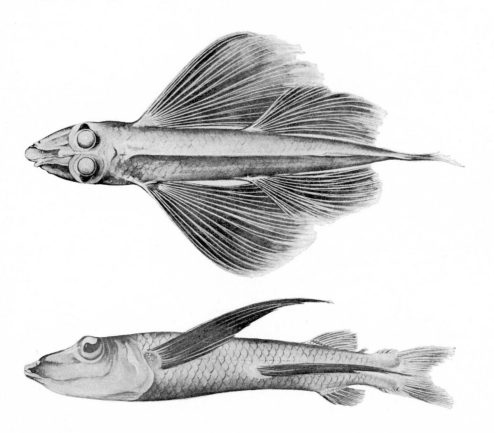

The generic name is from the Greek *dolichos* (long) and *pteryx* (fin or wing).

One specimen of this genus was captured at Ocean Station "Papa" (50 N, 145 W) in September, 1969. Its specific identity has not been determined with certainty but it probably represents an undescribed species. The specimen is currently being studied by C. G. Gruchy of the National Museum of Natural Sciences who has supplied the accompanying illustration, and information on the general characteristics.

Description Body elongate, cylindrical. Head length about 5.5 into standard length, somewhat flattened. Mouth terminal, very small. Snout about 13 into standard length. Premaxillaries lacking. Minute teeth present on vomer. Nares prominent. Eye large, tubular, diameter of base about 3.5 into length of head, primary lens dorsal, a lateral accessory lens present. Branchiostegals 2. Gill membranes attached to isthmus.

Fins Dorsal and anal in posterior third of body. A small adipose present. Caudal forked. Pectorals and pelvics both elongate.

Scales Cycloid, somewhat deciduous. Body and head surrounded by a transparent gelatinous covering.

Colour   Paired fins dark, unpaired fins slightly pigmented. Gelatinous body covering transparent. Peritoneum silvery. Body muscles yellowish (in alcohol). When fresh, the specimen was more transparent and blood in the gill region made that area pinkish-red.

Size   Total length of specimen 154 millimeters (6 inches). (This may be the largest specimen of the genus captured.)

Recognition   Noteworthy for its tubular eyes with lateral accessory lenses, very elongate pectoral and pelvic fins, and the transparent gelatinous body covering.

Distribution   The winged spookfish is known only from the North Pacific at 50 N, 145 W. The genus is represented by few rare species only, mostly from the Atlantic Ocean.

References   1 Cohen 1964.

BARRELEYE

Macropinna microstoma Chapman 1939

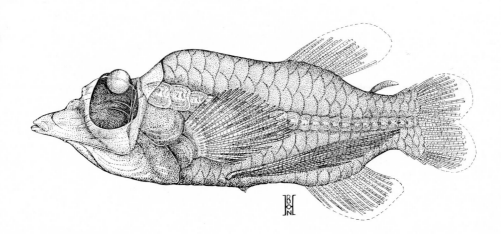

The scientific names are from the Greek *macro* (long) and *pinna* (fin); and *micro* (small) and *stoma* (mouth).

Description   Body rather deep, about 2.7 into standard length. Head large, wedgelike, its length about 2.0 into standard length. Mouth terminal, very small, directed forward, gape very small. Snout flat, shovel-like. Length of upper jaw about 5.6 into length of head, expanded posteriorly. No teeth evident. Interorbital space extremely narrow. Eye diameter about 2.8 into length of head, not round but cylindrical with pupils directed upward so that the cornea projects into the dorsal outline, base com-

159

pletely surrounded by a densely pigmented area. Except for some pigment around nostrils rest of head in front of eyes is transparent and the brain is clearly visible. Opercle oval with long diameter vertical. Preopercle with much expanded ventral section. Branchiostegal rays broad and thin. Gill membranes broadly united and attached to the isthmus so as to leave a broad free fold. Caudal peduncle deep, its least depth about 3.9 into length of head. Anus opening under the origins of the pelvic fins.

Fins   Dorsal (1), 11, inserted posterior to the greatest depth. Adipose, at the base of the caudal peduncle. Caudal forked, broad, and short. Anal 14, originating a little behind dorsal origin. Pectorals about 17 or 18, inserted well up on body. Pelvics 10, abdominal, originating high on side of body anterior to dorsal origin, longer than head, reaching base of caudal fin.

Scales   Cycloid, large, deciduous. Lateral line canal almost straight. Scales on lateral line canal 23 to 26.

Colour   Dark brown in adult.

Size   Length to 1.75 inches (4.4 cm).

Recognition   Distinguished by the shielded, upward-directed eyes, the small mouth, large head, shovel-like snout, and the long pelvic fins inserted high on the body.
This species goes through a remarkable transformation during its postlarval development.

Distribution   An uncommon bathypelagic species. Northern Baja California to the Gulf of Alaska[5] at depths from 54 to 487 fathoms (99–891 m).[3] In the northwest Pacific in the Kuril–Kamchatka Trench.[4] The only British Columbia records are from off the Queen Charlotte Islands.[2] There are no indications of schooling tendency in this species.[1]

References   1 Bradbury and Cohen 1958; 2 Chapman 1939; 3 Grinols 1965a; 4 Rass 1955; 5 Wilimovsky 1954.

FAMILY GONOSTOMATIDAE   LIGHTFISHES

This is a large and diverse group of small bathypelagic compressed fishes with photophores developed to varying extents, usually well developed. There are no barbels. Teeth are present in the jaws, may or may not be found on the vomer, palatines, pterygoids, and tongue. Gill openings are large and gill rakers nearly always well developed. Scales may be present or absent, if present they are large, cycloid, thin, and deciduous. Pectoral fins are usually low on the body. These are rarely seen species but abundant at depth where they probably play an important part in the economy of the oceans. Only one species recognized from off the British Columbia coast. Lightfishes and anglemouths.

VEILED ANGLEMOUTH

Cyclothone microdon (Günther 1878)

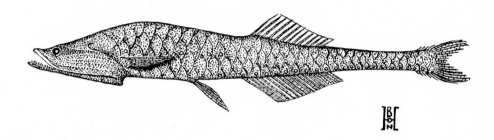

The scientific names are from the Greek *cyklos* (round) and *othoen* (veil); and *micros* (small) and *odons* (tooth).

The French name is *cyclothone jaune*.

Description   Body elongate, its depth about 6.7 into standard length, moderately compressed. Head wedgelike, its depth about 4.0 into standard length, dorsal profile almost straight, longest ventrally. Mouth terminal, very large, directed forward and only a little upward. Snout short, slightly concave in profile. Upper jaw very long, over 5 times length of snout. Lower jaw projecting forward beyond upper, and so extended backward that its articulation is the most posterior part of the head. The articulation also marks the deepest part of the head. Teeth on premaxilla large, weakly canine, and hooked inward. Similar teeth on palatines, and at the anterior end of the dentary outside of the mouth. On maxillaries very numerous fine teeth strongly graded in length, larger posteriorly, and directed forward. Posterior part of dentary with a palisade of slender conical teeth that increase only moderately in size from before backward. All arranged so that the jaws and throat act like a folding scoop net.[2] Interorbital space almost flat with a low central ridge, its width about 6 into length of head. Eye diameter about 10 into length of head. Gill opening much prolonged. Gill membranes free from each other and isthmus. Caudal peduncle slender, its least depth about 15 into standard length.

Fins   Dorsal (1), 12 or 13, placed well back on body. Caudal very deeply forked. Anal about 19, large, originating about below dorsal origin. Pectorals 9 or 10, small and narrow. Pelvics 5 or 6, abdominal, short.

Scales   Cycloid, large, about 30 rows in length. No lateral line canal. Two rows of photophores on body; a lower complete row near midventral line, from isthmus to base of caudal fin, with 31 to 35 photophores; a lateral row from above pectoral fin insertion to a point above anal origin, with 7 to 11 photophores, other photophores below eyes, and on gill cover.

Colour   Brown or black. Pale in midventral line. Dark rims on photophores.

Size   Length to 3 inches (76 cm).

Recognition   Notable for the huge mouth with large teeth anteriorly and many fine teeth along sides of jaws, no adipose fin, elongate angular body, two rows of photophores.

Distribution   Bathypelagic in the world's temperate and torrid oceans,[5] sometimes at great depths, to 2900 fathoms (5300 m).[4] In the north Pacific from California to the Bering Sea, the Kuril–Kamchatka Trench to the Okhotsk Sea and Japan.[3] Off northwestern British Columbia from 54 to 650 fathoms (100–1190 m).[1,3]

References   1 Chapman 1940; 2 Gregory 1933; 3 Grinols 1965a; 4 Leim and Scott 1966; 5 Matsubara 1955.

FAMILY STERNOPTYCHIDAE   SILVERY HATCHETFISHES

This is a compact family of thin small silvery fishes very compressed and deep. They are noteworthy for the presence of a "dorsal blade" formed by the external fusion of fin spine bases (pterygiophores) ahead of the ordinary dorsal fin. The mouth is large, directed upward, with small teeth, and the eye is large and directed upward. Scales are thin and so deciduous that they are seldom seen. There are numerous large and highly specialized photophores. The group is bathypelagic occurring in very deep water but occasionally individuals are encountered near the surface. Only one species recognized from off the British Columbia coast.

SILVERY HATCHETFISH

Argyropelecus lychnus lychnus Garman 1899

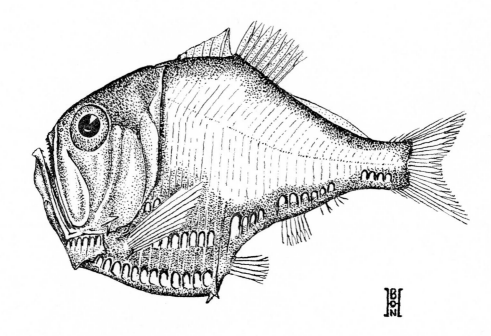

The scientific names are from the Greek *argyros* (silvery) and *pelecus* (hatchet); and *lychnos* (lamp).

This species was recorded as *Argyropelecus olfersii* (Cuvier 1829) by Clemens and Wilby 1946 and as *Argyropelecus sladeni* Regan 1908 in Clemens and Wilby 1961. The relationships of populations and the scientific names that should be used remain in some doubt.

Description   Body very deep forward about 1.5 into standard length, very compressed. In caudal part less than half as deep and even more compressed. Head deep, short, compressed, about 3 into standard length. Mouth terminal, large, directed strongly upward, upper jaw nearly as long as head. Teeth well spaced, needlelike and rather small. Snout extending into 2 closely placed longitudinal ridges joining in upper part of interorbital space and broadening above. Eye large, about 2.5 into length of head. Caudal peduncle much compressed, its depth about 7 to 8 into standard length.

Spines   On each side of the head, prominent, close to the midline at the nape. Two preopercular spines, 1 directed downward, the posterior 1 extending to the edge of the bone. A prominent bifid spine is at the posterior angle of the abdomen with 1 spine pointed down and the other forward. A less-developed single spine is pointed forward and down at the anterior end of the abdomen.

Fins   Dorsal (1), 9, almost square. It is preceded by a dorsal plate supported by 7 or 8 specialized extruded interspinal bones resembling fin spines but regarded as neural processes. It is not serrated. The adipose fin observed in related species is not apparent. Caudal forked, preceded above and below by several free spines. Anal fin

163

in 2 divisions, the second much reduced, 7 and 5. Pectorals 10 or 11, placed low on body. Pelvics 6, abdominal, directed backward.

Gill Rakers   Long and slender 17(18)(19) in the eastern Pacific.

Vertebrae   35 to 37.

Scales   Scales and lateral line canal absent (in specimen). Photophores numerous and large, arranged somewhat unevenly as follows: forehead, 1 in front and 2 behind each eye, 2 at the end of each maxillary, 2 above and behind the end of each maxillary, 2 above and behind the base of the pectoral, 6 shorter photophores extending to end of abdomen directly behind the base of the pectoral fin; series on either side, 6 in the branchiostegals, 6 along the isthmus, 12 in an abdominal series, 4 in a ventral series, 6 in a series above the anal fin, and 4 in subcaudal series.

Colour   Sides silvery with black edgings on the photophores, snout white-tipped with black, fins whitish, back and base of the caudal dark, iris black. On the displacement of the silvery superficial skin, the fish is dark brown and usually appears thus when preserved.

Size   Length to 2.33 inches (5.9 cm).

Recognition   Recognizable by its highly compressed deep body, silvery colour in life, and numerous large photophores.

Life History   Copepods have been found in the food.[3]

Distribution   The species is bathypelagic in the Atlantic and in the northeastern Pacific Ocean from Central and South America throughout California, Oregon, and Washington to British Columbia, at depths from 2222 fathoms[5] to 30 fathoms (4066–55 m) or less (one was found on the beach at Sooke Harbour). All British Columbia records are from the southern part of the province, including the Strait of Georgia.[1] It seems possible that with other ordinarily deepwater fishes, the hatchetfish is carried inshore by the counter current of the Fraser River.[2]

References   1 Barraclough 1956; 2 Barraclough and Waldichuk 1954; 3 Collard 1970; 4 Garman 1899; 5 Grinols 1965a; 6, 7 Schultz 1938, 1964. See also Barraclough 1954c, Schultz 1961.

FAMILY MELANOSTOMIATIDAE   SCALELESS DRAGONFISHES

Fishes of this family are compressed, generally slightly, usually slender fishes with a very short caudal peduncle, scaleless skin, and usually with light organs on the head and on the body in vertical rows. The jaws are large formed by both premaxilla and maxillary with erect teeth anteriorly and smaller denticles posteriorly. The palatine usually bears teeth and a chin barbel is present. Dorsal and anal fins are placed very far back. Pectoral fins may be absent, or like the pelvics they may be extravagantly developed. Bathypelagic fishes apparently usually from moderate depths.

1   No pectoral fins; pelvic fins ventral; snout concave; barbel very short; slender fish .... *Tactostoma macropus,* Longfin dragonfish, p. 167

or   2   Pectoral fins present; pelvic fins on side of body; snout blunt; barbel long (may be as long as body when intact); moderately sturdy fish .... *Bathophilus flemingi,* Highfin dragonfish, p. 165

HIGHFIN DRAGONFISH

Bathophilus flemingi Aron and McCrery 1958

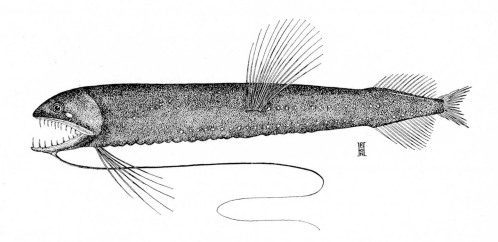

Scientific names from the Greek *bathos* (deep) and *philos* (living); and Dr R. H. Fleming, oceanographer at the University of Washington.

Description   Body elongate, greatest depth about 7 or 8 into standard length. Only slightly compressed and almost cylindrical. Head short, its length about 6 into standard length, slightly compressed. Mouth terminal, large, directed slightly upward, the upper jaw about 1.2 into length of head. Lower jaw projecting slightly. Teeth large, strong, sharp, and well spaced, on palatines but not on vomer. Interorbital wide and strongly convex. Eye diameter moderate, less than snout length. Lower jaws joined to isthmus by gill membranes.

Fins   Dorsal (1), 15 or 16, placed very far back on body and inserted on a slight elevation. Caudal small and deeply notched, the membrane almost continuous with those of the dorsal and

165

anal fins. Anal 16 or 17, placed slightly farther back than the dorsal, also inserted on a slightly deepened part of the body. Pectorals 4 to 7, rays long and fragile, membranes incomplete, jugular. Pelvics 15 to 17, abdominal, placed about on side of body, lacy, delicate.

Vertebrae   44 to 48.

Scales   Lateral line canal and scales absent. The epidermis is thin and comes off readily on handling. Folds or vesicles along the ventral surface of the body. There is a very long, delicate, finely tapered barbel originating below the lower jaws somewhat closer to the symphysis than the angle. It may be as much as 4 times body length. There are numerous light-producing organs as follows: a small organ in lower part of the eye; a larger circular organ approximately the size of the eye below and behind the eye; a lateral series of photophores extends back and up from near the pectoral base to above the pelvic insertion (15–17) and is broken there to continue at a lower level to a point between dorsal and anal origins (12–14); a ventral series (16–32) parallels the ventral profile for much of its distance, and is continued in a short series of 4 to 6 above the anal fin.

Colour   Black to dark brown.

Size   Length to 6.5 inches (16.5 cm).

Recognition   Notable for the lacy pectoral fins, the large pelvic fins high on the side of the body, the extremely long barbel under the chin, the broken and unbroken series of photophores on the side of the body, the dorsal and anal fins placed well back on the body one above the other, and the well-spaced strong teeth.

Distribution   Bathypelagic. In the northeast Pacific Ocean from Baja California through north and south California, Oregon, and Washington to British Columbia as far north as Bowie Seamount about 52.30 N, 136.20 W, at depths from 123 fathoms to 750 fathoms (225–1370 m).[2,3]

References   1 Aron and McCrery 1958; 2 Grinols 1965a; 3 Taylor 1967a. See also Barnett and Gibbs 1968a, b.

LONGFIN DRAGONFISH

Tactostoma macropus Bolin 1939

Scientific names from the Latin *tactus* (touch) and the Greek *stoma* (mouth — jaws almost touching); and *macros* (large) and *opus* (eye).

Referred to as the arrowfish by Clemens and Wilby 1946 and as arrow dragonfish in Clemens and Wilby 1961.

Description Body very elongate, greatest depth around midpoint about 11 into standard length, slightly compressed; depth immediately behind head 18 to 22 into standard length. Head short, its length 8 to 9 into standard length, moderately compressed. Mouth terminal, large, directed somewhat upward. Upper jaw length about 1.2 into length of head. Lower jaw strongly projecting and curved upward. Teeth numerous and various in size from minute to moderate-sized fangs irregularly placed in clusters. Teeth on upper jaws, palatines, and tongue, but absent on the vomer. Lower jaws placed very close together. Interorbital space broad and convex. Eye moderate, diameter nearly equal to snout. Lower jaws united by a membrane which is attached to the isthmus. About 13 branchiostegal rays. Caudal peduncle short.

Fins Dorsal (1), 14 to 16, placed very far back on body (origin about 84 percent of distance from snout to base of caudal). Caudal small and deeply notched. Anal about 19 or 20, immediately below dorsal. Pectorals absent. Pelvics 9 or 10, abdominal, placed well back, base broad.

Vertebrae About 82.[2]

Scales No scales or lateral line canal. The epidermis is extremely fragile. There is a small barbel at the throat rather less than half way from symphysis to angle of jaw not entering lower profile. There are numerous luminous organs as follows: a large suborbital photophore; several vague luminous patches on the head around the eye and on the operculum, smaller photophores between each pair of branchiostegal rays, 2 rows of smaller photophores on the side, below midside with about 66 photophores and another with about 57 ventral to it. They join in a single caudal series with about 12 to 17 photophores posteriorly.

Colour Jet black all over except for the dark gray on the posterior part of the lower jaw. When the thin epidermis is rubbed off, as is difficult to avoid, the dermis shows lead gray.[1] Young, rich brown.

Size Length to 13.5 inches (34.3 cm).

Recognition Identified by the very elongate body, the absence of pectoral fins, the pelvic fins placed low on the body, the two parallel lines of photophores on the sides, the dorsal and anal fins placed far back on the body, and the numerous large teeth.

Distribution Bathypelagic. In the northeast Pacific from off southern California to eastern Central Alaska. Off Oregon and Washington.[3] At depths from 17 to 220 fathoms (31–403 m) to 1000 fathoms (1830 m). The same or similar species is recorded off Japan.[4,5] Off the coasts of Vancouver Island and the Queen Charlotte Islands in British Columbia. One specimen now deposited at The University of British Columbia was taken by Captain Viggo Mark of the *Victor F* at 240 to 250 fathoms (440–460 m), 12 miles (19 km) southwest of Cape Spencer, Alaska (58.20 N, 136.40 W).

References   1   Bolin   1939a;   2 Chapman 1938; 3 Grinols 1965a; 4 Mead and Taylor 1953; 5 McAllister 1961.

FAMILY MALACOSTEIDAE   LOOSEJAWS

Fishes in the Malacosteidae are long, slim, and compressed. The skin is scaleless with scattered or variously arranged photophores. In several species a suborbital photophore is strikingly developed but it may be minute or absent. The jaws are greatly elongate, much longer than the rather small skull. The head is vertically movable, and there is no floor to the mouth. Teeth are well developed in both jaws; some are fanglike. A chin barbel may be present or absent; in some species it is extremely elongate. Bathypelagic fishes taken from near the surface to great depths (4000 m) in the warm, temperate, and tropical waters of the Pacific, Atlantic, and Indian oceans. Only one species from this family represented in the waters off British Columbia.

SHINING LOOSEJAW

Aristostomias scintillans (Gilbert 1915)

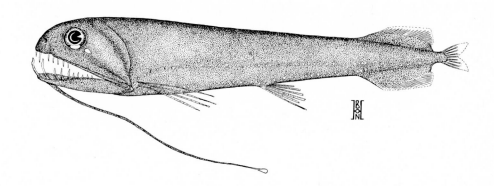

Scientific names from the Greek roots *aristo* (noble) and *stom* (mouth); and the Latin *scintillans* (sparkling).

Clemens and Wilby 1961 recorded this species under the common name loosejaw.

Description   Body elongate, depth about 5 to 5.5 into standard length, compressed. Head length, beyond end of jaw, about 4 into standard length, compressed, and deep. Mouth terminal, extremely large, directed forward. Snout short, about equal to diameter of eye. Upper jaw extending backward for more than twice distance from end of snout to the posterior margin of the orbit. Teeth on jaws long and sharp, very large in lower jaw some extending for about three-quarters of eye diameter, not straight or smoothly curved, flattened at ends. Teeth rather long and directed straight inward on midventral line of mouth. Interorbital space convex, width about 5 into length of head. Eye about 4.5 to 5 into length of head. Operculum extending to near tip of maxillary. Caudal peduncle compressed, and short, its least depth about 30 into standard length.

Fins   Dorsal (1), 21 to 23, far back on body. Caudal fin small and forked. Anal 25 to 29, almost mirroring dorsal but a little further back. Pectorals, 4 or 5, long, possibly free of membrane, placed low on body. Pelvics 6 or 7, free of membranes.

Scales   No scales or lateral line canal. Skin loose and delicate. An extremely long filamentous barbel originating at the symphysis of the lower jaw, extending more than half the length of the body, with a bulb at the end that might be luminous. Photophores in 2 series along lower part of the body, a lateral series extending from the branchiostegals to a point above the origin of the anal fin, and a ventral series from the branchiostegals to the end of the caudal peduncle. Two large luminous organs on the head, one an elongate triangle along the lower part of the eyeball, the other in a postocular position, large and oval.

Colour   Body and head black. Luminous organs attached to head reputed to be coloured; barbel bulb, pink; subocular, red; postocular, green.

Size   Length to 9 inches (23 cm).

Recognition   Noteworthy for the compressed body, the matching dorsal and anal fins placed far back, the reduced caudal peduncle and caudal fin, the pectoral and pelvic fins with elongate free rays, and the long filamentous barbel with an enlarged tip.

Life History   The loosejaw is reported to spawn in spring. It eats crustaceans and off California reaches a length of about 7 inches (17.8 cm) at an age of 7 years.[2]

Distribution   From central Baja California to British Columbia, through north and south California, Oregon, and Washington,[3] for several hundred miles offshore.[2] Depths recorded are for 551 fathoms (1010 m) off California to 123 fathoms (225 m)[3] and 16 fathoms (29 m) at 50.21 N, 138.44 W off British Columbia.[1,4]

References   1 Aron 1960; 2 Fitch and Lavenberg 1968; 3 Grinols 1965a; 4 McAllister 1961.

FAMILY CHAULIODONTIDAE   VIPERFISHES

Members of this family are rather small, slender, compressed fishes covered in life by a gelatinous membrane. Scales are large, deciduous and arise in much reduced scale pockets; like the gelatinous membrane they may disappear in preservative. There is a more or less hexagonal pigmented area beneath each scale, the pigment absent over the small light organs in each hexagon. The dorsal fin is well forward with its first ray greatly prolonged to a flaplike termination. Both dorsal and ventral adipose fins are present. Teeth on the mandible and premaxilla may be tremendous. Fine or moderate teeth may be present on maxillary and palatines. Head bones and attachments are modified so that the mouth can be opened wide enough to take in prey animals between the teeth. A small mental barbel is present. Luminous organs are present under each scale, in rows along the body, and on the branchiostegals. Bathypelagic species occurring from around 20 meters to great depths. Only one species of the family known from off British Columbia.

PACIFIC VIPERFISH

Chauliodus macouni Bean 1890

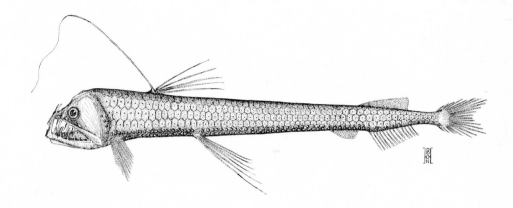

Scientific names from the Greek *chaulios* (exserted) and *odons* (tooth); and Professor J. C. Macoun, Geological Survey of Canada, a resolute pioneer of the Canadian west.

Clemens and Wilby 1946, 1961 used fanged viper-fish and fanged viperfish as the common names of this species.

Description Body very elongate. Depth below head about 7 to 10 into standard length, tapered fairly uniformly from head to caudal peduncle. Somewhat compressed. Head about 8 into standard length. Mouth terminal, directed slightly upward, very large, upper jaw about 7 into standard length. Teeth spectacularly developed in both jaws, well spaced, long, up to 18 into standard length; 4 on each side of premaxillary, the second, longest, greatly overlapping closed lower jaw, teeth on mandible extending beyond eye when jaws closed, the first longest, up to 7 on each side of jaw, some fixed and others movable. Eye moderate 3.3 to 4.4 into length of head. Interorbital space concave with a bony ridge above each eye and its width about same as eye diameter. Branchiostegal rays about 17, free from isthmus. Caudal peduncle short, compressed and slender, its depth 25 to 30 into standard length.

Fins Dorsal (1), 6 or 7, small, placed well forward, its first ray much produced (3 into standard length) in a long filament terminating in a minute flap. Adipose large, placed well back over posterior part of anal, higher posteriorly. Caudal deeply forked, rather small. Anal very long, narrow (2) sections separated by the anus, the anterior one lower, adipose, without evident rays; the second, 10 to 12, the rays in staggered row. Pectorals 10 to 12, thoracic. Pelvics 7 or 8, abdominal, long and narrow.

Gill Rakers No true gill rakers.

Scales The body in life is covered by a gelatinous membrane that is usually dissolved in preservative along with the scales. Scales are thin, cycloid, and either very deciduous or dissolve in preservative. About 56 scale rows in the length of the fish, and 5 horizontal rows. Scale areas are outlined with pigment and many of them are centred on small or moderately sized luminous organs. Scales are pigment free above the luminous organs. Two series of large photophores; a lateral series from above and in front of the pectoral fin to the anal fin; and a ventral series on each side of the midventral line from isthmus to end of

171

caudal peduncle. There is another series between the bases of the branchiostegals. On the head 1 small elongate photophore is below the centre of the eye (and behind it when the head is directed forward) and another smaller one immediately in front of eye. In smaller specimens a degenerate barbel or luminous organ is found behind the symphysis of the lower jaw.[5,7]

Colour   Dark brown to black. In preservative specimens showing a hexagonal reticulate pattern of scale pockets.

Size   Length to 9 inches (22.9 cm) and an age of at least 8 years.[3]

Recognition   Distinguished by slender form, hexagonal pattern to pigmentation, dorsal and ventral adipose fins, two rows of photophores along posterior part of the body, and the extravagantly developed fanglike teeth.

Life History   Viperfishes are predators on small animals, such as arrow worms and Crustacea. It is believed that luminous organs around the mouth and branchiostegals and on the end of the first dorsal ray extended over the mouth attracts small animals which are retained by the huge teeth. The arrangement of vital organs also permits the taking of larger food.

Distribution   Bathypelagic at depths from 876 fathoms (1600 m) from northern and southern California through Oregon, Washington, Alaska, the Bering Sea, the Kuril Islands, and southward toward Japan.[4] There are now numerous collections off British Columbia,[6] including specimens from the Strait of Georgia.[1,2]

References   1 Barraclough 1950, 1954a; 2 Barraclough and Waldichuk 1954; 3 Fitch and Lavenberg 1968; 4 Grinols 1965a; 5 Morrow 1964; 6 Taylor 1968; 7 Tchernavin 1953 (in Morrow 1964).

FAMILY SEARSIDAE (of ALEPOCEPHALIDAE)   TUBESHOULDERS

The Searsidae are deep-sea fishes having a characteristic shoulder organ — a large, round, black sac located immediately inside the upper portion of the cleithrum. The sac opens through the posterior end of a tube which is free between the pectoral fin and the lateral line. The maxillary forms the greater part of the upper jaw. There is no adipose fin. Upright fins are placed well back on the body. In the Searsidae scale arrangement on the head is reversed whereas in other members of the Alepocephalidae heads are scaleless. Only one species of the family has so far been recognized off the coast of British Columbia.

SHINING TUBESHOULDER

Sagamichthys abei Parr 1953

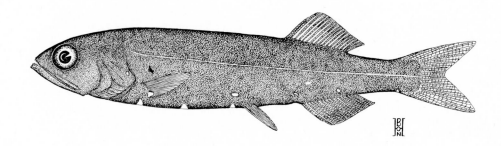

Scientific names from Sagami (Bay) Japan; and the Greek *ichthys* (fish); and Tokiharu Abe, Japanese ichthyologist.

Description   Body elongate, depth about 5 into standard length, moderately compressed. Head length about 3.6 into standard length, moderately compressed. Mouth terminal, large, directed forward and only slightly upward. Lower jaw projecting slightly. Upper jaw extending to behind posterior edge of orbit. Teeth small, subequal, in a single series within gape, in the premaxillaries and lower jaw. Maxillaries with a long very closeset comblike series of minute teeth. Slender curved teeth on vomer (2) and palatines (about 5). A short series of teeth external to the mouth on either side near the tip of the lower jaw. Interorbital rounded, width about 4 into length of head. Operculum with definite low ridges. Caudal peduncle compressed, its least depth about 12 into the standard length.

Fins   Dorsal (1), about 17 to 19, placed well back on body but somewhat ahead of anal. Caudal forked. Anal about 16 to 19, similar to dorsal. Pectorals about 14 to 17, rather small. Pelvics 9 or 10, abdominal.[4,5]

Gill Rakers   On first gill arch about 25[5] (25[4]).

Scales   Small, cycloid, about (104)107 to 109 in lateral line canal. Lateral line canal straight with about 48 pores. The arrangement of scales on the head is reversed from the usual one with each scale overlapping the one in front of it. The scales extend over the head to the snout. Photophores as circular or oval organs in the following positions: gular in the angle of the lower jaw (may be dumbbell shaped), opercular near posterior edge, pectoral near base of fin, supraanal, postanal above anal fin, infracaudal below caudal peduncle, and 4 or 5 on branchiostegals. In addition photophores as transverse bars or fusions across the ventral surface, the jugular at the throat, the thoracic at about the level of the tips of the pectoral fins, and an intraventral–supraventral organ just anterior to the pelvic fins.[5] There is a tubelike structure pointing posteriorly just above the pectoral fins.

Colour   In young, light blue-gray and colourless at posterior end. By 8 inches (20 cm) in length the colour is dark throughout.[1]

Size   Length to about 13 inches (33 cm).[1]

Recognition   Noteworthy for the tubelike projection above the pectoral fin (difficult to see in large dark specimens), the barlike photophores across the ventral surface, the extra-oral teeth on either side of the top of the lower jaw, and the reversed arrangement of scales on the head and adjacent body.

Life History   The young migrate at night from the deep water to depths of 200 meters (110 fathoms). Small crustaceans are abundant in the food.

Distribution   Found in the Antarctic, northwest Pacific off Japan. Off north and south California, Oregon, and Washington. Bathypelagic[2] to depths below 500 fathoms (915 m).[1]

Two specimens identified tentatively off British Columbia about 96 km (52 nautical miles) southwest of Tasu Harbour, Queen Charlotte Islands,[5,6] at about 125 and 300 fathoms (185–275 m and 510–595 m).

References   1 Fitch and Lavenberg 1968; 2 Grinols 1965a; 3, 4 Parr 1953, 1960; 5, 6 Taylor 1967b, 1968.

ORDER MYCTOPHIFORMES
(Iniomi)

A diverse group of fishes not characterized by any single feature. In general, the maxillary bone does not enter the gape, there is no mesocoracoid arch in the pectoral girdle, the innermost pelvic rays are fixed to the pelvic girdle. As in the Clupeiformes and Salmoniformes there are no spines so that fin and caudal rays are jointed and branched. There is usually an adipose fin and the gasbladder when present is closed. Ventral fins are usually abdominal and photophores are frequently present. Some species are hermaphroditic. For the most part they are fragile bathypelagic fishes.

FAMILY ALEPISAURIDAE   LANCETFISHES

Elongate, only slightly compressed fishes with flaccid bodies and large mouths awesomely armed with large fixed fanglike teeth. Body without scales. Adipose fin present. Dorsal fin very high and long. No gasbladder. Bathypelagic fishes of temperate, tropical, and arctic seas, in both Atlantic and Pacific oceans. Only one species so far recorded from waters off the British Columbia coast.

LONGNOSE LANCETFISH

Alepisaurus ferox Lowe 1833

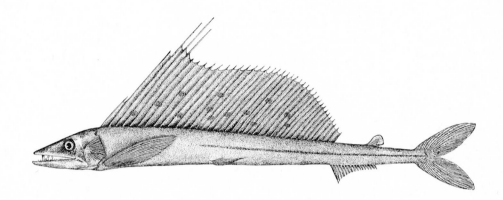

Scientific names from the Greek *a* (without), *lepis* (scale), and *saurus* (serpent); and the Latin *ferox* (ferocious).

Clemens and Wilby 1946 called this species *Alepidosaurus aesculapius* Bean 1882, handsaw-fish; in 1961 they used the names *Alepisaurus borealis* Gill 1862, Pacific lancetfish. In recent opinion Atlantic and Pacific stocks are one species with the older name becoming applicable to both. An additional species recognizable by a shorter snout has now been described from the Atlantic and found to occur also in the Pacific.[8]

The French name is *cavalo féroce*.

Description   Body very elongate, its depth about 10 (8–12.5) into standard length, compressed, greatest depth at head, from pelvic fins tapering evenly to caudal peduncle, moderately compressed. Head length about 6 into standard length, compressed, pointed, bones very light. Mouth terminal, very large, directed forward. Upper jaw extends beyond eye, nearly to preopercular bone. Snout long, over one-third length of head. Lower jaw slightly projecting. Teeth, in upper jaw, small, numerous, in single row in premaxillary; on palatines 1 or 2 long daggerlike teeth anteriorly separated from a second similar group, and 5 to 9 teeth of moderate size; in lower jaw a single row of various sizes of canine teeth and 1 or 2 daggerlike teeth, followed by a series of triangular teeth. Interorbital space flat or slightly concave between ridges, its width about 6 into length of head. Orbit of eye about 4.2 into length of head. Prominent radial ridges on operculum. Caudal peduncle narrow and compressed, its least depth about 36 into standard length, adipose lateral keels along midside posteriorly most prominent near caudal peduncle.

Fins   Dorsal (1), 36 to 45, very high and long, origin over opercular openings and extending to a point above anal origin, about 3 rays beginning with third or fourth much exserted, whole fin depressible into a groove. Adipose moderate in size, over posterior part of anal insertion. Caudal deeply and finely forked. Anal 14 to 18, generally low, highest anteriorly. Pectorals 12 to 15, middle rays longest, placed low on body. Pelvics 8 to 10, abdominal, weak.[1]

Scales   No scales. Lateral line canal high anteriorly, descending to run straight along midside.

175

Colour   Generally pale, iridescent, darker dorsally. Lateral adipose keel dark. All fins dark brown to black. Peritoneum black.

Size   Length to 6 feet 10 inches (208 cm) in an uncertainly identified Pacific Ocean specimen.[8] Five-foot (152-cm) specimens are not rare. The greatest weight recorded is nearly 10 pounds (4.5 kg).[7]

Recognition   Recognized by the long slender body, high, long dorsal fin, the adipose fin, and the irregular dagger-shaped teeth.

Life History   The anatomy of the longnose lancetfish shows it to be hermaphroditic — both sexes to be in one individual — and there is speculation about whether this is associated with solitary living. How the anatomy represents function is unknown.[8] Lancetfish are apparently voracious, the diet including, in California, pelagic molluscs and Crustacea, marine worms, coelenterates, salps, squid, octopus,[7] and elsewhere, hatchetfishes, lanternfishes, hake, rockfishes, agonids, other lancetfish, *Gilbertidia*, and spiny lumpsuckers. Curiously, in spite of the formidable mouth ingested food organisms seem to be little damaged. It is a good source of biological specimens, for example, the second Canadian record for *Allocyttus* sp. was from the stomach of a longnose lancetfish. Lancetfish in turn are fed upon by opah, sharks, albacore, and yellowfin tunas,[7] and fur seals. They are sometimes taken on halibut longline gear.

Distribution   Pelagic, or possibly bathypelagic, in Atlantic and Pacific oceans at depths from near surface to 400 fathoms (732 m)[9] or 700 fathoms (1280 m).[10] In Mediterranean Sea. Not recorded from Indian Ocean. In eastern Pacific from near equator close to surface,[6] California,[9] Washington,[2,3] British Columbia[1,4] including the Strait of Georgia, Alaska[5,12,13] including Aleutian Islands and Bering Sea, Kuril Islands, and around Japan,[11] and Okhotsk Sea.[9]

References   1 Cowan 1938; 2, 3, 4, 5, Crawford 1925, 1927a, b, 1929; 6 Fitch 1953; 7 Fitch and Lavenberg 1968; 8 Gibbs and Wilimovsky 1966; 9 Grinols 1965a; 10 Leim and Scott 1966; 11 Matsubara 1955; 12, 13 Wilimovsky 1954, 1964.

Family Anotopteridae   Daggertooths

Elongate cylindrical fishes compressed anteriorly, with long pointed jaws, without scales, and having little or no lateral line canal. No rayed dorsal fin but adipose fin present. Bones fragile. Mostly small but some moderately large. Bathypelagic fishes found in temperate waters of the Pacific and Atlantic oceans. Only one species recorded from off the British Columbia coast.

DAGGERTOOTH

Anotopterus pharao Zugmayer 1911

Scientific names from the Greek *an* (without) and *opterus* (dorsal — fin); and pharao (resemblance to — Egyptian king). The French name is *pharaon*.

Description   Body very elongate, its depth about 15 into standard length, compressed, more anteriorly, and less so posteriorly. Head elongate, its length about 4.3 into standard length, compressed. Mouth terminal, directed forward, with great gape and size. Maxillary extending to eye, about 7.7 into standard length. Lower jaw greatly projecting, about 5.9 of standard length, bearing a symphyseal knob about three-quarters as long as eye. Teeth vary in number between specimens. On premaxillary bone, teeth are small, numerous, and sharp, 19 to 55 on each side fixed and 5 to 16 depressible, on mandible 12 to 17 fixed and 0 to 13 depressible, on palatine large and daggerlike in 2 rows with 8 to 10 fixed and 2 to 6 depressible. Eye small, about 14 into length of head. Interorbital width about 17 into length of head. Caudal peduncle a slender continuation of a long tapered body, its least depth about 53 into standard length or 12 into length of head. Anus about two-thirds distance between pelvic and anal fins.

Fins   Dorsal, adipose only, small, originating very far back, about 0.9 distance from snout to anal base on body. Caudal, deeply forked. Anal small, 14 to 17, far back, originating about 0.9 distance from snout to caudal base, anterior rays longer. Pectorals 12 to 16, small, placed low on body. Pelvics 9 to 11, abdominal, very small.

Gill Rakers   No gill rakers.

Vertebrae   76 to 80.[8]

Scales   On under surface of the body, enlarged on lateral line canal. Pores on lateral line canal 75 to 83.

Colour   Silvery to dusky, almost black on caudal fin, and black on tips of pectoral fin rays. Adipose pale with dark anterior margin. Black on tips of jaws, branchiostegal membranes, inner surface of operculum, and peritoneum.

Size   Length to 4 feet 9.5 inches (146 cm) and 3 pounds 10 ounces (1.65 kg).[1,4]

Recognition   Identified by the very elongate body, absence of a rayed dorsal fin, and daggerlike teeth.

Life History   Daggertooth have been found to eat young rockfish, lingcod, young rock greenling, and each other. They, in turn, are eaten by albacore, Pacific lancetfish, halibut, steelhead salmon, blue shark, pomfret, and whales.[1,7,8,9]

Distribution   Probably bathypelagic. Over deep water from southern California, through British Columbia, southeast Alaska, Kamchatka, central north Pacific to Hokkaido.[2,3,6,9] In Atlantic off Labrador and Newfoundland, Greenland, Portugal,[5] offshore. Taken in the Antarctic.[6] Taken near the surface in the Pacific but may penetrate to great depths.[2] Appears to be widespread well off British Columbia and in the Gulf of Alaska.[7,8,10] Not in tropics.[2,3]

References   1 Fitch and Lavenberg 1968; 2 Grinols 1965a; 3 Hubbs, Mead, and Wilimovsky 1953; 4 Jow 1963; 5 Leim and Scott 1966; 6 Matsubara 1955; 7 Neave 1959; 8 Rofen 1966b; 9 Taylor 1959; 10 Welander, Alverson, and Bergman 1957.

FAMILY SCOPELARCHIDAE   PEARLEYES

Small, compressed, elongate or deep-bodied fishes with large mouths but jaws not prolonged or massive. Teeth are large, compressed, some depressible. The interorbital space is narrow, the frontal bones have longitudinal ridges. The eyes are more or less telescopic, directed upward or forward: there is a glistening spot on the eyeball which may be luminescent in life, but there are no other luminous organs. Scales cover the body and part of the head. There is no gasbladder. The one member of the family found off British Columbia differs from all the rest in having high instead of flat cleithral bones but in none are the bones external or free of the body. The family is bathypelagic and widely distributed in temperate and tropical oceans, and in the antarctic. One species of the family is known from British Columbia waters.

178

NORTHERN PEARLEYE

Benthalbella dentata (Chapman 1939)

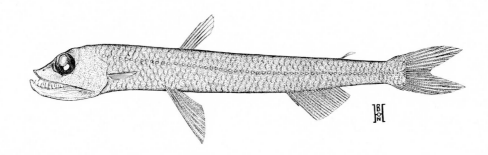

Scientific names from the Greek *benthos* (deep), the Latin *alba* (white), and *ella* (a diminutive); and the Latin *dentatus* (toothed — unusual arrangement of prominent teeth).

Clemens and Wilby 1946, 1961 recorded this species as *Neoscopelarchoides dentatus* Chapman 1939, and used pearl-eye and pearleye as common names.

Description   Body elongate, its depth about 8 into standard length, compressed, relatively little tapered. Head length about 5 into standard length, snout profile definitely concave, compressed. Mouth terminal, very large, directed forward and up. Upper jaw extending beyond upper edge of gill opening, and gape beyond posterior border of eye. Lower jaw extending beyond upper, curving upward. Teeth various and formidable; on upper jaw in a single row along edge of maxillary, not evident on premaxillary; on lower jaw long depressible fangs interspersed with somewhat smaller teeth through most of length, small normal teeth near symphysis; on tongue, a row of stout teeth, largest at the end, the one on the tip directed backward; on the palatines large teeth, the largest anterior and depressible; small stout teeth at the corner of vomer. Interorbital space very narrow, about

20 into length of head, relatively larger in small specimens, concave. Eye large, about 3.7 into length of head, the pupil directed forward and up in a deep black-covered cylinder. On the eyeball, behind and below the lens is a striking, oval, iridescent structure, probably luminescent. Gill membranes purple, free of isthmus, and each other. Caudal peduncle compressed, its least depth about 20 into standard length.

Fins   Dorsal (1), (6)7, short. Adipose very slender. Caudal long and forked. Anal (17)20(21). Pectorals (22)23(25), small. Pelvics 9, abdominal, large and expanded, inserted slightly ahead of dorsal insertion.

Scales   Cycloid, deciduous, their empty pockets giving the appearance of the scales being on the fish backward (as in the illustration) on the whole body but not on head. Lateral line canal scales enlarged, 56 to 58.

Colour   Brown dorsally, lighter below. Young up to about 3 inches in length (7.6 cm) translucent over body cavity.

Size   Length to 9.25 inches (23.5 cm).

Recognition   Noteworthy for having pelvic fins larger than pectorals, and inserted

179

anterior to dorsal fin, the spectacular and various dentition, and the pearly area on the lower part of the upturned telescopic eye.

Distribution   Bathypelagic over deep water from Mexico, through California, Oregon, Washington, and British Co-lumbia to Alaska at depths from 54 to 550 fathoms (100–1000 m).[2] Most British Columbia records are from the area off the Queen Charlotte Islands and Queen Charlotte Sound.[1,3]

References   1 Chapman 1939; 2 Grinols 1965a; 3 Taylor 1967b.

FAMILY PARALEPIDIDAE   BARRACUDINAS

The Paralepididae are slender-bodied elongate predatory fishes with long pointed compressed heads, long snouts, and large mouths armed with large, pointed, daggerlike teeth both fixed and depressible. There is no gasbladder. Dorsal and adipose fins are placed far back on the body. Bathypelagic over deep water.

KEY TO THE PARALEPIDIDAE

1   Origin of dorsal fin behind origin of pelvic fins; gill rakers with a row of 4 stout teeth on each base plate; upper jaw not extending back as far as anterior margin of orbit ....
.... *Lestidium ringens,* Slender barracudina, p. 181

or 1   Origin of dorsal fin anterior to origin of pelvic fin; gill rakers with many needlelike teeth on each base plate; upper jaw reaching as far as anterior part of eye .... *Notolepis rissoi rissoi,* Ribbon barracudina, p. 182

SLENDER BARRACUDINA

Lestidium ringens (Jordan and Gilbert 1881)

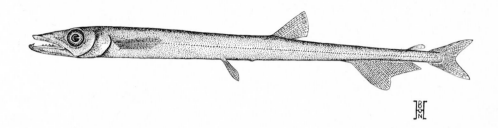

Scientific names from the Greek *lestos* (robber or harrier); and the Latin *ringens* (gaping).

Description   Body drawn out, its depth about 17 into standard length, deepest about one-third of length from snout, gently tapering to fine caudal peduncle, compressed. Parallel ridges along ventral surface from pelvic fins joining behind anus to form a vague keel as far as anal fin. Head long, slender, compressed, its length about 5.2 into standard length. Mouth terminal, large, directed forward and curving upward slightly in a long sigmoid curve. Upper jaw not quite reaching anterior margin of eye. Lower jaw terminating bluntly with an upturned tip fitting into a niche at the tip of the upper jaw, a slight knob at its lower tip, protruding slightly. Snout long. Teeth: in upper jaw, at anterior end 2 to 4 large depressible canines followed after a gap by a close row of small incurving canine teeth, becoming a closely placed palisade posteriorly; on vomer none; on anterior end of palatines a series of very large depressible canines each accompanied by a smaller fixed canine, the smaller teeth continuing posteriorly; in lower jaw large depressible canines each accompanied by a small fixed canine. Interorbital space concave with 2 moderate longitudinal ridges, its width about 7 into length of head. Eye diameter about 5.2 into length of head. Gill membranes free of each other and isthmus. Caudal peduncle slender, compressed, its least depth about 50 into standard length.

Fins   Dorsal (1), 9 to 12, short based and small, far back on body. Adipose moderately short based and low, very far back on body terminating behind end of anal insertion. Caudal forked, small. Anal 28 to 33, far back on body, long based, anterior portion much higher than rest of fin. Pectorals 11 or 12, moderately long and narrow. Pelvics 8 or 9, abdominal.

Scales   Limited to lateral line canal. Lateral line canal almost straight, ending at base of caudal fin.

Colour   Greenish brown above, silvery on sides and belly showing delicate iridescence.

Size   Length to 8.25 inches (20.9 cm).

Recognition   Known by the very slender body and head, the ridges between pelvic fins and anus continuing to anal fin as a vague low keel, the origin of dorsal fin posterior to origin of pelvics, and the scaleless body.

181

Life History   Examination of stomachs of slender barracudinas showed food to consist mainly of small fishes and fish larvae and to include also small crustaceans and cephalopods. In turn slender barracudinas are eaten by albacore, salmon, swordfish, and lancetfish.[1] Probably does much of its swimming vertically.[3]

Distribution   Bathypelagic[2] from Baja California near Cedros Island[1] through southern and northern California to 2140 fathoms (3920 m), Oregon to 221 fathoms (403 m) or less, Washington to 66 fathoms (122 m) to British Columbia. In British Columbia from 49.08 N, 127.25 W at 16 fathoms (29 m) and 51 N, 130 W at 27 fathoms (50 m), 51.26 N, 131.06 W, and about 45 miles (84 km) south of Tasu Sound. It has evidently a wide tolerance of depths.

References   1 Fitch and Lavenberg 1968; 2 Grinols 1965a; 3 Rofen 1966a. See also Harry 1953b.

RIBBON BARRACUDINA

Notolepis rissoi rissoi (Bonaparte 1841)

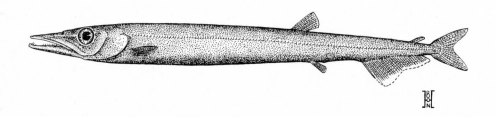

Scientific names from the Greek *notos* (back) and *lepis* (scale); and A. Risso, early European ichthyologist.

Clemens and Wilby 1961 recorded this species as *Notolepis coruscans* (Jordan and Gilbert 1881). It is now regarded as the same as the south Atlantic subspecies of *Notolepis rissoi*.[2,3,5,7]

Description   Body very elongate, its depth about 11 into standard length, greatest depth about midbody, body with a blunt keel from isthmus to origin of anal fin,

compressed. Head long, slender, wedge-shaped, compressed, its length about 4.1 into standard length. Mouth terminal, large, directed forward. Upper jaw extends back to anterior part of eye. Jaws about equal in length, tip of lower jaw slightly elevated and fits into notch at tip of upper jaw. Snout very long. Teeth in upper jaw with 4 to 6 large depressible canines near tip, a dense serrate row of fine teeth along main length of upper jaw turning backward and in, straighter posteriorly, palatine teeth large, depressible, canine, each with a small, straight, fixed tooth at its base, and smaller

182

fixed canines posteriorly. No teeth on vomer. Lower jaw with rather large, widely spaced, depressible canines, each accompanied by a smaller fixed canine. Interorbital space slightly concave with 2 longitudinal ridges, its width about 8.7 into length of head. Eye diameter about 7.5 into length of head. Operculum delicate and transparent. Opercular membranes free of each other and isthmus. Caudal peduncle slender and compressed, its least depth about 50 into standard length.

Fins   Dorsal (1), 10 or 11, small, placed behind midbody. Adipose short based and low. Caudal small, forked. Anal 29 to 32, far back on body, long based with anterior part highest. Pectorals 10 to 13, rather small. Pelvics about 12, abdominal.

Scales   Large, cycloid, deciduous, all over body and forward beyond eyes (said to be present only in adults). Lateral line canal along midside to posterior part of anal fin, slightly higher anteriorly.

Colour   Brown in alcohol specimens, darker dorsally and posteriorly. Bright silvery in life.

Size   Length to 9.25 inches (23.5 cm). The north Atlantic subspecies reaches 12 inches (30 cm).

Recognition   Known for the long slender body and head, its dorsal fin originating ahead of the pelvic insertion, the blunt lower jaw, the upper jaw extending back as far as the anterior edge of orbit.

Distribution   Erratically distributed through the Pacific, Indian, and South Atlantic oceans.[5] Off Honshu Island.[1,4] Rare in the northeast Pacific, from Mexico, and southern California to 1200 fathoms (2200 m).[1] In inshore waters of Juan de Fuca Strait[6] and Puget Sound.[8] Off the Canadian coast at 51.07 N, 131.04 W at 230 to 255 meters; 51.26 N, 131.09 W at 730 to 825 meters; and 51.30 N, 131.34 W at 155 to 185 meters.[7]

References   1 Grinols 1965a; 2, 3 Harry 1953 a, b; 4 Mead and Taylor 1953; 5 Rofen 1966a; 6 Schultz and DeLacy 1936; 7 Taylor 1967b; 8 Welander 1941.

FAMILY SCOPELOSAURIDAE   PAPERBONES, WEARYFISHES

Slender, small or moderate-sized, active fishes almost round anteriorly but progressively more compressed to caudal peduncle. The head is rather large; scales, mouth, and eyes large. Scales deciduous, teeth small and pointed. The pelvic fins are placed anterior to the dorsal fin, pectorals are long and placed well up on the side. There is an adipose fin over the posterior part of the anal fin. There are no photophores, and there is no gasbladder. The fish are bathypelagic in temperate and tropical seas. Only one species is known from off the British Columbia coast.

SCALY WEARYFISH

Scopelosaurus harryi (Mead, *in* Mead and Taylor 1953)

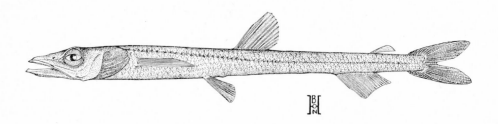

Scientific names from the fish names *Scopelus* (lanternfish) and *Saurus* (lizardfish); and R. R. Harry, U.S. ichthyologist.

Description   Body very elongate, its depth about 11 into standard length, only moderately tapered to caudal peduncle, little compressed anteriorly, more so posteriorly. Head elongate, its length about 4.0 to 4.3 into standard length, wedge-shaped, and slightly concave in profile. Mouth terminal, large, directed forward, curving downward from anterior end. Upper jaw extends to posterior margin of pupil. Lower jaw somewhat protruding, its tip barely entering dorsal profile. Teeth fine on both jaws, in 2 series on lower jaw, 1 inside and 1 outside closed mouth, minute on vomer, and scarce and small on palatines. Interorbital space broad and flat with 3 fine longitudinal ridges, its width about 4.5 into length of head. Eye large, its length about 5.5 into length of head, pupil elliptical, lens round, edge of orbit barely entering dorsal profile of head. Branchiostegals 10. Gill membranes free of isthmus and joined anteriorly. Caudal peduncle moderately compressed, its least depth about 22 into standard length.[2]

Fins   Dorsal (1), 11, origin immediately behind midbody, small, second and third rays longest. Adipose small. Caudal strongly forked and narrow. Anal 16 to 18, highest forward and lowest about its midlength. Pectorals 10 or 11, longest rays in lower half of fin, its length about two-thirds length of head. Pelvics 9 or 10, small, immediately ahead of anus.

Scales   Cycloid, large, deciduous, on head and body, on lateral line canal 63, 3 rows above lateral line canal and 3 below. Lateral line canal arching down anteriorly to opposite dorsal fin, then straight along midside.

Colour   Dark on head, body, and fins; peritoneum, gills, and mouth cavity black.

Size   Length to 8.5 inches (21.6 cm).[4]

Distribution   Off southern California,[1] British Columbia, and Japan.[3] British Columbia records from off Cape St. James at 52.26 N, 121.09 W (730–825 m) and off Tasu Sound at 52.11 N, 133.11 W (510–595 m).[4]

References   1 Fitch and Lavenberg 1968; 2 Marshall 1966; 3 Mead and Taylor 1953; and 4 Taylor 1967b.

Small fishes with compressed bodies, scales, large mouths, small teeth, and in most cases eyes directed laterally. The gape is formed entirely by the premaxillary bone and the maxillary extends beyond the anterior margin of the orbit. All species have photophores in specific limited series below the lateral line; in some cases secondary photophores are present, in general scales overlying photophores are modified to form lenses. The anal fin is large and placed far back, an adipose fin is present. Most species have gasbladders. There are many species, some of them are very abundant, in the oceans of the world. They are bathypelagic, usually at moderate depths although some are taken at substantial depths. They undertake vertical migrations and may be taken at the surface at night.

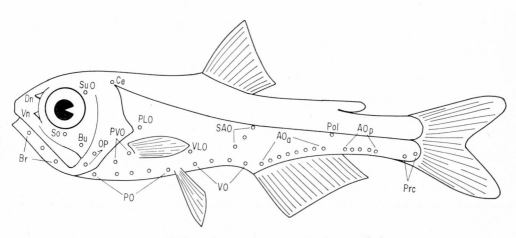

Paired photophores of a generalized myctophid

AOa	(1–7(9)) *Anterior anals*	OP	(1–2) *Operculars*	SAO	(3) *Supraanals*
AOp	(1–7(9)) *Posterior anals*	PLO	*Suprapectoral*	So	*Suborbital*
Br	(3) *Mandibulars*	PO	(1–5(6,7)) *Thoracics*	SuO	*Supraorbital*
Bu	*Buccal*	PVO	(1–2) *Subpectorals*	Vn	*Ventronasal*
Ce	*Cervical*	Prc	(1–4) *Precaudals*	VLO	*Supraventral*
Dn	*Dorsonasal*	Pol	(1(2)) *Posterolaterals*	VO	(1–4(5)) *Ventrals*

KEY TO THE MYCTOPHIDAE

1 Peduncular photophores in a continuous series; no posterolateral photophores .... *Protomyctophum thompsoni,* Bigeye lanternfish, p. 196

or 1 Peduncular photophores in 2 series separated by an interspace; 1 or 2 posterolateral photophores 2

2 Suprapectoral photophores below upper end of base of pectoral fin; lateral line very short, ending at about half length of retracted pectoral fin .... *Tarletonbeania crenularis,* Blue lanternfish, p. 202

or 2 Suprapectoral photophores above upper end of base of pectoral fin; lateral line complete 3

3 Rays in dorsal fin (15) 16 or more; posterolateral photophores 2, the second directly behind the first .... *Notoscopelus resplendens,* Patchwork lampfish, p. 195

or 3 Rays in dorsal fin 16 or fewer; posterolateral photophores 1 or 2, if 2, the second not directly behind first 4

4 Precaudal photophores 2, well separated at the posterior end of caudal peduncle .... *Symbolophorus californiense,* Bigfin lanternfish, p. 200

or 4 Precaudal photophores 4, either continuous, or divided 3 + 1 5

5 Pectoral fin long with its tip well behind vertical from origin of dorsal fin; a single large tooth on either side of the vomer .... *Ceratoscopelus townsendi,* Dogtooth lampfish, p. 187

or 5 Pectoral fin shorter, not reaching vertical below origin of dorsal fin; no large teeth on sides of vomer 6

6 Suprapectoral photophores directly over or behind base of pectoral fin; large luminous organ above base of pectoral fin and closer to it than to lateral line .... *Diaphus theta,* California headlightfish, p. 189

or 6 Suprapectoral photophores in front of pectoral fin; no large luminous area between base of pectoral fin and lateral line 7

7 Posterolateral photophores 1; precaudal photophores 4 in a single series .... *Stenobrachius leucopsarus,* Northern lampfish, p. 198

or 7 Posterolateral photophores 2; precaudal photophores usually 4, divided 3 + 1 8

8 Supraventral photophores closer to lateral line than to base of pelvic fin; photophores small .... *Lampanyctus regalis,* Pinpoint lampfish, p. 191

or 8 Supraventral photophores about midway between lateral line and base of pelvic fin .... *Lampanyctus ritteri,* Broadfin lampfish, p. 193

186

DOGTOOTH LAMPFISH

Ceratoscopelus townsendi (Eigenmann and Eigenmann 1889)

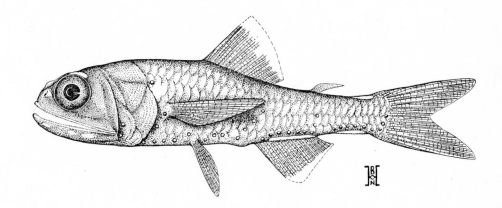

Scientific names from the Greek *cerar* (horn or snout) and *Scopelus* (a lanternfish); and C. H. Townsend, naturalist on the *Albatross*.

Clemens and Wilby 1961 used the common name fangtooth lanternfish for this species.

Description   Body rather elongate, its depth about 4 into standard length, compressed, greatest depth around pectoral insertion. Head deep, compressed, long, its length about 3 into standard length. Mouth terminal, large, directed forward and upward. Upper jaw extends beyond posterior margin of eye by about half distance from snout to posterior edge of eye. Lower jaw barely included. Snout short with a raised, transparent, flexible ridge from about mid-orbit to tip. Lips thin. Teeth on jaws small, sharp, conical, larger on palatines, a single tooth on either side of vomer. Interorbital space concave on either side of central ridge and between large luminous organs extending horizontally above upper rims of orbits, its width about 3 into length of head. Eye diameter about 3.5 into length of head. Opercular membranes free of each other and isthmus. Caudal peduncle very compressed, its least depth about 10 into standard length.

Fins   Dorsal (1), 13 or 14, large. Adipose short based and slender. Caudal forked. Anal 13 or 14, large, originating below posterior end of dorsal. Pectorals 5, long and slender, reaching beyond or nearly to anus. Pelvics 8 or 9, abdominal.

Scales   Cycloid, large, on lateral line canal about 37. Lateral line canal sloping gently downward and then straight. Photophores: on head: ventronasal small; first opercular small, second dorsal to it and larger; mandibulars 3, the first 2 closer: on body: thoracic 5, the last above the line for the rest of the series; ventrals 5, the third and the last slightly dorsal to the others; anals 7; peduncular 5 separated from ventrals and precaudals; precaudals 3 and 1, the first 3 along the ventral part of the caudal peduncle, the single photophore at the end of the lateral line canal; subpectorals at base of pectoral fin and below angle of operculum; suprapectoral above lower subpectoral, close to lateral line and between it and a vague luminous organ; supraventral beneath pectoral fin in its normal position; supraanal 3, roughly in line with last ventral photophore, the uppermost about lateral line canal, the lower slightly above line of anals. Prominent luminous organs: massive above posterior parts of eyes, elongate on either side of base of anal fin, above and below caudal peduncle, other luminous organs above and in front of pectoral fins, on midventral line behind pelvic fins, a faint Y-shaped median area between and ahead of pelvic fins, and other smaller organs.

Colour   Black with bluish metallic reflections from opercles and scales. Dusky on median fins, paired fins unpigmented.

Size   Length to 7.25 inches (18.4 cm).

Recognition   Recognizable by the massive luminous organs above the eyes, above and below the caudal peduncle, and along anal fin base, the single well-developed teeth on either side of the vomer, and the median crest on the snout.

Life History   Reported to eat crustaceans.[4]

Distribution   Circumglobal. Fairly common south of 35 N.[2,3] Off Japan[6] and Hawaiian Islands.[1] In eastern Pacific from off south and north California, Oregon to 220 fathoms (403 m), Washington to 123 fathoms (225 m),[5] off southern British Columbia at 48.59 N, 144.21 W at about 16 fathoms (29 m). Rare off British Columbia.[1] Generally in upper layers.

References   1 Aron 1962; 2 Bolin 1939b; 3 Briggs 1960; 4 Collard 1970; 5 Grinols 1965a; 6 Mead and Taylor 1953.

CALIFORNIA HEADLIGHTFISH

Diaphus theta Eigenmann and Eigenmann 1890

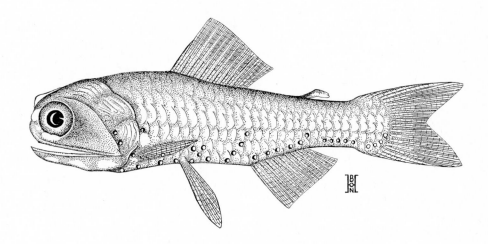

Scientific names from the Greek *dia* (divided) and *phos* (light); and *theta* (the Greek letter Θ) — both names in reference to the body photophores each of which is divided horizontally by a fine line of black pigment.

Theta lanternfish is a suitable and established alternative common name.

Clemens and Wilby 1946 listed this species as white-spotted lantern-fish, *Diaphus rafinesquii* (Cocco 1820).[4]

Description   Body elongate, depth about 3.9 to 4.4 into standard length, somewhat compressed. Head length about 3.2 into standard length, somewhat compressed. Mouth terminal, large, directed forward and upward. Upper jaw extending behind posterior edge of eye by about one-third snout to posterior margin of eye distance. Lower jaw included. Snout very short, blunt. Lips thin. Teeth very fine in both jaws. Interorbital space barely raised aside from central crest, its width about 3.6 into length of head. Eye diameter about 3.5 into length of head. Opercular membranes free of each other and isthmus. Caudal peduncle compressed, its least depth 9 to 10 into standard length.

Fins   Dorsal (1), 13 to 15. Adipose small, narrow based, slender. Caudal forked. Anal 12 to 14, origin behind end of dorsal insertion. Pectorals about 11, reaching pelvic insertion. Pelvics 8, abdominal.

Scales   Cycloid, large, 34 to 37 on lateral line canal. Lateral line canal sloping down slightly from anterior end and then straight along side to caudal base. Photophores: on head: dorsonasal large and circular; suborbital in 2 sections, an anterior elongate section, and a smaller posterior section; 2 operculars, the upper larger; 3 mandibular light areas: on body: thoracic 5, well spaced out, the fourth more dorsal than rest; ventral 5, well spaced, the second and third much elevated; supraanals (4)5(6); pedunculars (4)5 or 6(7); precaudals 4 in curve following ventral posterior edge of caudal peduncle; subpectorals 2, the upper at the pectoral base, the lower about halfway between it and first thoracic; suprapectoral above pectoral base and separated from it by the moderately large and prominent suprapectoral luminous organ; supraventral immediately above pelvic

189

base and at tip of pectoral fin; supraanals 3, in a line starting at the last of the ventrals; posterolateral above end of anal fin insertion and below lateral line canal. There is the luminous organ, mentioned above, dorsal to the base of the pectoral fin.

Colour   Brown to black on dorsal surface, lighter ventrally. Fins pale.

Size   Length to 4.5 inches (11.4 cm).

Recognition   Recognized by the four precaudal photophores, the large dorsonasal photophore, the elongate photophore below the eye, the large luminous organ above the base of each pectoral fin, the absence of large luminous organs on the caudal peduncle. Body photophores are divided by a curved septum that can be seen clearly under moderate magnification.

Life History   Off California food is recorded as euphausiids,[5] and copepods, euphausiids, and amphipods.[1] Larvae have been taken off California.

Distribution   Bathypelagic in the northeast Pacific Ocean and in the tropical mid-Pacific. Baja California through southern and northern California, Oregon from 16 to 900 fathoms (29–1650 m), Washington 11 to 584 fathoms (20–1070 m) and inshore[6] to Alaska[2,4,8] 922 fathoms (1690 m).[2] Off British Columbia along the whole coast[3,7] from 25 to 584 fathoms (46–1070 m); offshore, and inshore where it is taken by shrimp trawlers at 25 to 35 fathoms (46–64 m).

References   1 Collard 1970; 2 Grinols 1965a; 3 McAllister 1961; 4 Parr 1929a; 5 Paxton 1967; 6 Shimada 1948; 7 Taylor 1968; 8 Wilimovsky 1954.

PINPOINT LAMPFISH

Lampanyctus regalis (Gilbert 1892)

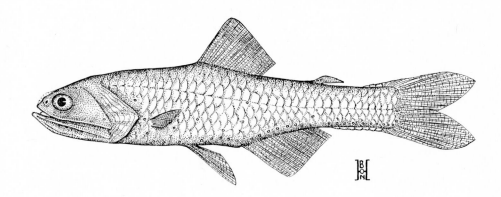

Scientific names from the Greek *lampas* (torch) and *nyctos* (night); and the Latin *regalis* (royal).

Pinpoint lanternfish is a suitable alternative name.

This species was called small-eyed lantern-fish, *Lampanyctus regalis* (Gilbert 1891) in Clemens and Wilby 1946, and pinpoint lanternfish in Clemens and Wilby 1961.

Description Body elongate, its depth about 5.3 into standard length, deepest anteriorly, compressed. Head about 3.5 into standard length, compressed. Mouth terminal, directed forward and up. Upper jaw extends behind eye by more than distance from snout to posterior margin of orbit. Jaws about equal, with lower jaw slightly projecting. Snout short and blunt, its length a little longer than diameter of eye. Teeth small and villiform, in bands or several rows around edges of jaws, on palatines and vomer. Interorbital space uneven with a median ridge, generally level, its width including thin bones over eyes about 3.7 into length of head. Eye diameter about 5.7 into length of head. Opercular membranes free of each other and of isthmus. Caudal peduncle compressed, its least depth about 9 into standard length.[5]

Fins Dorsal (1), 14 to 16, over point at mid-standard length. Adipose, moderate, rather short and rounded. Caudal forked. Anal 17 to 19, originating below middle of dorsal and ending under adipose. Pectorals 12, small. Pelvics 8, abdominal.

Scales Cycloid, large, 36 to 39 along lateral line canal, deeper along lateral line canal. Lateral line canal sloping down anteriorly and then becoming a straight line to caudal base. Photophores: on head: all obscure, ventronasal, buchal, 2 operculars and 3 mandibular reported: on body: all small; thoracic, 5, the fourth much elevated to level of upper pectoral rays, the first and second most separated of rest; ventrals, 5, in curved line from pelvic base to a little ahead of and to side of anus: anals, 6 to 8 or 9, all but last in a curved line above and between second and penultimate anal fin rays, the last much elevated and about halfway between the next to last and the posterolateral; penduculars 7 or 8, in line; precaudals, 4, the first 2 in line with penduculars and separated but little if at all from them, the third somewhat elevated, and the last at the end of the lateral line; subpectorals, the upper immediately in front of and immediately below first pectoral fin ray, the lower below and behind

191

the upper; suprapectoral anterior to upper subpectoral well below lateral line canal, in line with subpectorals; supraventral above ventral fin base on second scale below lateral line canal; supraanals with the upper in contact with lateral line canal above end of anal insertion, the second about midway between upper supraanal and last ventral photophores, the first a little ventral to the second and a little behind the third ventral. Luminous organs: prominent luminous organs on posterior edges of caudal peduncle involving about 3 scales dorsally and 4 to 7 scales ventrally, many minute luminous points on head.[3]

Colour   Rich brown to black, darkest dorsally and lighter below. Dusky on fins, inner rays of pelvics whitish.

Size   Length to at least 7.5 inches (19 cm).

Recognition   Recognizable by the very small photophores, three of them: upper supraventral, posterolateral and last precaudal in contact with lateral line canal. The eye is noticeably small.

Life History   Off California pinpoint lampfish have been found to feed on euphausiids.[2]

Distribution   Bathypelagic in the northeast Pacific Ocean from Mexico, through California to 891 fathoms (1630 m), Oregon to 750 fathoms (1375 m), and Washington to 536 fathoms (980 m)[4] to the Gulf of Alaska[7] and Kuril Islands. In British Columbia from 54 to 487 fathoms (99–891 m), most commonly reported off northern British Columbia.[1,6]

References   1 Chapman 1939; 2 Collard 1970; 3 Gilbert 1915; 4 Grinols 1965a; 5 Parr 1929a; 6 Taylor 1968; 7 Wilimovsky 1954. See also Moser and Ahlstrom 1970, Nafpaktitis and Nafpaktitis 1969.

BROADFIN LAMPFISH

Lampanyctus ritteri Gilbert 1915

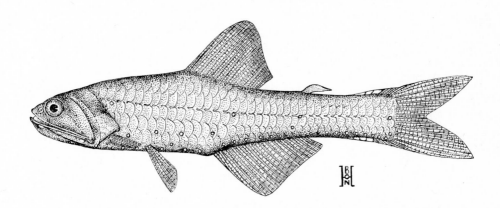

Scientific names from the Greek *lampas* (torch) and *nyctos* (night); and Dr Ritter, Director of the Scripps Institution of Oceanography, La Jolla, California.

Broadfin lanternfish is a suitable alternative name, and was used by Clemens and Wilby (1961).

Description   Body elongate, its depth about 5.1 into standard length, deepest at dorsal fin origin, compressed. Head about 3.9 into standard length, compressed. Mouth terminal, large, directed forward and up. Upper jaw extends beyond eye by more than distance from snout to posterior edge of orbit. Jaws about equal with lower jaw slightly projecting. Snout short and blunt, its length a little more than diameter of eye. Teeth small and villiform, in bands or several closely set rows on edges of jaws, on palatines, and vomer. Interorbital space uneven with a median ridge, generally level, its width including the transparent bones above the eye about 3.6 into length of head. Eye diameter about 5 into length of head. Opercular membranes free of each other and of isthmus. Caudal peduncle compressed, its least depth about 14 into standard length.[5]

Fins   Dorsal (1), 12 to 15, large. Adipose small, narrow based and slender, originating anterior to last anal ray. Caudal forked. Anal 17 to 19, large, origin below middle of dorsal base. Pectorals about 12, small, barely reaching pelvic insertion. Pelvics 8 or 9, depending on inclusion of rudimentary outer ray, abdominal.

Scales   Cycloid, large, 37 or 38 along lateral line canal, deeper along lateral line canal. Lateral line canal very slightly decurved anteriorly, almost straight throughout. Photophores: on head: suborbital very small and difficult to see in adults; buchal small; opercular 2; a small vague cervical spot at the upper edge of the gill cleft; mandibulars 3: on body: thoracic 5, in line except for fourth which is elevated to the level of upper pectoral rays and is barely behind third thoracic photophores, the fifth anterior to pelvic insertion; ventrals 4, the second slightly elevated from a general line, the first at base of pelvic rays, the fourth beside anus; anal 6 to 8, all but last in a smooth arch over anal fin from second to the third to last fin rays, the last elevated almost halfway to lateral line canal over second to last anal fin ray; penduculars 8 or 9 in line arching above contour of caudal peduncle; precaudals 4 or 3, all but last continuing line of penduculars and following contour of caudal base, the last at the end of the lateral line canal; subpectorals 2, the upper in front of and below origin of first pectoral fin ray, the lower vertically below it and opposite last pectoral fin ray base; suprapectoral on second scale in line below lateral line canal and well in advance of straight line joining sub-pectorals; supraventral directly above pelvic fin base and half distance from it to lateral line canal; supraanals, the third and upper one in contact with lateral line canal over interspace between first and second anal photophores, the first and second in a line parallel to lateral line canal and a little closer to ventral profile than lateral line canal, the anterior one over or slightly in advance of the third ventral photophore, the second vertically above the first anal fin ray. Most photophores divided horizontally by curved, dark, frail lines. Luminous organs: on posterior edges of caudal peduncle, involving 2 or 3 scales dorsally and touching base of caudal fin; ventrally involving 5 to 7 scales from second or third peduncular photophore to the first precaudal.

Colour Nearly black to metallic blue dorsally, lighter on sides, black in mouth and gill cavity. Fins dusky, marked with fine wavy lines.

Size Length to 7.5 inches (19 cm).

Recognition Recognizable by the moderate-sized photophores, most divided horizontally by a fine curved septum, the small eye, the supraventral photophores about half way between the pelvic fin base and the lateral line canal, and upper supra-anal photophore above the third anal fin ray.

Life History Broadfin lampfish have been found to feed on *Sagitta*,[2,3] young fishes and amphipods,[4] and *Sagitta,* young fishes, copepods, and euphausiids.[6]

Distribution Bathypelagic from off Mexico, through California at 350 to 599 fathoms (640–1095 m), Oregon to 750 fathoms (1375 m), Washington to 220 fathoms (403 m), and off British Columbia at 220 fathoms (403 m),[4] off southern British Columbia at 122 fathoms (223 m),[1] and northern British Columbia at depth.[7]

References 1 Aron 1958a; 2 Collard 1970; 3 Gilbert 1915; 4 Grinols 1965a; 5 Parr 1929a; 6 Paxton 1967; 7 Taylor 1968.

194

PATCHWORK LAMPFISH

Notoscopelus resplendens (Richardson 1844)

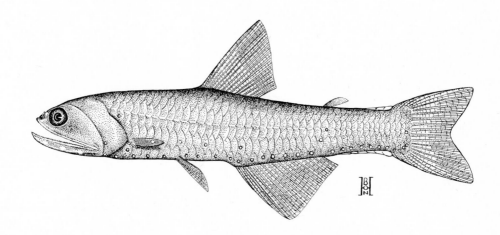

Scientific names from the Greek *notos* (back) and *Scopelus* (a lanternfish); and the Latin *resplendere* (to shine brightly).

Patchwork lanternfish is a suitable alternative name, and was used by Clemens and Wilby (1961).

Description Body elongate, its depth about 5 into standard length, compressed. Head length about 4 into standard length, compressed. Mouth terminal, very large, directed forward and upward. Upper jaw extending for more than half its length behind posterior margin of eye. Lower jaw slightly projecting. Snout short. Lips thin. Teeth very fine, close set in bands on both jaws, palatines, and vomer. Interorbital space about level, with a low median ridge, its width about 3.5 into length of head. Eye diameter about 4.5 into length of head. Opercular membranes free of each other and isthmus. Caudal peduncle very compressed, its least depth about 8 into standard length.

Fins Dorsal (1), about 15 to 17, rather large. Adipose small and slender. Caudal forked, large. Anal about 18 or 19, long based and moderately high, origin under posterior half of dorsal fin. Pectorals about 13, small, not reaching pelvic origin. Pelvics about 9, abdominal, small.

Scales Cycloid, rather large, 41 or 42 along lateral line canal. Lateral line canal sloping down slightly from anterior end, then straight to caudal base. Photophores: on head: dorsonasal elongate; opercular first small, at angle of jaw, second usual size; mandibular 2 or 3, vague: on body: thoracic 5 or 6, first close to operculum, others spaced out with the next to last dorsal to rest; ventrals 4 or 5, first under ventral fin, last near anus; anal 7 (to 9) in line; pedunculars 6 or 7 in continuation of anal line; precaudals (3)4 (5), 1 at end of lateral line, the others, smaller, in a continuation of the peduncular row at and around end of caudal peduncle; subpectorals 2, at and below pectoral base, suprapectoral almost at lateral line canal; supraventral above pelvic base and about half way to lateral line canal; supraanals 3, anterior one behind supraventral above space between ventrals 2 and 3, others almost in straight line with last ventral, behind second supraventral and near lateral line canal; posterolateral 2, above posterior end of anal insertion, the upper almost on lateral line canal. Luminous organs well developed on upper and lower edges of caudal peduncle.

Colour   Dark blue.

Size   Length to 5.3 inches (13.5 cm).

Recognition   Noteworthy for the two posterolateral photophores, the slender body, and high dorsal fin. There is a separate photophore on the caudal base at the end of the lateral line canal.

Distribution   Circumglobal. Atlantic Ocean south of 38 N, Indian Ocean, off Japan. In the eastern Pacific from southern California, and off Washington at 33 fathoms (60 m).[1] Off British Columbia at 49.24 N, 140.38 W at 16 fathoms (29 m) and at 52.17 N, 133.10 W. It no doubt occurs at greater depths.

References   1 Grinols 1965a.

BIGEYE LANTERNFISH

Protomyctophum thompsoni (Chapman 1944)

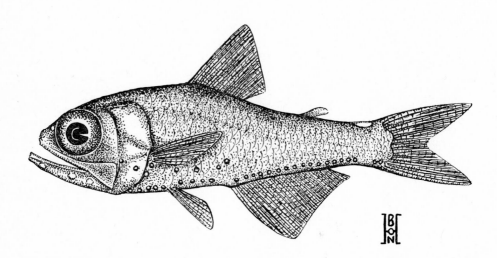

Scientific names from the Greek *protos* (primitive) and *Myctophum* (a generic name for a lanternfish); and W. F. Thompson, eminent U.S. fisheries scientist.

This species was recorded in Clemens and Wilby 1946 as big-eyed lantern-fish *Electrona thompsoni* Chapman 1944, and in 1961 as bigeye lanternfish *Electrona arctica* (Lütken 1892). Future consistency may require lampfish as the noun in the common name.

Description　　Body depth 3 to 3.2 into standard length, compressed. Head length about 3 into standard length, compressed. Mouth terminal, large, directed forward and up. Upper jaw extends beyond eye by one-third of snout to posterior margin of eye distance or less. Posterior end of maxillary expanded but maxillary not included in gape. Lower jaw distinctly projects. Snout short. Lips thin. Teeth fine, in jaws and on palatines. Interorbital space generally concave interrupted by a median transparent ridge, its width about 4 into length of head. Eye large, its diameter about 3 into length of head. Opercular membranes free of each other and isthmus. Caudal peduncle compressed, its least depth about 9 into standard length.

Fins　　Dorsal (1), 11 to 13. Adipose moderate. Caudal forked. Anal 22 to 25, very large, origin well ahead of posterior end of dorsal insertion. Pectorals about 14, reaching almost to anus. Pelvics about 8, abdominal.

Scales　　Cycloid, large, 35 to 39 along lateral line canal. Lateral line canal slopes gently down from anterior end and then straight. Photophores: on head: ventronasal small; opercular 1, small, above and behind maxillary; mandibulars, 3: on body: thoracic 5, in line; ventral, 4 in line; anals and peduncular in an uninterrupted line 15 to 18; precaudal 2, in horizontal line at lower end of caudal peduncle; subpectorals 2, below pectoral base, and anterior to and below it at edge of operculum; suprapectoral anterior to lower anterior subpectoral; supraventral above pelvic fin base, behind and slightly below upper subpectoral; supraanals 3, the first over the third ventral, and the third over the first anal photophore, the first is below the tip of the pectoral fin, the third about halfway between the lateral line canal and the ventral contour, the second supraanal is a little below the line joining the first and third. Luminous organs. Supracaudal (sometimes prominent) or infracaudal, on caudal peduncle, but not both on same individual.

Colour　　Metallic blue on dorsal surface, bright silvery ventrally.

Size　　Length to 2.75 inches (70 cm).

Recognition　　Recognized by the 15 to 18 photophores in a continuous series above anal fin and on caudal peduncle, large anal fin, and expanded posterior end of maxillary.

Distribution　　Bathypelagic. Baja California, north and south California, Oregon to 750 fathoms (1370 m), Washington to 220 fathoms (403 m), Gulf of Alaska,[4] Bering Sea, Kuril–Kamchatka Trench.[2] Generally distributed in deeper layers.[1] Commonly taken off northern British Columbia below 200 to 300 meter layers.[3] British Columbia records are from 17 to 379 fathoms (31–693 m).

References　　1 Aron 1962; 2 Grinols 1965a; 3 Taylor 1968; 4 Wilimovsky 1954.

NORTHERN LAMPFISH

Stenobrachius leucopsarus (Eigenmann and Eigenmann 1890)

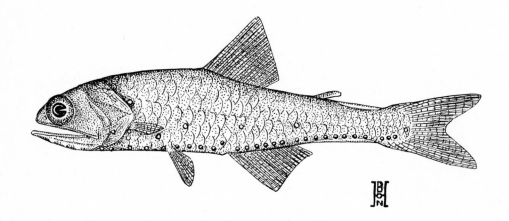

Scientific names from the Greek *stenos* (narrow) and *brachion* (arm); and *leucos* (white) and *psanos* (speckled).

Northern lanternfish is a suitable alternative name.

Clemens and Wilby 1946 and 1961 called this species *Lampanyctus leucopsarus* (Eigenmann and Eigenmann). In 1946 the common name used was small-finned lantern-fish, in 1961 smallfin lanternfish.

Description   Body elongate, depth about 5 into standard length, compressed. Head length about 3.5 into standard length, compressed. Mouth terminal, very large, directed forward and upward. Upper jaw extends beyond posterior rim of eye by more than half snout to posterior rim of eye distance. Jaws about even. Snout short and bluntly pointed. Lips thin. Teeth very small in narrow bands in both jaws. Interorbital space nearly flat with a median ridge, its width about 3.3 into length of head. Eye diameter about 4 into length of head. Opercular membranes free of each other and of isthmus. Caudal peduncle compressed, its least depth about 11 into standard length.

Fins   Dorsal (1), 12 to 15. Adipose small and slender. Caudal forked. Anal 14 to 16, origin below posterior third of dorsal. Pectorals about 11, slender and short, not reaching pelvic origin. Pelvics 8, abdominal.

Scales   Cycloid, large, 34 to 37 along lateral line canal. Lateral line canal sloping gently down and then straight along posterior end of side. Photophores: on head: ventronasal small; opercular 1 (or 2) above and behind end of maxillary, and one said to be at end of maxillary, but difficult to make out: on body: thoracic 5 or 6 in line except for fourth which is considerably dorsal to trend; ventral 3 or 4, along abdomen; anal 5 to 7; peduncular 6 to 8, the first above the posterior end of anal fin; precaudal 4, following ventral contour of the posterior end of the caudal peduncle; subpectorals 2, at base of pectoral fin and immediately below and somewhat ahead, both ahead of second thoracic; suprapectoral 1 at edge of operculum definitely below lateral line canal; supraventral about halfway between upper subpectoral and most posterior supraanal, above point a little behind pelvic insertion; supraanals 3 in a straight row starting above and behind last pelvic and extending up and back nearly to lateral line canal above first anal; posterolateral 1, close to lateral line canal above space between anal and peduncular series. Luminous organs: long series of luminous organs above and below caudal peduncle, supracaudal 5 to 8, infracaudal 7 to 9.

Colour   Gray to dark greenish blue on dorsal surface; lighter on ventral surface, black on operculum and fins, golden or claret on photophores in life.

Size   Length to 5 inches (12.7 cm).[3] (8.5 cm).[10]

Recognition   Distinguished by very small pectoral fins, luminous organs both above and below caudal peduncle, and single posterolateral photophore on posterior part of body.

Life History   Off Oregon yearling fish average about 23 millimeters in length, 2-year-olds about 41 millimeters, and 3-year-olds 59 millimeters. They may reach 8 years of age and the theoretical maximum size is around 85 millimeters. Spawning is mainly from December to March and maturity is reached at about 4 years of age.[10] Food includes fishes, copepods, and euphausiids separately or together.[4] Northern lampfish are eaten by yellowtail rockfish[8] and salmon.

Distribution   Bathypelagic. Generally distributed except in upper layers north of 45 N,[1] and occurs south as far as the California–Mexico border. Off California at 32 to 1083 fathoms (59–1980 m), Oregon to 900 fathoms (1650 m), Washington to 416 fathoms (762 m) and in Puget Sound,[9] British Columbia, and Alaska to 410 fathoms (750 m), Bering Sea 225 to 1625 fathoms (412–2970 m).[6] In the North Pacific Ocean from the Kuril–Kamchatka Trench to the Pacific coast of Japan.[6] In British Columbia from near the surface at Active Pass[2] to 1588 fathoms (2900 m) west of Moresby Island, Queen Charlotte Islands.[5] Abundant and found commonly over a wide range of depths from 150 to 600 meters off northern British Columbia[11] and off Kyuquot Sound.[7]

References   1 Aron 1962; 2 Barraclough 1967a; 3 Clemens and Wilby 1961; 4 Collard 1970; 5 Gilbert 1895; 6 Grinols 1965a; 7 McAllister 1961; 8 Pereyra, Pearcy, and Carvey 1969; 9 Shimada 1948; 10 Smoker and Pearcy 1970; 11 Taylor 1968.

BIGFIN LANTERNFISH

Symbolophorus californiense (Eigenmann and Eigenmann 1889)

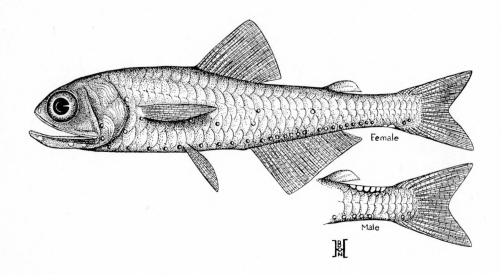

Female

Male

Scientific names from the Greek *symbolon* (mark) and *phoros* (bearer — near right angle of arrangement of supraanal photophores); and (State of) California.

Clemens and Wilby 1946 and 1961 recorded this species as *Myctophum californiense* Eigenmann and Eigenmann. In 1946 the common name was spelled bigfinned lantern-fish. Future consistency may require lampfish as the noun in the common name.

Description   Body elongate, depth about 4.6 to 5 into standard length, greatest depth over pectoral fin, compressed. Head length about 4 into standard length, compressed. Mouth terminal, large, directed forward and up. Upper jaw extends beyond posterior rim of eye by about half snout to posterior rim distance. Lower jaw slightly protruding. Snout short. Lips thin. Teeth fine in narrow bands on both jaws and on palatines. Interorbital space about 3 into length of head, concave but may be filled with inflated tissue. Eye diameter about 2.5 into length of head. Opercular membranes free of each other and of isthmus. Caudal peduncle compressed and slender, its least depth about 13 into standard length.

Fins   Dorsal (1), about 14 or 15. Adipose short based and slender. Caudal forked and small. Anal 19 to 22, higher anteriorly. Pectorals about 17, long, reaching beyond pelvic insertion but not as far as anus. Pelvics 8, abdominal.

Scales   Cycloid, large, 38 to 42 along lateral line canal. Lateral line canal sloping gently down toward tail in anterior part of body then straight along midside to caudal base. Photophores: on head: ventronasal small and embedded; operculars 2, first faint, second larger; mandibulars 2: on body; thoracic 5, the last at pelvic insertion, ventrals 4 evenly spaced in line between pelvic axil and side of anal fin origin; anals 7 along anterior three-quarters of anal fin; peduncular 9, the first 4 beside anal fin separated from anal photophores by a short gap; precaudals 2, on lower part of caudal peduncle; subpectorals 2, near base of lower pectoral fin rays and about midway between that one and first thoracic;

suprapectoral well in advance of pectoral fin base, about on line with lower subpectoral and second thoracic; supraventral over ventral fin insertion, closer to lateral line than midventral line, and overlaid by pectoral fin; supraanals 3, placed so that lines joining them have a marked angle approaching a right angle, the last 2 photophores and the last ventral in a straight line, the last photophore touching lateral line canal; postero-lateral touching lateral line canal above last anal. Luminous organs: a marked sex difference, males with 3 to 6 large organs in a row on dorsal edge of caudal peduncle; females with 3 to 8 organs on ventral part of caudal peduncle.

Colour   Black on dorsal surface, silvery on sides, dusky on bases of fins. Light from photophores pale green.

Size   Length to about 5 inches (12.7 cm).[3]

Recognition   Recognized by having two ventral precaudal photophores well separated from the peduncular, the anal and peduncular series of photophores separated over the anal fin, six or seven, eight to ten, and the sharp angle formed by the lines joining the supraanal photophores.

Life History   Five-year-old bigfin lanternfish are about 4 inches (10 cm) long. Spawning is in spring and summer.[3] Food is small crustaceans,[3] such as copepods and euphausiids either separately or together.[2] Lanternfishes are attracted to lights suspended over the water. They are eaten by albacore, jack mackerel, and rockfishes, by cephalopods, and by marine mammals and birds.[3]

Distribution   From near Cedros Island, Baja California[3] through northern and southern California, Oregon to 850 fathoms (1560 m), Washington to 270 fathoms (494 m),[4,6] British Columbia at 17 and 22 fathoms (31 and 40 m), off the west coast of Vancouver Island and northward,[1,4] and Alaska. Offshore from North America and Japan.[5]

References   1 Aron 1958a; 2 Collard 1970; 3 Fitch and Lavenberg 1968; 4 Grinols 1965a; 5 Mead and Taylor 1953; 6 Shimada 1948.

BLUE LANTERNFISH

Tarletonbeania crenularis (Jordan and Gilbert 1880)

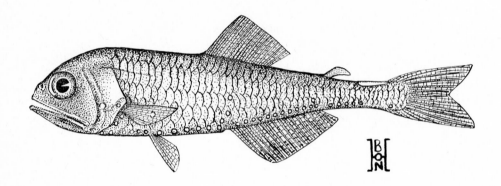

Scientific names from Tarleton Hoffman Bean, U.S. ichthyologist: and the Latin *crenula* (a small notch — slightly scalloped edges of the scales).

Description   Body elongate, its depth 4.2 to 4.8 into standard length, deeper anteriorly, compressed. Head about 3.8 into standard length, deep, compressed. Mouth terminal, large, directed slightly upward. Upper jaw extending behind eye by nearly 1 eye diameter. Jaws about equal. Snout short and blunt, its length less than diameter of eye. Teeth small, villiform, in several rows in both jaws. Interorbital space about 4.3 into length of head, nearly flat, with median ridge. Eye diameter 3.2 to 3.7 into length of head. Opercular membranes free of each other and of isthmus. Caudal peduncle compressed, its least depth about 18 into standard length.

Fins   Dorsal (1), 11 to 14, originating about middle of body. Adipose small, short based, and slender. Caudal forked. Anal 17 to 19 with a rather long base, originating a little behind origin of dorsal. Pectorals about 13, reaching beyond pelvic insertion. Pelvics 8 or 9 including outer rudimentary ray, abdominal.

Scales   Cycloid, moderate in size, in 45 to 50 oblique rows along body, margins crenulate. Lateral line canal short, less than length of head, with pores restricted to first few scales. Photophores: on head: dorsonasal small and deeply embedded; ventronasal not observed; supraorbital small and difficult to observe; operculars 2, close to preoperculum, the lower small, the upper larger and diffuse; mandibular 3: on body; thoracic (5)7(8), in line from isthmus to pelvic fin insertion; ventral (5)6(7) from pelvic axil to near anus, the second slightly dorsal to the rest of the line; anal (9)10(12), in line; penduculars 3 to 5 in line; precaudal 1, in line with anals and very close to midventral line, subpectorals 3, at pectoral base, and, above and below its line just under the operculum; supraventral above ventral insertion and immediately behind pectoral base; supraanals 3, above and slightly behind last ventral, behind and slightly above it, above anal fin origin near lateral line canal; posterolateral near lateral line canal near last anal. Luminous organs well developed in anterior part of eye, and in males only on dorsal edge of caudal peduncle from adipose to caudal fin.

Colour   Bright metallic blue on dorsal surface. Bright silvery on ventral surface.

Size   Length to 5 inches (12.7 cm).

202

Recognition   Recognizable by the slender caudal peduncle, the compression of head and body, by the reduced pelvic fins, and by the absence of a photophore on the body above the angle of the operculum.

Life History   Blue lanternfish are known to feed on euphausiids.[1] They in turn are eaten by albacore both in California and British Columbia. A mass mortality reported off Pebble Beach in California was associated with a drop in water temperature indicating strong upwelling of deep ocean water.[1]

Distribution   Bathypelagic. From tropical mid-Pacific, off Mexico and California to Alaska and the Pacific coast of Japan. From the surface where it is frequently encountered at night to depths of 387 fathoms (710 m) (off British Columbia).[3] Recorded from Puget Sound.[2,4] In British Columbia widely distributed off the west coast of Vancouver Island, Queen Charlotte Sound, Juan de Fuca Strait.

There appear to be three populations around the North Pacific Basin with different average characters and little geographic overlap. *Tarletonbeania taylori*[5] has been named as a separate species but is regarded here as a population of *T. crenularis*.[6]

References   1 Aughtry 1953; 2 DeLacy, Dryfoos, and Miller 1963; 3 Grinols 1965a; 4 Kincaid 1919; 5 Mead 1953; 6 Wisner 1959.

ORDER CYPRINIFORMES

The Cypriniformes are small to medium-sized freshwater fishes with soft-rayed fins, abdominal pelvic fins, and no adipose fins. Scales are cycloid and vary widely in size. Parietal, subopercular, and symplectic bones are present and intermuscular bones are developed. Anterior vertebrae are modified to be part of a Weberian apparatus. There are no vomerine teeth and typically no pyloric caeca. There are three to five branchiostegal rays. A gasbladder is present, often divided. Numerous species including suckers and minnows.

FAMILY CYPRINIDAE   MINNOWS

The Cyprinidae are usually small, but occasionally quite large, fishes without teeth on jaws, palatines, or vomer, and with the upper jaw formed by the premaxillary bone. Pharyngeals lie parallel to the gill rakers, are falciform, each with one, two, or three rows of blunt teeth. There are three branchiostegal rays on each side. Gill membranes are fused to the isthmus. Freshwater fishes. Minnows, including carp and goldfish, young carp occasionally getting far from land in brackish water.

CARP

Cyprinus carpio Linnaeus 1758

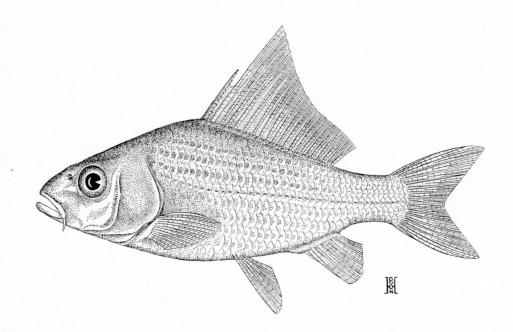

Scientific names from (the Island of) Cyprus, source of the European carp; and the Latin *carpio* (carp).

The French name for the species is *carpe*.

Description   Body sturdy, deep, and only moderately compressed, depth about 2.7 into standard length (3.0 in small marine specimens). Form in several aspects variable. Head slightly compressed, about 3 into standard length (as little as 2.6 in marine specimens). Mouth terminal, small, directed slightly upward. Upper jaw reaching to about two-thirds distance from snout to anterior margin of orbit. No teeth, inner part of mouth lined with numerous papillae. Interorbital space broad, domed, about 2.7 into length of head. Eye rather small, about 5 into length of head (3.3 in small marine

specimens). Branchiostegals 3, gill membranes fused to isthmus. Caudal peduncle sturdy and compressed.

Fins   Dorsal (1), 20(17–21) long based. The first long ray is modified by growth and/or coalescence to form a characteristic serrate spine. In small individuals taken in British Columbia salt water, the serrate spine is the second rather than first significant ray. Ray length is very variable with the serrate ray being anything from the longest to about 40 percent of succeeding rays. Caudal forked. Anal 6(7), short based with a similar serrate spine in first or in small specimens second position. Pectorals about 15 reaching about to base of pelvics. Pelvics about 8.

Scales   In British Columbia specimens in well-formed rows, large, cycloid, about 36 along the lateral line canal. Some domestic strains have scales much reduced in number or have no scales. Lateral line canal dipping down gradually from anterior end. Barbels on jaw, 2 on each side, a large one at the corner of outside end of the maxillary and the other on the upper lip about halfway along the jaw. These barbels develop late. The smaller is not evident on any of the small specimens taken in salt water and the barbel at the corner of the mouth is only noticeable on larger specimens (30 mm).

Colour   Green or bronze, lighter below.

Size   Reaches a length of 29 inches (74 cm) and weight of 10 pounds (4.5 kg) in British Columbia, 50 pounds (22.7 kg) in Washington State. Nothing over 1.5 inches (38 mm) recorded from British Columbia salt water.[2]

Recognition   Noteworthy for the serrate spines at the anterior parts of the dorsal and anal fins and by the gill membranes being attached to the isthmus.

Life History   Spawns in fresh water in June and July in weedy shallows or ditches. An 18.5 inch (47 cm) female contained 300,000 eggs. They uproot vegetation in feeding on plants and bottom organisms, make the water turbid and are regarded as a deterent to the well-being of fine fishes. They are recognized as food fishes in Europe and among some groups of North Americans but are underutilized in commerce. Remains of small carp have been found in the stomachs of a juvenile salmon off Point Grey.[1]

Distribution   Essentially a freshwater species introduced from Europe although originally of Asiatic origin, rather generally distributed in southern Canada from the lower St. Lawrence valley in brackish water to the lower Fraser, and throughout the United States, but not recorded from Alberta. At the mouth of the Vedder River and in Deas Island slough. Lower Squamish River. In the sea off Point Grey (in 1946)[2] and several records around East Point of Saturna Island in the Strait of Georgia in 1967.[1] The upper limits of salinity tolerance for carp have been found to be 5 or 6 parts per thousand[4,5] with survival for 36 days at 7.2 parts per thousand. The present observations support the suggestion of possible colonization of streams through salt water.[2,3]

References   1 Barraclough and Robinson 1971; 2 Carl, Clemens, and Lindsey 1959; 3 McCrimmon 1968; 4 Nakamura 1948; 5 Soller et al. 1965.

ORDER BATRACHOIDIFORMES
(Haplodoci)

The Batrachoidiformes have the bodies stout anteriorly with depressed heads. Scales are absent, or ctenoid and embedded. Gill openings are small and there are only three gill arches. The spinous dorsal fin is small with only two to four spines. The rayed dorsal and anal fins are long. Pelvic fins are thoracic with one spine and two or three rays.

FAMILY BATRACHOIDIDAE   TOADFISHES

Toadfishes are found mainly in tropical seas on the bottom or at modest depths, and occasionally bathypelagically. There are no scales and the numerous photophores are arranged in noteworthy lines, suggesting the name midshipman because of the resemblance to rows of buttons. In some species the spines of the head and dorsal fin are hollow and connected with poison glands at the base making them dangerous to handle. There is a gasbladder — in the local form specially adapted to make a humming sound leading to an alternative name, singing fish. They are of moderate size. One species known from British Columbia.

PLAINFIN MIDSHIPMAN

Porichthys notatus Girard 1854

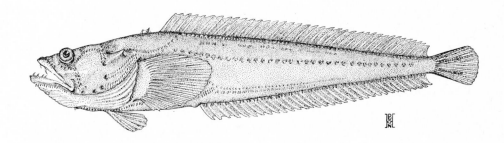

Scientific names from the Greek *poros* (pore) and *ichthys* (fish); and the Latin *notatus* (spotted).

Clemens and Wilby 1961 use the common name midshipman which will probably remain current in British Columbia.

Description   Body elongate, its depth about 5.5 into standard length, compressed, tapering evenly to caudal peduncle. Head wide and depressed, its length about 3.5 into standard length. Mouth terminal, large, directed somewhat upward. Upper jaw reaching line joining anterior margins of orbits. Snout short, middle of upper jaw extending beyond line between anterior edges of eyes by only slightly more than length of eye. Lips fleshy. Teeth, a pair of strong backwardly curved canines moderately spaced on vomer in upper jaw, 2 pairs widely spaced in lower jaw with smaller curved canines between them. A row of well-developed teeth on each palatine. Fine teeth along length of upper jaw and between largest teeth on lower jaw. Interorbital space very wide and flat, its width about 3.2 into length of head. Eyes strongly protruding, protrusible, small, the length about 6 into length of head, oval. Opercular membrane broadly joined to the isthmus. Branchiostegals 6. Caudal peduncle slender and much compressed, its least depth about 20 into standard length.[2]

Spines   A strong spine covered with skin on either operculum.

Fins   Dorsal (2), II — (33)35(37), well separated, the first fin very small with sharp spines, the rayed fin long, emarginate, even. Caudal rounded and narrow, free from dorsal and anal. Anal (29)31–33(37), long, even, emarginate, originating definitely behind origin of rayed dorsal and ending below end of dorsal. Pectorals about 18, broad. Pelvics I, 2, thoracic, the spine soft and broad, the rays much branched and flattened.

Vertebrae   Average of 10 in California 42.6 (41–44).[3]

Scales   Scales absent. Lateral line canals 4 on each side, beside dorsal fin, midlateral, lower side, and beside anal fin. Shorter rows of sensory pores on head and jaws. Two pairs of double nares, one near midline in upper jaw, opening in a papilla, the second pair opening front of the eyes. Photophores in rows on body and head including: on body, 2 dorsal rows, midlateral row, lower lateral row, anal row, 2 rows joined on belly, 2 rows roughly parallel lower jaw close to it and on throat, extending on next to last branchiostegal; on head, 2 rows on opercle and shorter rows around eyes, maxillary, etc. Cirri very numerous, and various in form and size, usually but not always associated with sensory pores, on lower jaw, free ends of maxillary, caudal fin, and elsewhere. A small anal papilla.

Colour   Olive brown to bronze or dark iridescent purple on dorsal surface, paler on sides with a golden yellow on ventral surface. White space under eye with a black crescent below. White on posterior edge of maxillary. In young there is a weak dark dorsal saddle.

Size   Length to 15 inches (38 cm).

Recognition   Noteworthy for the rows of luminous organs and cirri, for the protrusible eyes, the two large canine teeth on the vomer, and the very small spinous dorsal fin.

Life History   Spawning takes place in spring in shallow water or in the intertidal zone. A cavity is scooped out in sand or broken shell under rocks and the large pink or yellowish eggs are deposited in a single layer on the roof of the cavity where they are guarded by the fasting male which is usually effective in keeping the eggs clean and moist and in protecting them against intruders. The eggs are subspherical about 6 millimeters in diameter and attached to the rock by an adhesive disc. A nest usually contains 200 to 500 eggs with as few as 19 or as many as 789. The species may be polygamous. In about 16 to 20 days the young emerge from the eggs tail first at a length of 7 to 8 millimeters but they remain fixed by the yolk and the adhesive disc until they become free swimming at 32 to 34 millimeters. At this stage they avoid light and dig into the bottom during the daytime but come out at night to feed on small crustacean larvae.[1,6] Observations in aquaria suggest that burying themselves in the bottom is continued as a practice throughout life.[9] However, it has been captured at mid-depths and makes vertical migrations at night.[8] The adults are very resistant to exposure to air. The food of adults includes fishes and crustaceans.

An alternative name for the northern midshipman is singing fish. This recognizes the humming, growling, croaking, grunting sound made so loudly that the "oonk" can be heard for 40 feet (12 m).[1] Some observations indicate that the noise is related to aggression or defence but at other times the low intensity sounds suggest peaceful communication. The sound is produced within the gasbladder which is divided across by a diaphragm with a small central opening. Strong muscles attached to the walls of the gasbladder force the gasbladder gases through the opening to produce a considerable variety of noises. The gasbladder muscles are "striped muscles" associated with voluntary action.[4]

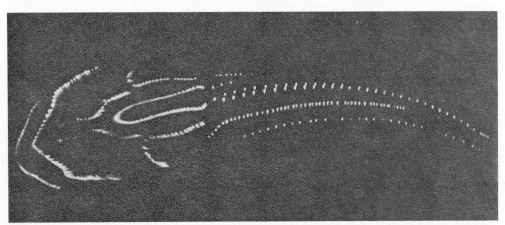

Plainfin midshipman displayed by its own lights. Photographed by J. A. MacDonald at Hopkins Marine Station; courtesy Dr Sharon Proctor. The luminescence was induced by the intraperitoneal injection of about 0.3 cc 1% adrenalin.

Under normal conditions and even under strong physical stimulation the photophores never or seldom emit light. They have been caused to do so in the laboratory by strong electric currents which produce bright luminescence for periods up to half a minute or by injections of adrenalin which gave much more persistent effects lasting up to several hours.[5]

Point Conception but confined to deeper water farther south.[7] In British Columbia the plainfin midshipman is common in the Strait of Georgia and on the west coast of Vancouver Island at least as far north as Nootka Sound. It occurs from the intertidal zone to depths of at least 145 fathoms (265 m).

Distribution   Known from the Gulf of California and Cape San Lucas[1] (and beyond as various races) to southeastern Alaska.[10] (Wilimovsky 1954 was unable to confirm the Alaska record). In the intertidal zone as well as in deeper water north of

References   I Arora 1948; 2 Buchanan 1935; 3 Clothier 1950; 4 Greene 1924; 5 Green and Greene 1924; 6 Hubbs 1920; 7 Hubbs and Schultz 1939; 8 Lavenberg and Fitch 1966; 9 Vancouver Public Aquarium 1969; 10 Wilimovsky 1954.

ORDER GOBIESOCIFORMES
(Xenopterygii)

The Gobiesociformes are small fishes with depressed heads and scales absent. Dorsal and anal fins are supported entirely by soft rays. The pelvic fins are united anteriorly to form, with a fold of skin, a large adhesive disc divided into anterior and posterior parts. Represented in shallow seas.

FAMILY GOBIESOCIDAE   CLINGFISHES

The clingfishes are small fishes, mainly tropical, but represented by two species in British Columbia where they are found in shallow water adhering to rocks and shells or hiding in burrows.

KEY TO THE GOBIESOCIDAE

1   Rays in dorsal fin 6 to 8; body elongate, slender; head small and narrow
.... *Rimicola muscarum,* Kelp clingfish, p. 212

or 1   Rays in dorsal fin 13 to 16; body stout, depressed anteriorly, compressed posteriorly; head large and broad ....
.... *Gobiesox maeandricus,* Northern clingfish, p. 210

NORTHERN CLINGFISH

Gobiesox maeandricus (Girard 1858)

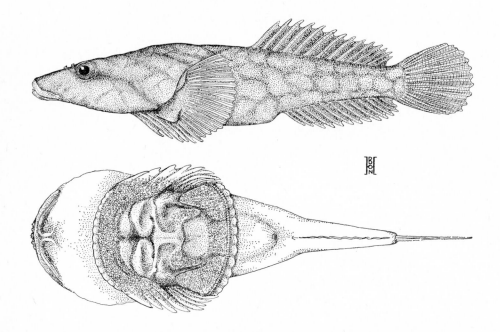

Scientific names from the fish names *goby* and *esox* (resemblance to either obscure); and the Latin *meandricus* (meandering — colour streaks).

Clemens and Wilby 1946 recorded this species as *Sicyogaster maeandricus* (Girard), the common cling-fish. Clemens and Wilby 1961 used flathead clingfish as the common name.

Description Body elongate, its depth 5 to 6 into standard length, depressed anteriorly and compressed posteriorly. Head large, depressed, its length about 2.5 into standard length. Mouth terminal, rather large, directed forward. Its opening extending about to the anterior margin of the eye. Snout bluntly rounded. Lower jaw included. Lips thick, the upper one extending as a veil over the mouth opening and lined on its anterior part by a cluster of papillae. The thickening of the lower lip divided into a symmetrical arrangement of folds. Teeth generally small and conical, larger at front and in bands there. Interorbital space wide and moderately arched, its width about 3 into length of head. Eyes small, about 7 into length of head. Gill membranes broadly joined and free of the isthmus. Caudal peduncle compressed and short, its least depth about 5 into length of head.[1]

Fins Dorsal (1), 13 to 16, far back on body and moderately long. Caudal well rounded. Anal 12 to 14, originating behind dorsal and ending below it. Pectorals about 21, short and broad, a fleshy palp between the base of the fin and the gill opening. Pelvics 4, united anteriorly by a papillose membrane, the rays are flexible and support the lateral rim of a prominent adhesive disc. The disc is completed posteriorly by a broad fringed fold of skin on the lower part of the body, separated from the pelvic fins by a deep notch.

Scales   Scales and lateral line canal present. A small anal papilla is present.

Colour   Light olive brown to cherry red, reticulated with darker or mottled with light shades. Dark radiating lines from eyes and joining the eyes through a series of reticulations. White bars between eyes and in young across back and on edge of caudal fin.

Size   Length to 6 inches (15.2 cm).

Recognition   Recognized by the adhesive disc, the large head with the body depressed in front and compressed behind, the single rayed dorsal fin set well back on the body.

Life History   Clings with its adhesive disc to rocks in intertidal zone and in tidal currents. Feeds on small crustaceans and molluscs.

Distribution   Known from southern California to southeastern Alaska.[2] There is a possible accidental occurrence off Baja California. Occurs along the whole coast of British Columbia and is common in the Strait of Georgia.

References   1 Briggs 1951, 1955; 2 Wilimovsky 1954. See also Schultz 1944.

KELP CLINGFISH

Rimicola muscarum (Meek and Pierson 1895)

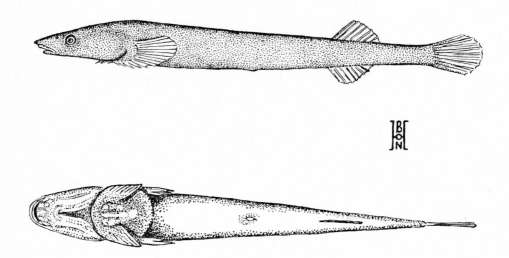

Scientific names from the Latin *rima* (crevice) and *cola* (inhabit); and *muscarum* (fly — speckled marking).

The first British Columbia specimens of this species were recorded as the slender cling-fish *Rimicola eigenmanni* (Gilbert 1890) (Clemens and Wilby 1946).

Description   Body elongate, depth about 8 into standard length, somewhat depressed through the anterior third. Head depressed, its length about 4 into standard length. Mouth terminal, moderate in size, directed slightly upward. Upper jaw not nearly reaching anterior margin of orbit. Lips thick, the upper well separated from the rest of the head, the lower with 2 series of blunt protuberances and ridges. Teeth fine and concentrated near the anterior parts of both jaws. Interorbital space broad and flat, its width about 2.3 into head length. Eye small, its diameter about 5 into head length. Snout about twice as long as eye. Gill membranes fused and free of isthmus.

Caudal peduncle rather long and evenly tapered, its least depth about 4 into head length.[1]

Fins   Dorsal (1), 6 to 8, first 1 or 2 rays embedded, placed far back on body. Caudal roundish, narrow. Anal 6 to 8, about opposite dorsal. Pectorals short and rather broad. Pelvics 4, thoracic, united anteriorly by wrinkled membrane to form the anterior portion of small adhesive disc which is completed posteriorly by a broad fold of skin from the ventral surface of body, the anterior and posterior segments of the disc separated by lateral clefts.

Scales   No scales or lateral line canal. There is an anal papilla, larger in males.

Colour   Light olive green to brown. In female sometimes sparsely covered with distinct brownish red spots about the size of the pupil of the eye.

Size   Length to 2 inches (5 cm).

212

Recognition Distinguished by the slender body, the small sucking disc with lateral clefts and the small size of the dorsal fin set far back on the body.

Distribution From Todos Santos Bay in Baja California[2] to central British Columbia. Records are from Agate Beach,[3] Ucluelet, Clayoquot Sound, Fitz Hugh Sound, and Goose Island.[4]

References 1 Briggs 1951, 1955; 2 Fitch 1952b; 3 Krejsa 1964; 4 Peden 1966c. See also Wilby 1936a.

ORDER LOPHIIFORMES
(Pediculati)

Most of the fishes in this order are short, round, or depressed and have the first dorsal spine very prominent, separated from the rest of the fin, and placed on head as a fishing lure, and often otherwise modified. The gill opening is never placed in front of the pectoral fins. The body is without ordinary scales but may be covered with spines. Pelvic fins are usually absent, but when present are thoracic consisting of one spine and five soft rays. Most are deep-sea fishes, but some are bathypelagic or drift with floating seaweed. Most species are small but some reach lengths of 4 feet (120 cm) and a weight of 50 or 60 pounds (22.7–27.3 kg) and are used for food.

FAMILY ONEIRODIDAE   DREAMERS

In the dreamers the body is usually stout, oval or globular, the pelvic fin is absent, the first dorsal spine is very long and directed forward, and is sometimes jointed. At its end there is a highly developed branched organ with various filaments or appendages called an esca. The whole assembly is called the illicium and is regarded as a fishing lure. It arises from a basal bone of the dorsal fin. The mouth is large with sharp depressible teeth. The rayed dorsal and anal fins are short, about equal in size and placed far back on the body, directed backward. Usually with scales, and black in colour. Members of this family have a complicated life history with the males remaining very small and failing to develop eyes, teeth, or illicium, and even becoming parasitic on the females. Complications arising from scarcity of specimens, the complex life history, and sexual dimorphism make positive identifications difficult, and in some cases it is necessary to assign specimens to species groups. Only females are dealt with, and males have not been recognized in the area under consideration.

213

KEY TO THE ONEIRODIDAE

1   Sphenotic spine present .... Genus *Oneirodes* 2

or   1   Sphenotic spine absent ....
.... *Chaenophryne parviconus,* Smooth dreamer, p. 214

2   Illicium about twice as long as basal bone; esca with 1 main element and a dense tuft of filaments ....
.... *Oneirodes eschrichti* group, Bulbous dreamer, p. 218

or   2   Illicium about as long as basal bone; esca with 2 main fingerlike elements
.... *Oneirodes acanthias,* Spiny dreamer, p. 216

SMOOTH DREAMER

Chaenophryne parviconus Regan and Trewavas 1932

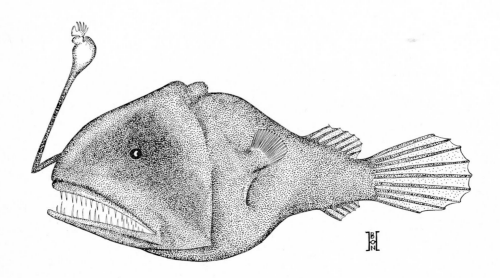

Scientific names from the Greek *chaenos* (gape) and *phrynos* (toad); and the Latin *parvus* (small) and *conus* (cone).

Description   Body very short, depth about 1.7 into standard length, width about 2 into standard length. Head large, its length about 1.8 into standard length, broad. Profile decurved. Top of head with a concavity, bounded by blunt ridges extending from behind eyes to premaxillaries. Mouth terminal, large, directed forward. Upper jaw

214

extending well beyond posterior margin of eye. Lower jaw somewhat protruding, its total length about half length of fish. Above mouth a long slender appendage, called illicium, arising from an exserted basal bone, its length about 3.8 into standard length, an intricate bulb at its end is important in making specific identifications. Lower jaw shallow. Teeth in both jaws irregular in size and spacing, 12 to 15 in upper jaw, 13 to 16 in lower jaw, 2 or 3 on each side of vomer. Interorbital space concave between high ridges, its width about 1.7 into length of head. Eye small, its diameter about 20 into length of head. Gill membranes united to body. Gill slits very small, opening behind and below pectoral fin. Caudal peduncle short and compressed, its least depth about 8.3 into standard length. No spines on head.

Fins Dorsal (1), 7, well back on body, directed up and back. Caudal 9, large. Anal 5, about half as long as caudal, ending about under same point, directed down and back. Pectorals small, 17, pediculate, directed upward. Pelvics absent.

Scales No scales or lateral line canal.

Colour Black except for pale on esca at end of illicium.

Size Length to 3.25 inches (8.3 cm).

Recognition Known for its heavy black body, gill openings below and behind pectoral fins, elongate appendage on snout with a complex end, absence of a sphenotic spine, and smoothly decurved profile.

Distribution Bathypelagic. Occurring in all oceans. Off Central America and in tropical mid-Pacific Ocean.[1] Rare in northeastern Pacific, known only from Oregon at 275 to 400 fathoms (504–733 m)[2,3] off the outlet of the Columbia River, and from a damaged head collected off Cape St. James at 51.26 N, 131.09 W at a depth of 730 to 825 meters.[4]

References 1 Bertelsen 1951; 2, 3 Grinols 1965b, 1966; 4 Taylor 1967b. See also Regan 1925, 1926, and Regan and Trewavas 1932.

SPINY DREAMER

Oneirodes acanthias (Gilbert 1915)

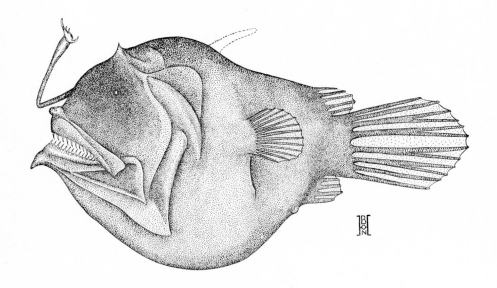

Scientific names from the Greek *onei-rodes* (dreamer); and *acanthias* (spine).

Description   Body very short, its depth about 1.5 into standard length, almost globular. Head large, deep and broad, its length about 1.5 into standard length, a deep wide groove extends between eyes from epiotic bones on top of head to premaxillaries. Mouth terminal, large, directed forward. A prominent knob on upper jaw from expanded end of maxillary. Upper jaw extends beyond eye. Lower jaw with a small sharp symphyseal process. Above mouth is a long, slender appendage called the illicium about 1.2 into head length. Its end is a complicated bulb called the esca whose detailed structure is important in identifying related species. The illicium is sometimes regarded as a dorsal fin (spine). Teeth in jaws large, in rows, unequal in size, irregularly spaced, curved inward, depressible, 13 in upper jaw, 15 in lower jaw, 3 or 4 teeth on either side of vomer. Interorbital space extremely concave between high frontal ridges, its width about 6.5 into length of head. Eye very small. Gill membranes joined to body. Gill openings very small, high on body, posterior to and below pectoral fins. Caudal peduncle short and compressed, its least depth about 5.5 into standard length.[1,5]

Spines   Strong sphenotic spines toward posterior ends of frontal ridges. A similar spine (sometimes bifid) directed out, posterior to and below corner of mouth. Below it a heavy flat triangular spine on lower posterior corner of opercular bones.

Fins   Dorsal (1), 5 to 6, short, directed backward, placed far back on body. Caudal with 9 rays, 4 of them bifid, fan shaped and rounded. Anal 4, below and balancing dorsal but somewhat smaller. Pectorals 13, pediculate. Pelvics absent.

Scales   Scales and lateral line canal absent.

Colour   Jet black except for unpigmented parts of esca.

Size   Length to 8 inches (20 cm).[2]

Recognition   Known for its sturdy black body, gill openings behind and below pectoral fins, the jointed appendage with a complicated expanded end on the snout, and the small eyes.

Life History   Unlike many related species male spiny dreamers are not parasitic on females but they are degenerate, lacking teeth, having relatively large heads, and eyes directed outward. Spiny dreamers attain maturity at quite a small size. They feed heavily on crustaceans.[2]

Distribution   Found in deep water from off Cedros Island, Baja California, through southern California from 794 to 891 fathoms (1450–1630 m), to the Gulf of Alaska at 54.13 N, 159.06 W.[4,6,8] The British Columbia record is from 510 to 595 meters at 52.11 N, 131.11 W off Moresby Island.[7]

References   1 Bertelsen 1951; 2 Fitch and Lavenberg 1968; 3 Gilbert 1915; 4 Grinols 1965a; 5 Regan and Trewavas 1932; 6 Schultz 1934a; 7 Taylor 1967b; 8 Wilimovsky 1954.

BULBOUS DREAMER

Oneirodes eschrichti Lütken 1871 group

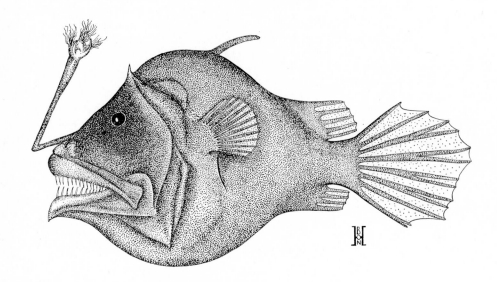

Scientific names from the Greek *oneirodes* (dreamer); and D. F. Eschricht, Danish naturalist.

Clemens and Wilby 1946 used the name bulb-fish *Oneirodes bulbosus* Chapman 1939[2] for this species, and in 1961 dreamer was used as the common name. Examination of many specimens leaves doubt about the exact status of the species and for the present it is best to refer British Columbia specimens to a group name covering either a single variable species or several similar species, as proposed by Bertelsen 1951.[1]

Description   Body very short, its depth about 1.6 into standard length. Head large, deep, and in intact specimens broad between opercular spines, its depth about 1.6 into standard length. A deep wide concavity extends from epiotic bones on top of head to premaxillary, its width about 6 into length of head. Mouth terminal, large, directed forward. Upper jaw extends about to posterior margin of eye. Above mouth a long slender appendage called illicium arises from a basal bone. When straightened illicium and basal bone go about 1.5 into length of head. It ends in an intricate bulb called esca whose detailed structure is used in identifying related species. A prominent knob on upper jaw is the expanded end of the maxillary bone. Lower jaw with a rounded symphyseal prominence. Teeth in both jaws, large, in irregular rows, unequal in size, directed inward, depressible, about 15 in upper jaw, about 19 in lower jaw, 2 to 4 on either side of vomer. Interorbital space extremely concave between highly raised frontal ridges. Eye very small, its diameter about 11 into length of head, protruding. Gill membranes united to body. Gill slits very small, high on side, opening behind and below pectoral fin. Caudal peduncle short and compressed, its least depth about 7 into standard length.[4,5]

Spines   Strong sphenotic spines toward posterior ends of frontal ridges. A similar spine directed out posterior to and below corner of mouth. Below it a heavy, flat, triangular spine on lower posterior corner of opercular bones.

Fins   Dorsal (2), 1 to 5 or 6, the first a fleshy, narrow, flaccid ray,[2] or a short skin tubercle,[6] originating about halfway between sphenotic spines and second dorsal; the second fin short, directed backward, placed far back on body. Caudal with 8 or 9 rays, 4 of them bifid, large rounded, fan shaped. Anal 4, placed almost balancing second dorsal, somewhat smaller. Pectorals about 13, pediculate. Pelvics absent.

Scales   Scales and lateral line canal absent.

Colour   Jet black except for unpigmented esca.

Size   Length at least to 3.1 inches (7.9 cm).

Recognition   Known for its sturdy black body, gill openings behind and below pectoral fins, jointed appendage with a decorated end on the snout, and the small eyes.

Distribution   The "group" is widely spread in tropical and subtropical seas; Atlantic, Indian, and Pacific oceans. In the northeastern Pacific from the Gulf of Panama and northern British Columbia off Moresby Island, 52.11 N, 133.11 W at 510 to 595 fathoms (935–1090 m)[6] and Graham Island 53.50 N, 133.54 W at 379 to 487 fathoms (695–890 m),[2,3] both of the Queen Charlotte Islands. At Ocean Station "Papa" 50 N, 145 W.

References   1 Bertelsen 1951; 2 Chapman 1939; 3 Grinols 1965a; 4 Regan 1926; 5 Regan and Trewavas 1932; 6 Taylor 1967b.

ORDER GADIFORMES
(Anacanthini)

The Gadiformes are an abundant and widely distributed group of modest-sized fishes found mostly but not entirely in the cool waters of the northern hemisphere. They are elongate fishes with tapering bodies. Mouths are moderate in size to large, with rather small teeth. Many species have barbels below the symphysis of the lower jaw. Scales are cycloid. Fins are supported by soft rays. There are two or three dorsal fins; some species have two anal fins. The pelvic fins are thoracic and their bases attached to the cleithra by ligaments. The body is covered with scales and there is a gasbladder not connected by a duct to the digestive tract. The tail may be greatly reduced, or the tail elements may be supplemented by structures derived from the neural and haemal spines of the posterior vertebrae, producing a "normal" appearing tail fin. There are altogether about six families and 400 species, of which one is a Canadian freshwater fish, two counting *Microgadus tomcod* which has freshwater populations. In British Columbia six families are represented as currently interpreted.

The fishes of this family resemble the cods in many important features. The species represented in Canadian Pacific waters differ from the cods by having a projecting upper jaw with a well-developed shelflike ridge along the snout and projecting below each eye. The posterior part of the gasbladder is tightly embraced by the ribs. Generally distributed deep-sea fishes. Moras, codlings, and related species.

PACIFIC FLATNOSE

Antimora microlepis Bean 1890

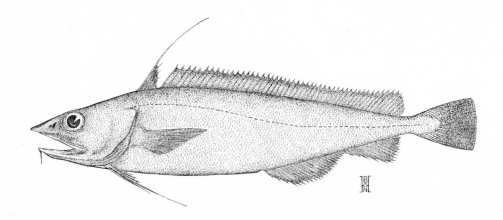

Scientific names from the Latin *anti* (opposite) and *mora* (another fish); and the Greek *micro* (small) and *lepis* (scale).

Clemens and Wilby 1946, 1961 recorded this species as long-finned and longfin cod, *Antimora rostrata* Günther 1878.

Description   Body elongate, depth about 5 into standard length, tapering gradually to a narrow caudal peduncle and tail, moderately compressed. Head, about 4.5 into standard length, depressed, pointed. Mouth subterminal, large, directed forward.

The snout is pointed to form a shelf over the mouth and extending back as a conspicuous keel under the eye. Maxillary extending to rear of eye. Teeth sharp and fine in bands on jaws and vomer. Eye large, its diameter 3.6 to 4.5 into length of head. Interorbital space flat and broad, about 5 into length of head. Caudal peduncle slender, its depth 25 to 30 into standard length.

Fins   Dorsal (2), 4 or 5, 50 to 55, first with a short base having its first ray much prolonged to about equal length of head; second long, highest at ends, lowest at about two-thirds from origin, ending abruptly, incised throughout except at posterior end. Caudal slender and truncate. Anal 39 to 42, deeply notched at about two-thirds from origin, ending abruptly, incised throughout except toward posterior end, originating below middle of second dorsal. Pectorals pointed, moderate, placed low on side. Pelvics 6 or 7, thoracic, placed very far forward, second ray much elongated — about as long as head.

Scales   Cycloid, small, about 115 rows. Lateral line canal faint, somewhat decurved and then straight. Well-developed barbel at tip of lower jaw.

Colour   Apparently variable from pale but definite blue gray or olive green throughout to deep violet or blue black. Darker on outer edges of fins and very dark on edge of caudal and fins on ventral part of the body. Dark on lower part of gill cover and branchiostegals.

Size   Length to more than 26 inches (66 cm).

Recognition   Recognizable by having a short dorsal fin followed by a long one, a single notched anal fin, all moderately incised, elongated first pectoral and first dorsal rays. There is a slender caudal peduncle. The sharp snout is continued into a ridge below the eye. The vent is more than halfway from snout to the end of the body.

Distribution   From Central America and the tropical mid-Pacific to the Bering Sea, Kamchatka, and Japan.[1,4,7] Canadian records are from off Cape St. James of the Queen Charlotte Islands at 1588 fathoms (1900 m);[2] off Kyuquot Sound in 250 fathoms (457 m);[5] and off Cape Scott in 1000 fathoms (1830 m).[3] The species may exist in significant quantities but it is unlikely to be exploited because of high fishing costs in deep water. A closely related species occurs in the Atlantic, and the same or a related species in the Indian Ocean.[6]

References   1 Alverson, Pruter, and Ronholt 1964; 2 Bean 1890; 3 Bourne and Pope 1969; 4 Grinols 1965a; 5 Ketchen and Wilson 1961; 6 Leim and Scott 1966; 7 Svetovidov 1948. Additional information from C. L. Hubbs by personal communication.

FAMILY GADIDAE   CODFISHES

The codfishes are represented in British Columbia waters by four species of moderate size, mostly from moderate depths. They have well-formed tail fins, two or three dorsal fins, and one or two anal fins. They are seasonally abundant, produce free floating eggs, and are valuable and potentially valuable commercially. The family is here taken to include cods, hakes, and related species.

KEY TO THE GADIDAE

	1	Dorsal fins 2; anal fins 1 .... *Merluccius productus,* Pacific hake, p. 225
or	1	Dorsal fins 3; anal fins 2 2
	2	Barbel evident; mouth opening under snout; first anal fin not originating under space between first and second dorsal fins 3
or	2	Barbels not evident; lower jaw projecting; first anal fin originating under space between first and second dorsal fins .... *Theragra chalcogramma,* Walleye pollock, p. 228
	3	Barbel small, its length about diameter of pupil; first anal fin originating under first dorsal fin .... *Microgadus proximus,* Pacific tomcod, p. 226
or	3	Barbel moderate, its length about equal to diameter of eye; first anal fin originating under second dorsal fin .... *Gadus macrocephalus,* Pacific cod, p. 222

PACIFIC COD

√ *Gadus macrocephalus* Tilesius 1810

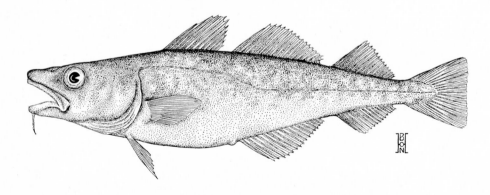

Scientific names from the Latin *gadus* (codfish); and the Greek *macros* (large) and *cephalos* (head).

Common usage may continue to refer to this species as plain "cod," or, as "gray cod" to distinguish it from the other species currently referred to as varieties of cod.

Description Body depth about 5 into standard length, greatest between one-third and two-fifths of length from snout, tapering toward tail, somewhat compressed. Head about 3.6 into standard length. Snout blunt. Mouth terminal, moderate, lower jaw included. Maxillary extending to below pupil of eye. Teeth on jaws small and sharp, outer row on each jaw much enlarged. Interorbital space rounded, about 3.9 into length of head. Eye small, about 6 into length of head. Anus below second dorsal fin. Least depth of caudal peduncle about 19 into standard length.

Fins Dorsal (3), distinctly separated, 10 to 13 — 13 to 16 — 14 to 17, first dorsal length about 1.6 into length of head. Caudal slightly forked. Anal (2), well separated, 16 to 19 — 15 to 18. Pectorals 19 to 22. Pelvics 6 or 7, thoracic.

Gill Rakers On first arch 20.88 for 27 British Columbia counts.

Vertebrae 50 to 53 for 9 British Columbia counts, mean 52.3.

Scales Cycloid, small. Lateral line canal high anteriorly, dipping gradually down to midside between middles of first and second dorsal fins. Moderate barbel just under end of lower jaw as long or longer than diameter of eye.

Colour Brown to gray on dorsal surface, shading into lighter hues on ventral surface. Brown spots numerous on back and sides. More or less dusky on fins. White on outer margin of all unpaired fins, wider on anal and caudal.

Size Length to 3 feet 3 inches (1 m).

Recognition Notable for three separate dorsal fins, anus below second dorsal fin, barbel below lower jaw as long as or longer than eye.

Life History Spawning takes place in winter. Eggs are about 1.02 millimeters (0.98–1.08 mm) in diameter. They show no oil globule. At first they are demersal and slightly adherent. The specific gravity is about 1.050 so they may sink in the water encountered.[25] Conflicting opinions are expressed for the western Pacific,[14,15,16,22] where eggs are reputed to be adherent or "benthonic." Eggs hatch in 8 or 9 days at 11 C and 17 days at 5 C, but will take about 4 weeks at 2 C in northern waters.[6] Hatching for a batch of eggs lasts over several days. Egg survival is high at 5 C. Newly hatched larvae are about 4.5 millimeters long. At 5 C the yolk sac is absorbed in about 10 days.[5] Young about 20 millimeters long have been found to eat copepods.[4] In Hecate Strait length at 1 year is 23 centimeters, at 2 years about 44 centimeters, and the theoretical maximum length is 94 centimeters. In the Strait of Georgia corresponding lengths are 26, 49, and 76 centimeters.[11] In the Strait of Georgia growth is rapid and continuous through the year.[7] First maturity for females is reached at about 40 centimeters body length and 2 or more, usually 3 years of age.[10] The length at which 50 percent are mature is 55 centimeters.[6] Half the males are mature at age 2. At 60 centimeters a female may produce 1.2 million eggs, at 78 centimeters 3.3 million.[16,24] Tagging in the Strait of Georgia shows congregations for spawning, and dispersal for feeding. The Japanese recognize travelling and stationary schools.[16] Cod move into deep water in autumn and return to shallow water in spring.[10] Feeding includes a wide variety of invertebrates and fishes including: worms, crabs, molluscs, and shrimps; herring, sand lance, walleye pollock and flatfishes.[9,15]

Distribution Mostly benthic but occasionally taken in quite shallow water.[1] Taken at depths to 300 fathoms (550 m). From Santa Monica in southern California through Alaska and the Bering Sea to the Chukchi Sea, past the Kuril Islands to Kamchatka, Okhotsk Sea, Sea of Japan, off Honshu, Korea and in the Yellow Sea to Port Arthur.[2,3,8,13,15,16,17,18,19,20,21,23] Toward the southern part of its centre of abundance cod occur in temperatures throughout the year between 6 and 9 C which is much warmer than farther north or west.[10] Informed current opinion is that the codfish of the North Pacific Basin belong to a single species of several more or less separate stocks.[7,26]

Utilization   The Pacific cod is now the most important of the trawl-caught bottom fishes of British Columbia. Landing figures in millions of pounds (454 metric tons) are given in the following tabulation:[12]

Year	Catch
1931–1935	0.8
1936–1940	1.5
1941–1945	1.2
1946–1950	2.0
1951–1955	5.1
1956–1960	8.0
1961–1965	9.7
1966	20.7
1967	11.2
1968	11.4
1969	7.6
1970	5.0

As the species has a fast growth rate and high natural mortality the current heavy exploitation is probably the best way to make efficient use of the resource. The catch is used for filleting and subsequent production of fish sticks, and fillet blocks for export.

References   1 Alverson 1960; 2 Alverson, Pruter, and Ronholt 1964; 3 Andriashev 1937; 4 Barraclough, Robinson, and Fulton 1968; 5, 6 Forrester 1964a, b; 7 Forrester and Ketchen 1955; 8 Grinols 1965a; 9 Hart 1949b; 10, 11 Ketchen 1961, 1964; 12 Larkin and Ricker 1964; 13 Matsubara 1955; 14 Moiseev 1953; 15 Nikol'skii 1961; 16 Okada 1955; 17, 18, 19 Phillips 1951, 1953b, 1958b; 20 Pinkas 1967; 21 Popov 1933; 22 Rass 1953; 23 Shmidt 1950; 24, 25 Thompson 1962, 1963; 26 Wilimovsky, Peden, and Peppar 1967; Schultz and Welander (1935) deal with distinctions between Pacific and Atlantic cods. Cobb (1927) provides a useful account of United States long-line fishing for cod across the North Pacific.

PACIFIC HAKE

Merluccius productus (Ayres 1855)

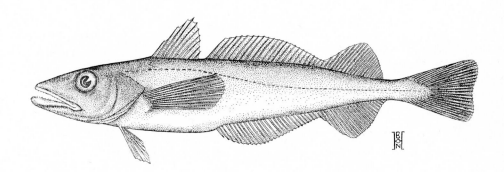

Scientific names from the Latin *merluccius* (ancient name — sea pike); and *productus* (drawn out).

Description   Body depth about 5 into standard length, moderately compressed. Tapering to a fine caudal peduncle from about one-third of length from anterior end of body. Head large, about 3.4 to 4.0 into standard length, pointed. Mouth large, terminal, directed slightly upward. Lower jaw somewhat protruding. Maxillary extending to below pupil. Snout longer than eye. Teeth strong, pointed, in bands, on both jaws, and on vomer. Eye large, about 4 to 5 into length of head, high, upper margin level with top of head. Three very low frontal ridges, 1 median and 2 diverging. Caudal peduncle slender.

Fins   Dorsal fins (2), 10 or 11(12)[5] — (39)41(44),[5] the first short based, third ray longest, second long, deeply notched. Caudal slightly forked or truncate. Anal long, 40 to 43 (41–44),[5] deeply notched, almost mirroring second dorsal. Pectorals 14 to 16, long, tip reaching beyond anus. Pelvics 6 to 8, thoracic.

Scales   Cycloid, small, deciduous. Lateral line canal moderately decurved, then straight. Scales along lateral line canal 147 to 166.[5]

Colour   Dark or metallic silver gray with black speckling on dorsal surface, bright silvery below. Brown on pectoral fins, black inside mouth and gill covers.

Size   Length to about 3 feet (91 cm).

Recognition   Distinguished by having two dorsal fins, the second dorsal and anal both long and deeply notched. There is no barbel. Mouth large with lower jaw protruding.

Life History   Males are recorded as being ripe in May in Puget Sound.[13] Off California spawning takes place at least from January to June.[1] Fecundity in California is reported as 33,000 for 37-centimeter females and 496,000 at 69 centimeters.[8] A case of hermaphrodism is reported.[9] Hake eggs are pelagic, spherical, clear, and smooth, with a single oil globule in the yolk. The diameter averages 1.12 millimeters (1.07–1.18 mm) and the oil globule diameter is just under one-third of a millimeter. Under usual conditions, hatching takes place in about 3 days or less.[1] Young larvae (5–11 mm) eat copepods and

225

their eggs in spring and early summer in the Strait of Georgia.[3,4,9,11] Hake are suspected of occasionally occupying intermediate water layers. The food of adult Pacific hake off the British Columbia coast consists primarily of euphausiids and sand lance, and to a lesser extent herring, smelt, anchovy, and shrimp. Evidence suggests that Pacific hake are mainly noctural feeders.[10] In northern California hake eat ocean shrimp, brill, other shrimp, slender sole, eulachon, tomcod, and other fishes.[6] Hake in turn are eaten by dogfish.[12]

Distribution   From the Gulf of California to the Gulf of Alaska and from the surface to 491 fathoms (900 m). Common along the whole British Columbia coast.[2,5,7]

Utilization   Because of its soft flesh, the Pacific hake has not yet had general use as a food fish. Its abundance suggests that it is an important potential source of animal protein.

References   1 Ahlstrom and Counts 1955; 2 Alverson, Pruter, and Ronholt 1964; 3 Barraclough 1967a; 4 Barraclough, Robinson, and Fulton 1968; 5 Ginsburg 1954; 6 Gotshall 1969; 7 Grinols 1965a; 8 MacGregor 1966b; 9 Millikan and Pattie 1970; 10 Outram and Haegele 1972 personal communication; 11, 12 Robinson, Barraclough, and Fulton 1968a, b; 13 Shippen and Alton 1967. See also Best 1963b.

PACIFIC TOMCOD

Microgadus proximus (Girard 1854)

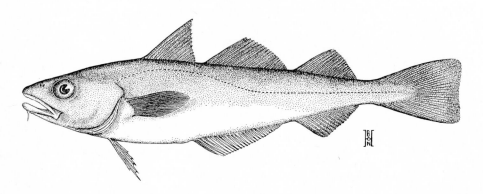

Scientific names from the Greek *micros* (small) and *gadus* (codfish); and the Latin *proximus* (next).

Description   Body depth about 5 into standard length, greatest near head, and tapering toward tail, somewhat com-

pressed. Head about 3.5 to 4 into standard length, somewhat depressed. Snout blunt. Mouth moderate, terminal, directed slightly upward, lower jaw included. Teeth in bands on jaws and vomer, outer row on jaws enlarged. Interorbital space moderately arched, and wide, about 2.7 to 3.9 into length of head. Eye rather small, diameter about 5 into length of head. Anus below first dorsal fin. Caudal peduncle slender.

Fins   Dorsal (3), 11 to 14 — 17 to 20, — 18 to 20, distinctly separate. Caudal truncate. Anal (2), 20 to 25 — 18 to 21. Pectorals about 19. Pelvics 6 or 7, thoracic.

Scales   Small and cycloid. Lateral line canal uniformly high anteriorly for about half body length, then curving down to midside. Barbel under edge of lower jaw, small, about as long as diameter of pupil.

Colour   Olive green dorsally, creamy white below, dusky on tips of all fins.

Size   Length to 12 inches (30.5 cm).

Recognition   Notable for having three spineless dorsal fins, a small barbel about as long as the diameter of the pupil under the chin, and the anus under the first dorsal fin.

Life History   Little is known about the life history. It is known to eat shrimps[2]

and is subject to parasitism by copepods that attach themselves to the inside of the mouth. In the aquarium injured tomcod may regenerate entire fins from stumps when treated with tetracycline.[4]

Distribution   Found from central California (Point Sal 34.59 N) at about 117 to 120 fathoms (260 m),[3] as far north as the Gulf of Alaska, Unalaska Island,[6] and Bering Sea.

In British Columbia never abundant but distributed along the whole coast at depths between 15 and 50 fathoms (27–92 m). A substantial school of small individuals was encountered off the beach at Lumberman's Arch in December 1968.[5]

Utilization   Not abundant enough to develop a market but highly regarded by fishermen who select it from catches for their own use. Formerly highly regarded by local inhabitants in Alaska as "Wachna."[1]

References   1 Cobb 1927; 2 Hart 1949; 3 Isaacson 1965; 4, 5 Lamb 1969, 1970 personal communications; 6 Wilimovsky 1964.

WALLEYE POLLOCK

Theragra chalcogramma (Pallas 1811)

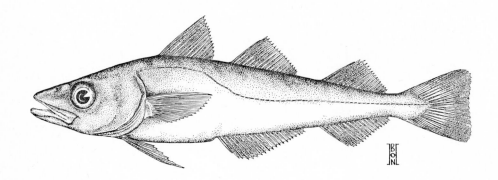

Scientific names from the Greek roots *ther* (beast) and *agra* (food — of fur seals); and *chalcos* (brass) and *gramma* (mark).

Clemens and Wilby 1946, 1961 spelled the specific name *chalcogrammus*.

The AFS Committee name "walleye pollock" is rejected by British Columbia fishermen as awkward. Plain pollock might be acceptable but may be confused with an Atlantic species in another genus. Whiting of Clemens and Wilby 1946 and 1961 is objected to by some because of conflict with a popular name for the Pacific tomcod. The name **bigeye** is proposed for popular use as current, descriptive, distinctive, and not confusing.

Description   Body depth about 6 into standard length, greatest a little over one-third of length from snout, tapering toward tail, somewhat compressed. Head about 3.7 into standard length. Snout pointed. Mouth terminal, moderate, lower jaw slightly projecting. Maxillary extending to front edge of pupil. Teeth on jaws small, slender and closely set, outer row on upper jaw slightly enlarged. Interorbital space flattened. Eye large, about 3.3 into length of head. Anus below space between first and

second dorsal fins. Caudal peduncle over 20 into standard length.

Fins   Dorsal (3), well separated, 10 to 13 — 13 to 16 — 15 to 19. Caudal slightly forked. Anal fins (2), well separated, 17 to 21 — 16 to 21. Pectorals expanded, 18 to 21. Pelvics 6 or 7, thoracic.

Vertebrae   Number 48 to 50 for 27 counts from southern British Columbia, mean 49.19.[18]

Scales   Cycloid, small. Lateral line canal arching high anteriorly, sloping down to midbody below middle of second dorsal.

Colour   Olive green to brown on the dorsal surface, frequently blotched or mottled. Silvery on sides. Lighter on ventral surfaces. Dusky to black on fins.

In young 2 narrow light yellow bands along sides, occasionally a short third band.

Size   Length to 3 feet (91 cm),[5] 80 cm.

Recognition   Three well-separated dorsal fins. Anus below space between first

228

and second dorsals. Minute or no barbel on lower jaw. Lower jaw slightly projecting.

Life History   The life history has been little studied. Young (4–22 mm) are recorded from the Strait of Georgia at the end of April and in May. Copepods and their eggs at that period appear to be practically the only food.[3,4,16,17] Eggs are 1.35 to 1.45 millimeters in diameter and pelagic.[12] Under aquarium conditions lengths in excess of 30 centimeters may be reached in the second summer.[9] At 7 years the length is 56 centimeters in Asian waters.[12] Food in British Columbia waters is recorded as shrimps, sand lance, and herring;[8] in Alaska as young pink, chum, and coho salmon (in one locality);[2] and in Asian waters, mysids, euphausiids, silver smelt, and capelin.[12] Bigeyes are eaten by fur seals.[6,13]

Distribution   Several populations of *Theragra* have been recognized as species or subspecies around the North Pacific Basin. Analysis led to the conclusion that such distinctions are not justified and in this account only one species is recognized.[18]

The range accordingly is from Carmel, central California,[14,15] through the Bering Sea to St. Lawrence Island and on the Asian coast to Kamchatka, Okhotsk Sea, and southern Sea of Japan.[11] It occurs from the surface to below 200 fathoms (386 m),[1,7] and is suspected to be bathypelagic at 200 meters.[12] Generally distributed and common in British Columbia.

Utilization   Because it is soft and often small, the bigeye has little market for human food. Relatively small quantities are landed as scrap fish for mink food.[10]

References   1 Alverson, Pruter, and Ronholt 1964; 2 Armstrong and Winslow 1968; 3 Barraclough 1967a; 4 Barraclough, Robinson, and Fulton 1968; 5 Clemens and Wilby 1961; 6 Cobb 1927; 7 Grinols 1965a; 8 Hart 1949b; 9 Lamb personal communication; 10 Larkin and Ricker 1964; 11 Matsubara 1955; 12 Nikol'skii 1961; 13 Okada 1955; 14, 15 Phillips 1942, 1943; 16, 17 Robinson, Barraclough, and Fulton 1968a, b; 18 Wilimovsky, Peden, and Peppar 1967.

FAMILY OPHIDIIDAE   CUSK-EELS AND BROTULAS

These fishes have long compressed bodies with thick loose skin enveloping the dorsal and anal fins. Pelvic fins are thoracic or jugular. Scales when present are cycloid, minute, and embedded. Many species of the family are known, mostly from warmer seas, and a few from great depths. Two species have penetrated fresh water in Cuba as cave dwellers; they are blind as adults, and like our forms are ovoviviparous. One species of the family is known from British Columbia.

RED BROTULA

Brosmophycis marginata (Ayres 1854)

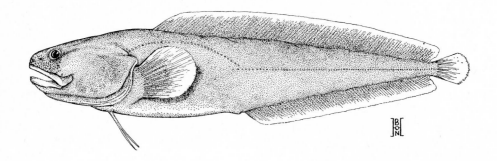

Scientific names from *Brosme* (cusk — a similar-appearing fish) and the Greek *phycis* (like); and the Latin *marginata* (edged).

Called red brotulid in Clemens and Wilby 1946.

Description   Body elongate, its depth about 4.9 into standard length, moderately compressed, tapered posteriorly. Head about 4.1 into standard length, compressed. Mouth terminal, large, directed forward. Jaws nearly even. Upper jaw extending well behind eye. Maxillary reduced to a dorsal plate above the premaxillary at the end of the jaw. Snout blunt in profile, and short. Teeth sharp, conical, moderate in size, in bands on jaws, vomer, and palatines. Interorbital slightly convex with 2 rounded frontal ridges and raised edges of the orbits, its width about 5.4 into length of head. Eye oval, small, its length about 9 into length of head. Gill membranes united and free of isthmus so that there is a broad free fold. Caudal peduncle very short and compressed, its least depth about 30 into standard length.

Fins   Dorsal (1), 92? to 102[3] (99–110[6]), long, rather low, base covered with loose skin. Caudal small and rounded rays 16(17).[6] Anal

70? to 74 (76)[1,3] (73–81)[6] long, rather low, base covered with skin. Pectorals about 20, rounded, almost pedunculate. Pelvics 2, thoracic, long slender filamentous outer ray twice length of inner ray.

Vertebrae   63, 64, 65 (in California).[1]

Scales   Skin rather loose on head and fin bases. Scales cycloid, small, embedded, about 170 rows. Lateral line canal in 2 parts, the upper anterior and arching downward ending about the halfway point in the standard length, directly over the anus, the lower part starts immediately below the end of the upper and continues along midside to the caudal fin. Numerous papillae on head, larger and more abundant on snout and lower jaw. Pores around head. Body typically covered with a coating of mucus.

Colour   Bright red to brown on dorsal surface, nearly white on ventral surface of the body, pale red on ventral surface of head, margins of dorsal and anal fins red, bright red on caudal and pectoral fins, lips pink. Mucus secretion reddish.

Size   Length to 18 inches (46 cm).

Recognition   Noteworthy for the thoracic pelvic fins each with a long and a short filamentous ray, the lateral line canal in two sections as it is broken in the middle, and the thick mucus secretion on head and body.

Life History   Like other members of its family the red brotula is ovoviviparous.[2] Fecundities of six individuals between 260 and 325 millimeters total length approximated 12,000 to 30,000 ova. Ova diameter in September and October averaged about 0.7 millimeter; by February the diameter was about 1.2 millimeters with no embryo evident; and in April or May the eggs were about the same size but contained crescentic embryos. In May, off Seattle, a 31-centimeter female, when captured extruded some 200 7-millimeter yolked larvae.[4]

Distribution   The red brotula is found from Ensenada, Baja California[5] to southeastern Alaska.[8,9] It is recorded from inshore waters of British Columbia. It is a species of moderate depths from 30 fathoms (55 m) in British Columbia, to 100 fathoms (183 m) off Oregon.[7]

References   1 Best 1957; 2 Breder and Rosen 1966; 3 Clemens and Wilby 1961; 4 DeLacy personal communication; 5 Fitch 1968; 6 Follett 1970; 7 Grinols 1965a; 8 Schultz and DeLacy 1936; 9 Wilimovsky 1954.

FAMILY ZOARCIDAE   EELPOUTS

The eelpouts have elongate slender bodies and rather large heads with overhanging upper jaws. Most of them are of moderate size or small. In most species, and in all encountered off British Columbia, both dorsal and anal fins are confluent with the caudal. Pelvic fins are thoracic when present but are frequently missing. Fins have no spines, only soft rays, and are covered with heavy skin so that ray number is difficult to determine with assurance. The lateral line canal may be present or absent, and if present, in one or two parts. Gill membranes are attached to the isthmus, and the gill openings may be much reduced. Bodies tend to be limp. There are numerous species as bottom-dwellers in the oceans of the world, some from deep water. Both oviparous and ovoviviparous species are encountered. At present 13 species are recorded from British Columbia but the status of some of the species is uncertain and complicated by errors, and by differences in the fish associated with size and sex. The family needs further study and review.

KEY TO THE ZOARCIDAE

	1	Pelvic fins present	2
or	1	Pelvic fins absent	7
	2	Teeth on vomer and palatines	3
or	2	No teeth on vomer	6
	3	Prominent mucous pores on jaws; depth about 15 into total length .... *Lycenchelys jordani*, Shortjaw eelpout, p. 238	
or	3	No mucous pores on jaws; depth 10 to 12 into total length .... Genus *Lycodes* 4	
	4	Pectoral fin rounded in outline; major axis of eye less than length of snout; linings of mouth and gill cavities, and of peritoneum not black	5
or	4	Pectoral fins usually notched in outline; length of major axis of eye greater than length of snout; linings of mouth and gill cavities, and peritoneum usually black .... *Lycodes diapterus*, Black eelpout, p. 243	
	5	Pelvic fins very small, their lengths about 2.5 into major axis of the eye; cartilaginous bars on ventral part of lower jaw inconspicuous .... *Lycodes brevipes*, Shortfin eelpout, p. 242	
or	5	Pelvic fins small, their lengths about 1.5 into major axis of eye; cartilaginous bars on ventral surface of lower jaw strongly developed .... *Lycodes palearis*, Wattled eelpout, p. 244	
	6	**Teeth on palatines, moderately slender fish** .... *Aprodon cortezianus*, Bigfin eelpout, p. 233	
or	6	No teeth on palatines or vomer .... *Lycodopsis pacifica*, Blackbelly eelpout, p. 245	
	7	Gill opening a small pore, about size of pupil of eye .... *Melanostigma pammelas*, Pacific softpout, p. 247	
or	7	Gill opening a substantial slit	8
	8	Scales present, minute; eyes oval .... Genus *Bothrocara*	9
or	8	Scales absent; eyes circular .... Genus *Lycodapus*	11

Bothrocara pusillum (Bean), the Alaska eelpout, is questionably reported from off the British Columbia coast. It has no pelvic fins; nearly uniform teeth are on jaws, vomer, and palatines. The lateral line is absent; and the length of the major axis of the eye is greater than the length of the snout. Three specimens of *Embryx crotalina*, the rattlesnake eelpout, now in the British Columbia Provincial Museum were taken in 1971 off the west coast of the Queen Charlotte Islands and off Cape Flattery at depths between 900 and 1200 meters. This very slender eelpout has scales on the body and parts of the head, and pelvic fins shorter than the diameter of the pupil of the eye. There are no teeth on palatines or vomer, and the lateral line is short and ventral.

232

BIGFIN EELPOUT

Aprodon cortezianus Gilbert 1890

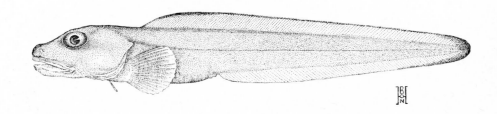

Scientific names from the Greek *a* (without), *pro* (before), and *odons* (tooth); and Cortez Bank (off San Diego).

In Clemens and Wilby 1946 the common name was spelled big-finned eel-pout.

Description   Body very elongate, its greatest depth about 9 into standard length, only moderately compressed, tapered to posterior end. Head large and compressed and convex but snout may be depressed and concave in front of eyes, head length about 4.3 into standard length. Mouth terminal, large, directed forward. Upper jaw extending to posterior part of pupil, including lower jaw, a fold of skin overhanging both jaws. A

233

cartilaginous stay on ventral surface of head parallel to mandibles. Teeth small in rows on upper jaw and palatines, absent from vomer; in an anterior patch on lower jaw, its outer, larger teeth continued as a row posteriorly. Bony interorbital narrow, about 18 into length of head. Eye oval, large, its length about 4 into length of head. Gill membranes joined to isthmus.

Fins   Dorsal (1), 105 to 108, confluent with caudal. Caudal rounded, not clearly distinguishable from dorsal and anal. Anal 89 to 93, confluent with caudal. Pectorals 18 to 21, large, margins entire. Pelvics 3, thoracic, much reduced, length about 1.7 into length of eye.

Gill Rakers   16 or 17 in first arch.[1]

Scales   Cycloid, small, embedded, on most of body except dorsal anterior part, not on head. Lateral line canal decurved slightly anteriorly, straight along midside thereafter, about as far as anus, faint.

Colour   Brown to blue black on back and sides, lighter ventrally. White on scale pockets. Dark above base of pectoral fins; black along anterior border of dorsal fin, on posterior parts of dorsal and anal fins, and on caudal. Light margins on pectoral fins. Gill cavity dusky and peritoneum jet black with its pigment vaguely showing through to exterior.

Size   Length to 18.5 inches (47 cm).[1]

Recognition   Notable for the absence of teeth on the vomer but presence on the palatines, the large entire pectoral fin, the broad depressed head, and the black peritoneum.

Distribution   Known from southern and northern[1] California, through Oregon,[2] and Washington,[4] and as far as Hakai Pass in central British Columbia at about 51.40 N.[5] Fairly common in the Strait of Georgia. Recorded from Barkley Sound.[3] Encountered at depths from 50 to 339 fathoms (92–620 m).[4]

References   1 Bali and Bond 1959; 2 Brock 1943; 3 Carl and Wilby 1945; 4 Grinols 1965a; 5 Palmen 1954.

TWOLINE EELPOUT

Bothrocara brunneum (Bean 1891)

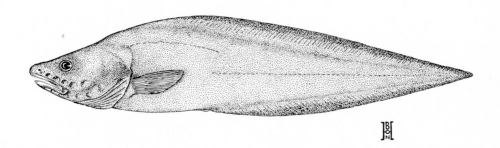

Scientific names from the Greek *bothros* (pitted) and *cara* (head); and the Latin *brunneum* (brown).

Description   Body elongate, its depth about 6 into standard length, moderately slender, compressed. Deepest ahead of dorsal fin. Head 4.2 to 5.2 into standard length, compressed, profile concave. Mouth terminal, oblique, moderate in size and gape, directed forward and up. Upper jaw overhanging lower. Maxillary extending to pupil of eye, overhung with folds of skin. Interorbital space slightly raised, its width about 4.5 into length of head. Teeth small and numerous on jaw and palatine, on vomer (10–20). Eye long, axis 5.2 to 6.5 into length of head, and shorter than snout. Gill membranes joined far forward to isthmus so that gill openings extend well under head.

Fins   Dorsal (1), 100 to 112, moderately high, beginning just behind head, confluent with caudal. Caudal narrow, bluntly pointed. Anal, 95 to 100, confluent with caudal. Dorsal and anal fins enveloped anteriorly in soft gelatinous tissue. Pectorals about 15 to 17, broad, entire, about half length of head. Pelvics absent.

Gill Rakers   Short and blunt, 17 to 20 on the first gill arch.

Scales   Cycloid, minute, covering body and fins. Lateral line canal in 2 parts: upper beginning above base of pectoral fin passing upward parallel to back, ending just behind vertical from anus; lower commencing on midbody above anus, passing above base of anal fin almost to posterior end of body, frequently becoming faint. Numerous mucous pores on head arising in depressions.

Colour   Uniform light gray or brown, semitranslucent, blue or black margins on dorsal and anal fins. Colour stronger posteriorly, transparent on narrow margins of unpaired fins. Light on lining of mouth. Black on peritoneum.

Size   Length to 26 inches (66 cm).

Recognition   This eelpout is recognizable by having two lateral line canals, the long axis of the eye being shorter than the snout, gill rakers short and stout, and no pelvic fins.

Distribution   From southern California to western Bering Sea (Kamchatka) and Sakhalin.[1,2,3] Common in deep water to 900 fathoms (1650 m) off Oregon.[4] The six Canadian specimens were taken on La Pérouse Bank, 48.44 N, 126.33 W between 301 and 318 fathoms (550–582 m).[5]

References   1, 2 Bayliff 1954, 1959; 3 Gilbert 1915; 4 Grinols 1965a; 5 Westrheim and Pletcher 1966.

235

SOFT EELPOUT

Bothrocara molle Bean 1890

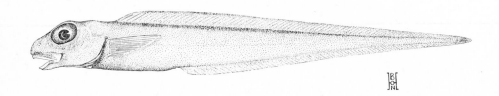

Scientific names from the Greek *bothros* (pitted) and *cara* (head); and the Latin *mollus* (soft).

The description and illustration for this species in Clemens and Wilby 1946, was based on a specimen of *Bothrocara brunneum*.[1]

Description   Body very elongate, its depth about 10 into standard length, compressed. Head about 4.2 into standard length, compressed. Mouth terminal, rather small, directed forward. Upper jaw overhanging the lower, and extending to anterior edge of pupil. Eye oval, its long axis 3.2 to 4 into length of head and longer than the snout. Gill membranes narrowly joined to isthmus.

Fins   Dorsal (1), about 112, moderately high, confluent with caudal. Caudal narrow, pointed. Anal, 89 to 101, confluent with caudal. Dorsal and anal fins enveloped anteriorly in soft gelatinous tissue. Pectorals about 13 to 14, entire, about half length of head. Pelvics absent.

Gill Rakers   Long and pointed, about 22 on first gill arch.

Scales   Cycloid, minute, covering body and unpaired fins. Lateral line canal indistinct, short, below base of dorsal fin. Head with numerous mucous pores, sometimes originating in pits.

Colour   Uniform light brown, semitranslucent. Blue or black towards margins of dorsal and anal fins. Colour more intense posteriorly. Transparent on margins of unpaired fins; light on lining of mouth. Black on peritoneum.

Size   Length to 10 inches (25 cm).[1,2]

Recognition   This eelpout is recognized by having a single poorly defined lateral line canal and the length of the major axis of the eye greater than the length of the snout. Gill rakers are long and pointed.

Distribution   From Mexico to the Bering Sea, recorded from all major regions but rare. Avacha Bay, USSR. All specimens from deep water down to 876 fathoms (1600 m).[3] The one British Columbia record from off Cape St. James, Queen Charlotte Islands at 51.23 N, 130.34 W at 876 fathoms (1600 m).

References   1, 2 Bayliff 1954, 1959; 3 Grinols 1965a.

LONGSNOUT EELPOUT

Bothrocara remigerum Gilbert 1915

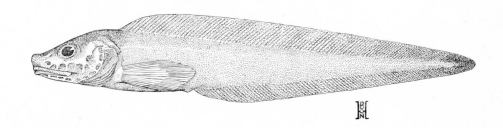

Scientific names from the Greek *bothros* (pitted) and *cara* (head); and the Latin *remus* (oar) and *gero* (bear).

Description Body elongate, its depth about 7.5 into standard length, compressed. Head length about 4.4 into standard length, compressed. Mouth terminal, moderate in size, directed forward. Upper jaw extends about to middle of pupil. Lower jaw slightly included. Snout, blunt, upturned at tip, concave dorsally, its length about 6.1 into length of head. Teeth in both jaws small, in bands; on palatines and vomer. Interorbital space narrow. Eye oval, its length about 3.8 into length of head. Gill membranes narrowly joined to isthmus.

Fins Dorsal (1), 107 to 117 (or greater spread), moderately high, confluent with caudal. Caudal narrow, rounded. Anal 93 or 94 (or greater spread), confluent with caudal. Dorsal and anal enveloped anteriorly in gelatinous tissue. Pectorals 13 to 16, rays exserted, the lower 4 short, upper part about four-fifths as long as head and reaching beyond anal origin. Pelvics absent.

Gill Rakers Slender and pointed, about 19 or 20 on first gill arch.[1]

Scales Cycloid, minute, covering body but missing on head; on vertical fins almost completely anteriorly, only near bases posteriorly; on bases of pectorals. Lateral line canal indistinct and wavy, anteriorly only. Large mucous pores on head usually arising in a depression.

Colour Brownish, darker ventrally and anteriorly. Black bands on anterior edges of dorsal and anal fins broadening to include whole fin membranes posteriorly. Mouth and gill chambers dark, peritoneum black.

Size Length to 22 inches (56 cm).

Recognition Distinguished by the projecting upper jaw with its upturned tip, the eye smaller than the snout, the pectoral fin reaching the anal fin, and the absence of pelvic fins.

Distribution Benthic. Taken in California to 822 fathoms (1500 m), Oregon to 900 fathoms (1650 m), and Washington to 822 fathoms (1500 m).[3] From British Columbia in Queen Charlotte Sound at 51.49 N, 131.17 W in 1050 fathoms (1920 m) (NMC 65-313).[4]

References 1 Bayliff 1954; 2 Gilbert 1915; 3 Grinols 1965a; 4 McAllister personal communication.

SHORTJAW EELPOUT

Lycenchelys jordani (Evermann and Goldsborough 1907)

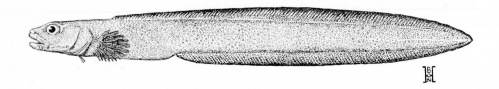

Scientific names from the Greek *lycos* (wolf) and *enchelos* (eel); and David Starr Jordan, eminent U.S. ichthyologist.

Description   Body very elongate, its depth about 15 into total length, compressed posteriorly, dorsal and ventral contours curving to a dull point. Head about 7 into total length, top of head flat. Mouth terminal, moderate in size, directed forward and up. Upper jaw reaching only to anterior edge of pupil, including lower jaw when mouth closed. Snout about 3.7 into length of head. Teeth small, villiform, on jaws in patches anteriorly, in single rows laterally, on palatines and vomer. There may be sexual dimorphism in dentition. Interorbital space narrow, about 13 into length of head, the bony part extremely narrow. Eye oval, its length about 4.5 into length of head.[1]

Fins   Dorsal (1), about 116, starting at a point about halfway along pectoral length in depressed position, deepest somewhat behind mid-length, confluent with caudal. Caudal not readily distinguishable from dorsal and anal, bluntly pointed. Anal 93, lower than dorsal, confluent with caudal. Pectorals about 16, broad and rounded, rays exserted. Pelvics thoracic, very small, length about diameter of eye.

Scales   Cycloid, on body and bases of upright and pectoral fins. Head, nape, and axil of pectoral fin naked. Prominent mucous pores on jaws.

Colour   Brownish olive. The scales are light in colour giving the body a finely spotted appearance. Head, pectoral fins, and edges of upright fins darker olive.

Size   To 13.25 inches (33.6 cm).

Recognition   Notable for the small pelvic fins, and rounded pectoral fins, the dappled body, without major colour pattern, the relatively short upper jaw, the rounded contours of the head, and the absence of a lateral line canal.

Distribution   Benthic in the northeast Pacific Ocean, recorded from Oregon at 900 to 1064 fathoms (1650–1950 m) and Alaska at 922 fathoms (1688 m).[3,4] The British Columbia record is a specimen taken at 50.54 N, 130.06 W in 1200 fathoms (2200 m) by Dr D. B. Quayle on September 11, 1964. It is recorded as BC 64-444.

References   1 Bayliff 1959; 2 Evermann and Goldsborough 1907; 3 Grinols 1965a; 4 Wilimovsky 1954.

238

BLACKMOUTH EELPOUT

Lycodapus fierasfer Gilbert 1890

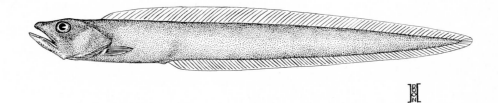

Scientific names from the Greek *lycodes* (wolffish — a related species) and, *apous* footless — no pelvic fins); and *fierasfer* (pearlfish — like).

Clemens and Wilby 1946 used pearly eel-pout as the common name for this species.

Description   Body very elongate, its depth about 11 into standard length, compressed, deepest ahead of anus, gradually tapered through posterior third. Head length about 6 into standard length, compressed, upper profile almost straight, with a minor bulge over eyes. Mouth terminal, moderate in size, directed forward and upward. Upper jaw extending to anterior part of eye. Lower jaw protruding and thick. Snout blunt and fairly long. Teeth usually small; on jaws and lower lip conical, curved inward, in bands; in a row of separated teeth on palatines; stronger on vomer. Interorbital space almost flat, its width about 9 into length of head. Eye oval, its length about 5 into length of head, or 1.8 into length of snout. Gill membranes united anteriorly but free of isthmus.[1]

Fins   Dorsal (1), 82 to 85, moderately long, confluent with caudal. Caudal narrow, bluntly pointed. Anal 70 to 74, low, quite even in height throughout; confluent with caudal. Pectorals about 6 to 8, small, slender, entire. Pelvics absent.

Scales   Scales and lateral line canal absent.

Colour   Pearly background, sparsely speckled with fine black dots. Black on jaws, mouth and gill cavities, and peritoneum.

Size   Length to 6 inches (15 cm).

Recognition   Noteworthy for the absence of pelvic fins and scales, bands of teeth in both jaws, translucent skin with a pearly background, black in mouth and gill cavities and on peritoneum, and the oblique mouth with projecting lower jaw.

Distribution   Gulf of Panama at 900 fathoms (1650 m) to Unmak Island, Alaska, including the Gulf of California to 1076 fathoms (1965 m), California to 603 fathoms (1120 m), Oregon at 400 to 1000 fathoms (733–1830 m), Washington to 584 fathoms (1070 m), and Alaska to 367 fathoms (674 m).[2] The only British Columbia record is for Howe Sound at 120 fathoms (219 m) from the mouth of a blackfin eelpout.

References   1 Bayliff 1959; 2 Grinols 1965a.

BIGTOOTH EELPOUT

Lycodapus grossidens Gilbert 1915

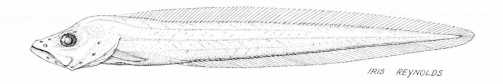

IRIS REYNOLDS

Scientific names from *lycodes* (wolffish — a related species) and the Greek *apous* (footless); and the Latin *grossus* (thick) and *dentalis* (of — teeth).

Description   Body very elongate, depth about 11 into standard length. Head length 5.5 to 6 into standard length, its width about 2.5 into its length. Mouth terminal, moderate in size, directed slightly upward. Upper jaw extending about to posterior edge of pupil. Snout blunt, its length about 3.7 into length of head. Lower jaw extends beyond upper. Teeth in both jaws curved canines, in bands anteriorly, narrowing markedly posteriorly (to a single row in lower jaw) outer row of teeth in lower jaw directed horizontally outward and sometimes very large, variable in size depending on sex, in upper jaw enlarged but less so, a single series of small teeth on palatines, and 1 or 2 small teeth on vomer. Bony interorbital space about 9 into length of head. Eye diameter about 4 into length of head. Gill membranes joined and free of isthmus.[1,2]

Fins   Dorsal (1), about 91, the first 10 or 11 rays unsegmented, low, confluent with caudal. Caudal about 6, pointed. Anal 72, the first 3 rays unsegmented, low, confluent with caudal. Pectorals 5 to 8, thoracic. Pelvics absent.

Scales   Scales and lateral line canal absent.

Colour   Light with sparse black speckling anteriorly becoming more pronounced posteriorly and on vertical fins. Silvery on abdomen masks black peritoneum. Dark inside of mouth and gill cavity.

Size   Length to at least 4 inches (10.2 cm).

Recognition   Recognized by the large canine teeth directed forward in the anterior part of the lower jaw and the projecting lower jaw.

Distribution   Benthic and rare. From Oregon at 400 to 850 fathoms (732-1556 m) and Alaska at 350 fathoms (642 m).[4] The only British Columbia record is of a specimen taken by Dr D. B. Quayle at 48.38.30 N, 126.44.30 W at 740 fathoms (1350 m) on September 7, 1964. It is recorded as BC 64-439.

References   1, 2 Bayliff 1954, 1959; 3 Gilbert 1915; 4 Grinols 1965a.

PALLID EELPOUT

Lycodapus mandibularis Gilbert 1915

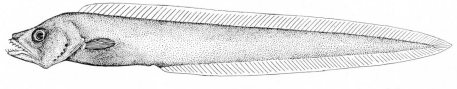

Scientific names from *lycodes* (wolffish — a related species) and the Greek *apous* (footless); and the Latin *mandibularis* (of the lower jaw).

Clemens and Wilby 1946 recorded this species as pale eelpout.

Description   Body very elongate, deepest and widest anteriorly, gradually tapering behind anus to tapered tail. Head length about 8 into standard length, dorsal profile about straight. Mouth terminal, moderately large, directed mostly forward. Upper jaw extends to posterior edge of pupil. Jaws about equal. Snout blunt, about one-third longer than eye. Teeth on both jaws, vomer, and palatines; on upper jaw, anteriorly in a broad patch in 3 ill-defined rows, a narrow band posteriorly; lower jaw with an anterior patch and a single posterior series of teeth; anterior teeth in both jaws may be much enlarged, curved, and canine; vomer with 2 or 3 teeth; and each palatine with about 8 teeth. Interorbital space slightly raised and almost flat, its width about 3 into length of head. Eye round, its diameter about 4.5 into length of head. Opercular membranes joined.

Fins   Dorsal (1), (86)90 or 91(100), long, low, smoothly contoured, confluent with caudal. Caudal with narrow tip, bluntly rounded. Anal 77 or 78, very low, smoothly contoured, confluent with caudal. Pectorals 8, small. Pelvics absent.

Scales   Scales and lateral line canal absent.

Colour   Almost white, faint speckling of black dots dorsally, more so posteriorly. Peritoneum, lining of gill cover, and posterior part of mouth dark.

Size   Length to 6.75 inches (17.3 cm).

Recognition   Recognizable by its terminal mouth with jaws about equal, absence of pelvic fins and scales, pale transparent skin, dark lining of mouth and gill cover, and dark peritoneum.

Distribution   Monterey Bay, central California to Alaska.[1] In California to 60 fathoms (110 m), Oregon to 750 fathoms (1370 m), Washington to 220 fathoms (403 m), and Alaska in 210 to 220 fathoms (385–403 m).[4] In British Columbia from 54 to 116 fathoms (99–212 m) off Graham Island (54.19 N, 133.13 W)[3] and Goletas Channel at about 200 fathoms (366 m).[2] Apparently pelagic.[4]

References   1 Bayliff 1959; 2 G. C. Carl personal communication; 3 Chapman 1940; 4 Grinols 1965a.

241

SHORTFIN EELPOUT

Lycodes brevipes Bean 1890

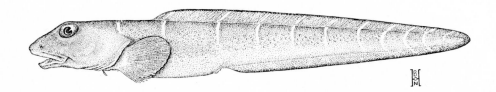

Scientific names from the Greek *lyco-des* (wolffish); and the Latin *brevis* (short) and *pes* (foot).

To distinguish North American from closely related but possibly distinct Asian relatives, eastern Pacific stocks are sometimes called *Lycodes brevipes brevipes*.[1]

Description   Body very elongate, its depth nearly 9 into standard length, compressed, tapered toward a blunt posterior end. Head large, slightly compressed, its length about 4.6 into standard length. Mouth terminal, large, directed mostly forward. Upper jaw extending to posterior part of pupil, overhanging lower jaw to such an extent that the jaws do not meet. A fold of skin overhangs upper jaw and a conspicuous fleshy lobe on each side of lower lip. Snout rounded in profile, extending beyond upper lip. Teeth rather small, on jaws hooked inward, on vomer, and palatines. Interorbital space narrow, width of bony part about 16 into length of head. Eye oval, its length about 4 into length of head. Opercular membranes fused to isthmus.

Fins   Dorsal (1), 85 to 102, confluent with caudal. Caudal not clearly distinguishable, narrowly rounded. Anal 74 to 89, confluent with caudal. Pectorals about 19 to 21, moderate in size, less than half head length, almost rounded with lower 7 rays moderately exserted. Pelvics 3, minute, thoracic.

242

Scales   Cycloid, small, embedded, covering body. Lateral line canal obscure, sloping from upper angle of gill opening toward base of anal fin, often incomplete.

Colour   Light brown on dorsal surface, paler below; white vertical bars across back of body and dorsal fin, 9 to 13, arranged so that the second bar is behind the dorsal insertion; narrow dark margins on dorsal and anal fins; pale on pelvic fins; creamy white to pink on peritoneum.

Size   Length to 11.75 inches (30 cm).

Recognition   Recognized by the minute pelvic fins, the undivided pectoral fins, the presence of teeth on the vomer and palatine bones, by having no more than one light stripe ahead of the dorsal fin insertion, and no extensive cartilaginous ridges on ventral surface of head.

Distribution   From Oregon through Washington and British Columbia to Alaska, the Bering Sea[2], and Okhotsk Sea.[2,3] At depths of 15 to 351 fathoms (27–642 m). Common near the centre of its range. In British Columbia in the southern Strait of Georgia and Queen Charlotte Sound. From the stomach of a lingcod off Victoria.

References   1 Andriashev 1937; 2 Grinols 1965a; 3 Matsubara 1955.

BLACK EELPOUT

Lycodes diapterus Gilbert 1891

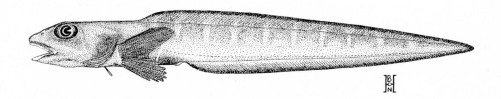

Scientific names from the Greek *lycodes* (wolffish); *di* (two) and *pteros* (fin — notched pectoral fin).

Clemens and Wilby 1946 recorded this fish as black-finned eel-pout, *Furcimanus diapterus* (Gilbert 1891). In 1961 they used the common name blackfin eelpout.

To distinguish the North American from northern (north Bering Sea) and Asian stocks the name *Lycodes diapterus diapterus* is sometimes used.

Description   Body very elongate, depth about 9 into standard length, slightly compressed, tapered toward posterior end. Head long, low, flattened above, its length about 5 into standard length. Mouth terminal, moderate in size, directed slightly upward. Upper jaw extending to anterior part of eye, overhanging lower jaw. Snout blunt. A moderate fold of skin overlying upper jaw. Teeth fine and pointed, on jaws, vomer, and palatines. Interorbital space flat, narrow, width of bony part about 18 into length of head. Eye oval, its length about 3 into length of head. Gill membranes fused to isthmus.

Fins   Dorsal (1), 90 to 124, confluent with caudal. Caudal bluntly pointed, boundaries with dorsal and anal not clearly distinguishable. Anal 97 to 107, confluent with caudal. Pectorals about 19, notched near middle to varying degrees with middle rays shorter than those above and below, lower rays moderately exserted. Pelvics 3, small, thoracic.

Scales   Cycloid, small, embedded, covering body. Lateral line canal sloping down from anterior end and then passing along lower part of side paralleling ventral profile, indistinct.

Colour   Dusky brown on dorsal surface, blue black ventrally. Fine prominent light spots over scales. Eight or 9 light vertical bars on side of body extending on dorsal fin and spreading or dividing on lower part of body, becoming faint or disappearing in adults. Blue black on pectoral, pelvic, and anal fins, blue black on lining of mouth and gill cavity, dusky to black on peritoneum.

Size   Length to 13 inches (33 cm).

Recognition   Distinguished by the dark linings of the mouth and gill cavity and the dark pigment on the ventral surface of body and fins. Ventral fin length about half diameter of eye.

Distribution   Southern California at San Diego to Washington,[2] British Columbia, Alaska and the southeast Bering Sea. Bering Island, northwest Bering Sea,[1,3,4] west Bering Sea, Sea of Japan,[3,4] Japan.

References   1 Bayliff 1959; 2 Chapman and DeLacy 1933; 3 Grinols 1965a; 4 Wilimovsky 1954.

WATTLED EELPOUT

Lycodes palearis Gilbert 1895

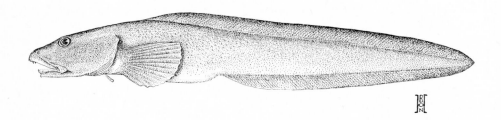

Scientific names from the Greek *lycodes* (wolffish) and the Latin *paleae* (wattles (on fowl)).

To distinguish North American from closely related but possibly distinct Asian relatives, eastern Pacific stocks are sometimes called *Lycodes palearis palearis*.[1]

Description   Body very elongate, depth about 8.1 into standard length, compressed, tapered evenly toward posterior end. Head long and low, slightly depressed, its length about 4.8 into standard length. Mouth terminal, large, directed forward. Upper jaw extending to pupil, overhanging lower jaw to such an extent that the mouth does not nearly close. Snout rounded in profile, somewhat bulbous and appearing broadly rounded from above. A fold of skin overhanging upper jaw. Prominent cartilaginous ridges on base of head parallel to lower jaws, ending abruptly close together, and close behind point of jaw. Lobed fleshy folds below lower jaws. Teeth moderate in size, conical, on jaws, vomer, and palatines. Interorbital space flat, narrow, width of bony part about 15 into length of head. Eye oval, its length about 5.6 into length of head. Opercular membranes fused to isthmus.

Fins   Dorsal (1), 94 to 105, confluent with caudal. Caudal not clearly distinguishable from dorsal and anal, narrowly rounded. Anal 83 to 90, confluent with caudal. Pectorals about 17, entire, rounded, with edges of lower 7 rays only gently fluted. Pelvics 3, small, thoracic.

Scales   Cycloid, small, embedded, covering body. Lateral line canal obscure.

Colour   Light brown to blue black on dorsal surface; narrow dark margins on dorsal and anal fins; pale on pelvic fins; creamy white to pink on peritoneum. In young, white vertical bars across body and sometimes extending to anal fin, second white bar entirely in front of dorsal fin.

Size   Length to 20 inches (51 cm).

Recognition   Recognizable by the small pelvic fins, the undivided pectoral fin, the presence of teeth on vomer and palatine bones, when white bars cross the body two of them being anterior to the dorsal insertion, having a lobed flap below the lower jaw and a prominent cartilaginous stay parallel to the lower jaw on the lower side of the head.

Life History   Spawning takes place in winter in Puget Sound, and the food there consists of small bivalves and shrimps.

Captive wattled eelpouts were sluggish feeders. Eggs are large, about 7 millimeters in diameter and tended to be ellipsoidal.[8]

Distribution   From Oregon,[1,9] Puget Sound in Washington,[2,5,8] through British Columbia,[3] Bering Sea, [2,4,9] Chukchi Sea, Okhotsk Sea,[1,4,6] Aniva Bay, and northern Sea of Japan,[6,7] Peter the Great Bay.[2] At depths from 30 to 155 fathoms (55–284 m). The status of the species is confused and part of the distribution should perhaps be credited to other species or subspecies. In British Columbia the species has been taken among the Gulf Islands at 30 to 50 fathoms (55–92 m) and off the Goose Islands in Queen Charlotte Sound at 110 fathoms (201 m).

References   1 Andriashev 1937; 2 Bayliff 1959; 3 Carl and Wilby 1945; 4 Grinols 1965a; 5 Halstead 1950; 6 Matsubara 1955; 7 Shmidt 1950; 8 Slipp and DeLacy 1952; 9 Wilimovsky 1954.

BLACKBELLY EELPOUT

Lycodopsis pacifica (Collett 1879)

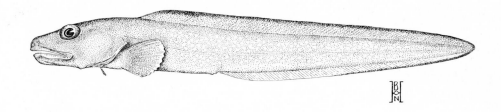

Scientific names from *Lycodes* a genus of related fishes and the Greek *opsis* (like); and Pacific (Ocean).

Clemens and Wilby 1946 spelled the common name black-bellied eel-pout.

Description   Body very elongate, its depth about 9 into standard length, compressed posteriorly, tapered evenly toward posterior end. Head long and low, slightly depressed, flattened above, its length about 4.7 into standard length. Mouth terminal, rather large, directed forward. Upper jaw extending back to middle of pupil, enclosing lower jaw. Snout rounded, slightly overhanging mouth, eyes entering dorsal profile. A fold of skin hanging over upper jaw. A fold of skin along posterior two-thirds of lower jaw. A firm but inconspicuous cartilaginous stay on bottom of head. Teeth small and conical on jaws only. Interorbital space flat and narrow, width of bony part about 16 into length of head. Eye oval, its length about 4.7 into length of head. Opercular membranes broadly fused to isthmus.

Fins   Dorsal (1), 90 to 107, confluent with caudal. Caudal not readily distinguishable from dorsal and anal, sharply rounded. Anal 70 to 90,

245

confluent with caudal. Pectorals broad, about 17, rays thickened, edge of fin slightly fluted. Pelvics 3, small, thoracic.

Scales   Cycloid, small, embedded, covering body, but not fins. Lateral line canal down midside of body through its anterior third.

Colour   Light gray to pale reddish brown, light spots over scales, pale vertical bars margined faintly with black across body, sometimes obscure in adults, black along margin of dorsal and in an elongate spot at its anterior end, black on margin of posterior end of anal fin, pelvic fins pale, jet black on peritoneum.

Size   Length to 18 inches (46 cm).

Recognition   Notable for the black peritoneum which is faintly evident through the skin, the absence of teeth on vomer and palatines, and the black spots along the anterior edge of the dorsal fin.

Life History   There are differences in body proportions between the sexes of blackbelly eelpouts, the males being larger with shovel-like snouts and large heads after reaching sexual maturity at about 17 centimeters. Most females are mature at 140 millimeters. Females have only one ovary. They produce from 7 to 52 eggs at a time with an average about 30. There is no evidence of viviparity but the adults may look after eggs and young. Most spawning takes place in November and December but there may be some from September to January. The life span is relatively short with few living beyond 5 years of age. In Burrard Inlet growth is nearly complete at age 4 when males are about 190 millimeters long and females 160 millimeters. Food is mainly bivalve molluscs. Polychaete worms, amphipods, and small crabs are also important foods, and brittle stars are also eaten. The blackbelly eelpout is the commonest member of its family in British Columbia where it is taken on muddy bottom, in depths between 10 and 120 fathoms (18–220 m).[3]

Distribution   Ensenada, Baja California, (Huntingdon Beach), southern California to Gulf of Alaska (Afognak and Unalaska islands).[1] The depths at which the species occurs may be related to latitude, viz: California to 218 fathoms (400 m), Oregon to 100 fathoms (183 m), Washington to 64 fathoms (117 m) (5 fathoms (9 m)[1]), British Columbia 10 to 120 fathoms (18–220 m), Alaska to 57 fathoms (104 m).[2] Common in British Columbia and frequently taken in shrimp trawls.

References   1 Bayliff 1959; 2 Grinols 1965a; 3 Levings 1969.

PACIFIC SOFTPOUT

Melanostigma pammelas Gilbert 1895

Scientific names from the Greek *melas* (black) and *stigma* (spot); and *pam* (all) and *melas* (black).

Description   Body very elongate, its depth 10 to 13 into total length, spindle-shaped, compressed posteriorly. Head length 7.0 to 7.7 into total length, its depth 9.9 to 10.7 into total length, and the width about the same. Mouth terminal, small, directed nearly forward. Jaws equal. Upper jaw extending back as far as anterior edge of pupil. Snout blunt and short, its length about 6 into length of head. Teeth in 2 rows on jaws (or in a single series laterally on lower jaw[3]) and in 1 row on palatines and vomer; dentition appears to vary between individuals; the outer rows of teeth or the median vomerine tooth may be enlarged. Eye large, its diameter about 3 into length of head. Gill opening a small pore above the base of the pectoral fin, its diameter one-half that of eye.

Fins   Dorsal (1), 84 to 88, origin over pectoral base but not distinguishable because of enveloping skin, confluent with caudal. Caudal narrow and pointed, with 6 to 8 rays. Anal 69 to 75 originating immediately behind vent, confluent with caudal. Pectorals 6 to 8, small and narrow. Pelvics absent.[3,7]

Gill Rakers   11 to 13.[7]

Vertebrae   86 to 89. [1,6,7]

Scales   Skin loose, without scales, the body becoming very wrinkled in preservative. Lateral line canal midlateral, accessory predorsal and dorsolateral lines. Pores on head: prenasal 1. suborbital 4, preoperculo-mandibular, 5 or 6.

Colour   Variable, black on head and abdomen, brownish elsewhere. Living colour in some cases silvery blue.

Size   Length to 4 inches (10.2 cm). The report of a 12-inch specimen is questioned.

Recognition   Noteworthy for the absence of pelvic fins, and for the small gill openings about one-half eye diameter in length and wholly above the base of the pectoral fin.

Life History   Specimens taken over green mud showed a variety of colours.[3] It is probably bathypelagic at depths greater than 500 meters. One capture was apparently from water at about 7 C. About 30 eggs about 2 millimeters in diameter are reported from one specimen.[7]

Distribution   Deep bathypelagic. From southern California as far south as San Diego from depths to 1084 fathoms (1984 m),[4] central California from 394 to 524 fathoms (720–958 m) to 53 to 118

247

fathoms (97–208 m), to Oregon at 900 meters,[5] and off British Columbia at 900 to 700 meters offshore from Calvert Island at 51.53 N, 131.25 W.[6] Alaskan records[2] are assessed as erroneous.[3]

References 1 Clothier 1950; 2 Evermann and Goldsborough 1907; 3, 4 Gilbert 1895, 1915; 5, 6 Grinols 1965a, 1966; 7 McAllister and Rees 1964. See also Yarberry 1965.

FAMILY DEREPODICHTHYIDAE   CUSKPOUTS

The fish in this family is slender and scaleless, and without a lateral line canal. Pelvic fins are extremely far forward, very close together, and much reduced, each consisting of only a single filament. The caudal fin is indistinguishably confluent with the dorsal and anal fins. The gill opening is short and vertical. Teeth are few, small, and irregular on jaws, vomer, and palatines. A single specimen of the family is known.

CUSKPOUT

Derepodichthys alepidotus Gilbert 1895

Scientific names from the Greek *dere* (throat), *pous* (foot), and *ichthys* (fish — position of the pelvic fins); and *alepodotus* (scaleless).

Description   Body very long and slender, its depth about 18 or 19 into total length. Head length about 8.5 into total length, moderately compressed, occiput flattened. Mouth terminal, moderate in size, directed forward and up. Upper jaw extends about to anterior edge of pupil, projects slightly, containing lower jaw of closed mouth, covered by thick skin of upper lip. Snout about 3.2 in length of head. Teeth few, small, and sharp, in narrow bands and irregular series on jaws, palatines and vomer. Exposed part of eye about 4.3 into length of head; eyeball fails to fill orbit. Gill slit vertical, its lower end slightly above base of lower pectoral rays, its length about 4 into length of head.

Fins   Dorsal (1), confluent with caudal. Anal, confluent with caudal, rays of both fins

248

concealed in thick integument. Pectorals long and slender, reaching halfway to vent, length about 1.3 into length of head. Pelvics 1, very close together, arising from a common raised base on midventral line, filamentous, placed far forward below eye.

Scales   Scales and lateral line canal absent. Large mucous pores on snout, lower part of head, and lower jaw.

Colour   Preserved specimen is light brown, dorsal and pectoral fins are whitish, the anal fin has a dark margin which shades into black posteriorly. Lips are dusky and the abdominal region blue black.

Size   Length to 4.3 inches (11 cm).

Recognition   Notable for the long slender form, the pelvic fins reduced to single filaments placed very far forward and arising from a common base, the long slender pectoral fin extending more than halfway to the vent, and the gill opening as a straight narrow slit about one-quarter as long as the head. There are no scales or lateral line.

Distribution   Only one specimen known from a depth of 1588 fathoms (2904 m) off the Queen Charlotte Islands at 52.39 N, 132.38 W.

References   Gilbert 1895.

FAMILY MACROURIDAE (CORYPHAENOIDIDAE)   GRENADIERS

The grenadiers are strongly tapered deepwater fishes with fine drawn-out tails whose minute tail fin is confluent with both dorsal and anal fins. They reach moderately large size and are found in all oceans. A ridge below the large eyes is produced into a rostrum over the inferior mouth. There is frequently a barbel below the tip of the lower jaw. There are two dorsal fins, the first much higher, usually with an initial spine that is armed with fine spinules. Dorsal and anal fins are low and smoothly contoured. Pelvic fins are thoracic, rather large, and usually with the first ray more or less prolonged. Scales are cycloid but are frequently beset with spines or ridges. Some of the five species known from off the Canadian coast are known from single or very few individuals, and their status cannot be regarded as certain. Grenadiers or rattails.

249

KEY TO THE MACROURIDAE

1 Interspace between dorsal fins longer than base of first dorsal fin; anus below interspace 2

or 1 Interspace between dorsal fins shorter than base of first dorsal fin; anus below second dorsal fin 3

2 Pelvic fin rays about 12, the fin extending to a point between the anus and the fourth ray of the anal fin ....
.... *Coryphaenoides cyclolepis,* Smoothscale rattail, p. 252

or 2 Pelvic fin rays about 10, the fin extending beyond the tenth ray of the anal fin .... *Coryphaenoides liocephalus,* Bearded rattail, p. 255

3 Pelvic fins about half as long as head with 6 to 8 rays; rostrum small and pointed; interspace between dorsal fins about 0.8 of first dorsal fin base; pectoral fin longer than pelvic fins; anus about below second dorsal origin
.... *Coryphaenoides pectoralis,* Pectoral rattail, p. 256

or 3 Pelvic fins about two-thirds length of head or longer; with 9 or 10 rays; rostrum with well-developed ridge below eye, interspace between dorsal fins about 0.5 of first dorsal fin base; pelvic fins longer than pectorals......... 4

4 Barbel about 1.5 into length of eye; no prominent knob at anterior end of suborbital ridge; dorsal fin with 11 to 13 spines ....
.... *Coryphaenoides acrolepis,* Roughscale rattail, p. 251

or 4 Barbel shorter than half length of eye; lateral suborbital ridges with prominent forward directed lateral knobs; dorsal fin with 12 to 14 spines .... *Coryphaenoides filifera,* Filamented rattail, p. 254

ROUGHSCALE RATTAIL

Coryphaenoides acrolepis   (Bean 1883)

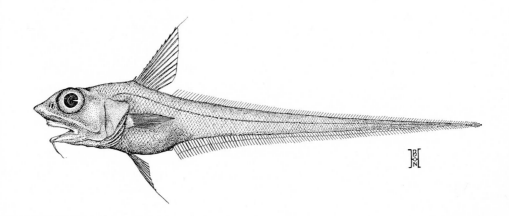

Scientific names from *Coryphaena* (a dolphin) and the Greek *oides* (like); and *acros* (sharp) and *lepis* (scale).

Description   Body elongate, its depth about 7.4 into total length, deepest immediately behind head, drawn out evenly into a long tail, compressed, more so posteriorly. Head about 4.7 into length, compressed. Mouth subterminal, large, directed forward and up. Upper jaw extends about to middle of eye, overhung by pointed rostrum of snout, includes lower jaw. Rostrum prominently extended under orbits. Teeth in villiform bands in both jaws, in upper jaw the outer largest. Interorbital space concave medially, its width about 4 into length of head. Eye oval, its length about 3.5 into length of head. Gill membranes united and joined to isthmus so as to leave a moderate free fold. Anus under second dorsal.

Fins   Dorsal (2), 11 to 13 — 111+, first fin short based, its first ray may be short and spinelike, the second long with moderate spines on its anterior edge, second fin very long, low, inconspicuous in a depression, extending to end of tail, 2 fins separated by about one-third base of first dorsal. Caudal very narrow and pointed. Anal about 94+, long, low. Pectorals about 20, long, narrow, length about half length of head. Pelvics about 10, thoracic, length about 1.3 into length of head.

Scales   Cycloid with weak keels and numerous spinules, about 195 rows in length, on body and head, except in axils. Lateral line canal decurved and then straight. Small barbel about 1.5 into length of eye under lower jaw.

Colour   Brown to black dorsally, paler below. Peritoneum and lining of gill chambers black.

Size   Length to 30 inches (76 cm).

Recognition   Distinguished by the pointed caudal fin, the presence of a fairly long barbel on the lower jaw, an interspace between the dorsal fins less than half the length of the base of the first dorsal fin, and the anus below the second dorsal fin.

Distribution   In the northeast Pacific from Baja California[3] through California,

Oregon, Washington to Alaska and the Bering Sea[2] and on the western side of the Kuril Islands, Kamchatka, and as far south as Sagami Bay, Japan. Taken at depths from 85 to 1350 fathoms (155–2470 m) throughout the range.

In British Columbia from Juan de Fuca Strait and off the northern part of the province between 1000 and 1500 fathoms (1830 and 2745 m).[1]

References   1 Bourne and Pope 1969; 2 Grinols 1965a; 3 Wilimovsky 1954.

SMOOTHSCALE RATTAIL

Coryphaenoides cyclolepis (Gilbert 1895)

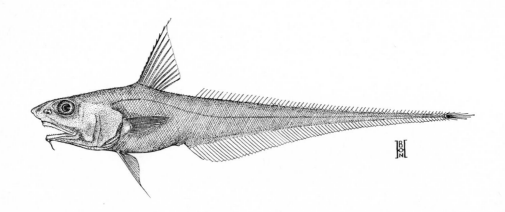

Scientific names from *Coryphaena* (a dolphin) and the Greek *oides* (like); and *cyklos* (circle) and *lepis* (scale).

Clemens and Wilby 1946 listed this species as smooth-scaled grenadier, *Dolloa cyclolepis* (Gilbert 1895). *Nematonurus* and *Moseleya* have also been used as generic names.[1]

Description   Body elongate, depth about 6.3 into standard length, deepest immediately behind head, tapering to a fine point, compressed, more so posteriorly. Head length about 4.5 into standard length, compressed, blunt. Mouth subterminal, large, directed forward and up. Upper jaw extends to posterior margin of pupil, overhung by rostrum of snout, includes lower jaw. Median and lateral rostral ridges ending in projections. Teeth small, in upper jaw in 2 series, a row of fine, hooked teeth along edge of jaw, an inner series of very small straight teeth directed inward from inner part of jaw; in lower jaw in a single series. Interorbital space flat, its width about 4.8 into head length. Eye moderate in size, oval, its length about 5 into head length. Gill membranes united and joined to isthmus so

252

as to leave a broad free fold. Anus below middle of space between dorsal fins.

Fins   Dorsal (2), II, 10 to 67, separated by more than length of base of first fin; first spine short, second very long and stiff with well-developed spinules directed forward and out; second fin very long, inconspicuous, anterior rays short, free of membrane, possibly torn, and lying in a shallow depression, extending to end of body confluent with caudal. Caudal very narrow and pointed. Anal about 77 long, low, extending to end of body. Pectorals about 20, slender, length about half head length. Pelvics 12, thoracic, outer rays long, extend about to anus.

Scales   On small (150 mm) specimens small, on head and body, keels small and spinules few or absent. On 217-millimeter specimen most scales on head and body heavily armed with 1 to 4 keels and up to many spinules. This is a difference to be expected as associated with size[2] or age. Small bare patches in axils. Lateral line canal decurved anteriorly, then straight. Barbel under lower jaw, length about 1.5 into snout length, thick at base.

Colour   Dark brown on dorsal surface. Lower part of head, gill chambers and membranes, and peritoneum black, showing through.

Size   Length to 9 inches (22.9 cm), at least.

Recognition   Distinguished by the pointed caudal fin, the barbel under the lower jaw, the interspace between the dorsal fins being longer than the base of the first dorsal, the anus below the interspace.

Distribution   Recorded only from deep water off the Queen Charlotte Islands, off Moresby Island in 1588 fathoms (2904 m), at 52.39 N, 132.38 W, and off Graham Island in about 1000 fathoms (1830 m) at about 53.33 N, 133.38 W, National Museum of Natural Sciences of Canada collection NMC 65-327.

References   1 Gilbert and Hubbs 1916; 2 Makushok 1963.

FILAMENTED RATTAIL

Coryphaenoides filifera (Gilbert 1895)

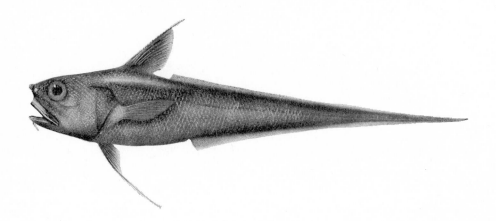

Scientific names from *Coryphaena* (a dolphin) and the Greek *oides* (like); and *filum* (thread) and *fero* (bear).

Clemens and Wilby 1946 listed this species as filamented grenadier, *Chalinura filifera* Gilbert 1895.

Description   Body elongate, deepest anteriorly, tapering to a fine point, compressed, more so posteriorly. Head large, rough, blunt, compressed. Mouth subterminal, large, directed forward and up. Upper jaw extends to posterior margin of pupil. Lower jaw included. Snout with rostrum overhanging mouth by about one-half distance between anterior tips of lateral suborbital ridges or about two-fifths of length of head. Teeth arrowlike; in upper jaw in bands with those in outer series enlarged, in lower jaw similar, in a single row of small teeth except in a band near symphysis. Eye diameter about 4 into length of head. Gill membranes joined to isthmus so as to leave a free fold. Anus below second dorsal.

Fins   Dorsal (2), II, 12 to 14 — (ray count of second dorsal, unknown), 2 fins separated by about half base of first dorsal fin; in first dorsal second spine very long and slender terminating in a long filament, nearly as long as head, smooth near base, but outer half strongly toothed, second dorsal low and inconspicuous, extending to end of body. Caudal very narrow and pointed. Anal, rays numerous, long and low, higher than dorsal, extending to end of body. Pectorals 20 to 22, long and slender. Pelvics 9 or 10, outside rays very long and filamentous, as long as head.

Scales   Cycloid with diverging ridges bearing small oblique spinules. Lateral line caudal decurved and then straight. Barbel short, one-twelfth to one-tenth length of head.

Colour   Dark brown, black on fins, nostrils, ventral surfaces of snout, lips, and gill membranes.

Size   Length to 21.5 inches (55 cm).

Recognition   Distinguished by the pointed caudal fin, the small barbel under the lower jaw, the interspace between the dorsal fins about one-half base of first dorsal, the anus below the second dorsal fin,

254

the long second spine on the first dorsal fin and long outside ray on the pelvic fin.

Distribution   Known only from three specimens taken at 1588 fathoms

(2904 m) of Moresby Island, Queen Charlotte Islands, British Columbia at 52.39 N, 132.38 W.

References   Gilbert 1895.

BEARDED RATTAIL

Coryphaenoides liocephalus (Günther 1887)

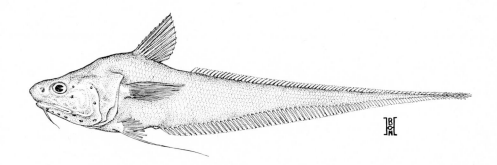

Scientific names from *Coryphaena* (a dolphin) and the Greek *oides* (like — possibly because of the high forehead); and *lios* (smooth) and *cephalos* (head).

Description   Body elongate, deepest near head, tapering to a fine point, compressed, more so posteriorly. Head length about 4.6 into standard length, compressed, blunt. Mouth subterminal, large, directed forward and up. Upper jaw extending beyond orbit. Snout rounded, bulging beyond maxillaries. Lower jaw included. Teeth small, pointed; in upper jaw in several rows, outer row largest, and arrow tipped; in lower jaw arrow tipped, in 1 row laterally and 2 at symphysis. Interorbital space 3.9 into length of head. Eye oval, its length

about 5.9 into length of head. Anus below space between dorsal fins. Pyloric caeca 9.

Fins   Dorsal (2), II, 9 — 114, separated by about 1.7 base of first fin; first fin short and high, first spine short, second spine long with a series of small spinules on its anterior edge; second fin very long, low, inconspicuous, middle rays longest. Caudal very narrow and pointed. Anal 113, long, low, rays longer than in second dorsal, extending to end of body. Pectorals about 20, long, narrow, length about 1.7 into length of head. Pelvics 10, thoracic, outer rays elongate extending to between fifteenth and twentieth anal ray.

Gill Rakers   Rakers 13 on inner side of first gill arch.

Vertebrae   84.

255

Scales   Cycloid or with 2 to 5 rows of weak spinules, varied in size and denticulation, about 145 diagonal rows along lateral line canal. Lateral line canal decurved above pectorals, then straight. Short barbel below lower jaw, its length about 1.3 into length of eye.

Colour   Dark brownish on posterior part of body and fins, not observed anteriorly. Black on lower jaw, mouth, gill cavities, and peritoneum.

Size   Length to 17 inches (43 cm).

Recognition   Distinguished by the pointed caudal fin, the long barbel under the lower jaw 1.3 times length of orbit, the space between dorsal fins about 1.5 times base of first dorsal, the anus below interspace.

Distribution   Known in British Columbia from a single specimen taken off Queen Charlotte Sound at 51.05 N, 132.22 W from a depth of 1510 fathoms (2760 m), National Museums of Canada collection NMC 65-321.[2] Three other specimens are known: one from near Yokohama, Japan, in 1875 fathoms (3430 m) at "Challenger" station 237, and two others from mid-Pacific in 2050 fathoms (3750 m) at "Challenger" station 246.[1,3]

References   1 Günther 1887; 2 McAllister personal communication; 3 Okomura 1970.

PECTORAL RATTAIL

Coryphaenoides pectoralis (Gilbert 1891)

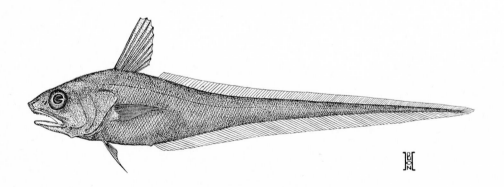

Scientific names from *Coryphaena* (a dolphin) and the Greek *oides* (like); and *pectoralis* (pectoral fin — long and narrow).

Description   Body elongate, its depth about 8 into total length, deepest immediately behind head, drawn out evenly in long tail, compressed, most so posteriorly.

Head about 6 into length, blunt anteriorly, little compressed. Mouth subterminal, large, directed forward and up. Upper jaw extends beyond orbit, overhung by small pointed rostrum of snout, and includes lower jaw. Teeth sharp, conical, in 2 or 3 rows in upper jaw, in 1 or 2 rows in lower jaw. Interorbital space about 3.5 into length of head, concave between 2 lateral ridges. Eye oval, its length about 4.2 into length of head. Gill membranes joined and fused to isthmus. Anus below second dorsal fin.

Fins   Dorsal (2), about 10 to 126, first fin fairly high, first ray long with a few weak small prickles on its anterior edge; second fin very long, low, inconspicuous, extending to end of tail, 2 fins separated by about three-quarters base of first dorsal fin. Caudal very narrow and pointed. Anal about 131, long, low, extending to end of tail. Pectorals about 17, triangular, long, narrow. Pelvics 6 to 8, thoracic.

Scales   Cycloid with several weak keels each with a weak spine, about 264 rows in length, on body except for axils, on head. Lateral line canal decurved, then straight. Small barbel, about 3 into length of eye, below lower jaw.[3]

Colour   Gray-brown on head and body, each scale with a prominent dark posterior border, fins and lateral line darker. Black in mouth, gill cavity, and on peritoneum.

Size   Length to 43 inches (109 cm).

Recognition   Distinguished by the pointed caudal fin, the presence of a barbel below lower jaw, the anus below second dorsal fin, the long narrow pectoral fin, and six to eight rays in pelvic fin.

Distribution   In the northeast Pacific from California through Oregon and Washington to the Bering Sea. On the Asian coast off Kamchatka, in the Okhotsk Sea, and off the Pacific coast of Japan. Off North America at depths between 325 to 900 fathoms (595–1650 m).[2]

British Columbia records were taken on longlines at 950 and 550 fathoms (1740 and 1000 m) at 50.31 N, 129.00 W and 53.01 N, 132.55 W.[1,4] One had two squid beaks in its stomach.

References   1 Bourne and Pope 1969; 2 Grinols 1965a; 3 Jordan and Evermann 1898; 4 McAllister personal communication.

ORDER ATHERINIFORMES
(Synentognathi, and related orders)

The Atheriniformes are long slender fishes for the most part with small specialized mouths, sometimes with the jaws extended as beaks, and the paired fins situated well back on the body. A large group of fishes best represented in the tropics in both fresh and salt water. Two species are known to occur in British Columbia.

FAMILY SCOMBERESOCIDAE   SAURIES

Sauries are long slender fishes with pointed snouts or beaks. There are about five finlets following the single dorsal fin which is composed only of soft rays, and there are five or more finlets following the anal fin, which has no spines. The lateral line canal is placed very low on the body. There are 9 to 15 branchiostegal rays, parietal bones are absent, nostril openings are single, and the rostral bones are joined by a suture. The sauries are marine surface fishes of minor commercial importance in some parts of the world. Sauries and billfishes.

PACIFIC SAURY

Cololabis saira (Brevoort 1856)[3]

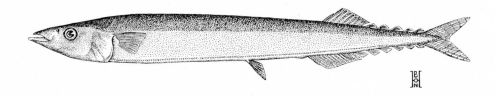

Scientific names are from the Greek roots *colos* (defective or curtailed) and *labis* (forceps — short beak); and the Japanese *saira* (spear — fish).

Description   Body elongated, compressed, depth about 7 into standard length, dorsal contour almost straight, lower profile without strong curves tapering gradually

258

to the caudal peduncle from a point about one-third from the tip of the lower jaw. Head compressed, its length about 4.5 into standard length. Mouth terminal, rather small, directed forward. Upper jaw extending about half distance to rear of pupil, the maxillary covered by a fold of the ethmoid cartilage, loosely hinged to the lower jaw. Lower jaw projecting to enter dorsal profile of head. Both jaws pointed. Teeth poorly developed. Interorbital space flat, raised moderately above level of orbits, about 5.5 into length of head. Eye diameter about 6 into length of head. Opercles thin and transparent. Gill membranes free from each other and isthmus. Caudal peduncle narrow and compressed, its least depth about 36–45 into standard length.

Fins Dorsal (1), 9 to 11, well back on body, followed by 5 to 6 free finlets. Caudal broadly and finely forked. Anal 12 to 14, well back on body but slightly ahead of the dorsal, followed by 5 to 7 finlets. Pectorals about 13, small, truncate, first ray notably flattened, placed high on the side, fin at rest partly lying under a low ridge on the body which is a continuation of the raised ridge of the cleithrum, to which the first ray is articulated so as to move forward and down when the fin is extended. Pelvics 6, abdominal.

Vertebrae 62 to 64, mean of 18 specimens, 63.4.[5]

Scales Cycloid, small, thin, deciduous, in 120 to 129 rows above the midline of the body. Lateral line canal distinct and very low on the body, close to the midventral line, from throat to caudal peduncle.

Colour Dark green to blue on dorsal surface, silvery below, small bright blue blotches distributed haphazardly on sides. Fins on lower part of body pale, others with darkened rays.

Size Length to about 14 inches (36 cm).

Recognition Identified by its slender form, dorsal and ventral finlets, low lateral line canal, and the pointed head.

Life History The eggs are demersal, separate, about 2 millimeters in diameter, with a group of about 20 filaments at one pole and a single longer thicker filament at about 90° to the pole. These filaments anchor the eggs to seaweeds, kelp, or rocks.[2,8] Eggs have been found on equipment at 50 feet (15 m) at 18 C off southern Vancouver Island. The larvae are relatively large, active, and pelagic. Juveniles are pelagic near the surface.[12] Food of adults includes fish eggs and larvae. Sauries in turn are taken as food extensively by albacore.[7] When alarmed the fish take a series of well-directed leaps, "skipping and soaring,"[9] but occasionally finish up on the deck of a boat.[4] They occur in widely spread schools or mixed in schools of other fishes. Pacific saury were notably abundant in California in 1931.[9]

Distribution Very generally distributed in the offshore waters of the Pacific, usually encountered at the surface, but, apparently also at considerable depths, at least as deep as 125 fathoms (229 m). From the southern Pacific and Baja California, through north and south California, Oregon, Washington, and the Gulf of Alaska[6,16] to Shimushira in the Kuril Islands, Japan,[14] and Goto Island off Kyushu.[8] In the tropical Pacific with young and adults observed between San Diego and Hawaii[11,12] and farther north.[1] Canadian records include Queen Charlotte Strait, and the Ain River, Masset Inlet, Queen Charlotte Islands, in brackish water about 200 yards (183 m) from the outlet,[10] as well as occurrences off the west coast of Vancouver Island,[13,15] and other exposed areas.

Utilization Never abundant enough in North American waters to attract a commercial fishery but actively sought off Japan with gillnets, and lift-nets and lights.[7]

References   1 Anon 1956; 2 Aplin 1939; 3 Brevoort 1856; 4 Chapman 1943; 5 Clothier 1950; 6 Grinols 1965a; 7 McHugh 1952; 8 Okada 1955; 9 Phillips 1932; 10 Pritchard 1933; 11 Schaefer and Reintjes 1950; 12 Schultz 1940; 13 Schultz, Hart, and Gunderson 1932; 14 Tanaka 1935; 15 Williamson 1930; 16 Wilimovsky 1954.

FAMILY ATHERINIDAE   SILVERSIDES

The silversides are small, slender, silvery fishes with two dorsal fins, the first small, and no finlets, and no beak. The lateral line canal is absent or may be a series of pores along the midside. There are five to seven branchiostegal rays. Parietal bones are present. Usually but not always with an anal spine and double nostrils. Pelvic fins are not, as in some related families, modified as secondary sexual appendages. Inshore and estuarial species, sometimes occurring in great enough schools to suggest possible commercial use. Silversides, topsmelt, grunnion, and related species.

TOPSMELT

Atherinops affinis affinis Jordan and Snyder 1913

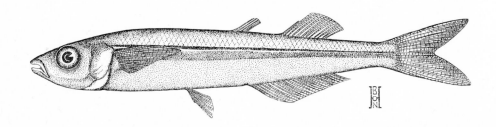

Scientific names are from *Atherina* (a genus of related fishes, from the Greek name, based on the Greek *ather* a spike or arrow — slender form), and from the Greek *ops* (like); and from the Latin *affinis* (related — to associated species).

Subspecies cannot be assigned with assurance to the only Canadian specimen of this variable genus. On the basis of likelihood it is assigned to the most northerly of a series of subspecies recognized along the west coast of North America.[2,5]

260

Description   Body elongate, depth about 7 into standard length, dorsal profile of body smoothly rounded. Head pointed, moderately compressed, dorsal profile flat and straight, its length about 5 into standard length. Mouth terminal, small, directed somewhat upward. Upper jaw not reaching halfway to anterior margin of orbit, not completely free from snout, slightly projecting. Snout length about 3.2 into length of head. Teeth very fine and bifid. Interorbital space about 3.5 into length of head, gently rounded. Eye diameter about 3.2 into length of head, near its midside. Gill membranes joined anteriorly, free of isthmus. Caudal peduncle compressed, its least depth about 15 into standard length.[1,3]

Fins   Dorsal (2), V — I, 11, spinous fin short and small, placed just behind midpoint of total length, rayed fin moderate in size and placed well back. Caudal forked. Anal I, 24, extending from points below middle of spinous dorsal to just beyond second dorsal. Pectorals 18, placed high on side, rather falcate. Pelvics I, 5, abdominal.[3]

Scales   Cycloid and deciduous, about 62 rows in the standard length of the fish. Lateral line canal not evident.

Colour   Blue gray to green above, silvery below. A striking bright silver band bordered above with blue extends the full length of the body.[4]

Size   Length at least to 14.4 inches (36.6 cm).[5]

Recognition   Noteworthy for its small separate spinous dorsal with five weak spines and the brilliant bar along each side.

Life History   Information on the life history of the northern subspecies of topsmelt has been obtained at Coos Bay, Oregon. There schools form near the entrance to the bay in March and April but later enter the sloughs and are found over the mudflats where they spawn from late May to early July. The eggs are attached to eelgrass just below low water. The largest eggs found in the ovaries were about 1.7 millimeters in diameter. Body lengths at the end of each year of growth are about: 1 year, 100 millimeters; 2 years, 185; 3 years, 220; and 4 years, 265. An age of 6 or 7 appears to be reached. Females grow rather faster than males throughout life with a continually increasing difference in length as the fish grow older. Young fish are relatively more slender than older ones.[5]

Distribution   From Monterey, California, including the mouths of streams to southern British Columbia. South of Monterey it intergrates with *Atherinops affinis litorales* Hubbs, and other subspecies extending the distribution to Guadaloupe Islands.

The most northerly and the only Canadian record is from Agate Beach, 4 miles (6 km) west of Sooke Harbour.[3]

References   1 Hubbs 1918b; 2 Jordan and Hubbs 1919; 3 Peden and Stewart 1964; 4 Roedel 1953b; 5 Schultz 1933.

ORDER BERYCIFORMES
(Berycoidei) (part of Berycomorphi)

The Beryciformes are short-bodied fishes in general occupying a debatable position between the soft-rayed and spiny-rayed fishes. Pelvic fins are thoracic with one spine and 3 to 13 soft rays, usually with more than five. The caudal fin has 18 or 19 rays. The maxillary is more or less protrusible, and an orbitosphenoid bone is present. The gasbladder is usually separate from the digestive tract. These are small tropical or deepwater fishes, represented off British Columbia by two species in one family.

FAMILY MELAMPHAEIDAE   MELAMPHIDS

The melamphids are small, only moderately compressed fishes with deep blunt heads, variously sculptured, and large scales. They are deep water, bathypelagic species. Several genera and species are recognized, two of them from off the British Columbia coast.

KEY TO THE MELAMPHAEIDAE

1   Prominent crest on top of head; rostral spine present; pectoral fin narrow based and slender .... *Poromitra crassiceps,* Crested melamphid, p. 264

or 1   No crest on top of head; rostral spine absent; pectoral fin with moderately long base and moderately expanded ....
.... *Melamphaes lugubris,* Highsnout melamphid, p. 263

HIGHSNOUT MELAMPHID

Melamphaes lugubris Gilbert 1890

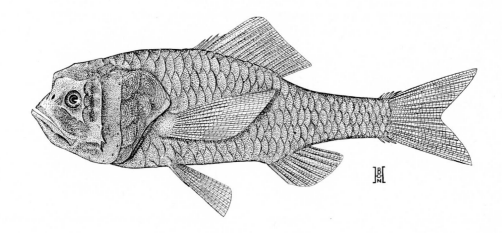

Scientific names from the Greek *melamphaes* (with darkness for light); and the Latin *lugubris* (mourning).

Clemens and Wilby 1946 recorded this species as high-snouted melamphid, *Melamphaes cavernosus* Chapman 1939.[1]

Description   Body depth about 3.2 into standard length, somewhat compressed. Head massive, blunt, moderately compressed, its length about 2.7 into standard length. Mouth terminal, large, directed forward and upward. Upper jaw extends to posterior part of eye. Lower jaw somewhat protruding, its lower parts very fragile. Snout blunt, short, and very high. Teeth fine, in bands on both jaws. Interorbital space wide, strongly convex, its width about 2 into length of head. Eye small, its diameter about 6.2 into length of head. Gill membranes free from each other and from isthmus. Side of head with 2 evident vertical ridges about 1 eye diameter apart, behind the second ridge the operculum is covered with large scales; in front of the first, and through the length of the top of the head are longi-tudinal fine striations. Caudal peduncle moderately compressed, its least depth about 8.5 into standard length.

There are 2 weak spines near the posterior angle of the preopercular bone.

Fins   Dorsal (1), III, about 16. Caudal forked, 3 or 4 free spines above and below rayed part of fin. Anal I, about 8, its origin about below end of dorsal insertion. Pectorals about 16, long and slender, reaching beyond anus but not as long as head. Pelvics I, 7, slender, thoracic.

Scales   Cycloid, very large, about 29 rows on body. Lateral line canal absent. Many pores in rows on head.

Colour   Dark brown or black. Black on throat and branchiostegals.

Size   Length to 3.5 inches (8.9 cm).

Recognition   Noteworthy for the massive sculptured head with its steep snout and many pores, the longitudinal lines on

263

top of head and anterior part of its side, and the two vertical bars on the sides of the head.

Life History   In the subarctic region young occur in surface layers (50–75 m) and half growns and adults at 200 to 250 meters. Further south in the transition zone young are found from 200 to 300 meters and older stages between 200 meters and as deep as 500 meters.[2,3]

Distribution   From off northern Baja California to the Bering Sea at depths off California of 822 fathoms (1500 m), to 200 fathoms (366 m) off Washington, and 322 fathoms (590 m) off Alaska. British Columbia records are from off Queen Charlotte Sound and off the Queen Charlotte Islands.

References   1 Chapman 1939; 2 Ebeling 1962; 3 Grinols 1965a.

CRESTED MELAMPHID

Poromitra crassiceps (Günther 1878)

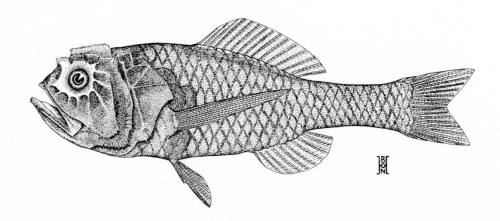

Scientific names from the Greek *poros* (pore) and *mitra* (stomacher — chest covering or head band); and *crass* (thick) and *ceps* (head).

This species was listed as *Melamphaes rugosus* Chapman 1939[1] in Clemens and Wilby 1946, 1961.

Description   Body stout at anterior end, depth about 3.5 into standard length, compressed at posterior end. Head large, deep, and only moderately compressed, its length about 2.5 into standard length. Two high transparent crests on either side of the parietal bone and a single ridge, split at its apex, between the nasals. The eye is centred in a flat plateau on the side of the head, the raised part buttressed by radiating ridges extending in all directions producing small cells on the surface of the head. Mouth

264

large, terminal, directed only slightly upward. The upper jaw extends to a point between the posterior margin of the eye. Snout blunt. Teeth small, villiform. Interorbital space very wide about 2.5 into length of head, much interrupted and complicated by various ridges. Eye small, its diameter about 6 into length of head. Opercles strongly braced with 3 radiating ridges between which are fine striations. Fine serrations or bristles on edge of opercular bone. Ridges under mandible and along midventral line of lower jaw. Branchiostegals 6. Gill membranes free from each other and the isthmus. Caudal peduncle compressed and fairly long, its least depth about 8 into standard length.[1]

Fins   Dorsal (1), III, 12. Caudal shallowly forked. Anal I, 9, short based. Pectorals 13, long, slender, longer than head. Pelvics I, 7.

Scales   Cycloid, large, deciduous in about 25 rows along midline of the body.

Colour   Black.

Size   Length to 6 inches (15 cm) but specimens exceeding 5 inches (12.7 cm) are uncommon. At 15 centimeters they are about 10 years of age.[2]

Recognition   Recognizable by its black colour, its sculptured head with crests over the eyes and spines on the forehead, and the long slender pectoral fin.

Life History   Small crustaceans are used as food. One specimen was found in the stomach of a salmon.[2]

Distribution   From Chile (about 33 S) to the Gulf of Alaska, through Central America, Mexico, California, Oregon, Washington, British Columbia at depths between 1800 and 380 fathoms (3300–700 m). Atlantic Ocean. Possibly Arctic Ocean. Bathypelagic.[3]

References   1 Chapman 1939; 2 Fitch and Lavenberg 1968; 3 Grinols 1965a.

ORDER ZEIFORMES
(Zeomorphi)

Zeiformes have deep compressed bodies, narrow caudal peduncles, and large eyes. The mouth is protrusible and the teeth poorly developed. They are of moderate size and marine. There is a spinous dorsal. The anal fin has one to four spines; the pelvic is thoracic with one spine and five to nine rays, and the caudal fin has 10 to 13 main rays. Post-temporal bones and the first vertebra are fused to the skull. Development is marked in the juveniles by the presence of rows of prominent horny protuberances along the sides. The protuberances later disappear. About 50 species in three families are recognized in tropical and temperate offshore waters. The status of the only Canadian species is uncertain as only the young are known. Dories, boarfishes, oreos, and related families.

OREO

Allocyttus sp.

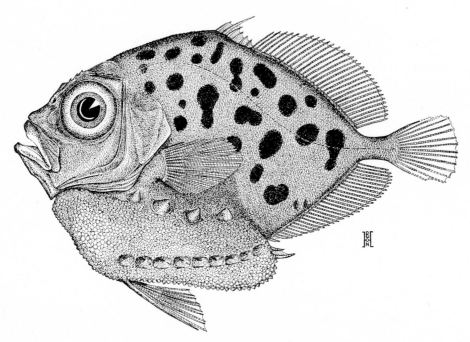

Generic name from the Greek *allo* (different) and *Cyttus* (a species of fish).

The first specimen of this species recorded from off the British Columbia coast was identified with *Allocyttus verrucosus* (Gilchrist 1908) in Clemens and Wilby 1961. It is a juvenile in a so-called oreosoma stage marked by horny protuberances along the sides. To date such juveniles have not been positively related to adults and the Canadian record cannot be identified with certainty. The adult of the oxeye oreo *Allocyttus folletti* Myers 1960 is recorded from California waters but this mid-Pacific specimen cannot be identified with it on the basis of available information.[1]

Description   Body very short, depth about 1.5 into standard length, much compressed. Head large, about 2.4 into standard length, compressed. Mouth terminal, moderate, directed upward, lower jaw slightly protruding. Upper jaw about 2.5 into length of head, a marked furrow across its anterior portion between the upper lip and prominent nasal bosses. Lips rather fleshy. Teeth on jaws small. Interorbital space level in general, concave with an elevated median section extending toward snout, about 3.2 into length of head. Nares extremely prominent. Eye large, about 2.8 into length of head. Operculum with a family of ridges radiating backward from a raised focus. Branchiostegals 7. Gill membranes free of the isthmus. Body below the head extending forward in a pouch behind and/or below the head. Caudal peduncle very narrow, about 17 or 18 into standard length, compressed.

Spines   A series of about 6 spines in a line over the orbit.

Fins   Dorsal (1), VI, 34, spinous and soft-rayed portions scarcely separated, if at all, but deeply notched. Caudal rounded. Anal III, 32. Pectorals 20. Pelvics I, 6 thoracic. All spines stout.[2]

Gill Rakers   On first arch 25.

Scales   Generally small, not overlapping, each with a raised centre, and apparently cycloid. Rows of enlarged scales on either side of the rayed portions of dorsal and anal fins. Scales on head except for chin and jaws. Scales enlarged on sides of belly and much enlarged toward midventral line. There are 4 or 5 large pointed scutes in a line between pectoral and anal fin insertions, and 9 or 10 in a line between pelvic and anal insertions. Lateral line canal in a strong upward arch from the back of the head about upper eye level to about three-quarters of standard length from snout, then approximately following midside of the caudal peduncle.
Adult fish have normal scales, mostly cycloid, without scutes, and even larger eyes.

Colour   From the single specimen examined apparently medium brown above with belly tan. Moderately dark spots in rough rows on the brown part of the body.

Size   The only specimens are 5 and 6 inches (13 and 15 cm) long. Adults (probably) reach 15.5 inches (39 cm).

Recognition   Noteworthy for its large eyes, stout spines on dorsal, anal, and pelvic fins, very slender caudal peduncle, arched lateral line canal, and horny tubercles on the ventral surfaces modified into rows of large protuberances.

Distribution   *A. folletti* is known from the coast of southern and central California. The first "Canadian" specimen is from about 50 N, 150 W at a surface temperature of about 10 C. A second juvenile about 6 inches (15 cm) in total length was taken at Ocean Station "Papa" (50 N, 145 W) by R. Pierce and is preserved in the national collection as NMC 69-338. It was taken from the stomach of a Pacific lancetfish about June 1969.

References   1 Myers 1960; 2 Welander, Johnson, and Hajny 1957. Additional information from Gruchy personal communication.

ORDER LAMPRIDIFORMES
(Allotriognathi)

The Lampridiformes are large, offshore, highly coloured fishes of striking form. **Fins** are soft rayed, the dorsal is always long and higher anteriorly, the anal may be long or may be much reduced, even to being a mere row of tubercles. Pelvics when present are under the pectorals, and the insertion may be horizontal. The gasbladder is closed. Premaxillary and maxillary are freely protractile so that the mouth is protrusible. Where known, the life history is complex involving striking changes in the relative sizes of the fins. These are fishes of intermediate depths offshore but they are occasionally encountered at the surface. Two species from different families are known from the British Columbia coast.

FAMILY LAMPRIDIDAE   OPAHS

The opahs are very deep, large, compressed fishes with long upright fins and forked tails. They occur in all oceans. Pectoral fins are inserted horizontally and may play an important part in locomotion. The only member of the family, the opah, moonfish, or Jerusalem haddock, is very striking because of it's unusual form, large size, and striking colour.

OPAH

Lampris regius (Bonnaterre 1788)

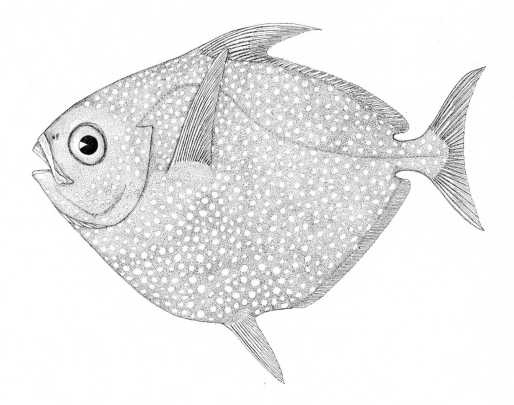

Scientific names from the Greek *lampros* (radiant); and the Latin *regius* (king's).

The French name for this species is *opah* or *poisson lune*.

Description Body very short, its depth about 1.5 into standard length, much compressed. Head length about 3.1 into standard length, compressed. Mouth terminal, moderate in size, directed forward and upward. Upper jaw extends about to anterior edge of orbit. Premaxillary bone protractile. Snout rounded. Teeth absent. Interorbital space smoothly arched, its width about 2.4 into length of head. Eye large, its diameter about 4.2 into length of head. Caudal peduncle compressed and rather slender, its least depth about 13 into standard length. Pits above and below base of caudal fin.

Fins Dorsal (1), 53 to 55[6] or 48 to 49,[1] originating at deepest part of body, first ray longest, high and falcate anteriorly followed by a low section somewhat higher at posterior end. Caudal broadly lunate. Anal 38 to 41[6] or 33 to 34,[1] long, nowhere high but higher at ends. Dorsal and anal fins recessed when depressed. Pectorals 20 to 24, long, falcate. Pelvics 14 to 17, abdominal, similar to pectorals in shape and a little longer.

Gill Rakers In first gill arch 13 or 14.

269

Vertebrae About 43.[3]

Scales Cycloid, minute. Lateral line canal arched strongly upward over pectoral fin curving gently down to midside.

Colour Dark steely blue dorsally shading into green with silver and purple iridescence, belly rosy, body covered with silvery spots in irregular rows, light mottling on caudal and dorsal fins, vermilion on fins and jaws, golden around eyes.[5,6]

Size The largest confirmed length is 4.5 feet (137 cm) or 160 pounds (73 kg). There are reports of 500-to 600-pound (228–273-kg) specimens.

Recognition Noteworthy for its compressed oval shape, falcate pectoral, pelvic, and anterior-dorsal fins, slender caudal peduncle, vermilion jaws, and silver spots on the body.

Life History Spawning probably takes place during the spring months. Food consists of such small fishes as hake, rockfish, and brotulas, and squids, and pelagic crabs.[3]

Distribution Pelagic and at depth, from the surface to more than 100 fathoms (183 m) in temperate and tropical oceans[4] and in northern extensions of warm water.[5] In the eastern Pacific from Cape San Lucas, Baja California, to the Gulf of Alaska. Off Icy Bay at 59.12 N, 141.42 W.[1] Off Japan. Off western Australia.[7] Canadian records off southern Vancouver Island.[2]

References 1 Bell and Kask 1936; 2 Cowan 1938; 3 Fitch 1951b; 4 Grinols 1965a; 5 Herald 1939; 6 Leim and Scott 1966; 7 Whitley 1948. See also Anon 1935d.

FAMILY TRACHIPTERIDAE   RIBBONFISHES

The ribbonfishes are elongate, much compressed fishes, widely distributed, bathypelagically but not necessarily at great depths. Because of their length and form they are of striking appearance. The dorsal fin runs the full length of the fish, and in adolescent specimens the upper lobe of the caudal fin is relatively overdeveloped. The way of life is relatively unknown. This family includes the so-called king-of-the-herring and king-of-the-salmon, the latter species being the one known from the coast of British Columbia.

KING-OF-THE-SALMON

Trachipterus altivelis Kner 1859

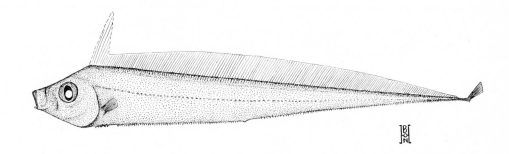

Scientific names from the Greek *trachys* (rough) and *pteron* (fin — narrow band of rough tubercles along the ventral surface replacing the anal fin); and the Latin *altus* (high) and *velum* (sail — high dorsal fin).

Clemens and Wilby 1946, 1961 called the king-of-the-salmon *Trachypterus rexsalmonorum* Jordan and Gilbert 1894. The spelling of the generic name is an unsupportable attempt to recognize its etymology. Recent work indicates the northeast Pacific stock is the same as that off Chile which was described earlier. The first name proposed is that recognized by usage.

Description   Body form and some meristic characters much subject to changes with development. Body greatly elongate, its depth about 9.7 into standard length, greatest depth close behind head, evenly tapered to very fine caudal peduncle, extremely compressed, especially dorsally and posteriorly. Young more robust.[7] Head obtusely pointed, its length about 7.7 into standard length, dorsal profile nearly straight, compressed. Mouth terminal, small, directed forward. Maxillary freely protractile, its posterior end not approaching line below anterior margin of eye. Teeth on jaws; in upper jaw, few and weak near median line; in lower jaw well-developed canine teeth in a "V" converging forward in symphyseal area, largest laterally. Interorbital space very depressed between abrupt orbital ridges, its width 6 into length of head. Eye round, large, its diameter 3.8 into length of head. Gill membranes united to each other and to isthmus. Caudal peduncle short, compressed, fine, its least depth about 200[1] into standard length. Anus sometimes placed asymmetrically.

Fins   Dorsal (1), 160 to 188, first 5 rays greatly elongated in young, becoming reduced with age, otherwise rather higher in centre, extending almost to caudal and ends abruptly. Caudal highly asymmetrical, dorsal lobe insignificant in the very young, becomes well developed in juveniles with 7 or 8 rays directed upward at a 45 degree angle to body axis, and eventually with growth is again much reduced; lower lobe is elongate in very young but becomes reduced to 5 or 6 short spines directed backward from the caudal base in older fish.[5] Anal absent. Pectorals 10 or 11, small, rounded. Pelvics 6 or 7, thoracic, elongate in young and juveniles, reduced to base in larger individuals.

Gill Rakers   12 to 16.

Vertebrae   90 to 94.[2]

Scales   Separate, elliptical, embedded in body, each with a pair of divergent spinous ridges,

271

larger on bases of dorsal fin rays and much enlarged toward midventral area where singly, or around the anus in fused groups, they provide a rasplike profile, absent in young. Lateral line canal straight along midside, as a series of discrete, short, nearly free tubes, 262 to 306.

Colour   In juveniles iridescent silvery with a series of about 4 dark blotches spaced above lateral line canal. Upright and pelvic fins, carmine red. Larger individuals very silvery[4] and greener with light spots around scales. Posterior end of dorsal fin dark in larger specimens.

Size   Standard length to about 175 centimeters representing a total length of about 6 feet. Larger individuals are reported. A ripe female about 167 centimeters standard length (5 feet, 6 inches) weighed only 4.04 kilograms (nearly 9 pounds).

Recognition   Recognized by its elongate, compressed body tapering to a fine caudal peduncle, the deep compressed head with a small mouth, the long dorsal fin, eccentric caudal fin, and lack of an anal fin.

Life History   Off California a female 167 centimeters in standard length caught in deep water was mature and ripe in November[2] but spawning may occur throughout the year. Young are identifiable by vertebral number at about 28 millimeters standard length. During development king-of-the-salmon go through a remarkable series of changes mainly involving fin dimensions and body form. It seems likely that the greatly elongate fins of the young may be floatation organs.[5] There is unconfirmed evidence from otoliths that growth in length is rapid, up to 40 centimeters after 1 year and 155 centimeters after 7 years.[6] Food of small individuals has been recorded as including copepods, annelid worms, and fish larvae. Larger individuals were found to have eaten copepods and euphausiids, small pelagic fishes, young rockfishes, squid, and Octopoda,[2,6] and they have been caught on queenfish *(Seriphus)* cut bait[2] and on a salmon spoon.

Distribution   Throughout the eastern temperate Pacific from Chile off Valparaiso, Central America, California, Oregon, Washington, and Alaska.[2,3] Halfway to Hawaii.[2] Off Barkley Sound.[4] From inside waters in Juan de Fuca Strait at Sooke and Sherringham Point,[1] Friday Harbor,[8] Pender Island and at the outlet of the Fraser River. Taken at least as deep as 270 fathoms (500 m) in California[2] and may be common in deep water.

References   1 Anon 1935a; 2 Fitch 1964; 3 Grinols 1965a; 4 Hart 1943d; 5 Hubbs 1926a; 6 Roedel 1938a; 7 Sette 1923; 8 Walker 1953.

ORDER GASTEROSTEIFORMES
(Suborder Gasterosteoidei)

The Gasterosteiformes is a small order of fishes found both in fresh and salt water. The dorsal fin is preceded by several free sharp spines. Anal, pectoral, and pelvic fins are also preceded by spines which may be stout and sharp. The pelvic fins are nearly thoracic with a spine and zero to two soft rays. There is no passage from the gasbladder to the digestive tract, no orbitosphenoid, no postcleithrum, and the pelvic girdle is not joined to the cleithrum. Two infraorbital bones are united with the preoperculum. The upper edge of the mouth is composed entirely of the premaxilla. These are abundant and adaptable fishes, and very flexible in form. Sticklebacks and tube-snouts. Two species in two families known from the salt water of British Columbia.

FAMILY AULORHYNCHIDAE   TUBE-SNOUTS

Tube-snouts are very slender, small, cylindrical, schooling fishes with heads greatly prolonged into a slender snout carrying at its end the small mouth and hinged upper jaw. The evident dorsal fin is placed well back on the body and is preceded by a row of about 25 isolated spines. The body is partly, but only partly, covered by rows of bony plates. There is only one species in the family, confined to the northeast Pacific.

TUBE-SNOUT

Aulorhynchus flavidus Gill 1861

Scientific names from the Greek *aulos* (tube) and *rhynchos* (snout); and the Latin *flavidus* (yellow).

Tubesnout as a spelling for the common name has merit.

Description Body very elongate, its depth about 15 to 20 into standard length, almost cylindrical but slightly depressed in middle section. Head elongate, shallow and narrow, its length about 4 into

273

standard length. Mouth terminal, very small, directed forward. Lower jaw flattened and protruding well beyond upper. Snout drawn out, flattened on top, with lower jaw forms a long tube, so that the upper jaw does not approach the eye. Premaxillaries hinged providing a free upper lip. Teeth very small, directed inward. Interorbital space flat, about 7 into length of head. Eye rather large and oval, its length about 6 into length of head. Caudal peduncle strongly keeled so that it is broader than deep over most of its posterior part, least depth about 80 into total length.

Fins   Dorsal (2), XXIV to XXVII — 9 or 10, the spinous portion represented by a series of small spines, free from membrane, the rayed part triangular and placed well back. Caudal, small, finely forked. Anal I, 9, spine small and broad, the fin mirroring the dorsal. Pectorals about 10, truncate. Pelvics I, 4, thoracic.

Vertebrae   53(53.9)55 (California 10 fish).[1]

Scales   Replaced by series of bony embedded plates. Lateral line canal almost straight.

Colour   On dorsal surface, pale mottled brown, varying from olive green to yellow brown. Creamy white on ventral surface. A bright silvery patch between operculum and pectoral fins extending on throat and bounded above by a dark band which extends forward through eye to snout. In breeding males pelvic fins bright red and snout phosphorescent.[5]

Size   Length to 7.0 inches (17.7 cm).

Recognition   Noteworthy for its elongate rigid spindle-shaped body, long tubular snout with a small mouth at the tip, and the numerous small free spines preceding the moderately sized triangular dorsal fin.

Life History   The tube-snout is a nest-builder and the breeding habits in California have been described.[4] Nest construc-

274

tion seems to be associated with the availability of (giant) kelp whose growing leaves are tied down to form the nest by strong strands extruded from the genital region of the male. Eggs are deposited by the female in masses 13 to 33 millimeters (0.5–1.3 inches) in diameter around the stems of the leaves between the main stock and the float, and adhere to each other rather than to the plant. Thus the egg masses are above the nest rather than within it. Usually nests are deeper than 35 feet (10 m). Eggs are about 2 millimeters in diameter, honey to dark reddish in colour. Males protect the nests. Hatching takes place in 2 or 3 weeks. In British Columbia spawning took place in April and the eggs hatched in May. In California maturity may be reached within a year.

Dr Charles W. Moffett observed that in the Friday Harbor area in late June tube-snouts concentrated around floats with heavy growths of the alga *Desmarestia aculeata* for spawning, females outnumbering males by as much as 10 or 20 to 1. Males established breeding territories about 2 feet (61 cm) apart, and defended them by lunging at intruding males or unprepared females. When females are ready they are accepted in sequence for egg-laying. Eggs are pink, deposited in small globular clusters adherent to algae, and guarded by the male. Egg clusters hatch in about 2 weeks, and hatching generally continues for 4 to 6 weeks. In 2 months young reach a length of about 2 inches (51 mm) and form small schools in shallow water and around structures.

Ordinarily the tube-snout swims slowly with rapid movements of the fins and the little mouth snapping continuously. There are sudden forward lunges, possibly involving the tail and it backs up slowly using the pectoral fins.[4] The body is rather rigid so the fish cannot turn quickly. Sometimes they form large schools.[2]

Food organisms recorded are small crustacean plankton such as amphipods, mysids, and crab zoea, and fish larvae, including its own young.

Distribution   Baja California to southeast Alaska.[6] In British Columbia rather generally distributed, common in the Strait of Georgia generally and in Burrard Inlet in December.[3] Usually found near the surface although adults may occur as deep as 100 feet (30 m).[4]

References   1 Clothier 1950; 2 Fitch 1952b; 3 Lamb personal communication; 4 Limbaugh 1962; 5 Moffett 1970; 6 Wilimovsky 1954.

FAMILY GASTEROSTEIDAE   STICKLEBACKS

Sticklebacks include both marine and freshwater forms, all of them small. They have 2 to 15 isolated spines anterior to the dorsal fin and these free spines are considered as representing the spinous dorsal. The last of the dorsal spines may be attached to the rayed fin. Pelvic fins are placed far forward on the abdomen and may be considered as thoracic. The sides are covered by a very variable number of bony plates replacing scales. One species, locally common, in British Columbia.

THREESPINE STICKLEBACK

Gasterosteus aculeatus Linnaeus 1758

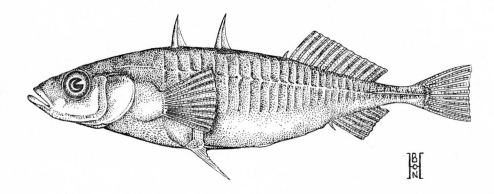

Scientific names from the Greek *gaster* (belly) and *osteo* (bone); and the Latin *aculeatus* (spined).

The French name is *épinoche à trois épines*.

Description   Body robust, finely tapered, moderately compressed, depth about 4 into standard length. (Frequently apparent sturdiness as here and in the illustration is caused by the body cavity stage of a tapeworm.) Head about 3.5 into standard length, compressed. Mouth terminal, rather small, directed somewhat upward. Dorsal profile continuous and almost straight. Head pointed. Upper jaw extending about halfway to anterior edge of orbit. Lips prominent. Teeth fine. Interorbital space about equal to eye diameter and about 4 into length of head. Opercles smooth. Branchiostegals 4. Gill membranes united to the isthmus. Caudal peduncle fine, its least depth about 20 into standard length, keeled, most strongly so immediately ahead of the tail fin where the width goes about 12 into standard length. A bony plate extending midventrally from between the pelvic fins.

Fins   Dorsal (2), III — 11 or 12, the first consisting of three isolated spines serrated (on the sides) and followed by a much reduced mem-

brane. Caudal slightly indented. Anal I, 8 or 9, the spine short. Pectorals 10, rather truncate. Pelvics I, 1 thoracic spine large and serrate, ray small. All spines lock into the erect position to give the fish a very formidable appearance.

Scales   Lateral line canal above midside following the dorsal contour. No real scales but each side may be armed by a series of up to 30 or more bony plates. The number seems to vary with habitat, sometimes none in fresh water and the higher numbers in full sea water. Variability is highly complex leading to differences in opinion about naming.[10,15]

Colour   Variable. In marine specimens silvery green to intense bluish black. In fresh water mottled brown. Young silvery.

Size   Length to about 4 inches (10 cm) although few reach that length.

Recognition   Two large and one small, free, serrated spines ahead of rayed dorsal fin, shallow keeled caudal peduncle, usually a series of bony plates along the side.

Life History   A very variable species in form and a most adaptable one to its environment. It is well established as a freshwater species where it forms distinctive populations in different waters, it commonly occurs in brackish waters of harbours where it schools in the eelgrass and around wharves, and in addition it is encountered far out to sea. It breeds in both fresh and salt water. Some observations on egg development in salt water raise doubts about the effectiveness of reproduction there.[20] In fresh water the male constructs an elaborate nest where he guards the eggs until the young leave but it is uncertain whether, or how, the practice holds under all conditions. The food of adults 25 to 87 millimeters (1–3.5 inches) total length in the southern Strait of Georgia in late spring and early autumn is dominated by copepods although a wide range of other organisms is found in the stomachs, including crustaceans (amphipods, euphausiids, larvae of decapods and barnacles, ostracods, and Cladocera), insects, young fishes (herring, bigeye, sand lance, searchers, rockfish), spider, and clam larvae.[1,2,3,4,5,6] Insects are important food in fresh water.[13,18,19] Sticklebacks are eaten by fur seals, [7,8] predatory fishes, and fish-eating birds.

Distribution   Found in both fresh and salt water through the north temperate area. In the Pacific from Baja California,[2] (in fresh water), central California through Washington,[9] British Columbia, the Bering Sea,[21] Aleutian Islands,[22] Kuril Islands,[14] Kamchatka,[17] Hokkaido,[14] Japan,[16] Korea.[14] In the Atlantic from Chesapeake Bay to Hudson Bay, from Spain to Norway, and Greenland. In Lake Ontario and the fresh waters of the Maritimes.[12] Very generally distributed and abundant throughout British Columbia. Occasionally recorded abundantly far off to sea.[11]

References   1, 2, 3 Barraclough 1967a, b, c; 4, 5 Barraclough and Fulton 1967, 1968; 6 Barraclough, Robinson, and Fulton 1968; 7 Clemens, Hart, and Wilby 1936; 8 Clemens and Wilby 1933; 9 De-Lacy, Dryfoos, and Miller 1963; 10 Hagen 1967; 11 LeBrasseur 1964; 12 Leim and Scott 1966; 13 Markley 1940; 14 Matsubara 1955; 15 Miller and Hubbs 1969; 16 Okada 1955; 17 Popov 1933; 18, 19 Robinson, Barraclough, and Fulton 1968a, b; 20 Vrat 1949; 21, 22 Wilimovsky 1954, 1964.

(Suborder Syngnathoidei)

These are strangely modified fishes for the most part of warm seas. The mouth is situated at the end of an elongated snout and is bounded dorsally by maxillary and premaxillary bones. The pelvic fins are absent in the British Columbia species and in many others but when present are abdominal. The British Columbia species has only the rayed second dorsal represented but in some species of the order a spinous dorsal is present. The gasbladder is without a duct to the digestive tract. This order includes seahorses and snipefishes as well as the local pipefish.

FAMILY SYNGNATHIDAE   PIPEFISHES

Body enclosed in an armour of encircling rings making it quite rigid and the fish inclined to posture in the water. There is a single rayed dorsal fin and pelvic fins are absent. Eggs are incubated in a specialized brood pouch along the abdomen of the male and sexual dimorphism is quite evident. One greatly elongate species is present in British Columbia waters.

BAY PIPEFISH

Syngnathus griseolineatus Ayres 1854

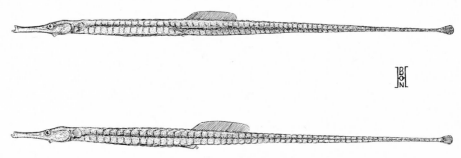

Male, *top;* Female, *bottom.*

Scientific names from the Greek *syn* (together) and *gnathos* (jaws); and the Latin *griseus* (gray) and *lineatus* (lined).

Clemens and Wilby 1946, 1961 used the shorter name pipefish for this species.

Description   Body drawn out, depth 25 to 30 into standard length, hexagonal in cross section anteriorly with the ventral side of the hexagon somewhat larger than the others. The 2 lateral surfaces become one near the dorsal fin so that the cross-section approaches becoming a truncate triangle. The male, posterior to the anus, has a midventral slit for about one-third of the fish length open into the brood pouch within the turned-in flaps of the body wall. Head elongate, about 8 into standard length, shallow and narrow. Mouth terminal, minute, directed somewhat upward. The part of the head in front of the eyes is modified into a long flexible tube constituting the snout. The effective upper jaw is very short extending only about one-tenth of the way to the orbit. No teeth. Interorbital space about 12.5 into length of head, almost flat with a low median ridge. Eyes a little longer than wide, the length about 9 into length of head. Operculum with faint striae nearly paralleling the margin and seeming to run continuously into the branchiostegals. Gill membranes broadly fused to each other and with the anterior part of the body leaving only a minute opening dorsally to the gill chamber. Caudal peduncle square in cross sections, very slender, its depth about 150 into standard length.

Fins   Dorsal (1), 36 to 41, short, about the same height throughout, placed about the middle of the body in the female, slightly forward in the male. Caudal very small, kite shaped. Anal, in female only, minute, 5, immediately behind anus. Pectorals about 13 small, rounded. Pelvics absent.

Scales   Replaced by bony plates; anteriorly, in 6 rows, 1 each dorsal and ventral, 2 on either side; posteriorly in 4 rows, 1 each dorsal and ventral and 1 on each side. No lateral line canal.

Colour   Colour variable, from pale green to dark green or brown depending on environment. Frequently pale olive green with narrow horizontal gray lines. Vague repetitive patterns may be related to the bony plates.

Size   Length to at least 13 inches (33 cm).

Recognition   Distinguished by the very elongate, flexible hexagonal and quadrilateral body, covered with bony plates, minute mouth and tail fin, and the absence of pelvic fins.

Life History   Among the San Juan Islands mating was observed in late June. In an elaborate ritual in which the male shakes himself, nods his head, and periodically assumes a rigid vertical S position, the female entwines herself about him[4] and presumably then transfers the fertilized eggs to the brood pouch of the male where the young develop until reaching a length of about three-quarters of an inch (19 mm). Running ripe females have been observed around the San Juan Islands in mid-July. However, in British Columbia males have been found carrying eggs as early as May 26 and young as late as August.

Individual pipefish are frequently observed drifting around in shallow water, swimming along with jerky movements around eelgrass beds and wharves. Occa-sionally they are observed farther from shore. Swimming appears to be by vibrating movements of the pectoral fin and undulations of the dorsal while the body postures in various positions.

The food consists mainly of small crustaceans, such as amphipods, copepods, and decapod larvae. It is sucked into the tubular mouth apparently by an inflation of the cheeks.

Distribution   From central California (Elkhorn Slough)[2] to southeastern Alaska.[5] Generally distributed in inshore protected areas. In British Columbia recorded from the Strait of Georgia,[1] Loughborough Inlet, and Queen Charlotte Islands. It is usually present at the entrance to Burrard Inlet.[3]

References   1 Barraclough, Robinson, and Fulton 1968; 2 Herald 1941b; 3 Lamb personal communication; 4 Moffett 1970; 5 Wilimovsky 1954.

ORDER PERCIFORMES
(Percomorphi, Acanthopterygii)

The Perciformes constitute a very large and very diverse group of marine and freshwater fishes in all parts of the world and at a wide variety of ocean depths. Usually there are two dorsal fins (sometimes modified), the first usually but not always spinous and well developed. The pelvic fin is under or before the pectoral, but frequently also extends posterior to its insertion. The pelvic fin has no more than one spine and six rays. The pelvic girdle is usually connected directly to the cleithrum. There are usually 17 principal rays in the caudal fin (occasionally fewer). The premaxilla usually carries the teeth of the upper jaw with the maxillary excluded from the gape. The eyes and skull are symmetrical. There is no orbitosphenoid, no mesacoracoid, and no Weberian apparatus, and the first vertebra is free of the skull. Intermuscular bones are absent. The gasbladder is closed. The lateral line canal system is normally developed (or in some cases highly specialized), and the scales are either ctenoid or cycloid.

Fishes in the family Percichthyidae were until recently assigned to the sea basses or Serranidae, a large, diverse and relatively unspecialized group of percomorph fishes with moderately large mouths, small sharp teeth on jaws and vomer, pelvic fins with one spine and five rays, and anal fins with three spines connected to the rayed portion of the fin by membrane. Recently the Percichthyidae were separated from the grouping since it was found that they had important characters in common (Gosline 1966). Notably, they lack a second spine below the main spine on the preoperculum; there are 25 or more vertebrae; the caudal fin is forked; the lateral line canal is complete and continuous, and the lateral line canals of the head are at least partly enclosed in bone; the premaxilla has two ascending processes; the maxilla is expanded posteriorly; the operculum has two (or three) backward-extending rounded protrusions; and there are no scaly processes at the bases of the pelvic fins. There is a gasbladder which may have anterior or posterior extensions. The separation is supported also by several less evident anatomical features. They are fishes of both fresh water and salt water. British Columbia has only one member of the new family, the temperate basses.

STRIPED BASS

Roccus saxatilis (Walbaum 1792)

Derivation of the generic name is uncertain. *Saxatilis* from the Latin (living among rocks).

The French name is *bar d'Amérique*.

Description   Body depth about 3.7 into standard length, compressed. Head about 3.1 into standard length. Mouth terminal, moderate in size, directed partly upward. Upper jaw extending to anterior part of the pupil. Lower jaw slightly projecting. Teeth fine on both jaws, palatines, and vomer; in parallel patch on base of tongue. Interorbital space somewhat elevated, its width about 3.4 into length of head. Eye about 8 into length of head. Preoperculum with weak serrations along edge. Caudal peduncle compressed and moderately deep, its least depth about 9 or 10 into standard length.

Spines   Two weak opercular spines directed backward.

Fins   Dorsal (2), VIII to X — I, 10 to 13, the fourth spine longest, the fins barely separated. Caudal forked. Anal III, 7 to 13. Pectorals 15 to 17, moderate in size. Pelvics I, 5, thoracic.

Scales   Ctenoid, moderate in size, 57 to 67. Lateral line canal almost straight along side.[8]

Colour   Olive green above, shading through silvery on sides to white on belly, with brassy reflections. There are 7 or 8 longitudinal dark stripes following scale rows, those above and close to lateral line, longer.

Size   There is an authentic-appearing record from California of 82 pounds (37 kg)[12] although 78 pounds (35.5 kg) is quoted officially.[11] On the Atlantic coast, the larger size of 125 pounds (57 kg) is reached[5] (AFS Newsletter Sept. 5, 1967).

Recognition   Noteworthy for its moderately compressed form, two only dorsal fins and the seven or eight longitudinal stripes following the scale rows.

Life History   Striped bass were introduced from New Jersey into the northern part of San Francisco Bay, California, in 1879. A second introduction was made in 1882, and in several subsequent years up until 1900 transfers were attempted within California. By 1884 an 18.5-pound (8.4-kg) striped bass appeared on the San Francisco market and in 1889 a 45-pound (20-kg) specimen. By 1889 a fishery was well established,[12] with only minor extensions of range. In California, ordinary movements are only moderately extensive and may be restricted by cold water barriers[9] and there are indications of homing to spawning grounds of origin in San Francisco Bay, which remains the centre of population.[9,13] However, a separate population was established and productive at Coos Bay, Oregon, by 1925, and was still growing in 1934[13] and producing in 1967.[6] Natural fluctuations in fishing success and species abundance appear to occur: in California general abundance declined from 1960 to 1968 while fish size increased,[7] suggesting that abundance and size may be related. Growth rates are fast and appear to be somewhat changeable. Representative fork lengths may be at age II 9.8 inches (25 cm); V 22.9 inches (58 cm), and IX 32.3 inches (82 cm) and growth continues at least to 20 years and large size.[2,10,13] All female striped bass are mature by the seventh year and about 87 percent in the fifth year. All males are mature in their fifth year and many in their third.[13] Females of moderate size produce about 500,000 eggs and large individuals more than 2,000,000. Striped bass are anadromous. Spawning takes place in spring, in fresh or slightly saline water at 15 to 24 C (60–75 F) in sloughs and frequently in accidental impoundments.[13] The eggs are demersal. They hatch in about 48 hours and the yolk sac is absorbed in about a week.[13] Access from nursery area can be impeded by water diversions[1] and precautions to avoid this are called for. Striped bass feed aggressively on a wide variety of marine and freshwater forms, including anchovies, shiner perch, striped bass, spring salmon, shrimps, carp[4,14,15] and feed especially actively in spring.[13]

Distribution   In coastwise waters. In the Pacific from southern California to southern British Columbia, not common south of Monterey, California,[11] or north of Coos Bay, Oregon. There are two Canadian records both for the summer of 1971 and spent females, from off Ecoole in Barkley Sound in July, and off Port San Juan in August.

In the Atlantic from northern Florida and Gulf of Mexico to the southern Gulf of St. Lawrence and St. Lawrence River, and in Shubenacadie Lake.[5]

Utilization   A very popular sports fish in California and formerly sought commercially. The fishery has been closed to commercial operations in California since 1935. There is a small commercial fishery at Coos Bay.[6]

References   1 Calhoun 1953; 2 Clark 1938; 3 Forrester, Peden, and Wilson 1972; 4 Johnson and Calhoun 1952; 5 Leim and Scott 1966; 6 Lyles 1969; 7 McKechnie and Miller 1971; 8 Merriman 1941; 9 Radovich 1963; 10 Robinson 1960; 11 Roedel 1953; 12 Scofield 1934b; 13 Scofield and Bryant 1926; 14 Shapovalov 1936; 15 Thomas 1967.

FAMILY BRANCHIOSTEGIDAE   TILEFISHES

The tilefishes are moderate- to large-sized, moderately compressed fishes of the temperate and tropical seas. Spines in the dorsal fin are soft, and the rayed portion of the fin is longer. Pelvic fins are thoracic. Only one species is known from British Columbia, and it a rarity. Tilefishes and ocean whitefish.

OCEAN WHITEFISH

Caulolatilus princeps (Jenyns 1842)

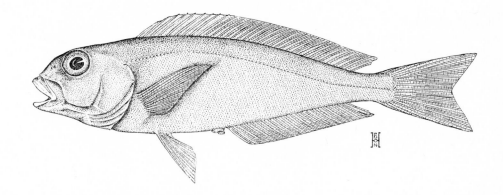

Scientific names from the Greek *caulos* (stem) and from *Latilus* (another fish); and the Latin *princeps* (leader).

Description   Body depth about 3.8 into standard length, moderately compressed. Head with strongly arched profile, its length about 3.6 into standard length. Mouth terminal, rather small, directed obliquely forward and upward. Upper jaw not quite reaching anterior margin of eye, slightly longer than lower jaw. Snout narrow at end. Teeth in jaws in villiform bands bounded on the outside by rows of small canines, largest posteriorly. Interorbital space raised, almost flat across centre of head, broad, its width about 3.7 into length of head. Eye subcircular, its length about 4.5 into length of head. Posterior edge of preoperculum finely and evenly serrate. Gill membranes joined and fused to the isthmus so as to leave a moderate free fold. Caudal peduncle compressed, its least depth about 13 into standard length, abruptly narrowed from base of caudal fin.

Fins   Dorsal (1), IX, 24 or 25, no notch between spinous and rayed parts, spines flexible, generally smooth contour. Caudal forked, upper lobe slightly longer. Anal II, about 23. Pectorals about 18, falcate. Pelvics I, 5, thoracic, extending well beyond anus.[1]

Scales   Ctenoid, fine, covering body, sides of head, and top of head as far as eyes, about 125 along side. Lateral line canal a flattened sigmoid, rising a little at the anterior end and then arching down to midside on the caudal peduncle, on base of caudal fin.

Colour   Warm brown on upper part of body, paler below. Fins tinged with yellow or green. Pectoral fin with a yellow streak in centre. Dorsal and anal fins with a blue stripe near edge.

Size   Length to 40 inches (100 cm) in California.

Recognition   Notable for the rather robust form with an unnotched, long dorsal fin with about 9 spines and 24 rays, the absence of teeth from the roof of the mouth, and the fine serrations along the posterior edge of the preopercular bone.

Distribution   Ecuador and Galapagos Islands, southern California, Washington off Willapa Bay. Not common north of Point Conception, California.[3] A single Canadian record from offshore between Barkley Sound and Clayoquot Sound, 48.41 to 49.07 N at 30 to 210 fathoms (55–384 m).[2]

References   1 Jordan and Evermann 1898; 2 Pattie and Baker 1969; 3 Roedel 1948b.

FAMILY ECHENEIDAE   REMORAS

The remoras are moderate-sized fishes with more or less cylindrical bodies and with the spinous dorsal fin highly modified to form on the top of the head and anterior body a sucking disc to attach the animal (presumably for rides) to larger fishes, turtles, etc. The disc is divided once longitudinally and several times across the body by laminae. There is no gasbladder, scales are cycloid, and the pelvic fins are thoracic. There are no spines in the upright or pelvic fins. For the most part these are fishes of the warm seas. One species is known from British Columbia. Remoras, whalesuckers, and sharksuckers.

WHALESUCKER

Remora australis (Bennett 1840)

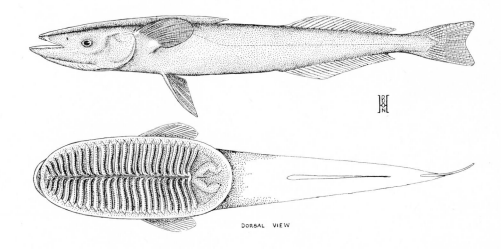

DORSAL VIEW

Scientific names from the Latin *remoral* (delayer); and *australis* (southern).

Clemens and Wilby 1946, 1961 used the name *Remilegia australis* (Bennett) for this species.

Description   Body elongate, greatest depth (behind pelvic fins) about 7 into standard length, about round in cross section in posterior half. Head much depressed, its top and the anterior part of the dorsal body highly modified to make a large-rimmed adhesive disc facing dorsally. In it some 25 cells are divided into right and left divisions by a central longitudinal membrane. The rim of the disc is denticulate, its length about 3.5 into standard length. Mouth terminal, moderate in size, directed slightly upward. Lower jaw projecting but narrower than upper jaw. Upper jaw fused with disc, part of which constitutes snout. Gape fails to reach eye. Teeth all fine, in bands, those in mouth villiform, those on edges of jaws somewhat larger. Interorbital space very wide, nearly 2 into length of head, consti-

tuting part of the adhesive disc. Eye small, lenticular, its length about 10 into length of head. Branchiostegals 8. Gill membranes free of the isthmus and each other. A groove in abdomen from between pelvic fins to anus. Caudal peduncle very little compressed, its least depth about 22 into standard length.

Fins   Dorsal (2), XXV to XXVII — 20 to 23, the spinous portion forming the adhesive disc, rayed fin low and rather fleshy. Caudal small and moderately forked. Anal 20 to 24, mirroring rayed dorsal. Pectorals about 24, short, and rounded. Pelvics I, 5 thoracic, recessed into deep grooves in the abdomen, where the fin membrane is secured.

Scales   Embedded and minute. Lateral line canal high anteriorly starting close to disc, reaching midside about at the posterior end of disc and continuing straight to caudal fin.

Colour   Brown or gray on ventral surface, lighter on dorsal surfaces. Fine light border on rayed dorsal and anal fins.

285

Size   Length to 20 inches (51 cm).

Recognition   Notable for the large sucker on the top of the head with about 25 lamellae.

Distribution   A fish of the tropical seas, including the Indian Ocean, the south-west Atlantic and Gulf of Mexico. **Off** western North America from Baja California to Vancouver Island. Canadian records include Sechart in Barkley Sound, Vancouver Island, and Goose Island in Queen Charlotte Sound.

FAMILY CARANGIDAE   JACKS

The carangids are moderate-sized fishes of variable form from terete to moderately compressed, well represented in warm seas. They have deeply forked tails and slender caudal peduncles. Usually there are two dorsal fins but the spinous fin may be absent or reduced to a few isolated spines. It is always shorter based than the rayed dorsal. There is one only or no anal or dorsal finlet. The premaxilla is protractile. Scales may be cycloid or absent. The lateral line canal frequently has well-developed plates in a row which is high at the anterior end. Only one species of the family occurs off the British Columbia coast and it is of fairly regular occurrence during the warm weather months. Jacks.

JACK MACKEREL

Trachurus symmetricus (Ayres 1855)

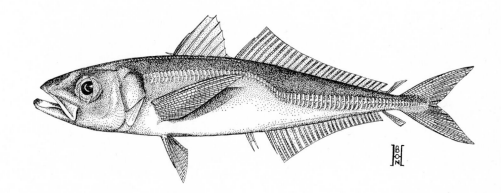

Scientific names from the Greek *trachus* (rough) and *oura* (tail — in the ancient name of a related species, *trachouros)*; and the Latin *symmetria* (symmetrical — regularly formed).

Regarded as a scad by Clemens and Wilby 1946 and thus identified as *Decapterus polyaspis* Walford and Myers 1944. Clemens and Wilby 1961 preferred the common name mackereljack to emphasize that the species is not related to the true mackerels. The present name follows usages in California where the species is familiar and of British Columbia fishermen, and agrees with the AFS recommendation.

Description   Body elongate, depth about 4.5 into standard length, fusiform. Head bluntly pointed, its length 4.2 into standard length. Mouth moderate, terminal, directed slightly upward with end of maxillary reaching nearly to anterior edge of orbit. Lower jaw protruding. Teeth small. Eye large, diameter 3.6 to 5.2 into length of head, partly covered anteriorly and posteriorly by strong transparent membranes. Caudal peduncle slender, its least depth around 30 into standard length.

Fins   Dorsal (2), almost continuous at base, VIII — I (or no spine), (28)32 to 33(38), anterior fin especially depressible in groove. Some small individuals show an additional forward-directed spine at the first dorsal origin but **this** seems to be embedded in skin in larger fish. Anal (2), (I)II — (22)29(33); anterior fin depressible in groove; posterior fin high anteriorly and low posteriorly. The last rays of both dorsal and anal fins become progressively more finletlike in structure and appearance with growth and in large specimens appear as finlets, but usually a fine connecting membrane or its remnants can be detected in carefully handled individuals. Pectorals 22 to 24, length about 4.5 into standard length, apparently longer proportionately in larger specimens. Pelvics I, 5, thoracic.

Gill Rakers   (51)56(61).

Vertebrae   (23)24(25).

Scales   Cycloid. Two lateral line canals. The main lateral line canal starts at about the level of the top of the eye, continues straight back to about the level of the origin of the second dorsal fin, where it slopes sharply downward to midside, continuing then to the base of the caudal fin. Line is composed of heavy scutes, especially in straight part. The accessory lateral line canal extends along base of dorsal fin to some point between the fourth spine or the fifth ray. Scales in main lateral line canal total 99(87–111) with 52(41–59) in curved portion, 46(40–55) in straight part.[6]

Colour   Metallic blue or green above, often mottled with lighter shades. Silvery on sides and belly.

Size   Length to 28 inches (71 cm).

Recognition   Two dorsal fins close together and about same height. Lateral line canal composed of bony shields along entire length. The last ray of dorsal and anal fins is sometimes free especially in large specimens but is not notably widely spaced from the preceding ray.[8]

Life History   Half the females are mature at about 280 millimeters total length and 2 years of age and all are mature at 3 years and around 310 millimeters. A California specimen 215 millimeters standard length contained 53,000 maturing eggs. Eggs when spawned are spherical, and pelagic near surface. Spawning is most concentrated off southern and Baja California between February and May,[1] and takes place mainly in the middle of the night.[2] Food is variable, often predominately macroplankton but at other times based mainly on lanternfishes or squids. They take anchovy as bait. School feeding on accumulations of blue lanternfish and saury attracted to a light seemed to be well organized with each jack mackerel selecting and running down a particular prey.[4] Laboratory experiments[5] showed that in jack mackerel night vision is good enough to allow schooling on a starry moonless night and effective feeding on a full moonlight night.

Distribution   From at least as far south as San Juanico Bay, 25.15 N, and tropical mid-Pacific,[3] 600 miles (970 km) off California,[1] and north to northeast Alaska.[9] Between May and September experimental fishing showed jack mackerel catches to move northward from about latitude 45 N to the whole of the eastern Gulf of Alaska at water temperatures between 11 and 17 C.[7] It is taken both in seines at the surface and in trawls on the bottom. Quite abundant at the surface off the southern part of Vancouver Island in early autumn. In British Columbia taken to 220 fathoms (403 m). British Columbia records include off Nootka, Selwyn Inlet, Queen Charlotte Islands, offshore rather generally, between May and October.

Utilization   The jack mackerel, judging from the abundance of young in the plankton, is one of the more abundant fishes in California and it supports a moderate fishery for canning. Only large individuals seem to occur on British Columbia fishing grounds. Substantial catches by seiners have failed to find profitable markets.

References   1 Ahlstrom and Ball 1954; 2 Farris 1963; 3 Grinols 1965a; 4 Grinols and Gill 1968; 5 Hunter 1968; 6 MacGregor 1966a; 7 Neave and Hanavan 1960; 8 Roedel 1953b; 9 Wilimovsky 1954; Other pertinent references are Anon 1934; Roedel 1948b; Roedel and Fitch 1952; and Walford and Myers 1944. See also Fitch 1956, Hart 1935, Roedel 1953a.

The pomfrets are large, strongly compressed, pelagic or bathypelagic fishes. Adults have blunt snouts and are deep bodied anteriorly tapering to a shallow caudal peduncle. Dorsal and anal fins are long based, each with two or three spines at the origin. The caudal fin is lunate and the pectoral fins long and pointed. Changes in form during development complicate the assessment of species. There is one species off the coast of British Columbia; it occurs abundantly but erratically offshore and infrequently inshore. Pomfrets and breams.

(PACIFIC) POMFRET

Brama japonica Hilgendorf 1878

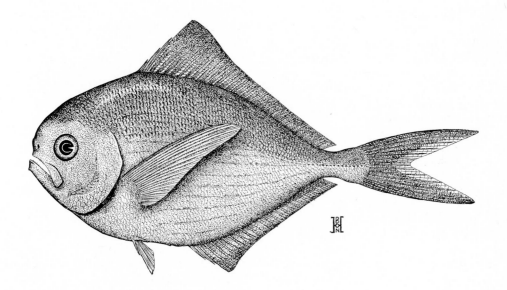

Scientific names from the Latin *brama* (a European minnow with some similarity in form); and Japan.

This species was called pomfret *Brama raii* (Bloch 1791) in Clemens and Wilby 1946 and 1961.

Brama raii or *Brama brama* Bonnaterre (1788) has been regarded as inhabiting the temperate and tropical oceans of the world.[6,9] However, although individual adults cannot be distinguished, young of north Pacific stocks differ clearly from those taken elsewhere.[8,10] The stock is accordingly regarded as representing a different species and the oldest acceptable name is applied.

289

Description   Body depth about 2.2 into standard length, very compressed, deepest around midlength. Head deep, compressed, its length about 3.6 into standard length. Mouth terminal, large, directed forward and up. Upper jaw extending about to centre of pupil. Snout blunt, slightly concave. Lower jaw blunt. Jaws even. Teeth on jaws and palatines slender. Interorbital space much elevated and convex, its width about 3 into length of head. Eye rather deeper than long, its diameter about 4 into length of head. Gill membranes free from each other and isthmus. Caudal peduncle compressed, its least depth about 15 into standard length.

Fins   Dorsal (1), III, 30 to 33, long, relatively high anteriorly, curving down and rather low posteriorly. Caudal deeply and finely forked. Anal II to III, 25 to 27, long and low, highest anteriorly. Pectorals about 22, falcate, longer than head, upper rays supported by cartilaginous folds. Pelvics I, 5, subthoracic, groups of long, modified scales at the outer angles of the bases.

Scales   Cycloid, rather small, each with anchors up and down, precisely arranged in longitudinal rows on body, on bases of fins, and all over head. Lateral line canal forming an arch on anterior two-thirds of body and then straight along midside, 80 to 84 scales in its length.

Colour   Steel gray above, silvery below with brighter bands along scale rows. Dusky to black on snout and all fins except pelvics. Orange streaks on operculum.

Size   Length to 4 feet (122 cm),[3] largest seen 19 inches (48 cm), probably reaches 3 feet (91 cm).

Recognition   Recognizable by the compressed body, long falcate pectoral fins, large tail, and blunt head.

Life History   Fishing experiments show that the area of availability to surface gillnets moves northward with the advance of the season from below latitude 50 N in early summer to the Gulf of Alaska generally in late summer,[8,12,13] and that availability is strongly related to water temperature.[7,11] Inshore and perhaps elsewhere the species appears and disappears erratically.[14] In the north Atlantic also pomfret are only seasonally abundant, occurrence is erratic, and availability is related to water temperature.[2,11,16] Squid, fish, and crustaceans have been found in the food.

Distribution   At least as far south as Guadaloupe Island,[5] southern California, Oregon, Washington,[15] Gulf of Alaska,[17,18] Aleutian Islands,[19] but not common in Bering Sea.[8] Kamchatka, Pacific coast of Japan, and tropical mid-Pacific.[6] Occasionally abundant in British Columbia,[4,14] and sometimes taken inshore.[1]

Utilization   Reported to be a good food fish but not so far found consistently enough to provide a basis for an industry.

References   1 Anon 1939; 2 Clark 1928; 3 Clemens and Wilby 1961; 4 Cowan 1938; 5 Fitch 1950; 6 Grinols 1965a; 7 Hanavan and Tanonaka 1959; 8 Hitz and French 1965; 9 Leim and Scott 1966; 10 Mead personal communication; 11 Mead and Haedrich 1965; 12 Neave and Hanavan 1960; 13 Pinckard 1957; 14 Pritchard 1930b; 15 Schultz and DeLacy 1936; 16 Stephen 1928; 17 Van Cleve and Thompson 1938; 18, 19 Wilimovsky 1954, 1964.

The manefishes are moderate-size or small, compressed fishes found bathypelagically or at bottom at moderate depths. The head is blunt and deep, and the eyes large. The dorsal fin is long based. The anterior rays of the dorsal fin are very much prolonged and fit into a fleshy sheath beside the dorsal fin when the fin is not erected. A similar sheath beside the anal fin receives the greatly elongated pectoral fin rays. Uncommon fishes, only a few specimens known from off the coast of British Columbia.

MANEFISH

Caristius macropus (Bellotti 1903)

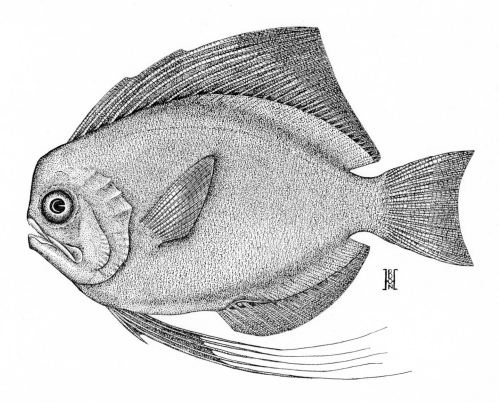

Scientific names from the Greek *caristios* (topsail); and *macro* (large) and *pez* (foot).

Description   Body very short, its depth about 1.7 into standard length, much compressed. Head short, its length about

3.4 into standard length, very deep, its depth about 1.6 into its length, compressed. Mouth terminal, moderate in size, directed forward and up. Snout vertical to overhanging, and short. Upper jaw extending beyond posterior margin of eye. Lower jaw included. Teeth fine, conical, curved inward, irregular, on jaws, vomer, and palatines. Interorbital space extremely high, its width about 2.7 into length of head. Gill membranes free from each other and isthmus, overlying second gill coverings which meet and fuse with isthmus. Caudal peduncle about 7 into standard length, compressed.

Fins   Dorsal (1), 32[4] of which some appear to be spinous, long, anterior rays very long, their tips extending three-quarters of distance to caudal peduncle, originating far forward over centre of eye, membrane delicate, the base of the anterior three-quarters of fin covered on each side with a fleshy sheath originating on the dorsal part of the body anteriorly and originating increasingly higher on the side of the fin until it disappears posteriorly. Caudal shallowly forked and almost pedunculate. Anal 22, rays long, joined by frail membrane, fin accompanied by folds similar to those beside dorsal but more developed, originating at pelvic insertions and continuing nearly to end of fin. Pectorals 17(14–19), rather pointed. Pelvics I, 5, rays very much elongated to about four-fifths standard length, thoracic.

Gill Rakers   On first gill arch about 21.

Vertebrae   37 to 40.[4]

Scales   Cycloid, irregularly arranged and of uneven sizes, generally moderate in size, large on head, as far as snout, small on fin sheaths and on bases of caudal and pectoral fins. Lateral line canal high, following dorsal contour of body, not discernible on posterior part of body and irregular elsewhere.

Colour   Dark brown, fin membranes black except on caudal which may also be dark brown.

Size   Length to 12.1 inches (30.7 cm).

Recognition   Recognized by the long high dorsal fin, which like the anal is sheathed at the base, the compressed body with a high steep forehead, and the long pelvic fins.

Life History   Manefish stomachs have been found to include fish remains,[1] their young are in turn eaten by albacore and lancetfish off California.[1] What the manefish does in life is not known but it may be noted that the dorsal, anal, and pelvic fins are received very tidily between the appropriate sheaths.

Distribution   Off Japan.[2] In the northeast Pacific from about Cedros Island, Baja California, to California, Oregon, and British Columbia. In British Columbia off Esteban Point[4] and Moresby Island (52.17 N, 133.10 W),[3] Queen Charlotte Islands. Bathypelagic at moderate depths. Rare. Similar fishes from the North Atlantic and possibly South Atlantic are regarded as different species.

References   1 Fitch and Lavenberg 1968; 2 Grinols 1965a; 3 Taylor 1967b; 4 Welander, Alverson, and Bergman 1957. See also Scott, Kohler, and Zurbrigg (1969).

The drums are sturdy elongate fishes with both spinous and rayed portions of the dorsal fin well developed, either separately or joined. Characteristically they are marine fishes of shallow inshore waters although some are known from fresh water. The upper jaw is formed by the premaxilla. Pelvic fins are thoracic. The anal fin has one or two spines. Abdominal muscles contract against the gasbladder to produce sounds, leading to the common group names croakers and drums. The group includes well-regarded sports and commercial fishes. Two species have been known to wander into Canadian waters. Drums, croakers, and seabass.

KEY TO THE SCIAENIDAE

1   Lower jaw projecting; anal fin II, 8 or 9; spines in first dorsal IX or X
.... *Cynoscion nobilis,* White seabass, p. 295

or   1   Lower jaw not projecting; anal fin II, 10 to 12; spines in first dorsal XII
to XV .... *Genyonemus lineatus,* White croaker, p. 294

WHITE CROAKER

Genyonemus lineatus (Ayres 1855)

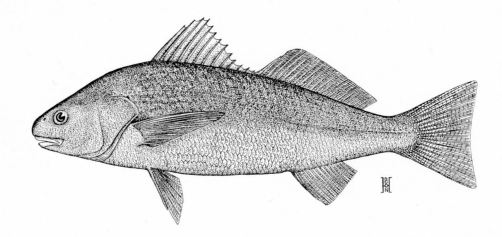

Scientific names from the Greek *genys* (lower jaw) and *nema* (barbel); and the Latin *lineatus* (striped).

This species was recorded as king-fish in Clemens and Wilby 1946 and is popularly called kingfish in California.

Description   Depth (3.5)3.4(4.0) into standard length, rather compressed. Head (3.2)3.4(3.6) into standard length. Anterior profile generally convex but may be flat or concave at eyes. Snout rounded. Lower jaw included. Maxillary usually extends to middle or posterior edge of pupil but may be longer. Eye 4.5 to 4.7 into length of head in 10 centimeter specimens, about 7.5 into length of head at 30 centimeters. Caudal peduncle depth (10.2)11.0 (11.6) into standard length.

Fins   Dorsals (2), (XII)XIII to XIV(XV) — I, (21)22(24), spinous dorsal only slightly incised. Caudal only slightly indented. Anal II, 11(12), free edge sloping backward. Pectorals (16)17(19). Pelvics I, 5, thoracic, fleshy appendages at base, first ray with free threadlike tip.[1,2]

294

Vertebrae   25.

Scales   Ctenoid. Lateral line canal high on body toward head sloping down to middle of side of caudal peduncle. Pores along lateral line canal 52 to 54. Slits and pores around mouth. Minute barbels on lower jaw.

Colour   Silver with brassy lustre and fine black stippling. Light below. Faint wavy lines follow scale rows upward and backward. First dorsal fin rather dusky, other fins aside from ventrals often yellowish. Small but conspicuous black spot on inside of pectorals extending a little on body. Peritoneum whitish.

Size   Length to 13 inches (33 cm).

Recognition   Lower jaw included. Dorsal fins XII to XV, I, 21 to 24. Anal II, 11 to 12. Chin with minute barbels (hard to see). Conspicuous black spot at inside of each pectoral fin at upper corner of base.

Life History   Spawning lasts from November until May. Sexual maturity is reached at about 13 to 15 centimeters. Feeding is active and versatile, including many bottom invertebrates.

Distribution   Central Baja California to Mayne Bay, Barkley Sound, Vancouver Island, B.C. There is only one British Columbia record.

Utilization   A schooling fish, sometimes used as bait in California, but generally unimportant.

References   1 Roedel 1948b; 2 Skogsberg 1939. See also Isaacson 1964.

WHITE SEABASS

Cynoscion nobilis (Ayres 1860)

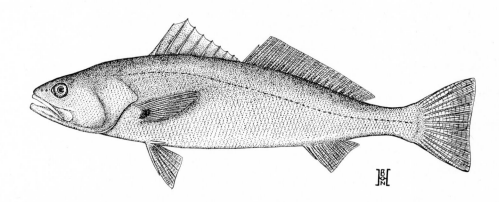

Scientific names from the Greek *kyon* (dog) and *skion* (name of a related European fish); and the Latin *nobilis* (noble).

Description   Body depth (4.2)4.5 (5.2) into standard length, rather compressed. Head (3.5)3.7(3.8) into standard length, profile flat or slightly convex above eye. Snout rather pointed. Mouth moderate. Tip of lower jaw projecting to various degrees. Maxillary reaches posterior edge of pupil or posterior margin of eye, its length 2.3 to 2.4 into length of head. Eye (5.3)6.1 (6.7) into length of head in small specimens

(18–32 cm), (8.1)9.1(9.8) in larger individuals (84–95 cm). Caudal peduncle depth (11.8)13.7(17.2) into standard length.

Fins   Dorsal (2), IX to X — I, (20)21(23), 2 fins contiguous, spinous portion slightly incised, triangular, with second or third spine longest; the second fin rather low. Caudal slightly lunate. Anal II, 8(9), free margin sloping backward. Pectorals I, (14)16. Pelvics I, 5, thoracic, fleshy appendage at base.

Scales   Ctenoid, on body and head to tip of snout. Lateral line canal high anteriorly, then arching down and straight along side of body. Pores along lateral line canal (75)81(87). Snout and chin with minute, scarcely visible pores.[2,3]

295

Vertebrae 24.

Colour Dorsally metallic blue, when fresh with copper luster. Whitish or silvery below. Dusky blotch at base of inner side of pectorals. Inner sides of pelvics dusky. Peritoneum nearly white.

Young (less than 30–35 cm) with dusky cross bars on back and extending to sides.

Size Length to 4 feet (122 cm) and weight to 80 pounds (36 kg).

Recognition Projecting lower jaw. Contiguous or touching spinous and rayed dorsal fins. Dorsal fins X — I, 20 to 23, anal II, 8 to 9, much shorter than rayed dorsal. Pectorals longer than 0.5 into length of head, reaching about to tips of pelvics.

Life History Spawning in California occurs from March to August near kelp beds. Fifty percent of the females are mature at 28 inches (71 cm) and half the males at 24 inches (61 cm). All are mature by 29.5 inches (75 cm).[1] The species is mainly a fish eater taking anchovies, pilchards, herring, and smelts as well as squids and crayfish.

Distribution Gulf of California to southeastern Alaska,[4] uncommon north of San Francisco. Canadian records are from Victoria, Sherringham Point, and Toba Inlet. It is observed in Juan de Fuca Strait and on the west coast of Vancouver Island.

Utilization The white seabass is an excellent food fish and is highly regarded by anglers in California.

References 1 Clark 1930; 2 Roedel 1948b; 3 Skogsberg 1939; 4 Wilimovsky 1954. See also Bonham and Olson 1955, Starks 1919.

FAMILY PENTACEROTIDAE ARMORHEADS

The armorheads are moderate-sized compressed fish with small mouths and fine teeth. The anal fin has three spines. The pelvic fins have one spine and five rays, and are thoracic. The bones of the head are sculptured with radiating lines. The armorheads are offshore species in the deeper parts of all oceans. They are rare off British Columbia, more abundant in the western Pacific Ocean.

PELAGIC ARMORHEAD

Pentaceros richardsoni Smith 1849

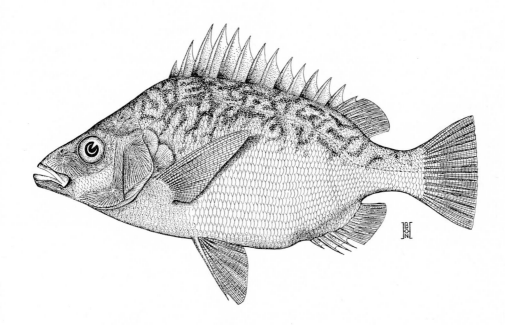

Scientific names from the Greek *penta* (five) and *ceros* (horns — or plates); and John Richardson, famous naturalist and explorer.

This species was named boarfish, *Pseudopentaceros richardsoni* (Smith 1849) in Clemens and Wilby 1961.

Description Body depth about 2.3 to 2.7 into standard length, compressed, ovate. Head compressed, bluntly pointed, length about 3 into standard length. Mouth rather small, terminal, directed slightly upward, upper jaw not extending half way to back of orbit, lower jaw slightly projecting. Snout slightly bulbous. Teeth fine, conical, in bands or patches on both jaws and vomer. Interorbital space broad, raised above orbits but flat, less than 3 into length of head. Eye about 4 into length of head. Opercles, preopercles and subopercles, cleithral, nasals, frontals, and other bones of cranium marked by strong radiating striations. Caudal peduncle compressed, its depth about 11 into standard length.

Fins Dorsals (1), XIII or XIV, 9 or 10, with long base, spines longitudinally ridged and in 2 series originating on either side of the mid-dorsal line, spinous portion moderately incised, rayed part of fin on raised peduncle and higher than spinous section. Caudal gently rounded. Anal IV, 7 to 9, on raised peduncle with 4 spines ridged and staggered. Pectorals 17, shorter than head. Pelvics I, 5, the spine strong, red, and strongly ridged, thoracic.

Gill Rakers On first arch (including rudiments) about 7 + 17.

Vertebrae 24.

Scales   Weakly ctenoid, overlapping on back and sides, embedded and separate on lower part of body, those near midventral line thickened with radiating striae. Lateral line canal curving strongly upward anteriorly and following shape of dorsal contour to caudal peduncle. Scales parallel to lateral line canal 70 to 76, pores about 69 to 72. Four sensory pores on lower jaw.

Colour   Bluish brown or gray on dorsal surface with pale vermiculations, and all paler below. Orange on spines of anal and pelvic fins. Various shades of red on head.

Size   Reported to reach 21 inches (53 cm). Specimens 12 inches (30 cm) in length are not uncommon.

Recognition   Notable for: strongly striated scaleless head bones, four anal fin spines, staggered longitudinally, striated spines on anal and dorsal fins, and thickening of the ventral scales.

Life History   The pelagic armorhead is taken in dragnets, gillnets, or on setlines at depths from the surface to 220 fathoms (400 m). One specimen caught on a surface longline 35 miles (56 km) off the west coast of the Queen Charlotte Islands and brought in to the Vancouver Aquarium was quite tame by the time it arrived from off the west coast of Vancouver Island[5] and fed on cooked shrimp the day after arrival. It fed well intermittently and swam actively in the aquarium. Observations suggest that in nature it takes moving food, near the surface, at night.[6] It did not bother chinook salmon smolts kept in the same tank. It grew nearly 3 inches (75 mm) (from 10–13 inches) in 3 years in the Vancouver Public Aquarium.[6]

Distribution   Very widely distributed and recorded from seas off South Africa, New Zealand, and from Japan, where it is not uncommon and is reported to support a fishery.[2,3] From California,[1,2] Oregon,[7,8] Washington and from well off the west coast of Vancouver Island about 50 N, 145 W,[4] and off Queen Charlotte Islands.

References   1 Fitch and Lavenberg 1968; 2 Follett and Dempster 1963; 3 Grinols 1965a; 4 Neave 1959; 5, 6 Vancouver Public Aquarium Staff 1969, 1970; 7 Wagner and Bond 1961; 8 Welander, Johnson, and Hajny 1957.

FAMILY EMBIOTOCIDAE   SURFPERCHES

The surfperches constitute a small rather uniform group of small and medium-sized species from the shallow waters of the north Pacific. All are compressed, more or less elliptical in outline, with a furrow or groove along either side of the dorsal fin; and all are ovoviviparous. Spinous and rayed dorsal fins are continuous. The dorsal fin has not more than 11 spines. The anal fin has three spines and 15 to 35 rays. Pelvic fins are thoracic with one spine and five rays. The caudal fin is deeply forked. There are no vomerine teeth. Scales are cycloid. The lateral line canal is continuous and high on the side. One species occurs in fresh water in California; the rest are all marine, for the most part living in bays or in the surf. Nine species have been recorded from British Columbia. Surfperches, seaperches, and viviparous perch.

KEY TO THE EMBIOTOCIDAE

1   Scale rows along lateral line canal less than 50 2

or   1   Scale rows along lateral line canal 59 or more 3

2   Frenum present .... *Brachyistius frenatus,* Kelp perch, p. 303

or   2   Frenum absent .... *Cymatogaster aggregata,* Shiner perch, p. 304

3   Frenum present 4

or   3   Frenum absent 6

4   Spinous part of the dorsal fin lower than rayed portion so that there is a marked step between the 2 sections of the fin 5

or   4   Spinous part of the dorsal fin incised but its outline about same height as rayed portion so that the 2 sections of the fin run into each other in a smooth arc .... *Phanerodon furcatus,* White seaperch, p. 310

5   Colour reddish with striking blue horizontal stripes ....
.... *Embiotoca lateralis,* Striped seaperch, p. 306

or   5   Colour pattern not marked, a dusky bar or 2 over back, generally silvery overlain with brown; a dark spot on preoperculum behind end of maxillary .... *Rhacochilus vacca,* Pile perch, p. 312

6   Distinct row of small scales along base of anal fin as far as last ray ....
.... Genus *Amphistichus* 7

or   6   No distinct row of small scales along posterior half of base of anal fin ....
.... Genus *Hyperprosopon* 8

7   Lengths of third to sixth dorsal fin spines greater than succeeding spines leading to a broad shallow notch in the profile of the whole dorsal fin
.... *Amphistichus koelzi,* Calico surfperch, p. 300

or   7   Lengths of dorsal fin spines beyond the fourth about equal and the 2 sections of the dorsal fin are smoothly contoured together ....
.... *Amphistichus rhodoterus,* Redtail surfperch, p. 301

8   Pelvic fins tipped with black ....
.... *Hyperprosopon argenteum,* Walleye surfperch, p. 307

or   8   Pelvic fins plain .... *Hyperprosopon ellipticum,* Silver surfperch, p. 309

CALICO SURFPERCH

Amphistichus koelzi (Hubbs 1933)

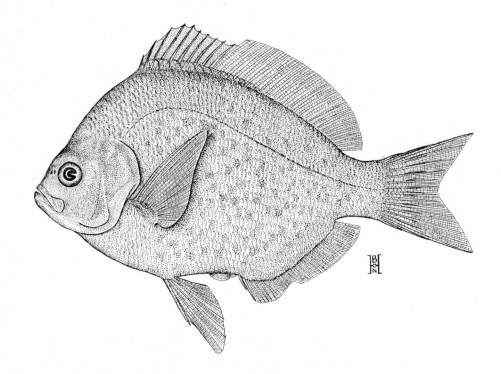

Scientific names from the Greek *amphi* (double) and *stoichos* (series — biserial teeth); and Walter Koelz, U.S. ichthyologist.

Description   Body short and compressed, depth about 2.0 into standard length. Head compressed, its length about 3.3 into standard length. Mouth rather small, terminal, and directed upward. Upper jaw length is about 2.8 into length of head and the maxillary extends as far as the anterior part of the orbit. Lower jaw somewhat protruding. There may be a narrow frenum joining the lower lip and lower jaw but it is usually absent. Interorbital space rounded, about 3.2 into length of head. Eye diameter about 3.6 into length of head. Caudal pe-duncle compressed and relatively deep, its least depth about 2.0 into length of head.

Fins   Dorsal (1), (IX)X(XI), (24)26(28), the spinous portion almost same height as the rayed portion but shorter. Caudal forked. Anal III, (26)29(32). Pectorals (25)27(29), ends appear frayed. Pelvics I, 5, thoracic.

Scales   Cycloid, rather small, (61)66(68) in lateral line canal. Lateral line canal usually somewhat less curved than dorsal contour of fish. A sheath of scales along the anterior part of the dorsal fin demarked from the body scales by a dark furrow. A definite row of small scales extending along base of anal fin to its last ray.

Colour   Generally silvery overlaid lightly with brassy tones. Back bluish or olivaceous.

Lower head and lower anterior part of body tinged with red. Sides with series of brown speckles which form rough narrow vertical bars. Pectorals plain, other fins usually reddish.[4]

Size   Length to 9 inches (22.9 cm)[2] in Canada, 12 inches (30.5 cm) in California.

Recognition   A much compressed fish with longest rays of spinous dorsal fin about on general contour of rayed dorsal. A vague pattern of narrow reddish bars each formed by a series of spots on the sides.

Distribution   Santo Tomos Bay in northern Baja California[4] to Shi Shi Beach 10 miles (16 km) south of Cape Flattery.[2] Found in surf.[3] Uncommon north of California.

There is no truly Canadian record. The northern record is about 20 miles (32 km) from the Canadian border and the species is included on that basis.

References   1 Hubbs 1933; 2 Peden and Best 1966; 3 Roedel 1953b; 4 Tarp 1952.

REDTAIL SURFPERCH

Amphistichus rhodoterus (Agassiz 1854)

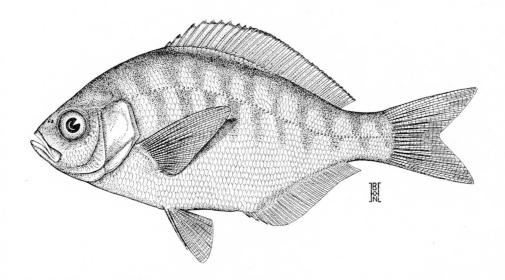

Scientific names from the Greek *amphi* (double) and *stoichos* (series — biserial teeth); and *rodoteros* (rosy).

The common names assigned to this species by Clemens and Wilby were porgy in 1946 and redtail seaperch in 1961. The scientific name used was *Holconotus rhodoterus*.

301

Description   Body short and compressed, depth about 2.1 into standard length. Head compressed, its length about 3.2 into standard length. Mouth terminal, rather small, and directed slightly upward. Upper jaw length about 2.6 into length of head. It extends to below the orbit. The snout is short. Lower jaw somewhat protruding. No frenum attaching edge of lower lip to jaw. Teeth fine. Interorbital space well rounded, its width about 3.2 into length of head. Eye relatively small, its diameter about 4.4 into length of head. Caudal peduncle short and relatively rather deep, its least depth about 2.2 into length of head.

Fins   Dorsal (1), (IX)X, (25)27(28), rather long in the base, the spinous portion slightly higher than rayed portion. Caudal broadly forked. Anal III, (28)29(31), highest at anterior end. Pectorals 27(28). Pelvics I, 5, thoracic.

Scales   Cycloid, rather small, (60)63(67). Lateral line canal parallels dorsal contour rather accurately throughout its length. A sheath of scales along the anterior two-thirds of the dorsal fin on either side demarked from the body scales by a furrow. A definite row of small scales extending along base of anal fin to the last ray.[2,3]

Colour   Generally silvery overlaid lightly with a brassy cast. Light green above. Sides with a series of about 9 to 11 narrow vertical dark bars, posteriorly, broken and staggered along the lateral line. Caudal and anal red.

Size   Length to a little over 16 inches (41 cm).

Recognition   Notable for having the spinous part of the dorsal fin slightly higher than the rayed portion, no frenum, and a somewhat projecting lower jaw. There is a colour pattern of narrow dark vertical bars on the side, in the posterior part of the body staggered at the lateral line canal. There are 11 to 13 rakers on the lower limb of the first gill arch.

Distribution   Halfmoon Bay in central California to the central west coast of Vancouver Island. An important species of viviparous perch in central California. In shallow surf and around old structures.[1]

British Columbia records from Esquimalt Harbour, Hesquiat Harbour, and Tofino area.

References   1 DeMartini 1969; 2 Roedel 1953b; 3 Tarp 1952.

KELP PERCH

Brachyistius frenatus Gill 1862

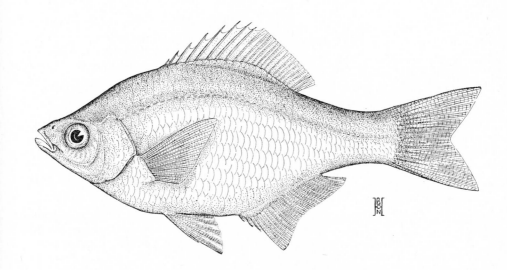

Scientific names from the Greek *brachys* (short) and *istion* (sail); and the Latin *frenatus* (bridled).

This species was recorded as the brown sea-perch *Brachyistius brevipinnis* (Günther 1862) by Clemens and Wilby 1946 and was assigned the common name kelp sea-perch in Clemens and Wilby 1961.

Description   Body compressed, depth about 2.5 into standard length. Head compressed, its length about 3.2 into standard length. Mouth small, terminal, directed slightly upward. Snout short. Upper jaw length about 4.0 into length of head reaching about three-quarters of the way to orbit. Lip joined to lower jaw by a frenum. Teeth moderately well developed. Interorbital space rounded, its width 3.3 into length of head. Eye, rather small, about 3.5 into length of head. Caudal peduncle sturdy and long, its least depth 2.1 into length of head, and its length about 1.7 into length of head.

Fins   Dorsal (1), (VII)VIII(IX), (13)14(16), spinous portion lower than soft-rayed part. Caudal forked. Anal III, (21)23(24), branched and unbranched soft rays alternating as arranged in fin. Pectorals (17)18. Pelvics I, 5.

Vertebrae   31 to 34, average 32.8.[1]

Scales   Cycloid, large, on lateral line canal (37)41(44). Lateral line canal approximately paralleling dorsal contour from head to caudal peduncle. A sheath of large scales along anterior three-quarters of dorsal fin separated from body scales by a furrow. A scaled peduncle at base of anterior part of anal fin.[3]

Colour   Variable. Olive brown to coppery above lateral line, with dark pigment under each scale, bright below lateral line. Dark on axilla. Fins either pale or rosy.

Size   Length to 8 inches (20 cm).

Recognition   Notable for its large scales, frenum joining lower lip and jaw, and the large caudal peduncle.

303

Life History   Occur to depth of 15 fathoms (27 m), usually around kelp. They eat crustaceans, and, in California mature in the first year.

Distribution   From Turtle Bay, central Baja California[2] to southern British Columbia at Departure Bay and southwest Vancouver Island. Characteristically in kelp beds.

References   1 Clothier 1950; 2 Fitch 1952b; 3 Tarp 1952.

SHINER PERCH

Cymatogaster aggregata Gibbons 1854

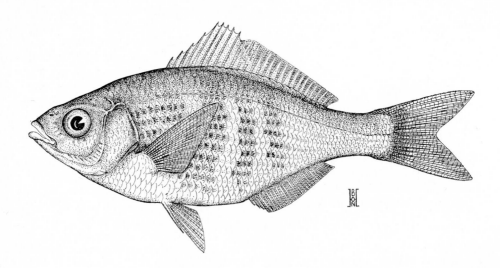

Scientific names from the Greek roots *cymo* (foetus) and *gastro* (belly); and the Latin *aggregatus* (crowded together).

Assigned the common name yellow shiner by Clemens and Wilby 1946 and shiner seaperch by Clemens and Wilby 1961.

Description   Body compressed, depth about 2.5 into standard length. Head compressed, about 2.9 into standard length. Mouth rather small, terminal, directed slightly upward. Upper jaw length about 3.6 into length of head, about four-fifths length of snout. Edge of lower lip free from lower jaw — no frenum. Teeth fine. Interorbital space rounded, about 3.2 into length of head. Eye rather small, its diameter 3.6 into length of head. Caudal peduncle compressed and slender, its least depth about 2.7 into length of head.

304

Fins Dorsal (1), (VIII)IX(XI),(19)20(22), spinous section higher than rayed part. Caudal forked. Anal III, (22)24(25) edge sigmoid, branching of rays irregular; males with an obvious anal gland at the base of the spines and anterior rays and an accompanying sharp break in the outer contour of the fin. Pectorals 19(20). Pelvics I, 5, thoracic.[8]

Vertebrae 33 to 37, average of 10 specimens, 34.6.[2]

Scales Cycloid, large, on lateral line canal (36)40(43). Lateral line canal approximately paralleling dorsal contour becoming closer toward tail. A sheath of scales along the side of the anterior three-fourths of dorsal fin demarked from scales of body by a furrow.[8]

Colour Always shining but otherwise very variable from bright silvery to almost black in breeding males. Characteristically with silvery longitudinal bars following lines between scale rows, separated by strong dark bars produced by pigment spots under the scales. Darker or greenish dorsally. The pattern frequently complicated by about 3 yellow vertical bars that partly interrupt the longitudinal dark bars.

Size Length to about 6 inches (15 cm).

Recognition Notable for its large scales (under 43 along lateral line canal) and slender caudal peduncle (its least depth at least 2.4 into head length), and absence of a frenum.

Life History In California the period between breeding and producing young is about a year.[5] Special anatomical provisions assure a supply of oxygen and nutrients to the young in the ovaries.[9] Formation of sperm by males is promoted by lengthening days of late winter and spring. In females early egg development is promoted by warmer temperatures but maturation of the egg preliminary to fertilization is advanced by the cool temperatures of early winter.[10] In British Columbia the breeding season with its complicated mating behaviour by the males lasts from April to July, and the sperm is stored in a compartment of the ovary for 5 to 6 months until November or December when the sperms penetrate the ovary fertilizing the eggs and gestation starts.[11] Five to 17 (mean 10), more in larger individuals,[4] (8–36)[1] young are born, tail first, in June or July, less commonly in May or August. Faster development of the embryo is caused by warmer water.[10] At birth young are 5.6 to 7.8 centimeters long. Females are rather larger than males at birth and throughout life.[10] Males are mature at birth[3,6] and the scales show a spawning check at 1 year of age. Females do not breed at 1 year of age but 99 percent are gravid in the second year. An age of 5 years and length of 128 millimeters was encountered.[4] At Yaquimma Bay, Oregon, females increase in mean length from 9.3 centimeters at 1 year to 13.6 centimeters at 6 years, and the number of embryos from 5.8 to 20. Larger and older females also produce larger young at birth.[12] Food differs with sex, age, and season. The early food is mainly copepods. Mussels and algae are taken at later stages, and adults are observed nipping the appendages off barnacles around wharves. Feeding activity is stimulated by light, and especially by sunrise.[4]

Distribution From Point Banda in northern Baja California to Port Wrangel in southern Alaska.[7]

In British Columbia common generally in shallow water through the summer. In winter in deep water down to 40 fathoms (73 m). Taken at 70 fathoms (128 m) on LaPérouse Bank.

Utilization Used to some extent as fresh fish in Canada and as bait in California.

References 1 Clemens and Wilby 1961; 2 Clothier 1950; 3 Eigenmann 1894; 4 Gordon 1965; 5, 6 Hubbs 1917, 1921; 7 Roedel 1953b; 8 Tarp 1952; 9 Turner 1952; 10, 11 Wiebe 1968a, b; 12 Wilson and Millemann 1969.

STRIPED SEAPERCH

Embiotoca lateralis Agassiz 1854

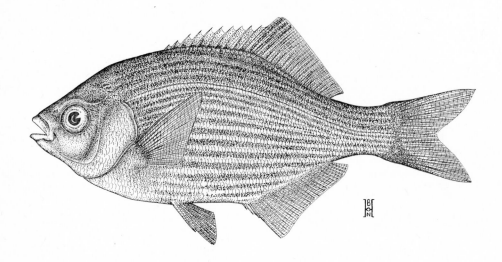

Scientific names from the Greek *embios* (living) and *tocos* (bring forth); and the Latin *lateralis* (lateral — blue stripes).

The species was recorded as blue seaperch, *Taeniotoca lateralis* (Agassiz 1854), by Clemens and Wilby 1946.

Description   Body short, compressed, depth about 2.2 into standard length. Head compressed, its length about 3.1 into standard length. Mouth small, terminal, directed slightly upward. Upper jaw about 3.6 into length of head and not quite reaching the anterior edge of the orbit. Broad frenum attaching lower lip to the jaw. Teeth moderate and pointed. Interorbital space broadly rounded, its width 2.8 into length of head. Eye diameter about 3.4 into length of head. Caudal peduncle compressed and fairly deep, its least depth 2.2 into length of head.

Fins   Dorsal (I), (X)XI, 23(24)25, spinous portion definitely lower than soft-rayed part.

Caudal broadly forked. Anal III, (29)30(33). Pectorals (21)22(24), triangular. Pelvics I, 5, thoracic.

Scales   Cycloid, (59)63(65) along lateral line canal. Lateral line canal somewhat farther from dorsal profile anteriorly. A row of scales forming a sheath along the base of each side of the dorsal fin for the first three-quarters of its length. Marked by a furrow and dark line especially prominent opposite the rayed portion of the fin and continuing to its end.

Colour   Copper ground colour with dark brown overlay on back. A series of about 15 blue horizontal stripes below lateral line. Head with several series of blue spots and stripes. Fins coppery. Dark areas on anterior part of rayed dorsal, base of caudal fin, anterior part of anal, and distal halves of pelvics.[4]

Size   Length to about 15 inches (38 cm).

Recognition   Notable for the relatively low spinous dorsal with the longest

306

spine about half the length of longest soft ray, the broad frenum joining lower lip to jaw, about 15 horizontal blue stripes below lateral line canal. (Note colour illustration, Plate III.)

Life History   Viviparous. In British Columbia young are liberated in June and July, as many as 44 at a birth.[1] Newly born young have longer fins and an orange cast on fins and body.[2] Recorded food items are small crustaceans, worms, mussels, and herring eggs. In captivity striped seaperch are very aggressive with dominant individuals herding the rest into compact schools in a corner of the tank.[2]

One of the more beautiful of British Columbia fishes.

Distribution   From Point Cabras in northern Baja California to Port Wrangel in southeast Alaska.[3] Not uncommon in British Columbia. Of minor commercial importance in northern California.

References   1 Fraser 1923; 2 Lamb personal communication; 3 Roedel 1953b; 4 Tarp 1952.

WALLEYE SURFPERCH

Hyperprosopon argenteum Gibbons 1854

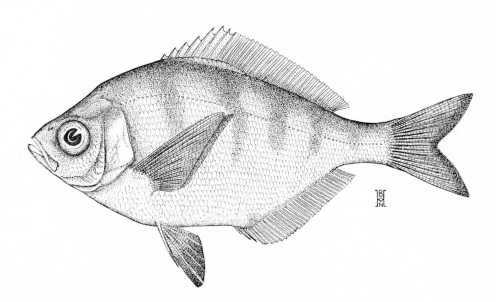

Scientific names from the Greek *hyper* (above) and *prosopon* (face — upward direction of "face"); and the Latin *argenteum* (silvery).

Clemens and Wilby 1946 and 1961 assigned the common names wall-eyed seaperch and walleye seaperch respectively.

Description   Body short, compressed, depth about 2.2 into standard length. Head compressed, its length about 3.2 into standard length. Mouth terminal, rather small, directed upward. Length of upper jaw about 2.6 into length of head, usually reaching orbit. Lower lip not bound to lower jaw by frenum, projecting. Teeth fine. Interorbital space raised moderately, about 3.2 into length of head with a low median ridge. Eye rather large, its diameter about 2.8 into length of head. Caudal peduncle compressed, its least depth about 2.4 into length of head.

Fins   Dorsal (1), (VIII)IX(X), (25)27(28), spinous part slightly higher than rayed part into which it passes evenly, highest about middle, base long. Caudal forked. Anal III, (30)32(35), rather low with long base. Pectorals 25(27)28. Pelvics I, 5, thoracic.[4]

Gill Rakers   On lower limb of first gill arch 21 or more.

Vertebrae   33 to 37, average of 11 specimens, 34.3.[1]

Scales   Cycloid, small, on lateral line canal (68)69(73). Lateral line canal swings upward from origin approximately following contour of body to caudal peduncle. A scaled sheath along the base of the dorsal fin marked off throughout its length by a furrow.

Colour   Dark blue dorsally, sides and belly silvery with young having narrow golden vertical bars. Tips of pelvic fins black. Dusky on edge of caudal.

Size   Length to 12 inches (30 cm).

Recognition   The spinous portion of the dorsal fin is higher than the soft-rayed part. The tips of the pelvic fins are black, there is no frenum, and the scales are small (more than 65 along lateral line canal).

Life History   In California courting males drive away intruders of their own species but not others. Viviparous. The gestation period is at least 5 or 6 months. Five to 12 young about 40 millimeters long are produced.[2] Of significant importance commercially in California.[3]

Distribution   From Santa Rosalia Bay, Baja California[3] to southern British Columbia (Esquimalt Harbour). Common along sandy beaches in California.

References   1 Clothier 1950; 2 Rechnitzer and Limbaugh 1952; 3 Roedel 1953b; 4 Tarp 1952.

SILVER SURFPERCH

Hyperprosopon ellipticum (Gibbons 1854)

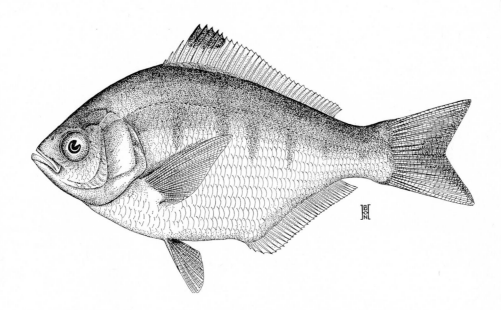

Scientific names from the Greek *hyper* (above) and *prosopon* (face — upward direction of "face"); and the Latin *ellipticum* (elliptical — outline of body).

Description   Body very short, compressed, depth about 2.2 into standard length, notably oval in profile. Head compressed, its length about 3.4 into standard length. Mouth rather small, terminal, directed upward. Upper jaw about 2.9 into length of head, barely reaching anterior edge of orbit. Lower jaw projecting. Lower lip not bound to jaw by frenum. Teeth fine. Interorbital space raised well above level of eyes, moderate, its width about 2.9 into length of head. Eye diameter 3.3 into length of head. Caudal peduncle compressed and fine, about 2.0 into length of head.

Fins   Dorsal (1), (VIII)IX(X), (25)26(28), spinous portion definitely higher than soft-rayed

portion and tapering evenly into it, base long. Caudal forked. Anal III, (29)31(34), rather low with long base. Pectorals (26)27(28). Pelvics I, 5.[2]

Gill Rakers   On lower limb of first gill arch 17 or 18.[2]

Scales   Cycloid, medium in size (59)62(67) along lateral line canal. Lateral line canal swings upward rather sharply from its point of origin at the head, then parallels the dorsal contour to the caudal peduncle. A row of enlarged scales along the base of the spinous dorsal.[3]

Colour   Dark green dorsally, sides and belly silvery. A series of narrow vertical bars of pale golden pink on body wall. Pectoral fins colourless. In British Columbia specimens dark on end of caudal fin and free edge of spinous dorsal.

Size   British Columbia specimens to 10 inches (25 cm).

Recognition   The spinous portion of the dorsal fin is higher than the soft-rayed part. The pelvic fins are without pigment. There is no frenum. Scales are moderate in size, always less than 69, and usually less than 65 along the lateral line canal.

Distribution   Southern California about 34 N to Schooner Cove,[2] Vancouver Island, about 49 N. That and near Ucluelet are the only records north of Clallum County, Washington.[1] The 12 adults from Ucluelet were taken on May 26, 1970, in water about 12.5 C. Most were gravid females averaging about 24 centimeters long.

References   1 Lamb personal communication; 2 Peden 1966c; 3 Tarp 1952.

WHITE SEAPERCH

Phanerodon furcatus Girard 1854

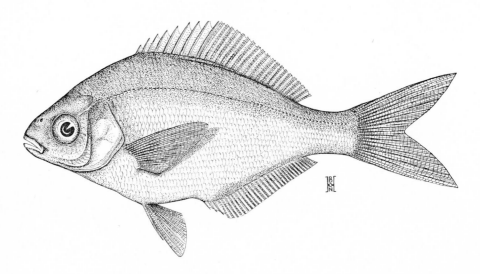

Scientific names from the Greek *phaneros* (evident) and *odons* (tooth); and the Latin *furcatus* (forked — tail).

Description   Body compressed, depth about 2.5 into standard length. Head compressed, its length about 3.3 into standard length. Mouth terminal, small, directed slightly upward. Upper jaw about 4.0 into length of head, reaching little more than halfway to orbit. Lower lip attached to lower jaw by a frenum. Teeth fine. Interorbital space rising moderately, its width about 3.0 into length of head. Eye small, 3.8 into length of head. Caudal peduncle rather slender, its depth about 2.5 into length of head, long.

Fins Dorsal (1), (IX)X(XI), (20)23(26), base rather long, rays of spinous portion shorter than soft rays. Caudal finely forked. Anal III, (29) 31(34), base length and height moderate. Pectorals 20(21). Pelvics I, 5, thoracic.[3]

Vertebrae 38 to 42, average of 17 specimens, 39.1.[1]

Scales Cycloid, moderate, on lateral line canal (56)61(62). Lateral line canal approximately paralleling dorsal contour but comes continually closer in progressing backward. A scaly sheath is on the sides of the dorsal fin.

Colour Greenish above but predominately silvery. Dark line at base of posterior part of dorsal fin. Fins usually yellowish except for edging of dark on tail fin, and usually a dark spot on edge near anterior end of anal fin.

Size Length to 12 inches (30 cm).

Recognition Notable for the frenum attaching the lower lip to the lower jaw, deeply forked tail, and the rather low dorsal fin having spinous section deeper and running into the soft-rayed part almost in a smooth curve.

Distribution Northern Baja California to Vancouver Island. Uncommon in Canada but the most important of the commercial viviparous perches in California.[2] Most common in sheltered bays.

References 1 Clothier 1950; 2 Roedel 1953b; 3 Tarp 1952.

PILE PERCH

Rhacochilus vacca (Girard 1855)

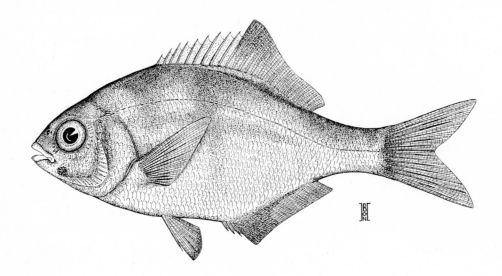

Scientific names from the Greek *racos* (ragged) and *cheilos* (lip); and the Latin *vacca* (cow — re viviparity).

Clemens and Wilby 1946 recorded this species as *Damalichthys vacca,* the dusky sea-perch. Clemens and Wilby 1961 used the same scientific name and the common name pile seaperch.

Description   Body short, compressed, depth about 2.3 into standard length. Head compressed, its length about 3.0 into standard length. Mouth small, terminal, directed slightly upward. Upper jaw and snout about same length, 3.9 into length of head. Lower jaw attached to lip by frenum. Teeth small. Interorbital space raised coming to a blunt ridge, its width about 2.8 into length of head. Eye variable in size among individuals, its diameter averaging about 3.8 into length of head. Caudal peduncle least depth about 2.5 into length of head.

Fins   Dorsal (1), (IX)X(XI), (21)22(25), rayed portion much higher than spinous portion, the anterior part of the soft dorsal is much the highest part of the whole fin with the first or second ray the longest. Caudal deeply forked. Anal III, (27)28(30). Pectorals (19)21(22). Pelvics I, 5, thoracic.

Vertebrae   33 to 38, average of 10 specimens, 34.6.

Scales   Cycloid, (58)64(69) in lateral line canal. Lateral line canal rather flatter than dorsal profile. A scaley sheath on each side of the dorsal fin for the first two-thirds of the length. This is set off by a furrow in the first two-thirds of the length of the fin and the line of the furrow continues alongside the fin as a dark line to its end.

Colour   Above, dark gray or brown pigment with a silvery luster which dominates the colour on the sides and belly. Darker blotches on the back and sides, dark vertical bars on juveniles. Fins dusky.

Newly born young are pinkish and the rayed portions of the fins are relatively higher.[3]

312

Size   Length to 17.4 inches (44.2 cm).

Recognition   Notable for the shape of the dorsal fin with a rather low spinous portion and the anterior end of the soft-rayed part much higher than any other section, a frenum connecting the lower lip and lower jaw, and the deeply forked tail fin.

Life History   In California breeding has been observed in July and it has been assumed that the gestation period was about 15 months[7,8] but there is conflicting evidence.[5] Tagging in Oregon showed movements to be very limited.[4] In British Columbia young are born in August. In confinement pile perch show strong territoriality.[3] The pile perch eats mussels in large numbers and strongly developed pharyngeal teeth are adapted to crushing the shells which are later encapsuled in mucus and voided with the faeces.[1]

Distribution   From San Martin Island, northern Baja California to southeast Alaska.[6,7,9]

It is common around the coast of Vancouver Island and in Burrard Inlet.[3] Frequents rocky shores and old piers.

Utilization   A moderately important commercial species in California. In Canada not highly regarded and taken mostly off docks by anglers.

References   1 Brett personal communication; 2 Eigenmann and Ulrey 1894; 3 Lamb personal communication; 4 Morgan 1961; 5 Randolph 1898; 6 Roedel 1953b; 7 Tarp 1952; 8 Wales 1929; 9 Wilimovsky 1954.

FAMILY SPHYRAENIDAE   BARRACUDAS

Barracudas are moderately large to large fishes. They have a subcylindrical form with long pointed head and a projecting lower jaw. The mouth is large as are the deep-set teeth which occur on the palatine bones and both jaws. The first dorsal is spinous and depressible with five spines; the second dorsal is placed far back on the body. The pelvics have one spine and five rays and are placed under the first dorsal. The pelvic girdle is not attached directly to the cleithrum or postcleithrum. The caudal fin is forked. The lateral line canal runs down and back. The barracudas are most abundant in the warmer seas but one species occurs occasionally off British Columbia.

PACIFIC BARRACUDA

Sphyraena argentea Girard 1854

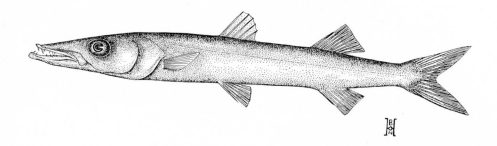

Scientific names from the Greek *sphyraena* (ancient name for this type of fish, from *sphyra,* hammer); and the Latin *argenteum* (silvery).

Clemens and Wilby 1946 called this species barracuda.

Description Body elongate, depth about 8.5 into standard length (in a small specimen, deeper in old individuals), deepest in middle, only somewhat compressed, taper mostly confined to caudal peduncle. Head very long, its length about 3 into standard length (in small individuals, about 4 in large ones), wedge shaped. Mouth terminal, large, directed forward. Upper jaw not reaching as far as anterior margin of eyes. Snout long. Lower jaw extending well beyond upper, small symphyseal knob. Teeth in upper jaw very small, sharp, spaced, at tip of jaw and on palatines very large and daggerlike. In lower jaw irregular, largest teeth near 2 ends, sometimes piercing upper jaw at tip of snout. Interorbital space flat and rather wide, its width about 6.5 into length of head. Eye diameter about 6.5 into length of head in small individuals, relatively smaller in large specimens. Gill membranes separate and free of isthmus. Caudal peduncle compressed, its least depth about 19 into total length.

Fins Dorsal (2), V — I, 9 or 10, widely separated. Caudal strongly forked. Anal I, 8 or 9, similar to second dorsal, and a little behind it. Pectorals about 16, small. Pelvics I, 5, abdominal, situated well forward.

Scales Cycloid, small, in about 274 rows above lateral line canal. Lateral line canal sloping down anteriorly, then straight along midside, about 166 scales.

Colour Bluish or brownish dorsally, silvery ventrally.

Size Length to about 4 feet (122 cm).

Recognition Recognized by two widely spaced dorsal fins, the first with five spines and the second with one spine and 9 or 10 rays, the elongate head and large mouth with large daggerlike teeth, elongate subterete body, and pelvic fins about midbody.

Life History Information on life histories has been obtained in California.[2,6] Spawning takes place at irregular intervals from April to September. Each female spawns several times during the season. First spawners produce an estimated 42,000 eggs, and large fish up to 484,000 per spawning. All males and about 75 percent of females are mature at 2 years. All are mature at 3 years. Eggs are pelagic, and when first released 1.2 to 1.6 millimeters in diameter, and rather lopsided. Newly hatched larvae are about 2.5 millimeters long. In about 4 days they begin to take on adult characters including the protruding lower jaw, and start feeding. At 1 year of age barracuda average about 35 centimeters long. A 71-centimeter barracuda is 4 or 5 years old and weighs about 3 pounds (1.36 kg). They are known to reach at least 11 years of age. As their appearance suggests barracuda are voracious feeders eating a variety of pelagic fishes such as anchovies and pilchards. In turn barracuda are eaten by seals, sea lions, and porpoises. They are schooling fish living fairly close to shore. They migrate north during summer and apparently move southward in autumn. They evidently respond to changes in water temperature.

Distribution   Gulf of California[4] and Magdalena Bay[2] to Prince William Sound, Alaska,[3] and Kodiak Island.[5] Pelagic. In British Columbia taken at Sooke,[1] Queen Charlotte Sound, and Prince Rupert.

Utilization   In California considered desirable as a table fish, and also sought for sport.

References   1 Cowan 1938; 2 Pinkas 1966; 3 Quast 1964; 4 Roedel 1948b; 5 Van Cleve and Thompson 1938; 6 Walford 1932. See also Walford 1929.

FAMILY TRICHODONTIDAE   SANDFISHES

Sandfishes are sturdy anteriorly tapering to a moderately deep caudal peduncle. There are two dorsal fins, spinous and rayed, a forked caudal fin, a large pectoral fin, and a thoracic pelvic fin with one spine and five rays. The anal fin is long. The mouth is rather large and both jaws are outlined with a straining fringe. The family is distributed through the north Pacific Ocean. So far only one species has been recorded in British Columbia.

(PACIFIC) SANDFISH

Trichodon trichodon (Tilesius 1811)

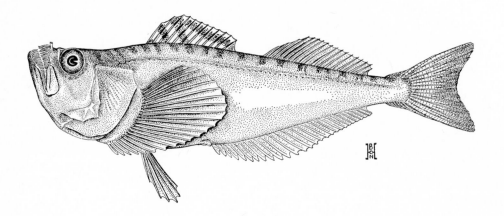

Scientific names for the species from the Greek *trichos* (hair) and *odons* (mouth).

Clemens and Wilby 1946 and 1961 used unqualified sand-fish and sandfish as common names for this species.

Description   Body rather elongate, depth about 3.6 into standard length, deepest near dorsal origin, tapering to caudal peduncle, compressed. Head length about 3.4 into standard length, dorsal profile almost straight and in line with long axis of body, compressed. Mouth terminal, moderate in size, directed almost straight upward. End of upper jaw in natural position under anterior part of eye. Lower jaw very deep, slopes down nearly to end of upper jaw at an angle about 30 degrees to vertical. Nares prominent and narrow. Lips on both jaws strikingly fringed with fleshy palisades. Teeth moderate in size, conical, well spaced, recurved, on jaws, vomer, and palatines. Interorbital space broad and flat, narrowest between anterior angles of orbits, its width about 3.1 into length of head. Eye diameter about 4.5 into length of head. Gill membranes fused well forward, and free of isthmus. Caudal peduncle compressed, its least depth about 14 into standard length. Anal papilla slender. A pair of anal palps on either side of anus.

Spines   Preopercular 5, radiating, middle one longest.

Fins   Dorsal (2), XIII to XV — I, 18 to 20, separated by about 1 eye diameter, both highest anteriorly and both curving gently down to body. Caudal moderately forked. Anal about I, 28 or 29, long and low. Pectorals 21 or 22, firm with lower edges turned forward. Pelvics, I, 5, thoracic.

Scales   Absent. Lateral line canal high, following dorsal contour, about 46 pores.

Colour   Light brown on dorsal surface, silvery ventrally, dark along midside, mid-dorsal line in irregular patches, and lateral line. Spinous dorsal with dark streaks paralleling free edge. Upper parts of pectorals and caudal with darkened edges, and vague dark blotches on rayed dorsal. Anal, pelvics, and lower parts of pectorals light.

Size   Length to 12 inches (30.5 cm).

316

Recognition   Recognized by the up-ward-turned, fringed mouth, the stout pectoral fin with out-turned edges, and absence of scales.

Life History   Clemens and Wilby[2] report capture of a sandfish on February 23, 1936, at Wickaninnish Bay from a depth of about 1 foot (30 cm) in sand. It was a 12-inch (30.5-cm) female which extruded mature eggs when disturbed. Found in stomach of a chinook salmon.

Distribution   From northern California as far south as San Francisco Bay through Oregon, Washington,[3] Alaska, the Aleutian Islands,[5] and Bering Sea[4] to Medniji Island and Kamchatka.[1] Known from both coasts of Vancouver Island, Hecate Strait, and outlet of the Skeena River.

References   1 Andriashev 1937; 2 Clemens and Wilby 1946; 3 Schultz and DeLacy 1936; 4, 5 Wilimovsky 1954, 1964.

FAMILY BATHYMASTERIDAE   RONQUILS

The ronquils have elongate rather slender bodies with high straight lateral line canals and long-based dorsal and anal fins, both composed of soft rays. Pelvic fins are thoracic, each with one spine and five rays. Two members of the family are found in British Columbia. Ronquils and searchers.

KEY TO THE BATHYMASTERIDAE

1   First 3 or 4 rays in the dorsal fin unbranched, the remainder branched; scales ctenoid .... *Bathymaster signatus,* Searcher, p. 318

or   1   First 20 to 30 rays in dorsal fin unbranched, the remainder branched; scales cycloid .... *Ronquilus jordani,* Northern ronquil, p. 319

SEARCHER

Bathymaster signatus Cope 1873

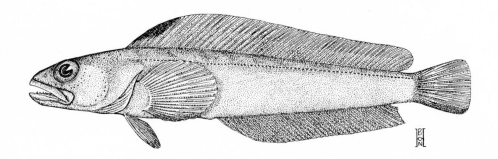

Scientific names from the Greek *bathys* (deep) and *master* (searcher); and the Latin *signatus* (marked).

Description   Body elongate, depth about 5.5 into standard length, compressed. Head length about 3.3 into standard length, only moderately compressed. Mouth terminal, large, directed forward. Upper jaw extending to posterior margin of orbit. Teeth in jaws moderate in size, in a row on upper jaw, in clusters in lower jaw. Pads of small teeth in mouth and in rows on vomer and palatines. Snout short, as long as eye or a little shorter. Interorbital space narrow, its width about 8 into length of head. Eye oval, its length about 4.3 into length of head, the long axis directed forward and down. Gill membranes free of each other and isthmus. Caudal peduncle short, strongly compressed, its least depth about 14 into standard length.

Fins   Dorsal (1), about 47, first 3 or 4 rays not branched, rest branched, high, even, tapering slightly toward posterior. Caudal, narrow, gently rounded. Anal, 32 to 34, high, with height about even through length. Pectorals about 21, rounded. Pelvics I, 5, thoracic.

Scales   Ctenoid, moderate in size, extending on dorsal and pectoral fin membranes for nearly half their heights, absent from head and cheeks. Lateral line canal following dorsal contour from head to caudal peduncle, about 100 pores. Numerous pores, mostly raised, on upper part of head and snout, and around eyes.

Colour   Brown on the dorsal surface with dark markings, lighter ventrally with yellow to orange streaks. Yellow on head in some areas and yellow mottling on fins. Black blotch on anterior part of dorsal fin for first 3 to 5 rays, conspicuous. Pelvic fin dusky and some dark marks on other fins. Eyes reputed to be blue.

Size   Length to 12 inches (30.5 cm).

Recognition   Notable for the naked head with its raised pores, the ctenoid scales, and only three or four unbranched rays in the dorsal fin.

Life History   In April and June young between total lengths of 7 and 25 millimeters (0.28–1 inch) were encountered commonly in surface waters of Saanich Inlet and were found to be living almost exclusively on copepods, their larvae and eggs.[1]

Distribution   From northern British Columbia to the Bering Sea and Pribilof Islands, and on the Asian coast from Petropavlosk to Cape Olytorsky and the Commander Islands but not recorded from Okhotsk Sea. Adults in Canada reported mostly from the northern part of British Columbia, Milbanke Sound, and the west coast of the Queen Charlotte Islands.

References   1 Barraclough, Robinson, and Fulton 1968.

NORTHERN RONQUIL

Ronquilus jordani (Gilbert 1888)

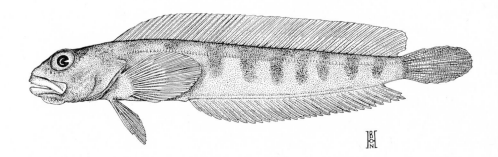

Scientific names from the Spanish *ronquilus* (a similar fish); and David Starr Jordan, U.S. ichthyologist who first recognized the species.

Clemens and Wilby 1946, 1961 used the unqualified common name ronquil for this species.

Description   Body elongate, its depth greatest immediately anterior to anus, about 5.6 into standard length, moderately compressed. Head length about 3.6 into standard length, only moderately compressed. Mouth terminal, large, directed forward. Upper jaw projecting to about middle of orbit. Snout low and short, about length of eye. Teeth rather small, in single rows on upper jaw and on sides of lower jaw, in patches at tip of lower jaw, vomer, and palatines. Interorbital space narrow, its width about 11 into length of head. Eye oval, its length about 4 into length of head. Gill membranes free of each other. Caudal peduncle short, strongly compressed, its least depth about 13 into standard length.

Fins   Dorsal (1), 41 to 48, first 20 to 30 rays unbranched, rest branched, moderately high, and about same height throughout. Caudal rounded. Anal 31 to 34, rays moderately exserted, about same height throughout, terminating slightly ahead of or below dorsal termination. Pectorals about 17, rounded, rays slightly exserted, more so and thickened, ventrally.

319

Scales   Cycloid, small, on body but not on fins, on cheeks below level of eye. Lateral line canal following dorsal contour from head to caudal peduncle, about 93 pores. Lines of moderate well-spaced pores on head around eyes, on cheeks, and top of head. In males an even fleshy pad from snout to occiput.

Colour   In the 2 sexes distinctive. On males, orange dorsally; dull olive green below; vague darker vertical bars on sides, fine yellow longitudinal lines below lateral line canal, and yellow on upper part of pectoral fin; golden bars below eye and across middle of cheek; black on top of head and across occiput, and behind eye; dusky blotch at anterior end of dorsal fin; black, margined with yellow on dorsal and caudal fins; iridescent light blue margined with black on anal fin with golden spots at base; pelvic fins and lower parts of pectorals black. On females, olive green dorsally, lighter ventrally; yellow longitudinal lines on sides; reddish on occiput; dusky blotch on anterior part of dorsal fin; bright orange on edges of dorsal and caudal; pale light blue margined with brown on anal; white on pelvic fins.

Size   Length to 6.75 inches (17.1 cm).

Recognition   Recognized by having the first 20 to 30 rays of the long even dorsal fin unbranched with the rest branched, cycloid scales, small scales on the cheeks behind and below the eyes, and pores on head relatively inconspicuous.

Life History   Northern ronquil are taken at depths of 10 to 90 fathoms (18–165 m) in British Columbia. Females with fully developed salmon coloured eggs have been taken in March, and ripening individuals have been taken in Puget Sound in February. Young ronquil under one-half inch (5–11 mm) in length have been taken at the surface off the outlet of the Fraser River and in Saanich Inlet. They were found to be eating Cladocera and other crustaceans such as copepods and barnacle larvae, clam larvae, and polychaete worms.[1,2,3]

The so-called ronquil may include two species, one with a blunt snout and 90 to 98 lateral line pores, and another sharper-snouted species with more lateral line pores.

Distribution   Monterey Bay, California to the Aleutian Islands and the Bering Sea. [4,5] Throughout British Columbia both in the Strait of Georgia and on the outside coast.

References   1 Barraclough 1967a; 2 Barraclough, Robinson, and Fulton 1968; 3 Robinson, Barraclough, and Fulton 1968b; 4, 5 Wilimovsky 1954, 1964.

In the clinids the body is elongate and moderately tapered. The dorsal fin is long, extending practically the full length of the body, but is not confluent with the caudal. It is almost entirely composed of spines and has raised sections at both ends. Pelvic fins are thoracic with one spine and three or four rays. Teeth are small and conical. Two species of this family are represented in British Columbia records. Clinids, kelpfishes, and related species.

KEY TO THE CLINIDAE

1   Scales in longitudinal series above lateral line canal more than 175; dorsal soft rays (7)8 or 9(10), evenly spaced; no ocelli on sides of body ....
.... *Gibbonsia metzi,* Striped kelpfish, p. 322

or   1   Scales in longitudinal series above lateral line canal fewer than 175; dorsal soft rays (5)6 or 7(8), first rays closer together than posterior rays; one or more dark spots of varying intensities on sides ....
.... *Gibbonsia montereyensis,* Crevice kelpfish, p. 323

STRIPED KELPFISH

Gibbonsia metzi Hubbs 1927

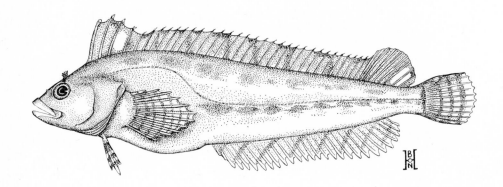

Scientific names from P. W. Gibbons, an early naturalist of Alameda, California; and C. W. Metz, perceptive student of the genus.

Description   Body elongate, depth about 4.6 into standard length, strongly compressed. Head length about 4.2 into standard length, compressed, snout narrow. Mouth terminal, moderate in size, directed slightly upward. Upper jaw extending to anterior part of eye. Lower jaw somewhat protruding. Lips thickened. Teeth small, conical, on jaws and vomer. Interorbital space convex, its width about 6.5 into length of head. Eye diameter about equal to interorbital width. Gill membranes fused to each other and free of isthmus. Caudal peduncle much compressed, short, its least depth about 17 into standard length.

Fins   Dorsal (1), XXXIV to XXXVII, (7) 8 to 9(10), long, the first 3 spines more closely spaced and higher than those following, long, rays at posterior end of fin longer than spines immediately ahead, posterior 2 rays separated from rest of fin by widened spaces between preceding 2 rays. Caudal rounded. Anal II, 24 to 27, posterior rays somewhat lengthened. Pectorals about 12, rounded. Pelvics I, 3, thoracic.

Vertebrae   Number about 49.

Scales   Cycloid, minute (more than 180 rows above lateral line canal). Lateral line canal following dorsal contour anteriorly beyond end of pectoral fin, then straggling down to midside continuing there sparsely to caudal peduncle. Flaplike cirri over each eye, small cirri over nostrils, slender cirri at tips of dorsal spines.

Colour   Red or brown, weakly striped or mottled with darker shades.

Size   Length to 7.25 inches (18.4 cm).

Recognition   Noteworthy for the long dorsal fin with posterior rays and anterior spines higher than rest of fin, and no ocelli.

Distribution   From Hondo Canyon, 175 miles south of Ensenada, Baja California to Oregon–California border. In British Columbia at Ucluelet and Maquinna Point, Nootka Island. Usually taken in shallow water as in tide pools.

References   Hubbs, C. L. 1927; Hubbs, Clark 1952.

CREVICE KELPFISH

Gibbonsia montereyensis Hubbs 1927

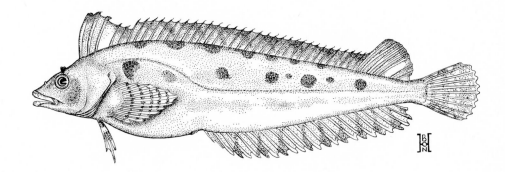

Scientific names from P. W. Gibbons, an early naturalist of Alameda, California; and Monterey, California.

Clemens and Wilby (1946) called this species spotted kelpfish, *Gibbonsia elegans montereyensis*. Later work[2] showed that *Gibbonsia montereyensis* should be regarded as a distinct species separate from *Gibbonsia elegans*. However, the name *Gibbonsia montereyensis montereyensis* (Clark Hubbs 1952) is recommended to separate the form found in British Columbia and elsewhere on exposed coasts from closely related populations occurring in more sheltered areas.

Description   Body elongate, depth about 4.3 into standard length, compressed. Head length about 4.6 into standard length, compressed, narrow toward snout. Mouth terminal, rather small, directed forward. Upper jaw extending about to anterior margin of orbit. Lips thickened. Jaws about equal. Teeth fine and conical on both jaws and vomer. Interorbital space convex, its width about 7 into length of head. Eye diameter about equal to interorbital width. Gill membranes fused to each other and free of isthmus. Caudal peduncle much compressed and short, its least depth about 18 into standard length.

Fins   Dorsal (1), XXXIV to XXXVI, (5)6 to (7)8, long, first 3 spines longest and somewhat set apart from the 2 following so that the spinous part of the fin is slightly notched, outline of rest of spinous part of fin even, rays considerably longer than spines, the last 3 rays separated from rest of rays by widened spaces. Caudal rounded. Anal II, 23 to 28, rays in posterior part of fin longest. Pectorals about 12. Pelvics I, 3, thoracic.

Vertebrae   About 49 to 51.

Scales   Cycloid, very small, but fewer than 175 rows above lateral line canal. No scales on caudal fin or posterior part of caudal peduncle. Lateral line canal after extending straight back from opercle, arcs gently down to midside where it extends to caudal peduncle. Flaplike cirri over each eye, small cirri over nostrils, fine cirri at tips of dorsal spines.

Colour   Very variable with several recognizable phases, reddish, green, dark and silver bars, which intermix freely. There is usually a strong dark ocellus above the lateral line canal behind the pectoral fin and there may be additionally several or a series of dark spots of various intensities. Fins weakly pigmented at bases, anal and pectorals most so. Head often with pigment bars radiating from eye.

Size   Length to 4 inches (10 cm).

Recognition   Recognized by the long dorsal fin with anterior spines and posterior rays both longer than rest of fin. Usually ocelli on side behind head or a series of dark spots.

Distribution   San Tomas Bay and as far as Descanso Bay, Baja California.

through California to north of Point Conception. In British Columbia at Ucluelet, not known between.

References   1 Hubbs, C. L. 1927; 2 Hubbs, Clark 1952.

FAMILY STICHAEIDAE   PRICKLEBACKS

The pricklebacks have long slender compressed bodies. The dorsal fin is long, extending to the end of the body and, sometimes only, confluent with the caudal fin. It is composed entirely of spines. The anal also is long, and it also may or may not be confluent with the caudal fin. The lateral line canal is faint, incomplete, or absent, or there may be four main branches with vertical side branches on either side of the body. Pelvic fins may be present or absent; when present there is one spine and three or four rays. The teeth are small and conical. The pricklebacks are circumboreal bottom fishes. There are 14 species recorded from British Columbia waters. Pricklebacks, cockscombs, warbonnets, and shanny.

KEY TO THE STICHAEIDAE

1   Pelvic fins present 2

or 1   Pelvic fins absent 10

2   Cirri prominent on head 3

or 2   No cirri on head 5

3   Cirri arising in interorbital area dominating over others; dorsal spines more than 65; pelvic fins I, 3 ....
.... *Bryozoichthys marjorius,* Pearly prickleback, p. 331

or 3   Cirri arising in interorbital area not dominating; dorsal spines less than 65; pelvic fins I, 4 .... Genus *Chirolophis* 4

4   Large cirri in interorbital area and on anterior dorsal fin spines; anal fin rays 44 to 51; teeth in jaws in broken rows; no ocelli on dorsal fin ....
.... *Chirolophis decoratus,* Decorated warbonnet, p. 332

or 4   Cirri from snout to dorsal fin origin nearly uniform in size; anal rays 37 to 42; teeth flattened, in cutting edges in jaws; row of ocelli on dorsal fin ......
.... *Chirolophis nugator,* Mosshead warbonnet, p. 333

5   Spines in anal fin 0 to II 6

or 5   Spines in anal fin III to V 9

6   Spines in dorsal fin 44 to 57 8

or 6   Spines in dorsal fin 57 to 72 .... Genus *Lumpenus* 7

7   Spines in dorsal fin 57 to 60; lower 5 rays of large pectoral fin exserted; snout markedly overhanging ....
.... *Lumpenus maculatus,* Daubed shanny, p. 336

or 7   Spines in dorsal fin 66 to 72; pectoral fin moderate in size without exserted lower rays; snout barely extending beyond lower jaw ....
.... *Lumpenus sagitta,* (Pacific) snake prickleback, p. 337

8   Spines in dorsal fin 44 to 45; anal spine I; sides with vague Y-shaped dark marks; a row of black spots along base of dorsal fin ....
.... *Allolumpenus hypochromus,* Y-prickleback, p. 327

or 8   Spines in dorsal fin 55 to 57; anal spines II; about 25 vertical light bars intercepting olive brown colour on sides ....
.... *Plectobranchus evides,* Bluebarred prickleback, p. 339

	9	Snout longer than eye and overhanging mouth; no vertical bars in colour pattern .... *Lumpenella longirostris,* Longsnout prickleback, p. 334
or	9	Snout shorter than eye, barely extending beyond anterior end of lower jaw; 10 to 12 white vertical bars crossing upper part of side .... *Poroclinus rothrocki,* Whitebarred prickleback, p. 340

	10	Anal fin confluent with caudal fin; no crest on top of head 12
or	10	Anal fin free of caudal fin; median crest on top of head .... Genus *Anoplarchus* 11

	11	Width between attachments of posterior margins of gill membranes to isthmus 1.7 to 4.1 percent of standard length; anal rays 36 to 40 (in British Columbia) .... *Anoplarchus purpurescens,* High cockscomb, p. 329
or	11	Width between attachments of posterior margins of gill membranes to isthmus 0 to 1.9 percent of standard length; anal rays 40 to 44 .... *Anoplarchus insignis,* Slender cockscomb, p. 328

	12	Spines in anal fin II or III .... *Phytichthys chirus,* Ribbon prickleback, p. 338
or	12	No spines in anal fin .... Genus *Xiphister* 13

	13	Distance from tip of snout to origin of dorsal fin approximately equal to length of head .... *Xiphister mucosus,* Rock prickleback, p. 343
or	13	Distance from tip of snout to origin of dorsal fin about 1.5 times length of head .... *Xiphister atropurpureus,* Black prickleback, p. 341

Y-PRICKLEBACK

Allolumpenus hypochromus Hubbs and Schultz 1932

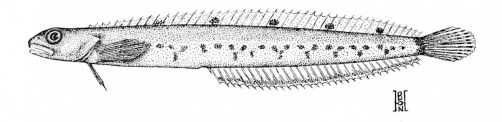

Scientific names from the Greek *allo* (other) and *Lumpenus* (a related fish); and the Greek *hypo* (below) and *chroma* (colour).

Called Y-blenny in Clemens and Wilby 1946.

Description   Body very elongate, depth about 8 or more into standard length, compressed. Head about 5 to 6 into standard length, compressed, bluntly rounded anteriorly. Mouth terminal, moderate in size, directed forward. Upper jaw extends to middle of pupil. Moderate teeth in jaws and on vomer. Interorbital space narrow, about 8 into length of head, almost flat directly behind orbits, concave before and after. Eye large, oval, its length about 4 into length of head entering dorsal profile. Opercular membranes united, joined to isthmus at middle line. Caudal peduncle compressed, its depth about 19 into standard length.

Fins   Dorsal (1), about XLIV, free from caudal. Caudal ovally rounded. Anal I, about 31. Pectorals large, pointed. Pelvics I, 3, thoracic, origins contiguous, long, length about 3 into length of head.

Scales   Cycloid over whole body, but not on head. Lateral line canal absent.

Colour   In preservative, light brown, a row of 5 black spots along base of dorsal fin and 2 additional spots on upper and lower base of caudal fin, a less definite series of dark markings along sides, some of those on lower part forming distinct Y's.

Size   Length to 2.9 inches (7.4 cm).

Recognition   Notable for united gill membranes joined to isthmus at the centre, the Y-shaped markings, spots at the base of the dorsal fin, the long pelvic fins, the dorsal fin with about 45 spines, and the anal fin with one spine and 31 rays.

Life History   Young about 13 millimeters in length were taken in Saanich Inlet in June. They were found to be eating copepod larvae.[1]

Distribution   Known only from southern British Columbia, Departure Bay,[2] Baker Pass, and Saanich Inlet.[1]

References   1 Barraclough and Fulton 1968; 2 Hubbs and Schultz 1932.

SLENDER COCKSCOMB

Anoplarchus insignis Gilbert and Burke 1912

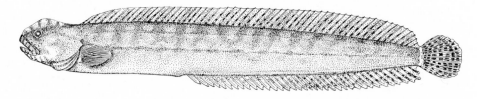

Scientific names from the Greek *anoplos* (unarmed) and *archos* (anus — no spine); and the Latin *insignis* (no signal).

Description   Body elongate, depth 6.8 to 9.5 into standard length, slightly compressed forward, and greatly compressed posteriorly. Snout to origin of anal fin 2.3 to 2.5 into standard length. Head rather short, slightly compressed, its length 5.6 to 7.4 into standard length, fleshy crest between snout and occiput. Snout steep, rounded in profile. Mouth terminal, moderate, directed somewhat upward. Maxillary reaching point below posterior margin of eye. Lips fleshy. Small conical teeth on jaws, fine teeth on vomer and palatines. Eye small, its diameter 26 to 36 into standard length. Nasal tube restricted distally, placed midway between anterior edge of orbit and snout. Opercle with posterior edge fleshy. Branchiostegal rays 5. Width between attachments of posterior margin of gill membrane to isthmus 0 to 1.9 percent of standard length; occasionally posterior margins of gill membranes joined to produce a narrow free fold. Caudal peduncle short and deep.

Fins   Dorsal (1), LVII to LXIV, spines weak anteriorly but strong over anal fin, mod-

erately high, a little higher posteriorly, base long with origin over or slightly before pectoral, well notched but joined to caudal. Caudal short and rounded. Anal 40 to 46, moderately high, a little higher posteriorly, base long, margin incised between rays, rounded posteriorly, and barely joined to base of caudal fin. Number of spines and rays related to latitude. Pectorals 9 or 10, bluntly pointed. Pelvics absent.

Vertebrae   62 to 68.

Scales   Small, cycloid, embedded, on posterior part of body and extending from between seventh and eighth anal ray. Rudimentary lateral line canal on midside and even more reduced lateral line canal between it and dorsal fin. Pores on head in 7 paired series; suborbital 6, anterior to nasal tube 1, above eye 3, postorbital 7, occipital 3, preopercular 6, mandibular 4, and an unpaired pore on nape.

Colour   Dark, or with a broken or variegated dark and light pattern usually with dark and light bars accentuating each other across jaw. Frequently dark markings near anterior portion of dorsal fin and on the posterior margin of each gill cover. Rarely individuals partly or completely bright red.

Size   Length at least to 4 inches (10.2 cm).

Recognition   A prickleback with a moderate fleshy crest from snout to occiput, in British Columbia 41 or more anal fin rays (some have 40) and 59 or more dorsal spines (some have 57 or 58), and 63 to 65 vertebrae. The width across the isthmus where it meets the gill membrane is less than 1.9 percent of the standard length and there may be a complete fold.

Life History   It is found in the intertidal zone and to depths of 7 to 100 feet (21–30 m).

Distribution   Known from **Puget** Sound, Washington, to Attu Island of **the** Aleutian Chain. Canadian records are **from** Sooke, Howe Sound, Pender Harbour, **Port** McNeil and Port Simpson.

References   Gilbert   and   **Burke** 1912; Peden 1966b; Peppar 1965.

HIGH COCKSCOMB

Anoplarchus purpurescens Gill 1861

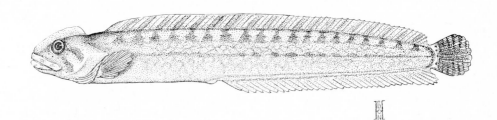

Scientific names from the Greek *anoplos* (unarmed) and *archos* (anus — no spine); and the Latin *purpureus* (purple).

The common name crested blenny was used in Clemens and Wilby 1946, and cockscomb prickleback in 1961.

Description   Body elongate, depth 6.85 (5.8–8.1)[5] into standard length, compressed. Head small, 6.2 (5.4–6.8) into standard length, moderately pointed, a prominent fleshy crest or cockscomb above posterior part of head. Mouth terminal, moderately large, oblique. Lower jaw included. Lips fleshy on both jaws. Teeth on jaws small and conical, on vomer and pala-

tines minute and in bands. Eye small, its diameter 24 to 30 into standard length.[4] Opercle with posterior edge fleshy. Branchiostegal rays 5. Gill membranes broadly fused with isthmus. Isthmus width 1.7 to 4.1 percent of standard length.[4] Caudal peduncle short, deep, compressed.

Fins   Dorsal (1), (LV)LVII(LVIII), spines quite flexible toward head, long, its base (1.12) 1.19(1.30)[5] into standard length. Caudal with broad base and convex outer margin. Anal 39 or 40, extending from immediately behind anus to base of caudal fin. Pectorals moderately large with convex free ends. Pelvics lacking.

Vertebrae   (58)60(61) in southern British Columbia. Vertebral number and fin ray numbers are higher in collections from farther north.[4]

329

Scales Small, cycloid, embedded, restricted to posterior part of body. Lateral line canal only faintly visible, a short line of spaced pores. Lines of sensory pores on head, but no cirri, spines, or barbels.

Colour Very variable. May be light to dark gray with olivaceous overtones, brown to dark brown with or without reddish overtones, or purple to almost black. Females are less varied in colour than males, but show more pattern, usually having green grayish backgrounds with brownish reticulations, or dark brownish backgrounds with subdued reticulation. Belly pale. In the male, the cockscomb and under surface of the head are pale, rather yellowish, and without speckling. In the female, the head is more speckled and mottled. There is a gray bar across the base of the caudal peduncle. At breeding season the male develops bright orange colours on its anal and pectoral fins, and reddish on the caudal and dorsal fins.[5]

Size Length to 7.8 inches (20 cm), but it is questionable that this size is reached in British Columbia.

Recognition Absence of pelvic fins. Presence of fleshy crest above posterior part of head. Scales on posterior part of body only. Pale band marking base of caudal fin. Fewer than 41 rays in anal fin. Isthmus more than 2.0 percent of standard length.

Life History Female cockscombs tend to be slightly larger, to grow a little faster, and to be somewhat more numerous than males. In southern British Columbia lengths of about 4.5 inches (11.4 cm) were reached by both sexes after 3 years. They matured after 2 or 3 years of age. In southern British Columbia females produce some 2700 eggs in a single spawning act. After spawning the eggs are about 1.4 millimeters in diameter. In late winter egg masses are placed under or between rocks or shells and are guarded by the female who bends her body around the mass, fanning the eggs continuously by rhythmic undulations of the posterior part of her body.[6] In southern British Columbia eggs hatch in about 3 weeks or less, producing larvae less than a third of an inch in length (7.5 mm) with an oil globule still evident in the oval yolk sac. The young eat almost entirely copepods.[1,2] By June the most advanced young may be over an inch (30 mm) long, fully pigmented, and similar to the adults, cockscomb and all. Marking experiments showed movements ordinarily to be restricted to 50 feet (15 m) but gave no indication of strong homing tendency. However, defence of territory is displayed at spawning time. Local populations have been reported from Puget Sound[7] but may be based on contaminated samples. An important food is green algae (32 percent) with polychaete worms, amphipods, other worms, molluscs, and crustaceans filling the diet.[5] The only animal definitely known to feed on cockscombs is the common garter snake (at Friday Harbor, Washington).[3]

Distribution Point Buchon, California, to Attu Island in the Aleutians. British Columbia records are from the mouth of the Fraser River, Saturna Island, Vancouver, Jervis Inlet, and Queen Charlotte Sound. The species is widely distributed mainly in the intertidal zone and above the 10-foot (3-m) depth level.

References 1 Barraclough and Fulton 1968; 2 Barraclough, Robinson, and Fulton 1968; 3 Batts 1961; 4 Peden 1966b; 5 Peppar 1965; 6 Schultz and DeLacy 1932; 7 Sribhibhadh 1959.

PEARLY PRICKLEBACK

Bryozoichthys marjorius McPhail 1970

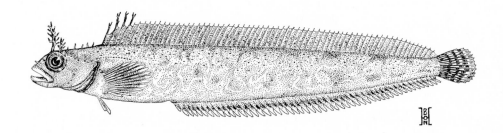

Scientific names from *Bryozoa* (moss animalcules) and the Greek *ichthys* (fish); and Mrs D. (Marjorie) McPhail.

Description Body elongate, depth 7 to 8 into standard length, slightly compressed. Head about 6 into standard length, mouth terminal, moderate in size, directed slightly upward. Upper jaw moderate, its length about 3 into length of head, reaching point below pupil of eye. Snout short, its length about 5 into length of head. Teeth small, acutely conical, in narrow ill-defined bands on jaws, vomer, and palatines. Interorbital space narrow, bony part almost flat, covered with soft tissue. Eye, large, greater than snout, its diameter about 4 into length of head. Gill membranes united and free from isthmus. Caudal peduncle compressed and short, its least depth about 20 into standard length.

Fins Dorsal (1), LXVII to LXXI, originating above dorsal base of pectorals. Caudal truncate to slightly rounded. Anal I, 53 to 55, membrane incised for about one-fifth ray length. Pectorals 15 to 16. Pelvics I, 3, thoracic.

Vertebrae 71 to 73.

Scales Very small, ctenoid, covering entire body, including nape, but not on head. Lateral line canal short, extending to a point about halfway down pelvic fin. Pores on head, mandible 4, a single short cirrus on snout; 2 long (length postorbital 7, interorbital 7, preopercular 6. Cirri: about 3 into length of head) cirri fused at base above anterior margin of orbit; 3 short cirri in row across posterior interorbital space; about 18 short cirri on occiput; multifid cirri on the first 4 dorsal spines; a short cirrus on posterior edge of maxillary and another immediately below it on the lower jaw. No cirri at symphysis of lower jaw. Shorter scattered cirri on opercular siphon and there may be cirri between the lateral line canal pores.

Colour (In alcohol.) Light tan with 9 dark blotches at base of dorsal fin and a series of irregular pearly white areas along the side. Fine dark spots on sides and dorsal fin. A dark pigmented area around eye and extending in a dark band below the eye. Supraorbital cirri dark with pale bands. Pectoral fins pale. Pelvic fins dusky. Anal fin pale at base, with a dark strip distally except for creamy tips of exserted rays. Caudal pale with 2 to 4 distinct dark ventral stripes.

Size Length to 9 inches (22.9 cm).

Recognition A prickleback with large complex cirri originating in the interorbital area. Teeth not in a single cutting edge.

Distribution So far known only from the type locality Forrester Island about

331

10 miles into southeast Alaska from the continuation of the Canadian boundary, and south of Unalaska Island in the Aleutian chain.

References   McPhail 1970.

DECORATED WARBONNET

Chirolophis decoratus (Jordan and Snyder 1903)

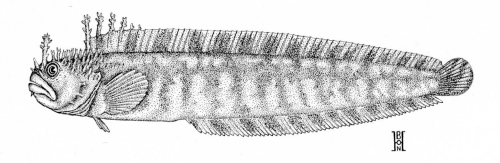

Scientific names from the Greek *chiros* (hand) and *lophos* (crest); and the Latin *decoratus* (ornamented).

Called the decorated blenny in Clemens and Wilby 1946 and decorated prickleback *Chirolophis polyactocephalus* (Pallas 1811) in Clemens and Wilby 1961.[2]

Description   Body elongate, depth about 6 into standard length, moderately compressed. Head about 6 into standard length. Mouth terminal, moderate in size, directed forward and up. Upper jaw moderately long, its length about 2.3 into length of head, reaching point below posterior edge of pupil. Snout short, its length about 5 into length of head. Lips thick. Teeth small, conical, in a series of broken rows in the jaws. Interorbital space narrow, about 6 into length of head, bony part almost flat but covered with soft tissue. Eye moderate in size, subcircular, its length about 5 into length of head. Gill membranes united and free of isthmus. Caudal peduncle compressed and very short, its depth about 25 into standard length.

Fins   Dorsal (1), LXI or LXII, originating above dorsal base of pectoral, extending a little on caudal. Caudal rounded. Anal I, 44 to 51, free of caudal, membranes excised except for about last 6 rays. Pectorals about 14, rounded, all rays flattened. Pelvics I, 4, thoracic.

Scales   Cycloid, small, ahead of pelvic fin. Lateral line canal short, extending about halfway to tip of pectoral fin, pores 6 to 15. Pores on head below jaws, around and between eyes, on preoperculum and around cleithral region. Cirri: a median cirrus on snout; a pair of cirri under lower jaw; large cirri fused together at base on anterior part of interorbital space, and 2 large

332

cirri at postorbitals. About 30 substantial fleshy cirri between interorbital and dorsal origin. Many additional cirri on anterior upper sides, and on the first 4 or more dorsal spines. Smaller cirri on preoperculum, operculum, and under lower jaw.

Colour   Pale brown with white to cream markings, paler below. Irregular light areas on upper part of body, and vertical light bars below. Dark bars run down from eyes. Prominent dark bars on the dorsal, caudal, and anal fins.

Size   Length to 16.5 inches (42 cm).

Recognition   A prickleback with a large complex cirrus originating in front of eyes and with a heavy development of cirri on the first four or more dorsal spines.

Distribution   Washington[1] to the Aleutian Islands[4] and Bering Sea.[3] It occurs at depths from 10 to 50 fathoms (18–91 m) throughout the inshore waters of British Columbia.

References   1 DeLacy, Dryfoos, and Miller 1963; 2 Makushok 1958; 3, 4 Wilimovsky 1954. 1964. See also Schmidt 1942.

MOSSHEAD WARBONNET

Chirolophis nugator (Jordan and Williams 1895)

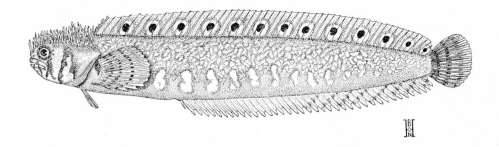

Scientific names from the Greek *chiros* (hand) and *lophos* (crest); and the Latin *nugator* (fop — elegant appearance).

Clemens and Wilby 1946 used the common name ornamented blenny for this species, and in 1961 called it mosshead prickleback.

Description   Body elongate, depth about 7 into standard length, compressed, only moderately tapered toward caudal peduncle. Head small, length about 8.3 into standard length, compressed. Mouth terminal, small, directed forward. Jaws about equal. Upper jaw extending to posterior edge of pupil. Lips thick. Teeth flattened, in closely set rows in jaws. Interorbital space about 4 into head length. Eye round, about 5.3 into length of head. Gill membranes united and free of isthmus.

333

Caudal peduncle short, compressed, its depth about 17 into standard length.

Fins   Dorsal (1), LIII to LV, long, reaching caudal fin but barely doing so, moderately high. Caudal rounded. Anal I, 37 to 42. Pectorals about 14, lower rays slightly exserted, rounded. Pelvics I, 4, thoracic.

Scales   Cycloid, small, embedded. Lateral line canal short, not extending to tip of pectoral fin, high. Cirri numerous, fleshy, branched, on top of head in a dense mat from anterior part of eyes to origin of dorsal fin and first spine.

Colour   Variable. Male brownish, sometimes with a red tinge; pale spots rimmed with darker on sides of body; spots fainter, smaller, and more numerous dorsally on sides; light on lower part of head with several brown streaks; white on pelvic fins and anterior part of anal fin; other fins with brown pigment spots in bands forming faint bars. Females nearly plain brown on body. In line spread along middle of dorsal fin about 13 dark spots each surrounded by a clear area to form prominent ocelli.

Size   Length to 4.8 inches (12.2 cm).

Recognition   Noteworthy for the dense cluster of evenly sized cirri on top of head extending to first dorsal spine, anal fin with one spine and 37 to 42 rays, and about 13 ocelli spaced out along the dorsal fin.

Life History   A gravid female was found at Sooke on January 9, 1963. Eggs are large, about 2 millimeters in diameter. The species is found under rocks at low tide in the intertidal zone.

Distribution   Northern California to southeastern Alaska near Sitka[2] and Umnak Island,[1] Alaska. Most Canadian records are from the Strait of Georgia area.

References   1 Hubbard and Reeder 1965; 2 Quast 1968.

LONGSNOUT PRICKLEBACK

Lumpenella longirostris (Evermann and Goldsborough 1907)

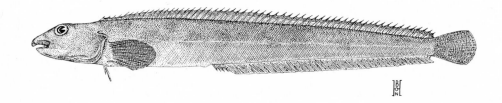

Scientific names from *Lumpenus* (a related fish) and the Latin diminutive *ella*; and the Latin *longus* (lang) and *rostrum* (beak).

This species was called long-snouted blenny in Clemens and Wilby 1946 and longsnout blenny in 1961.

Description   Body very elongate, depth about 8.5 into standard length, compressed. Head rather small, its length about 5.4 into standard length. Mouth terminal, rather small, directed forward. Upper jaw not reaching orbit. Lower jaw included and overhung by fleshy snout. Teeth, on jaws small and conical, absent elsewhere. Interorbital space, concave, bony part about 2.5 into length of eye but space extended by soft tissues. Eye oval, in a soft socket, its length about 4.6 into length of head. Gill membranes united far forward where they are joined to the isthmus. Caudal peduncle barely discernible, compressed, its least depth about 22 into standard length.

Fins   Dorsal (1), LXI to LXXI, spines stiff and sharp with exposed points, free from caudal fin. Caudal rounded. Anal III to V, 36 to 42, originating immediately behind anus, free from caudal. Pectorals moderate in size, rounded. Pelvics I, 2 or 3, spines fine and sharp, small, thoracic.

Scales   Cycloid, small, on body and head. Lateral line canal short and faint. Line of pores on head.

Colour   Bluish brown on dorsal surface, silvery to sooty blue on ventral surface, sooty blue on cheeks, opercles, and gill membranes. Fins dark. Preserved specimens sometimes paler.

Size   Length to 10.5 inches (26.7 cm) or more.

Recognition   Notable for its stiff spines with naked tips, the long fleshy snout overhanging the lower jaw, the anal fin (usually) with three to five spines, and the dark fins.

Life History   Young 4 to 33 millimeters long were taken at the surface in the southern Strait of Georgia in April. They were found to be eating copepods almost exclusively.[1,2]

Distribution   Burrard Inlet, British Columbia (Deep Cove and North Arm) at 50 to 65 fathoms (92–119 m) to southeast Alaska.[3] Recorded from Smith Sound and Prince Rupert Harbour.

References   1, 2 Barraclough 1967a, b; 3 Wilimovsky 1954. See also Makushok 1958.

DAUBED SHANNY

Lumpenus maculatus (Fries 1837)

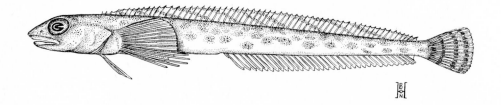

Scientific names from the Danish and German *lumpen* (a European remotely similar fish); and the Latin *maculatus* (spotted).

The French name for this species is *lompénie tachetée*.

Description   Body very elongate, its depth about 11.5 into standard length, deepest about end of pectoral fin, compressed. Head length about 5.3 into standard length, slightly compressed. Mouth terminal, moderate in size, directed forward. Upper jaw extends to below middle of pupil and well beyond tip of lower jaw. Snout rounded over upper jaw. Lower jaw included. Lips thickened. Teeth moderately large, conical, in rows in jaws; at anterior end, several rows in upper jaw and a small patch in lower jaw; on head of vomer, and on palatines. Interorbital space narrow and nearly flat, its width about 11 into length of head. Eye and pupil large and oval, length about 4 into length of head. Gill membranes united and attached to isthmus so as to leave a broad free fold. Caudal peduncle very compressed and short, its least depth about 33 into standard length.

Fins   Dorsal (1), LVII to LX, long, low, even, becoming gradually lower posteriorly. Caudal rounded. Anal I to II, 34 to 36. Pectorals 14 to 16, nearly as long as head, lower 5 rays greatly lengthened and exserted. Pelvics I, 3 or 4, thoracic.

Scales   Small, cycloid, on body and posterior sides of head. Lateral line canal not evident.

Colour   In alcohol, grayed green with patches of black dots on sides and back, on dorsal and caudal fins dots arranged in oblique or vertical bars. Other fins clear or only vaguely marked. A horizontal bar through eye to snout in some samples.

Size   Greatest length seen, 6.2 inches (16 cm).

Recognition   Noteworthy for the overhanging snout, the pectoral fin nearly as long as head, the large eye, the short but distinct caudal peduncle. Dorsal (LVII–LX) and anal (I–II, 34–36) are usually diagnostic among Canadian pricklebacks.

Distribution   Puget Sound[2,4] through British Columbia in Queen Charlotte Strait near north Malcolm Island,[4] and at the Aleutian Islands,[6] Bering Sea,[3] Arctic Alaska,[5] Robben Island,[3] Atlantic and Pacific stocks have been separated[1] but British Columbia specimens have many characters closest to Atlantic samples.[4] Including Atlantic stocks range extends through the North Atlantic to Spitzbergen Island. In British Columbia to depths of 180 to 300 feet (55–91 m) on hard sand bottom.

References   1 Andriashev 1954; 2 Chapman and DeLacy 1933; 3 Matsubara 1955; 4 Peden 1966c; 5, 6 Wilimovsky 1954, 1964.

(PACIFIC) SNAKE PRICKLEBACK

Lumpenus sagitta Wilimovsky 1956

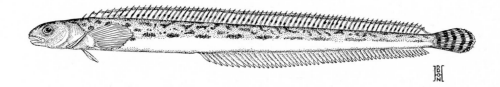

Scientific names from the Danish and German *lumpen* (a European remotely similar fish); and the Latin *sagitta* (arrow — long slender fish).

Clemens and Wilby 1946 called this species eel-blenny, *Lumpenus anguillaris* (Pallas 1811). The technical unsuitability of that name has been pointed out and the current new one proposed.[8]

Description   Body very elongate, its depth about 12 into standard length, moderately compressed, more so posteriorly. Head length nearly 10 into standard length. Dorsal head profile changes direction at posterior end of snout and anterior part of interorbital. Mouth terminal, rather small in size, directed forward. Upper jaw not reaching anterior margin of eye. Lower jaw included. Snout blunt. Lips thickened. Teeth in jaws, small, columnar, oval, well separated. Interorbital space almost flat, its width about 7 into length of head. Eye oval, its length about 3.7 into length of head. Gill membranes joined and fused to isthmus. Caudal peduncle compressed, its least depth about 30 into standard length.

Fins   Dorsal (1), LXVI to LXXII, free from caudal with even outline, low. Caudal narrow with oval free end. Anal I, 45 to 50, spine short, slender, sometimes absent, free from caudal. Pectorals about 17, large, bluntly pointed. Pelvics I, 3, thoracic.

Scales   Cycloid, covering entire body and head. Lateral line canal straight.

Colour   Pale green on dorsal surface, cream ventrally. Brown or green bars along midside and streaks or spots on upper part of sides. Brown bars and dots on dorsal fin form bands parallel to fin margin and, on caudal fin, produce vertical bars. Other fins pale. Lining of mouth pale.

Size   Length to 20 inches (51 cm).

Recognition   Known by its very elongate body, the gill membranes united to isthmus without a free fold and the dark bars along the side of the body.

Life History   Young snake pricklebacks 5 to 52 millimeters long occur abundantly near the surface in April and May off the outlet of the Fraser River. Food at this stage is almost entirely copepods.[1,2,3,4,5] Larger individuals can be caught on hooks using marine worms as bait. The snake prickleback is a restless fish in captivity and jumps out of aquaria.[7]

Distribution   From northern California to the Bering Sea, Washington,[6] Aleutian Islands.[9] Common in a variety of locations through British Columbia, at depths to 113 fathoms (207 m).

References   1, 2 Barraclough 1967a, b; 3 Barraclough and Fulton 1967; 4 Barraclough, Robinson, and Fulton 1968; 5 Robinson, Barraclough, and Fulton 1968a; 6 Schultz and DeLacy 1936; 7 Vancouver Public Aquarium Staff 1969; 8, 9 Wilimovsky 1956, 1964.

RIBBON PRICKLEBACK

Phytichthys chirus (Jordan and Gilbert 1880)

Scientific names from the Greek *phytos* (plant) and *ichthys* (fish — habitat); and *cheir* (hand).

This species was called belted blenny in Clemens and Wilby 1946.

Description   Body very elongate, its depth about 8.6 into standard length, little changed through anterior three-quarters of fish length, compressed. Head small, moderately compressed, its length about 8 into standard length. Mouth terminal, moderate in size, directed upward. Snout short and rounded. Jaws about equal. Upper jaw extending about to anterior margin of eye. Lips thick. Teeth in jaws moderate, blunt, conical, well spaced, about 4, large, near symphysis of lower jaw. Interorbital space convex with an extension of a fleshy median ridge on snout, narrow, its width about 10 into length of head. Eye round, its diameter about 7 into length of head. Gill membranes united and free of isthmus.

Fins   Dorsal (1), (LXIX)LXXV(LXXVIII), long, low, joining caudal. Caudal rounded. Anal II or III, 40 to 50, joining caudal. Pectorals about 15, very small. Pelvics absent.

Scales   Cycloid, small, over entire body. Lateral line canals 4, the upper 3 extending straight through length of body to caudal fin, the lower to near anal origin, many vertical branches anteriorly joining those of the opposite side across the belly. A small flap above the gill slit.

Colour   Olive green to olive brown dorsally, yellow to green ventrally, frequently with darker markings on side, small white spots sometimes evident along midside, 4 light and dark streaks reaching back and down from eyes, fins green to brown tinged with yellow.

Size   Length to 8 inches (20 cm).

Recognition   Noteworthy for the absence of pelvic fins, the four lateral line canals along the anterior side of the body, and the anal fin with two or three spines and 40 to 50 rays. The status of this form is somewhat in doubt and more than one species may be confused under the name.

Life History   The food of adults includes Crustacea and red and green algae. Young about an inch in length (25–32 mm) were found to be eating copepods, and *Oikopleura*.[1]

Distribution   Southern California to Adak Island[3] and the Bering Sea.[2] Common along the entire British Columbia coast in the intertidal zone where it is found under stones.

References   1 Robinson, Barraclough, and Fulton 1968a; 2, 3 Wilimovsky 1954, 1964.

BLUEBARRED PRICKLEBACK

Plectobranchus evides Gilbert 1890

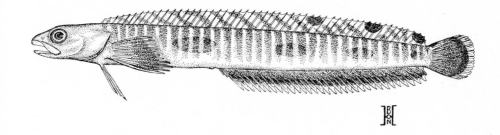

Scientific names from the Greek *plectos* (enfolded) and *branchos* (gill); and *evides* (comely).

Clemens and Wilby 1961 recorded this species as black-and-white prickleback.

Description   Body very elongate, its depth about 10 into standard length, compressed, only moderately tapered. Head slender and compressed, its length about 4.8 into standard length, convex over eyes. Mouth terminal, moderate in size, directed forward and upward. Upper jaw extends to below pupil, includes lower jaw. Snout short. Lips prominent, covering teeth. Teeth conical; in upper jaw very small, in bands; in lower jaw small in rows; on vomer in a small group; and on palatines moderately well developed in rows. Interorbital space very narrow, slightly concave, its width about 14 into length of head. Eye large, oval, its length about 4.1 into length of head. Gill membranes united and connected to isthmus so as to leave a broad free fold. Caudal peduncle compressed, reduced to token length, its depth about 21 into standard length.

Fins   Dorsal (1), LV to LVII, barely meeting caudal, low, even in contour. Caudal rounded. Anal II, 34 or 35, almost reaching caudal, low, even in contour. Pectorals about 15, broad, lower 6 rays elongated. Pelvics I, 3, thoracic, spine short, rays long.

Scales Cycloid, covering body and posterior part of head. Lateral line canal indistinct. An obvious pore between posterior margins of eyes, others behind and in front of eyes, and in rows on back of head and lower edge of gill cover.

Colour Dusky olive brown dorsally, paler below. About 25 vertical light bars, narrower than intervening spaces, about 3 vague dark blotches spaced along side imposed on other pattern. Dorsal fin with oblique dark bars, some intensified to make black blotches, especially toward posterior end. Caudal, anal, and pectoral fins with dark bars parallel to edge leaving a pale margin. Sometimes a dark spot on inner dorsal margin of caudal fin. Pelvics without markings.

Size Length to 5.2 inches (13.2 cm).

Recognition Recognized by pelvic fins, each with a short free spine and three rays, anal fin with two spines, white vertical bars on sides of body, black spots at posterior end of dorsal fin and upper anterior edge of caudal fin.

Distribution Southern California[2] to central British Columbia. Canadian records from Ladysmith Harbour at 47 fathoms (86 m) and Tahsis Inlet at about 70 fathoms (128 m).[1]

References 1 Barraclough 1959; Schultz and DeLacy 1936.

WHITEBARRED PRICKLEBACK

Poroclinus rothrocki Bean 1890

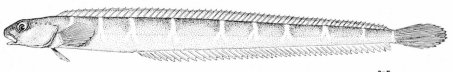

Scientific names from the Greek *poros* (pore) and *Clinus* (the generic name of a similar fish); and Dr J. T. Rothrock, botanist at the University of Pennsylvania.

Clemens and Wilby 1946 used the common name white-barred blenny for this species.

Description Body very elongate, its depth about 13 into standard length, mod-

erately compressed. Head length about 7.8 into standard length, barely compressed. Mouth terminal, moderate in size, directed forward. Upper jaw reaching anterior part of eye, includes lower jaw. Snout blunt. Lips rather thick. Small teeth in jaws, on vomer, and palatines. Interorbital space narrow and convex, its width about 10 into length of head. Eye large, oval, its length about 3.5 into length of head, not entering profile.

340

Opercular membranes united to each other and to isthmus. Caudal peduncle moderately compressed, very short, fine, its depth about 30 into standard length.

Fins   Dorsal (1), LVII to LXVII, membrane just reaching base of caudal. Caudal long, narrow, bluntly pointed. Anal III, 40 to 44, second spine stronger than third. Pectorals about 13, broad and rounded. Pelvics I, 3, spines short and sharp rays relatively long.

Scales   Cycloid, small, covering body and cheeks. Lateral line canal almost straight down centre of side.

Colour   Light brown on dorsal surfaces, lighter ventrally. About 10 to 12 white vertical bars edged with brown in a series on upper part of body, spreading or dividing to become confluent with pale ventral colouring. Small brown smudges at bases of membranes between spines of posterior part of dorsal fin.

Size   Length to 10 inches (25 cm).

Recognition   Noteworthy for the series of white vertical bars along the upper part of the body, the pelvic fin with a short sharp spine and three moderately long rays, the anal fin with three spines, and the large bluntly rounded tail fin.

Distribution   From southern California to Unalaska Island and the Bering Sea,[2,3] Washington.[1] In British Columbia at Burrard Inlet, Porlier Pass and Rennell Sound, Queen Charlotte Islands, at depths of 25 to 70 fathoms (46–128 m).

References   1 DeLacy, Dryfoos, and Miller 1963; 2, 3 Wilimovsky 1954, 1964.

BLACK PRICKLEBACK

Xiphister atropureus (Kittlitz 1858)

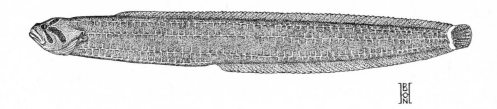

Scientific names from the Greek *ziphistus* (sword belt); and the Latin *ater* (black) and *purpureus* (purple).

Clemens and Wilby 1946 called this species black blenny, *Epigeichthys*

atro-purpureus. In 1961 they spelled the scientific name *Epigeichthys atropurpureus*.

Description   Body very elongate, its depth about 8.8 into standard length,

341

compressed. Head small, its length about 7.7 into standard length. Mouth terminal, rather large, directed forward and up. Upper jaw extends to midorbit. Snout bluntly rounded and short. Teeth on jaws conical, a few enlarged and effective at anterior ends of both jaws. Interorbital space convex and narrow, its width about 10 into length of head, a marked protuberance at its anterior end. Eye small and round, its diameter about 6 into length of head. Gill membranes broadly joined leaving a wide free fold. A fold of skin at the upper corner of the gill opening.

Fins   Dorsal (1), LXV to LXXIII confluent with caudal, low, snout to origin of dorsal fin about 1.5 times length of head. Caudal small and rounded, directed somewhat upward. Anal 40 to 52, low, confluent with caudal. Pectorals as minute flaps. Pelvics absent.

Scales   Not discernible. Lateral line canals 4. Glandular pits on head and body.

Colour   Dark reddish brown to black with head pale enough to display 3 dark light-edged bands radiating from each eye. Light band sometimes prominent across base of caudal fin and extending on dorsal and anal fins.

Size   Length to 12 inches (30.5 cm).

Recognition   Noteworthy for the absence of pelvic fins and the minute pectoral fins, the four lateral line canals, the absence of an anal spine, the dark bands with light margins radiating from the eyes, and in having the dorsal origin about half a head length behind the head.

Life History   Young between 6 and 22 millimeters long have been taken at the surface in the southern Strait of Georgia in May and June.[1,5,6] They were eating copepods and their nauplii, and clam larvae. Juveniles and adults are intertidal animals and are found under rocks at low tide.

Distribution   Baja California to southeast Alaska and Kodiak Island.[3,7] Generally distributed along the British Columbia coast. Records for Attu, Agattu, and Atka islands are based on *Anoplarchus purpurescens* and a misapplied name.[2,4]

References   1 Barraclough, Robinson, and Fulton 1968; 2 Gilbert and Burke 1912; 3 Hubbard and Reeder 1965; 4 Hubbs 1927; 5, 6 Robinson, Barraclough, and Fulton 1968 a, b; 7 Wilimovsky 1954.

ROCK PRICKLEBACK

Xiphister mucosus (Girard 1858)

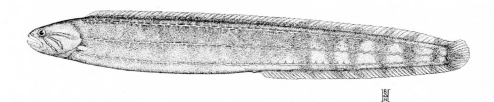

Scientific names from the Greek *ziphistus* (sword belt); and the Latin *mucosus* (slimy).

Clemens and Wilby 1946 used rock blenny as the common name for this species.

Description   Body very elongate, its depth about 8 into standard length, compressed. Head small, its length about 7.3 into standard length. Mouth terminal, rather large, directed forward and up. Upper jaw extending to posterior edge of orbit. Snout blunt, round, and short. Teeth on jaws small and conical, larger in anterior part of upper jaw. Interorbital space convex, its width about 8.7 into length of head. Eye small and round, its diameter about 8 into length of head. Gill membranes broadly joined leaving a wide free fold.

Fins   Dorsal (1), LXXI to LXXVII, confluent with caudal. Snout to origin of dorsal fin about equal to length of head. Caudal small and rounded, directed somewhat upward. Anal 46 to 50, low, confluent with caudal. Pectorals minute flaps, about 12. Pelvics absent.

Scales   Cycloid, minute, over entire body. Lateral line canals 4, numerous vertical branches, lowermost joining those of other side. Numerous glandular pits on head and body.

Colour   Greenish black with several dusky white bars on posterior part of body, 2 dark bands diverging back from each eye, each band double with a paler centre.

Size   Length to 20 inches (51 cm).

Recognition   Noteworthy for the absence of pelvic fins and the minute pectoral fins, the four lateral line canals, the absence of an anal spine, the dark bands with light centres diverging from the eyes, and the dorsal originating about as far from the snout as the posterior edge of the operculum.

Distribution   Southern California to southeast Alaska. Throughout British Columbia. From the intertidal zone to at least 10 fathoms (18 m). The food consists largely of algae.

Gunnels are small fishes having long slender compressed bodies. The dorsal fin is long, extending from the back of the head to the caudal fin which is confluent with both dorsal and anal. The dorsal fin is composed entirely of spines. When pelvic fins are present they are thoracic and have one spine and one ray. Teeth are small and conical. The lateral line canal is short or absent. The gunnels are found in shallow water in the northern parts of the Atlantic and Pacific oceans. Six species are recorded from the waters of British Columbia.

KEY TO THE PHOLIDAE

	1	Pelvic fins absent	2
or	1	Pelvic fins present .... Genus *Pholis*	3

	2	Dorsal fin spines 90 to 94; anal spine I, long, thin, and flexible, extending beyond rays; pectoral fin short but relatively broad, and longer than distance from end of snout to posterior edge of orbit; a row of dark dots along midside .... *Apodichthys flavidus,* Penpoint gunnel, p. 345
or	2	Dorsal fin spines 83 or 84; anal spines I or II, the spine next to the rays stout and rounded; pectoral fin minute, its length less than distance from the snout to posterior edge of orbit; colour without pattern but may be bright red or green .... *Xererpes fucorum,* Rockweed gunnel, p. 350

	3	Dorsal spines fewer than 82; anal spines fewer than 40	4
or	3	Dorsal spines more than 82; anal spines more than 40	5

	4	Series of dark markings on back along base of dorsal fin in shape of V's or U's .... *Pholis ornata,* Saddleback gunnel, p. 348
or	4	Series of dark markings on back along base of dorsal fin each shaped as a pair of brackets ( ) .... *Pholis laeta,* Crescent gunnel, p. 347

	5	Dorsal spines 87 to 90; anal rays 50 to 53; a series of light patches on back along base of dorsal fin each marked with scattered dark points .... *Pholis clemensi,* Longfin gunnel, p. 346
or	5	Dorsal spines 84 to 86; anal rays 41 to 44; colour usually but not always red .... *Pholis schultzi,* Red gunnel, p. 349

PENPOINT GUNNEL

Apodichthys flavidus Girard 1854

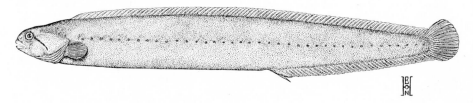

Scientific names from the Greek *apous* (without feet) and *ichthys* (fish — fish without pelvic fins); and the Latin *flavidus* (yellow(ish)).

Clemens and Wilby 1946 used the common name pen-point blenny for this species.

Description   Body very elongate, its depth about 8 into standard length, greatest depth about midlength, strongly compressed. Head small, its length about 7.5 into standard length, compressed. Mouth terminal, small, directed forward and up. Snout short. Jaws about even. Upper jaw extends to upper part of eye. Lips thickened. Teeth small, conical. Interorbital space narrow and convex with a raised fold of skin on snout and anterior part of interorbital space, its width about 9 into length of head. Eye round, its diameter about 5 into length of head. Gill membranes united and free of isthmus.

Fins   Dorsal (1), XL to XLIV, low, continuous with caudal. Caudal rounded, somewhat elevated dorsally. Anal I, 38 to 42; the spine large, thin, flexible, V-shaped in cross section with the concave side forward, completely recessed between fleshy folds (like a pen nib), low, confluent with caudal. Pectorals small, rounded, about 14. Pelvics absent.

Scales   Cycloid, small. Lateral line canal absent.

Colour   Very variable depending upon diet as well as environment, from green through brown to red, the green colour from pigments dispersed through skin, the red in special pigment cells, the brown from a combination.[5] Dark dots spaced in a broken line along midside of body, sometimes also light spots. Narrow dark line down and back from eye to operculum, sometimes through eye. Some fresh specimens may show a silvery line margined with orange and black from middle of maxillary through lower part of eye to nape or opercle.

Size   Length to 18 inches (46 cm).

Recognition   Noteworthy for the large pen nib-shaped anal spine, and the absence of pelvic fins.

Life History   Pairs of penpoint gunnels have been found coiled around masses of white eggs near low tide in Burrard Inlet in January.[1] The food includes small Crustacea and molluscs. Growth appears to be rapid during the first year from 20 to 40 millimeters in April and May to 100 to 120 millimeters by the end of summer.[3]

Distribution   Southern California to southeast Alaska[4] and Kodiak Island.[2] In British Columbia on both coasts of Vancouver Island, the Strait of Georgia. Common in Burrard Inlet in September.[3] Queen Charlotte Islands.[1]

References   1 Clemens and Wilby 1961; 2 Hubbard and Reeder 1965; 3 Lamb personal communication; 4 Wilimovsky 1954; 5 Wilkie 1966.

LONGFIN GUNNEL

Pholis clemensi Rosenblatt 1964

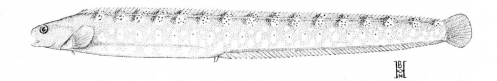

Scientific names from the Greek *pholas* (one who lies in wait); and Dr W. A. Clemens, Canadian zoologist and educator.

Description   Body very elongate, its depth 11 to 12 into standard length, laterally compressed, groove extending back from pectoral base curving down to anus separating side from belly. Head short, 8 to 9 into standard length. Snout slightly shorter than eye, blunt, steep, and slightly inflated in profile. Mouth small, terminal, oblique. End of closed lower jaw about below level of pupil. The end of the lower jaw is below the anterior margin of the orbit. Teeth strong, bluntly conical, slightly recurved, in 2 rows in both jaws, in upper jaw inner row better developed, 3 to 5 teeth on head of vomer, obscured by papillae on roof of mouth. Eye 36 to 50 into standard length, placed high on head, but not entering dorsal profile. Gill membranes united but free of isthmus.

Fins   Dorsal (1), LXXXVII to XC (mean 88.3), continuous from nape to caudal, spines sharply pointed with tips hooked backward, fin except for tips of spines covered with thick skin. Caudal small and confluent with dorsal and anal. Anal II, 50 to 53 (mean 51.7), skin normal. Pectorals ovoid, 13 or 14. Pelvics I, 1, spine thick and sharp, thoracic, minute.

Scales   Minute, partly imbricated, covering whole body but absent on head and fins. Lateral line canal absent. Sensory pores on head large but few.

Colour   In life variable, magenta and silver, fading in preservation to brown and tan. Dark marks at base of dorsal fin in about 15 light targets, and vague darker inverted U's on lower part of the body. Head somewhat darker above with a light mark running back from eye.

Size   Length to about 5 inches (12.7 cm).

Recognition   Noteworthy for the presence of a small pelvic fin, and 87 to 90 dorsal spines.

Distribution   Known only from the northern State of Washington, Juan de Fuca Strait, and the Strait of Georgia as far northwest as Walsh Cove on the east side of West Redondo Island. It has been taken at moderate depths from 4 to 35 fathoms (8–64 m). The Walsh Cove specimen is at the British Columbia Provincial Museum (Peden 1972 personal communication).

References   Rosenblatt 1964.

CRESCENT GUNNEL

Pholis laeta (Cope 1873)

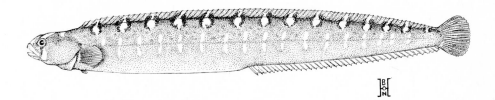

Scientific names from the Greek *pholas* (one who lies in wait); and the Latin *laeta* (joyful).

The common name bracketed blenny was used for this fish by Clemens and Wilby 1946.

Description   Body very elongate, its depth about 8.4 into standard length, compressed. Head small, its length about 8 into standard length, compressed. Mouth terminal, small, directed forward and upward. Upper jaw extends to anterior part of eye. Lower jaw slightly protrudes. Snout blunt, about as long as diameter of eye. Teeth small, conical, on both jaws, vomer, and palatines. Interorbital space narrow, 7 or more into length of head, convex from a fleshy pad extending along snout. Eye small, its diameter about 5.5 into length of head. Opercular membranes united and free of isthmus.

Fins   Dorsal (1), LXXIV to LXXX, confluent with caudal. Caudal rounded, directed slightly upward. Anal II, 35 to 37, confluent with caudal. Pectorals about 11, small, rounded, length about 2.2 into length of head. Pelvics I, 1, thoracic, minute.

Scales   Cycloid, very small. Lateral line canal absent.

Colour   Yellowish green; darker on dorsal surface; slightly mottled on sides; black markings in series along base of dorsal fin and extending on it as pairs of dark brackets, each pair enclosing an orange or yellow area which extends beyond the brackets on the body and on the fin to its margin; a light area on each side of the head margined with black; a green spot sometimes on the opercle; orange on the anal fin, sometimes on caudal fin.

Size   Length to 10 inches (25 cm).

Recognition   Recognizable by the series of crescent-shaped markings along dorsal surface at base of caudal fin, and the minute pelvic fins in thoracic position, each with one spine and one ray.

Distribution   Northern California to the Bering Sea and through the Aleutian Islands.[1,2,3,4] Common throughout British Columbia at depths down to 30 or 40 fathoms (55 or 73 m), and frequently found in the intertidal zone where it occurs in tide pools or under rocks protected by seaweed.

References   1 DeLacy, Dryfoos, and Miller 1963; 2 Schultz and DeLacy 1936; 3, 4 Wilimovsky 1954, 1964.

347

SADDLEBACK GUNNEL

Pholis ornata (Girard 1854)

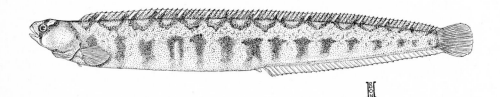

Scientific names from the Greek *pholas* (one who lies in wait); and the Latin *ornatus* (ornamented).

Clemens and Wilby 1946 used the common name saddled blenny for this species.

Description   Body very elongate, its depth about 8.3 into standard length, compressed. Head small, its length about 8 into standard length, compressed. Mouth terminal, small, directed forward and partly upward. Upper jaw extends to anterior part of eye and forward beyond lower jaw. Snout rounded, shorter than eye. Teeth small, conical, in both jaws. Interorbital space narrow, convex and padded with soft tissue, its width about 8.5 into length of head. Eye small, its diameter about 4.2 into length of head. Opercular membranes broadly united and free of isthmus.

Fins   Dorsal (1), LXXIV to LXXIX, confluent with caudal. Caudal rounded. Anal II, 35 to 38, confluent with caudal. Pectorals about 12, small, rounded, length about half length of head. Pelvics I, 1, thoracic, minute.

Scales   Cycloid, very small. Lateral line canal absent.

Colour   Olive green to brown on dorsal surface; yellow, orange, or red on ventral surface; dark bar through posterior margin of eye, bar divided across top of head; dusky bars in series along sides of body broadest at midside and disappearing ventrally; dark markings in a series along base of dorsal fin in the shape of U's or V's enclosing green or brown areas darker than body colour; orange sometimes on pectoral, anal, and caudal fins; sometimes anal fin light green with a series of white bars.

Size   Length to 12 inches (30 cm).

Recognition   Recognized by the series of U- or V-shaped black markings along the base of the dorsal fin, the minute thoracic pelvic fins, each with one spine and one ray.

Distribution   Northern California through Oregon and Washington,[2] to the Bering Sea,[3] and the Sea of Japan as far as Peter the Great Bay.[1]

Moderately abundant along British Columbia coast but exact status uncertain because of frequent misidentifications. Occurs most frequently near the outlets of streams on muddy bottom at depths between 10 and 20 fathoms (18 and 37 m). It is recorded as feeding on small crustaceans and molluscs.

References   1 Matsubara 1955; 2 Schultz and DeLacy 1936; 3 Wilimovsky 1954.

RED GUNNEL

Pholis schultzi Hubbs 1933[4]

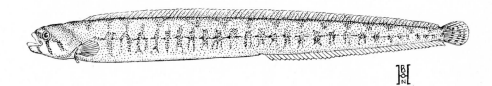

Scientific names from the Greek *pholas* (one who lies in wait); and Dr L. P. Schultz, Curator of Fishes, U.S. National Museum.

Description   Body very elongate, its depth about 10 into standard length, compressed. Head small, its length about 8.5 into standard length, compressed. Mouth terminal, small, directed forward and upward. Upper jaw extending to anterior margin of pupil. Lower jaw slightly protruding. Lips thick. Snout blunt, and convex through to occiput. Teeth small, conical, tending to be in 2 rows on both jaws. Interorbital space narrow, convex, fleshy, less than diameter of eye. Eye small, its diameter about 4.2 into length of head. Opercular membranes united and free of isthmus.

Fins   Dorsal (1), LXXXIV to LXXXVI, confluent with caudal. Caudal rounded. Anal II, 41 to 44, confluent with caudal, spines moderate, in a pouch between anus and anal fin origin. Pectorals 11 or 12, small, rounded. Pelvics I, 2, thoracic, minute.

Scales   Cycloid, very small, embedded, covering body. Lateral line canal absent.

Colour   Body usually bright, dark red, but sometimes light brown or greenish brown. Ventral surface lighter. Sides of body fairly plain or with variously developed serial patterns of light spots, blotches or streaks tending to blend into paler ventral surface. A series of single or paired small black spots along midside. Series of about 16 small, evenly spaced, light markings along dorsal fin, anterior ones sometimes obscured. Anal fin with a series of many dark and light vertical bars. Head with light bar passing ventrally from posterior portion of each maxillary, both bars accentuated anteriorly and posteriorly with black bars; a few similar light bars may radiate from dorsal portion of eye; the more ventral light bars may be conspicuously white or filled in with some red or brown.[1]

Size   Length to 3.1 inches (7.9 cm).

Recognition   Recognized by having minute pelvic fins each with one spine and one ray, 84 to 86 dorsal spines and 41 to 44 soft rays in the anal fin.

Life History   So far recorded in Canada from areas exposed to ocean surge at depths down to 15 feet (4.6 m) below the intertidal zone. United States records seem to support the idea that the preferred habitat includes exposure to ocean conditions. Red and green algae or eelgrass were present where Canadian specimens were taken.

Distribution   Northern California through Oregon and Washington[3] to southern British Columbia. In British Columbia north and west to Ucluelet and Schooner Cove on the west coast of Vancouver Island.[1]

References   1 Peden 1966a; 2 Hubbs 1933; 3 Schultz and DeLacy 1936; 4 Schultz and Hubbs 1961.

ROCKWEED GUNNEL

Xererpes fucorum (Jordan and Gilbert 1880)

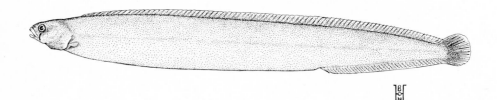

Scientific names from the Greek *kseros* (dry) and *cerepes* (creeper); and the Latin *fucorum* (of the seaweed, *Fucus*).

Clemens and Wilby 1946 called this species fucus blenny.

Description   Body elongate, depth about 8 into standard length, compressed. Head small, its length about 10 into standard length, compressed. Mouth terminal, small, directed forward and upward. Upper jaw barely reaching anterior edge of eye. Upper and lower jaws meet nearly evenly. Snout bluntly rounded, shorter than eye diameter. Lips thickened. Teeth small, conical, on jaws and vomer. Interorbital space narrow, about 8 into length of head, convex with a fleshy pad of skin extending back along snout. Eye small, its diameter about 5 into length of head. Opercular membranes united and free of isthmus.

Fins   Dorsal (1), LXXXIII or LXXXIV, confluent with caudal. Caudal rounded, slightly turned dorsally. Anal I, 32 to 38 confluent with caudal; the counted spine strong, long, rounded, sharp, arising from a pouch; a first short, enlarged, rounded spine reputedly present but difficult to find. Pectorals about 12, very small, rounded, length about equal to eye diameter. Pelvics absent.

Scales   Cycloid, small, difficult to distinguish. Lateral line canal absent.

Colour   Bright green to red, essentially without pattern, dark spots sometimes in a series along midside, narrow dark line running down from eye.

Size   Length to 9 inches (22.9 cm).

Recognition   Recognized by the bright uniform coloration, the rounded spine at the origin of the anal fin, and the absence of pelvic fins.

Life History   As indicated by the name the rockweed gunnel is found most frequently in masses of rockweed (*Fucus*). The food of adults includes small crustaceans and molluscs. A small 1-inch (25-mm) specimen taken at the surface was found to have eaten *Oikopleura*.[2]

Distribution   Baja California to central British Columbia, Oregon,[3] and Washington.[1] British Columbia records include: off Victoria, Ucluelet, Vargas Island, Courtenay, Comox, Nootka Island, Brooks Peninsula, Hope Island, and Goose Island (BC 58-550).

References   1 DeLacy, Dryfoos, and Miller 1963; 2 Robinson, Barraclough, and Fulton 1968a; 3 Schultz and DeLacy 1936.

The wolffishes are long, large fishes with dorsal fin consisting entirely of spines and confluent or nearly confluent with caudal and anal fins. Pelvic fins are absent. Teeth are strong in both jaws, and on palatines and vomer and are developed as canines and molars. The lateral line canal may be absent or dual. The greatly drawn-out wolf-eel is the only member of the family represented off the British Columbia coast where it is moderately common in deep water.

WOLF-EEL

Anarrhichthys ocellatus Ayres 1855

Scientific names from the Greek *anarhichas* (an ancient name for a related species); and the Latin *ocellatus* (eye-like — spots).

Description   Body very elongate, depth about 15 into standard length, deeper in large individuals, less deep in small ones,[5] compressed and evenly tapered to a narrow caudal base. Head length about 11.4 into standard length, longer in large individuals,[5] compressed. Mouth terminal, large, directed forward and upward. Upper jaw extends beyond posterior margin of eye. Snout short, blunt, and narrow, blunter in males.[7] Lips retracted. Teeth in anterior part of each jaw strong, conical canines (worn down in old individuals[5]), on sides of lower jaw strong molars, on vomer in 2 series, on palatines molars in 2 series meeting molars of lower jaw. Interorbital space convex, its width about 5.4 into length of head. Eye round, its diameter about 7.5 into length of head. Gill membranes broadly fused to isthmus.

Fins   Dorsal (1), CCXXVIII to CCL, spines flexible, low, continuous to end of body. Caudal very small, slender, pointed, demarked from dorsal and anal by notches. Anal 200 to 233, low, continuous to posterior end of body. Pectorals about 20,[4] small and rounded. Pelvics absent.

Vertebrae   Very numerous, 241,[2] more than 247.[5]

Scales   Cycloid, minute, buried in skin. Lateral line canal absent.

Colour   Grays, browns, or dark green, sometimes orange in young, with large rounded black spots of various sizes ringed with light colour, covering body and dorsal fin. Anal fin and core of caudal light, mottling increasing with age.[9]

351

The wolf-eel is subject to marked variations both in colour and in meristic characters. Young fish are pale or bright in ground colour and the upright fins are much higher than in large individuals.

Size   Length to 8 feet (2.4 m).

Recognition   Recognized by its very elongate body, large canine and molar teeth, absence of pelvic fins, separation of caudal fin from dorsal and anal fins by slight notches, and large dark spots surrounded by light colour.

Life History   Two 3.25-inch (83-mm) wolf-eels caught at the surface in the Strait of Georgia had eaten a 15-millimeter walleye pollock.[1] Large specimens in captivity ate crustaceans, sea urchins, mussels, clams, and other hard-shelled invertebrates.

A female taken with her egg mass to the Aquarium remained coiled around the eggs fasting until the young hatched.[6,9]

Distribution   From southern California at La Jolla at 400 feet (122 m),[4] through Oregon and Washington[8] to the Gulf of Alaska[10] and Krenitzen Islands in the Aleutians.[11] In British Columbia from the Strait of Georgia and Hecate Strait and from the outside coasts, at depths to 123 fathoms (225 m).[3]

References   1 Barraclough 1967b; 2 Clothier 1950; 3 Grinols 1965a; 4 Hubbs and Barnhart 1944; 5 Kanazawa 1952; 6 Lamb personal communication; 7 Makushok 1958; 8 Schultz and DeLacy 1936; 9 Vancouver Public Aquarium Staff 1969; 10, 11 Wilimovsky 1954, 1964.

FAMILY PTILICHTHYIDAE   QUILLFISH

Quillfish are extremely elongate with a dorsal fin extending from the back of the head to the end of the body. The anterior part of the dorsal fin is composed of small hooklike spines, and the posterior part of the membrane is supported by delicate unbranched rays. The anal fin is supported entirely by fragile rays. The gill membranes are free from the isthmus. Scales and lateral line canal are absent. Pelvic fins are absent. The family includes only one species; it is uncommon through the northern Pacific Ocean, and occurs off British Columbia.

QUILLFISH

Ptilichthys goodei Bean 1881

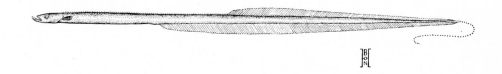

Scientific names from the Greek *ptilon* (quill) and *ichthys* (fish); and Dr G. B. Goode, U.S. ichthyologist.

Description   Body drawn out, its depth about 35 into standard length, tapering almost to a point through the last five-sixths of its length, only slightly compressed. Head small, its length about 15 into standard length. Mouth terminal or dorsal, small, directed strongly upward. Upper jaw not quite reaching as far as anterior edge of orbit. Lower jaw greatly projecting and turned upward. Teeth on jaws closely set, sharp, and conical, 1 regular row in each jaw. Interorbital space relatively wide and smoothly arched. Eye small, its diameter about 5 into length of head. Branchiostegals 3. Gill membranes broadly united and free of isthmus.

Fins   Dorsal (1), XC, 137 to 145, spinous portion composed of very short stiff curved spines, starting at nape and extending about two-fifths of distance to end of body. Rayed portion continuing through remaining three-fifths much higher at its anterior end and tapering to zero at posterior end. Rays slender, unsegmented, unbranched, with continuous membrane. Two sections of fin continuous. Fin continuing to caudal. Caudal much reduced and completely confluent with dorsal and anal. (Undamaged specimens are reported to have a long caudal filament.) Anal 185 to 196, starting at a point about one-quarter from nape to caudal and continuing on caudal. Deepest near middle. Rays as in dorsal. Pectorals 13, small. Pelvics absent.

Vertebrae   236 to 240.

Scales   No scales or lateral line canal.

Colour   In preservation very pale. White with isolated pigment spots, organized into a weak row along the midventral line of the abdomen. Amber green,[9] yellow or orange, and a dark longitudinal stripe have been reported on the body of some specimens. May be very variable.

Size   Length to 13.5 inches (34 cm).

Recognition   Recognized by the very long slender body, small jaws with the lower protruding, and the minute hooked spines in the anterior part of the dorsal fin.

Life History   Taken occasionally at surface, mainly around lights at night,[5,8] but inhabits deeper water in daytime.[5] It has been suggested that it buries itself in bottom mud.[6] There is one record of it being eaten by a coho salmon.

Distribution   Occasionally encountered. From northern Washington,[2,3,7] through British Columbia to Unalaska Island[10] and the Bering Sea,[4,11] Kamchatka, Kuril Islands, and the Okhotsk Sea.[1,5] In British Columbia, off Porlier Pass[7] Juan de Fuca Strait, in Flamingo Inlet, and off

353

Haystack Island, in inside waters, and off Kyuquot Sound on the west coast of Vancouver Island.

References   1 Andriashev 1937; 2 Chapman and DeLacy 1933; 3 DeLacy, Dryfoos, and Miller 1963; 4 Evermann and Goldsborough 1907; 5 Grinols 1965a; 6 Makushok 1958; 7 Schultz 1929; 8 Walker 1953; 9 Williamson 1927; 10, 11 Wilimovsky 1954, 1964.

FAMILY CRYPTACANTHODIDAE   WRYMOUTHS

In the wrymouths the body is very elongate, the dorsal fin starts close to the head and is confluent with the caudal and anal fins. The dorsal fin is entirely supported by spines. The anal is also long, and is supported by two spines followed by many soft rays. Pelvic fins are absent. The head is flattened and shows prominent pores. The mouth is directed strongly upward. Gill membranes are free of the isthmus. Two species of this family are recorded from British Columbia waters.

KEY TO THE CRYPTACANTHODIDAE

1   Maxillary extending beyond eye by at least 1 eye diameter; scales on posterior part of body ....
.... *Delolepis gigantea,* Giant wrymouth, p. 355

or   1   Maxillary not extending beyond eye; no scales on body ....
.... *Lyconectes aleutensis,* Dwarf wrymouth, p. 356

GIANT WRYMOUTH

Delolepis gigantea Kittlitz 1858

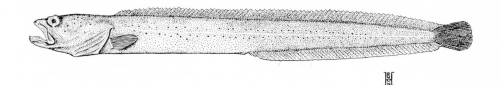

Scientific names from the Greek *delos* (visible) and *lepis* (scale); and the Latin *gigantus* (huge).

Description   Body very elongate, depth about 11 into standard length, compressed. Head depressed, its length about 4.8 into standard length. Mouth terminal, large, directed forward and upward. Upper jaw extending beyond posterior margin of eye. Lower jaw thick and protruding. Snout shallow with profile low. Lips thickened. Teeth small, fairly sharp, conical, directed inward on jaws, on vomer and palatines. Interorbital space wide and concave, a raised area across its posterior end extending into 2 rounded parietal ridges. Eye small, sunk, its diameter about 17 into length of head. Operculum extends well back over insertion of pectoral fin, gill membranes united and fused with isthmus.

Fins   Dorsal (1), LXXIII to LXXVII, confluent with caudal. Caudal quite distinct, margin oval. Anal II, 43 to 49, confluent with caudal. Pectorals about 11, length up to at least 5 times eye diameter. Pelvics absent.

Scales   Cycloid, small, buried on anterior half of body and not evident at all ventrally. Lateral line canal slightly decurved anteriorly, then straight down midside to caudal fin, faint.

Colour   Pale brown, tinged with yellow and violet, lighter on ventral surface. Markings variable. One colour phase with dark stripe along base of dorsal fin, dark above and below lateral line with pale area between, irregular dark spots in series above and below lateral bands. Other phase almost uniform light fawn, dark band along lateral line. Occasionally top of head to tip of lower jaw chalky white.

Size   Length to 3 feet 10 inches (117 cm).

Recognition   Notable for the absence of pelvic fins, the projecting lower jaw with the maxillary reaching behind eye, the scales exposed on the posterior part of body, and pale brown coloration with darker longitudinal bands.

Distribution   Northern California to Unalaska Island and Bering Sea, Oregon and Washington.[1,2,3] In British Columbia recorded from Victoria, Nanaimo, English Bay, Barkley Sound, Pender Harbour, Comox, Hardy Bay, Alert Bay, and Kingcome Inlet at depths of 18 to 70 fathoms (33–128 m). No doubt common also to the north and west.

References   1 Schultz and DeLacy 1936; 2, 3 Wilimovsky 1954, 1964.

DWARF WRYMOUTH

Lyconectes aleutensis Gilbert 1895

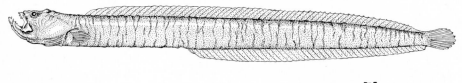

Scientific names from the Greek *lycos* (wolf) and *nectes* (swimmer); and Aleutian (Islands).

Clemens and Wilby 1946, 1961 used the common name red devil for this species.

Description   Body very elongate, depth about 14 into standard length, moderately compressed anteriorly, more so posteriorly, deepest ahead of anus, only slightly tapering over most of length. Head length about 7.7 into standard length, profile in line with dorsal contour of body to nasals, rather square in cross section. Mouth terminal, moderate in size, and directed almost straight upward. Gape extending little more than halfway to eye, but heavy maxillary bone extending to below centre of eye. Upper jaw overlaid by tubule of nostril. Lower jaw heavy, much projecting, when closed dorsal to upper jaw, a pair of toothed crests at symphysis, with uneven margins. Lips retracted. Teeth blunt, scattered along upper jaw and on anterior part of lower jaw, in a row at posterior ends of lower jaw, stubby on vomer. Interorbital space wide, about 5 into length of head, ridges on parietals, frontals, and nasals, nearly meeting between posterior ends of orbits. Eyes very small, and round, diameter about 16 into length of head, on top of head. Suborbital ridges high and blunt.

Gill membranes united to isthmus without a free fold.

Fins   Dorsal (1), LX to LXIX, continuous with caudal, low, even outline but spines readily become exposed. Caudal oval. Anal III, 45 to 49, continuous with caudal, spines weak, shorter than first rays. Pectorals small, about 12. Pelvics absent.

Scales   Scales absent. Lateral line canal indistinct. Skin loose and wrinkled.

Colour   In life bright red from blood showing through transparent skin. In preservation, dull gray, paler below, with a lighter stripe down midside.

Size   Length to 10.75 inches (27 cm), at least.

Recognition   Distinguished by the absence of pelvic fins, the almost vertical jaws, the projecting lower jaw, the nostril projecting over the maxillary, the transparent skin red in life, and the absence of scales.

Life History   In May off outlet of Fraser River and in Saanich Inlet, young 6 to 28 millimeters long were eating copepods almost exclusively.[1,4] In July almost ripe females with eggs about 1.8 millimeters in diameter were taken at 15 fathoms (28 m) off the San Juan Islands. They have been reported to live partly buried in the bottom.[5]

Distribution From northern California at 191 fathoms (350 m) through Oregon at depths to 100 fathoms (183 m), Washington, and Aleutian Islands[3,6] to the Bering Sea.[3] In British Columbia of general occurrence in the southern Strait of Georgia at depths to around 40 fathoms (73 m), Quatsino Sound[2] and probably elsewhere.

References 1 Barraclough, Robinson, and Fulton 1968; 2 Carl personal communication; 3 Grinols 1965a; 4 Robinson, Barraclough, and Fulton 1968a; 5 Schultz 1930; 6 Wilimovsky 1964.

The graveldiver has an elongate slender body that is deeper toward the caudal end than at midbody. Dorsal and anal fins consist of rays; they start about midbody and are completely confluent with the caudal fin. Gill membranes are united and free of the isthmus. Teeth are small and conical, on the jaws. These fish are found in the intertidal zone and bury themselves in loose bottom materials. Only one species of the family is known and it is from the northeast Pacific.

GRAVELDIVER

Scytalina cerdale Jordan and Gilbert 1880

Scientific names from the Greek *scytalina* (viper — diminutive); and *cerdale* (wary one).

Clemens and Wilby 1946 called this species burrowing blenny.

Description Body very elongate, depth about 19 into standard length, barely compressed anteriorly, more so posteriorly. Head slender, its length about 7 into standard length, moderately depressed. Mouth terminal, large, directed forward and somewhat up. Upper jaw reaching posterior margin of eye. Jaws about equal. Lower lip thickened, papillae on upper lip. Lower jaw deep. Snout blunt anteriorly and concave through most of its length. Both upper and lower jaws pitted by prominent pores, largest in lower jaw, where there are 4 pairs. Two large strong blunt canine teeth at anterior ends of upper and lower jaws, larger in lower jaw. Numerous other strong blunt conical teeth in jaws and on vomer and palatines. Interorbital space concave, moderate in width, its width about 7 into length of head. Eye very small, round, directed upward, its diameter about 15 into length of head. Operculum greatly expanded dorsally, entering dorsal profile. Gill membranes united, free from isthmus.

Fins   Dorsal (1), 41 to 51, confluent with caudal, inserted just ahead of midpoint of body and a little more ahead of anal insertion, anterior rays not distinguishable without dissection. Caudal round, directed partly upward. Anal 36 to 41, confluent with caudal, rays obscure. Pectorals about 8, rays difficult to count, small, oval, fleshy. Pelvics absent.

Scales   Scales and lateral line canal absent.

Colour   Brownish purple or pink dorsally, paler below, all vaguely banded, speckled, mottled, or vermiculated with lighter or darker hues. Possibly pale pink in life.

Size   Length to 6 inches (15 cm).

Recognition   Recognized by the elongate, rounded, scaleless body with dorsal and anal fins, confluent with the rounded caudal, on posterior half of body; the absence of pelvic fins; the inflated opercles; and the striking pores in the lower jaw.

Distribution   Central California.[5] Puget Sound and San Juan Islands[3] through British Columbia and southeastern Alaska at Baranof Island (57 N, 135 W),[4] to the Aleutian Islands (Agattu[1,6]) and the Bering Sea.[2] Not commonly reported but possibly more abundant than records indicate. In British Columbia recorded at Sooke, Esteban Point, Maquinna Point, Kaisun Bay (Moresby Island, Q.C.I.). It occurs in tide pools and on beaches burrowing in sand and gravel.

References   1 Gilbert and Burke 1912; 2 Quast 1968; 3 Schultz 1930; 4 Schultz and DeLacy 1936; 5, 6 Wilimovsky 1954, 1964.

FAMILY ZAPRORIDAE   PROWFISHES

The prowfish has a stout, compressed body, blunt head, and no pelvic fins. The upright fins are long and evenly contoured, the dorsal supported by spines, and the anal by three inconspicuous spines and numerous soft rays. The caudal peduncle is well formed and supports a broad tail fin. Gill membranes are united with a broad free fold. The mouth is directed upward. Teeth are small and present on the jaws and in the pharynx, but not in the oesophagus. There is only one species in the family and it is distributed along the Pacific coast of North America.

PROWFISH

Zaprora silenus Jordan 1896

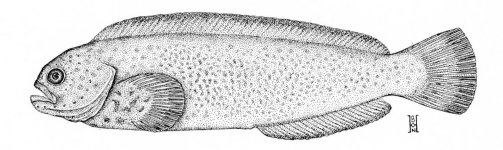

Scientific names from the Greek *za* (an intensifying prefix) and *prora* (prow); and *Silenus* (a drunkard Greek demigod who fell in a marsh on a revel and became covered with slime).

Description Body elongate, depth (2.9 to 4.2[1]), about 4.6 (for large specimens) into standard length, compressed. Head length (2.9 to 3.4[1]), about 5.3 (for large specimens) into standard length, compressed, blunt anteriorly, with a high "brow." Mouth terminal, moderate in size, directed forward and up. Jaws about even but area below lower jaw protruding. Upper jaw extending to anterior part of eye. Snout short and blunt. Lips widened with rough scales along edge. Teeth on jaws only, moderate in size, in a single row, sharp, flattened. Interorbital broadly arched, the width of the bony section about 3 into length of head. Whole interorbital width about 2.5 into length of head. Eye moderate, nearly round, its diameter about 4.5 into length of head in large individuals, and 2.7 in small. Opercular membranes fused, attached to the isthmus at its tip. Caudal peduncle compressed and deep, its least depth about 10 into standard length.

Fins Dorsal (1), LIV to LVII, long, moderate in height. Caudal broad and rounded. Anal 29 or 30, moderate in height. Pectorals 24 or 25, round. Pelvics absent.

Scales Ctenoid, small, elongate, in oblique rows, about 200, on head except snout and around eyes, on bases of all fin rays. No lateral line canal. Several rows of much enlarged pores on head and lower jaw, usually in an unpigmented spot, sometimes in a light ring emphasized by a darkened outline.

Colour Gray, green, or rich brown on dorsal surface and sides, shading into tan ventrally. Irregular dark spots on body, larger on base of pectoral fin. Yellow or orange on sides of head near pectoral fins and in mouth. Fins darker than body especially near edges. There are radiating marks around eyes. Some individuals have light yellow blotches on sides.

Small individuals have more prominent vertical bars on dorsal and anal fins, and the head pores are not in light areas.

Size Greatest length recorded 34.5 inches (88 cm).

Recognition Noteworthy for the high blunt snout, the absence of pelvic fins, the absence of a lateral line canal, and the large pores, ringed with white on the head.

Life History Young up to 72 millimeters (2.85 inches) long are pelagic or bathypelagic and are taken in plankton nets at 16 to 195 fathoms (29–357 m) off the west coast of British Columbia.[1] Later stages have been taken close to bottom on lines or purse seines. The young have been found associated with the large orange jellyfish *Cyanea*.[6]

Distribution   From California to the Gulf of Alaska,[10] through Oregon,[8] Washington,[3] British Columbia. From the Gulf of Alaska through the Aleutian Islands, Kodiak Island,[4,7] Akutan Island,[7] Krenitzen Islands,[11] Umnak Island,[6] Attu,[6,11] and into Asian waters at the Commander Islands,[5]

the west coast of Kamchatka,[9] and Hokkaido.[3,5,10] Not uncommon and generally distributed in British Columbia, Nanaimo Harbour, Juan de Fuca Strait, Anthony Island,[2] and Rivers Inlet at moderate depths, 40 to 65 fathoms (73–119 m).

References   1 Chapman and Townsend 1938; 2 Dymond 1928; 3 Grinols 1965a; 4 Kendall 1924; 5 Matsubara 1955; 6 Scheffer 1940; 7 Schultz 1934b; 8 Schultz and Harvey 1945; 9 Shmidt 1950; 10, 11 Wilimovsky 1954, 1964. See also McAllister and Krejsa 1961.

FAMILY AMMODYTIDAE   SAND LANCES

In the sand lances the body is very long, slender, and subcylindrical. Dorsal and anal fins are long and even, and without spines. In our species the pelvic fin is absent; when present it is jugular. The caudal peduncle is distinct and the tail forked. The head is long and pointed with a projecting lower jaw. Teeth are absent, and the gill rakers long and slender. Scales are cycloid and small. The lateral line canal is high and straight. There is a fleshy ridge extending for the length of the body, low along the side, and there are fine diagonal folds along the length of the body. There is no gasbladder. These are small fishes, sometimes forming great schools, at others burying themselves in the bottom sand. Sand lance are found in the oceans of the world. Few species are assigned to the family and only one of these is recognized off the coast of British Columbia.

PACIFIC SAND LANCE

Ammodytes hexapterus Pallas 1811

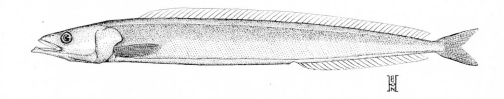

Scientific names from the Greek *ammos* (sand) and *dyo* (dive or burrow); and *hex* (six) and *pteros* (fins or wings — vertical fins plus longitudinal folds and lateral line and/or dorsolateral angle possibly appeared as six longitudinal fins or wings?).

Alternative spellings for the common name are sandlance, and sand launce.

Clemens and Wilby 1946 named this fish sand-lance *Ammodytes tobianus personatus* Girard 1856.[7]

Description   Body very elongate, depth about 9 into standard length, or more in small specimens, somewhat compressed, ventral surface flattened. Head long, about 4.5 into standard length, slender, somewhat compressed. Mouth terminal, moderate in size, directed forward and up. Upper jaw extending to anterior part of eye. Snout low, long, pointed. Lower jaw closes outside upper, with a projection directed forward and down. Teeth not evident. Interorbital space convex, its width about 5 into length of head. Eye small, its length about 7 into length of head. Opercular membranes free of each other and of isthmus. Caudal peduncle compressed, its least depth about 37 into standard length.

Fins   Dorsal (1), 54 to 59, long, low. Caudal deeply forked. Anal 24 to 30, terminating ahead of dorsal, and less than half its length.

Pectorals about 13, narrowly rounded, placed low on body. Pelvics absent.

Scales   Cycloid, small. Side of body with about 150 diagonal folds running down and back to ventrolateral angle of body where a delicate longitudinal fold runs the length of the body from throat to caudal peduncle. Lateral line canal high on body, paralleling dorsal contour from head to caudal peduncle.

Colour   Gray or green above, silvery below, iridescent or metallic hues in life.

Size   Length to 8 inches (20 cm) in British Columbia, at least to 10.25 inches (26 cm) in Bering Sea.

Recognition   Noteworthy for the elongate, only slightly compressed body with high lateral line canal, close diagonal creases running down and back on sides, longitudinal fold running length of body along ventrolateral curve, long low dorsal and anal fins, absence of pelvic fins, well-forked caudal fin, and distinct caudal peduncle.

Life History   The sand lance leads a varied life, sometimes offshore, sometimes in large schools stemming tidal currents in channels, at others burying themselves more or less completely in beach sand, and possibly also in deep water. In surface water off the outlet of the Fraser River and in Saanich

Inlet in early summer larvae up to 25 millimeters, postlarvae 25 to 75 millimeters, and adults are abundant and feeding mainly on copepods, their eggs and nauplii, but also on a wide variety of other foods.[2,3,4,5,6,10,11] Sand lance are frequently taken as food by chinook and coho salmon, lingcod, halibut, fur seals, and by many other marine vertebrates. It is not regularly used as human food but is said to be excellent.

Distribution   From southern California to Alaska and the Bering Sea,[13] Arctic Canada at Port Harrison, and the outlet of Clearwater River, Hudson Bay,[9]

Chukchi Sea,[12] Anadyr Gulf,[1] through the Aleutian Islands[14] and Commander Islands,[12] Okhotsk Sea,[12] Kuril Islands,[8] and Sea of Japan as far south as 44 N. Abundant through British Columbia in a wide range of habitats.

References   1 Andriashev 1937; 2, 3, 4 Barraclough 1967a, b, c; 5 Barraclough and Fulton 1967; 6 Barraclough, Robinson, and Fulton 1968; 7 Clemens and Wilby 1946; 8 Matsubara 1955; 9 McAllister 1964; 10, 11 Robinson, Barraclough, and Fulton 1968a, b; 12 Shmidt 1950; 13, 14 Wilimovsky 1954, 1964.

FAMILY GOBIIDAE   GOBIES

The gobies are small fishes, mainly of tropical seas, but occasionally in temperate seas or fresh water. They are characterized by a fusion of the thoracic pelvic fins to form a flaring cone which may be used for attachment. Gill openings are small, tails rounded, and the bodies covered with scales. Usually there is no gasbladder, and there are no parietals. Gobies are sedentary fishes frequently lying partly buried in the sand on the bottom. The family includes the smallest fishes in the world — a Philippine species whose adults are less than a half-inch (11 mm) long. Three species are recognized in British Columbia.

KEY TO THE GOBIIDAE

1   Scales large, 25 to 28 rows along lateral line canal; median crest on top of head from between posterior ends of orbits to dorsal fin origin ....
.... *Coryphopterus nicholsi,* Blackeye goby, p. 365

or   1   Scales small or moderate in size, at least 60 rows along lateral line canal; no crest on head 2

2   Upper jaw extending beyond posterior margin of eye; dorsal fin spines IV or V .... *Clevelandia ios,* Arrow goby, p. 363

or   2   Upper jaw extending about as far as pupil of eye; dorsal fin spines VII .... *Lepidogobius lepidus,* Bay goby, p. 366

ARROW GOBY

Clevelandia ios (Jordan and Gilbert 1882)

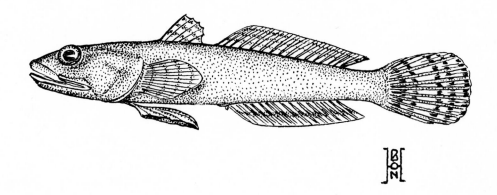

Scientific names from D. Cleveland, President, San Diego Society of Natural History; and from the Greek *ios* (arrow).

Description   Body elongate, depth about 6.8 into standard length, little tapered, moderately compressed. Head large, about 3.5 into standard length. Mouth terminal, large, directed mostly forward. Upper jaw extending well behind orbit, in all for about two-thirds length of head, includes lower jaw. Upper lip thickened. Teeth in jaws, fine, sharp, spaced apart. Interorbital space narrow, flat between raised orbits which enter profile, its width about 7 into length of head. Eye small, its diameter about 6 into length of head. Gill membranes joined to isthmus. Caudal peduncle compressed and relatively deep, its least depth about 12 into standard length.

Fins   Dorsal (2), IV or V — 15 to 17, well separated, moderately high, flowing outline. Caudal rounded. Anal 14 to 17, ends anterior to end of rayed dorsal. Pectorals about 20, pointed. Pelvics 5, thoracic, large, median edges fused, lateral edges joined by a membrane for about one-third length of fin to form a hollow cone free of body. A fleshy ridge in a trough from pelvic insertion to anus.

Scales   Cycloid, small, in about 70 oblique rows above midside. Lateral line canal absent. Rows of pores on lower part and sides of head.

Colour   Pale gray, green, or tawny with fine black and orange speckling. Dark bars formed by black spots on all fins but pelvics. Green and iridescent white spots on sides. Males with conspicuous dark bands on anal fin.

Size   Length to 2 inches (5.1 cm).

Recognition   Recognized by having the pelvic fins joined to make a hollow cone free of body, the slender body, and the large mouth extending for about two-thirds length of head.

Life History   In California arrow gobies spawn from December to August, mainly in March through June. All are mature at 34 millimeters standard length. Eggs are about 0.7 to 0.8 millimeter in diameter in California but about 0.85 millimeter in Washington. They are laid in groups, up to 1100 mature at once. Eggs sink and are non-adhesive. There is no parental care of young.[3] Eggs hatch in 10 to 12 days at 15

363

to 15.5 C to produce pelagic larvae 2.7 to 3.8 millimeters long. These grow rapidly reaching about 7 millimeters in 10 days.[11,12] Larvae 4 to 6 millimeters long have been taken in the Strait of Georgia[1] and Saanich Inlet,[2] and were found to be eating floating eggs of marine animals, copepods and their nauplii, and barnacle larvae. Adults live in sheltered bays and estuaries. They are very tolerant of extreme conditions of temperature and salinity.[3,5,10] Ordinarily they are active but when threatened and at low tide they take shelter in the burrows of ghost shrimps and mud shrimps,[7,8,9,13] where they sometimes get nipped. Fish down to 21 millimeters in length have been found in burrows.[3] When burrowing in sand and mud they are well hidden although presence may be indicated by spurts of water behind the gill covers. Adults eat diatoms, green algae, tintinnids, eggs and young of their hosts. They place pieces of food too large for them to handle near crabs to be torn up so that they can have the smaller pieces. Arrow gobies have been found in the food of *Sebastes* sp.,[3] staghorn sculpin,[9] whitespot greenlings,[6] and terns.[3]

Distribution Southern California through Oregon and Washington[4] to the Strait of Georgia.[14] In British Columbia vicinity of Victoria, and southern Strait of Georgia.

References 1, 2 Barraclough and Fulton 1967, 1968; 3 Carter 1965; 4 De-Lacy, Dryfoos, and Miller 1963; 5 Hubbs 1916b; 6 Jordan and Gilbert 1882; 7, 8, 9, 10 MacGinitie 1930, 1934, 1935, 1939; 11, 12 Prasad 1958a, b; 13 Ricketts and Calvin 1956; 14 Schultz and DeLacy 1936.

BLACKEYE GOBY

Coryphopterus nicholsi (Bean 1881)

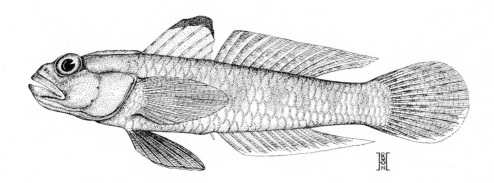

Scientific names from the Greek *cory-phos* (head or summit — crest on head), and *pteros,* (fin — reaching dorsal fin); and Captain H. E. Nichols, U.S.N., its discoverer.

Clemens and Wilby 1946 listed this species as large-scaled goby *Rhinogobiops nicholsii* (Bean 1881) and in 1961 used the name crested goby *Coryphopterus nicholsii* (Bean 1881), but the common name is applied to another species. Bluespot goby is another applicable name.

Description   Body elongate, its depth 5 to 6 into standard length, compressed. Head length about 3.7 into standard length. A scaleless crest on the mid-dorsal line extends from behind the eyes to the first dorsal fin. Mouth terminal, moderate in size, directed forward. Lower jaw protruding. Upper jaw extends to anterior part of eye. Lips thick. Interorbital space narrow, concave, with a median groove, its width about 8 into length of head. Eye somewhat protruding, its length about 3.7 into length of head. Gill membranes broadly joined, and attached to isthmus. Caudal peduncle much compressed and quite deep, its least depth about 8 into standard length. A small anal papilla.

Fins   Dorsal (2), V to VII — 12 to 14, the posterior part of the rayed portion extending well back over the caudal peduncle. Caudal rounded. Anal 11 or 12, almost mirroring rayed dorsal. Pectorals 22. Pelvics 6, thoracic, united to form a hollow cone free of body.

Scales   Cycloid, large, covering body except in front of pelvic fins and dorsal surface anterior to line joining dorsal fin origin and pectoral insertion, about 25 rows along midbody. Lateral line canal absent. A low fleshy crest medially from top of head to dorsal origin.

Colour   Pale   orange-olive   irregularly streaked horizontally with purplish brown, flecked with metallic green, faint iridescent stripe below eye, pale yellow barred with fine wavy vertical orange lines on vertical fins. Jet black on tips of first 5 spines and intervening membranes of dorsal, and on pelvic fins except their base. Light margins on other vertical fins. Eyes dark.

Size   Length to 4.75 inches (12 cm).

Recognition   Recognized by a combination of fused pelvic fins, large scales, fleshy crest on top of head, dark eyes, and black edge on the spinous dorsal.

Life History   Individuals 3.5 to 16 millimeters long (0.14–0.63 inch) occur

365

close to the surface in the low salinity water at the outlet of the Fraser River. Their stomachs contained copepods and their nauplii, Cladocera, barnacle larvae, bivalve larvae, and tintinnids.[1,2,3] Larger individuals are taken close to bottom in relatively shallow water of less than 20 fathoms (37 m). They are very territorial in their behaviour.

Distribution   From Baja California to the Queen Charlotte Islands. On both coasts of Vancouver Island and north to Skidegate Inlet.

References   1 Barraclough 1967a; 2, 3 Robinson, Barraclough, and Fulton 1968a, b.

BAY GOBY

Lepidogobius lepidus (Girard 1854)

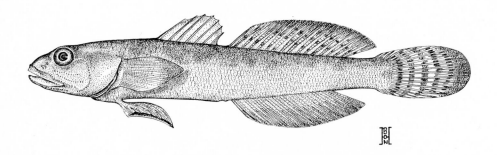

Scientific names from the Greek *lepis* (scale) and the Latin *gobio* (a kind of small fish); and the Latin *lepidus* (pretty).

Clemens and Wilby 1946 and 1961 used the common names fine-scaled goby and finescale goby for this species.

Description   Body elongate, its depth about 7.4 into standard length, compressed, slightly tapered. Head rather large, its length about 4.1 into standard length, slightly compressed. Mouth terminal, moderate in size, directed forward and up. Upper jaw extending about to middle of pupil; includes lower jaw. Snout blunt. Lips thick. Teeth in jaws, small, conical, in several irre-

gular rows, largest anteriorly. Interorbital space slightly convex, its width about 9 into length of head. Eye diameter about 4.4 into length of head. Opercular membranes fused to isthmus with no free fold. Caudal peduncle compressed, its depth about 11 into standard length.

Fins   Dorsal (2), VII — 16 to 18, close together, rayed part about same height throughout and same as spinous dorsal. Caudal ovally rounded, large. Anal 15 or 16, smooth profile, originating behind rayed dorsal origin and terminating anterior to it. Pectorals about 20, rounded. Pelvics 5, thoracic, fused at median margins, lateral rays of 2 fins joined directly by a membrane to form a hollow cone free from the body. Deep furrow from base of pelvics to anus.

366

Scales   Cycloid, small, covering body and posterior parts of head, in oblique rows along sides of body, about 86. Lateral line canal absent. Rows of pores on lower sides and ventral surfaces of head.

Colour   Pale olive green; mottled with dark dorsally, and on dorsal and anal fins, on pectoral fin faintly, and in weak vertical bars on caudal fin.

Size   Length to 4 inches (10 cm).

Recognition   Recognized by having pelvic fins joined to make a hollow cone free of body, fine scales, and moderate mouth extending to below pupil of the eye.

Distribution   Baja California to southern British Columbia. Washington. In British Columbia from the Strait of Georgia and its approaches, at Victoria, Esquimalt, Burrard Inlet, Howe Sound, Baynes Sound, Denman Island, Comox, on shallow muddy bottoms down to 30 fathoms (55 m).

References   See DeLacy, Dryfoos, and Miller 1963; Schultz and DeLacy 1936.

FAMILY TRICHIURIDAE   HAIRTAILS

Hairtails are very elongate fishes with compressed slender bodies, pointed heads, and no scales. The dorsal fin is long, and low, of spines and rays. The caudal peduncle is extremely slender, and the tail fin either finely forked or absent. Pectoral fins are small and placed low on the body; pelvics are absent or represented by small scales under the pectoral fins. In some species the pelvic girdle is joined to the cleithrum by a ligament. There is a single record of a member of this family from British Columbia.

FROSTFISH

Benthodesmus simonyi (Steindachner 1891)

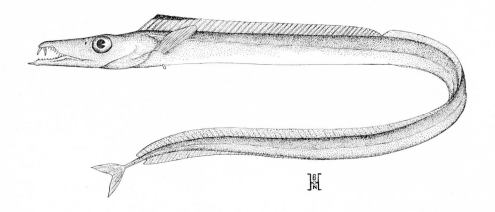

Scientific names from the Greek *benthos* (deep) and *desmos* (joined); and Professor Oskar Simony of Mathematics and Physics, Hochschule für Bodenkultur, Vienna, eclectic and collector.

The French name for this species is *sabre d'argent*.

Clemens and Wilby 1946 recorded this species as frost-fish *Benthodesmus atlanticus* Goode and Bean 1895. The later 1961 identification is retained here, although with question as the only northeast Pacific specimen cannot be found and the illustration appears to have been based on a mutilated specimen or an inadequate account.

Description   Body drawn out, its depth about 24 into standard length, deepest at head, tapered evenly. Head wedgelike, compressed, its length about 7 into standard length. Mouth moderately large, terminal, directed forward. Jaws slender and pointed, the lower somewhat projecting and having a short fleshy forward-directed appendage. Teeth generally moderate in size, 2 or 3 large, sharp canines on each side of upper jaw. Interorbital space narrow, concave longitudinally, the width of the bony part about 15 into length of head, with a weak ridge medially. Eye diameter about 6 into length of head. Branchiostegals 7. Caudal peduncle extremely slender, its least depth about 400 into standard length, depressed with its width about twice its depth, producing a slight keel.

Fins   Dorsal (2), XLVI or XLVII — 92 to 106, long low, barely separated. Caudal small based and finely forked. Anal I or II, 91 to 98, extending from anus to caudal peduncle, not quite as far as dorsal, the first 60 rays not protruding beyond skin but making a hard ridge along ventral edge of body. Pectorals about 12, insertion almost horizontal, and partly under operculum, rounded. Pelvics I, the fins reduced to scales below pelvic base, or even absent.

Scales   Scales absent. Lateral line canal prominent, tubelike, from upper angle of operculum sloping down to midside.

Colour   Grayed silver, slightly darkened dorsally, and dark brown on snout, lower jaw, and posterior part of body. Black along anterior upper edge of first dorsal, rest of fins transparent white.

Size   Length without caudal to 48 inches (122 cm).

Recognition   Recognized by the long slender compressed body, the prominent lateral line canal, the few prominent large teeth, and the finely forked tail supported by an extremely fine caudal peduncle.

Distribution   The only northeast Pacific specimen is recorded from Juan de Fuca Strait near Bentinck Island, an area of strong tidal mixing. *Benthodesmus simonyi* is reported from the Caribbean Sea and warmer areas of the North Atlantic, the genus from tropical and subtropical seas, presumably from deep water.

References   See Gilbert 1917; Goode and Bean 1882; Maul 1953; Steindachner 1891; Tucker 1953.

FAMILY SCOMBRIDAE

MACKERELS AND TUNAS

The scombrids include many kinds of temperate and tropical marine fishes displaying a wide variety of sizes but all having terete streamlined forms and recessible dorsal and pectoral fins as an adaptation to fast swimming. There is a slender, keeled caudal peduncle and a lunate or finely forked tail fin. There are two dorsal fins, the second, rayed portion, followed by a series of finlets. The anal fin has one to three weak spines at the origin followed by rays, and it also is followed by a series of finlets. Pelvic fins are thoracic. The head is conical with a fixed premaxilla. Scales are small and cycloid. Most species are wide-ranging animals of the open seas, individuals crossing the oceans and some species represented in several oceans. Five species have been found in waters off British Columbia but only two can be regarded as regular visitors.

KEY TO THE SCOMBRIDAE

1   No keel on side of caudal peduncle; dorsal fins separated by about length of base or first dorsal fin .... *Scomber japonicus,* Chub mackerel, p. 374

or   1   Keel(s) on sides of caudal peduncle; dorsal fins separated by less than diameter of eye 2

2   Spines in dorsal fin more than 16 .... *Sarda chiliensis,* Pacific bonito, p. 373

or   2   Spines in dorsal fin less than 16 3

3   Gill rakers on first gill arch more than 50; distinct corselet of large scales on anterior part of body, the posterior part scaleless or nearly so .... *Euthynnus pelamis,* Skipjack tuna, p. 371

or   3   Gill rakers on first arch fewer than 45; corselet indistinct or absent, scales covering body .... Genus *Thunnus* 4

4   Pectoral fins extending beyond posterior end of anal fin .... *Thunnus alalunga,* Albacore, p. 376

or   4   Pectoral fins not extending as far as origin of second dorsal fin .... Thunnus thynnus, Bluefin tuna, p. 379

SKIPJACK TUNA

Euthynnus pelamis (Linnaeus 1758)

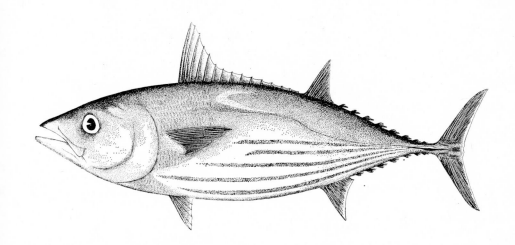

Scientific names for this species from the Greek *eu* (true) and *thynnos* (tunny); and *pelamis* (tunny).

The French name for this species is *thonine à ventre rayé*.

Clemens and Wilby 1946, 1961 called this species *Katsuwonus pelamis,* and in 1946 used skipjack as the common name.

Description   Body depth under first dorsal fin about 3.6 into standard length, robust. Head length about 3.3 into standard length, smoothly conical. Mouth terminal, moderate in size, directed forward and slightly up. Upper jaw extends to anterior part of eye. Teeth in jaws only, in single series, weak. Interorbital space broad, in raised smooth arch, its width about 3.8 into length of head. Eye almost round, its diameter about 6 into length of head. Caudal peduncle with a strong lateral keel on either side and secondary keels above and below, slender, its least depth about 45 into standard length. No gasbladder.

Fins   Dorsal (2), XV or XVI — (14)15 (16), first fin long based with first spine longest,

last 9 or 10 spines shorter and gently graded, making a strongly concave free margin, depressible into a mid-dorsal groove; second fin much lower (about two-thirds as high) than first with short base; fins close together; second fin followed by 8 (or 7) finlets. Caudal rather shallowly lunate. Anal (14)15(16), approximately same size and shape as second dorsal, but behind it; followed by about 8 finlets. Pectorals sharp, triangular. Pelvic I, 5, thoracic, triangular.[2]

Gill Rakers   On first arch (53)57(63).

Vertebrae   40 or 41.

Scales   Cycloid, moderate in size, a corselet of modified scales covers anterior part of body bounded by a curving line including dorsal base, pectoral area, and throat, few scales on rest of body. Lateral line canal straight and high on anterior part of body continuing through a curve to a straight line along midside posteriorly from a point below the second dorsal fin.

Colour   Very dark blue with metallic hues above, silvery below, dirty white on lower parts of head, throat, and around ventral fins. On lower part of sides 2 to 6, usually 4, dark longitudinal stripes, very rarely missing.[6] First dorsal spine and membrane pale; second dorsal, other fins, and finlets dusky; pelvics white along free edge; occasionally vertical light bars along sides.[9]

Size   In the Pacific, skipjack tuna may reach about 39.4 inches (1 m) and 25 kilograms. A British Columbia specimen was 25.5 inches (65 cm). Larger sizes are reported for the Atlantic Ocean.

Recognition   Usually recognizable immediately as a tuna with several (4 or 5) dark longitudinal stripes on the lower part of the body. There is a major concavity in the profile of the first dorsal fin, and the pectoral fin is short and triangular.

Life History   Spawning seems to take place throughout the year in tropical waters[10] including those off the Marshall Islands and Central America.[5] The smallest mature males encountered were 39.1 centimeters long and females 34.0 centimeters. A specimen 49.5 centimeters long was found to contain 856,000 maturing eggs. Eggs have a diameter about 1.12 millimeters and a single oil globule. Young grow rapidly and fish are believed to reach fork lengths of 75 to 85 centimeters in fourth year[1] but the rate of growth is not known with certainty. Food includes a wide variety of tropical fishes and invertebrates. Feeding is very active and skipjacks have been found to take food up to 14 percent of their body weight per day.[4] In turn they have been found to

be eaten at one stage or another by a considerable range of large pelagic fishes. Skipjack tuna form schools and are highly migratory both along shore and across wide stretches of ocean.[10]

Distribution   Skipjack tuna are found in the tropical and subtropical seas of the world; Pacific, Atlantic, and Indian oceans. In the western Pacific seasonal northerly migrations in small schools reach southern Hokkaido.[8] Off Central America[10] and north to California. Gulf of California. Only two Canadian records in the Pacific: Barkley Sound[3] and the entrance to Juan de Fuca Strait.[7]

Utilization   Skipjack tuna supply an important part of the world's tuna catch and contribute to the general pool of tuna products for freezing and subsequent canning. They are mainly taken by pole and line and by seine fisheries. There is no fishery off Canada but Canadian fishermen seining for bluefin tuna have made small landings.

References   1 Brock 1954; 2 Godsil and Byers 1944; 3 Hart 1943d; 4 Magnuson 1969; 5 Marr 1948a; 6 Matsumoto, Talbot, Collette, and Shomura 1969; 7 Neave 1959; 8 Okada 1955; 9 Strassburg and Marr 1961; 10 Waldron 1962. See also Schaefer and Marr 1948.

PACIFIC BONITO

Sarda chiliensis (Cuvier 1831)

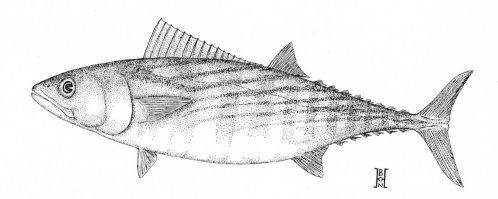

Scientific names for this species from *sarda* (an ancient name for the European species); and Chile, South America.

Clemens and Wilby 1946 listed this species as bonito, *Sarda lineolata* (Girard 1858).

Description Body depth 4.3 to 5.0 into standard length, fusiform. Head length 3.7 to 4.0 into standard length, like rest of body notably free from discontinuities. Mouth terminal, moderate, upper jaw 2.0 to 2.2 into length of head. Lower jaw projecting. Teeth in jaws moderately large and sharp, about 20 on each side. No teeth on vomer. Interorbital space wide and smooth. Eye length about 6.5 into length of head. Caudal peduncle slender, its least depth about 25 to 30 into standard length, a keel on either side.

Fins Dorsal (2), XVIII or XIX — I, 14 to 16, almost contiguous, first dorsal entire. Dorsal finlets (7)8(9). Caudal strongly lunate. Anal II, (10)11(12). Anal finlets 6 or 7. Pectorals short and triangular. Pelvics I, 5, thoracic. Origins of first dorsal, pectorals, and pelvics almost in same vertical plain (pectorals slightly in advance).[1,6]

Gill Rakers On first arch (20)24(27).

Vertebrae (44)45(46).

Scales Cycloid, small, covering body. Corselet along base of first dorsal to near upper end of gill opening, then scooping around nearly to end of pectoral fin and back to throat at isthmus. Plate of scales around pelvics extends beyond tips of fins. Lateral line canal trends down from opercular margin to pectoral insertion where it rises sharply and then drops in an irregular line to midside on caudal peduncle.

Colour Metallic blue dorsally, silvery below. Eight to 10 broad, oblique, parallel black lines sloping up and back, somewhat irregularly, from midside, or below it posteriorly, very rarely missing.

Size Length to 40 inches (102 cm).

Recognition Long first dorsal fin contiguous with second dorsal. Finlets. Dark stripes on upper part of body.

Life History Spawns off southern California.[2] On Asian coast makes northward migrations in spring in small schools. Pacific bonito feed on sardine, anchovies, squid, and other pelagic fishes.

Distribution   Pelagic but not uncommon inshore. In subtropical eastern Pacific and off Japan. Off northern Chile, Peru, and Mexico. From southern California to Luck Point and outlet of Copper River in Alaska.[4,5] Canadian records from Victoria, Sooke, west coast of Vancouver Island, Rivers Inlet, and off Yellow Point in the Strait of Georgia.[3] In Puget Sound.[4]

Utilization   Well thought of as a sports fish in California. Used there in canning but not highly regarded for that purpose.

References   1 Godsil 1954; 2 Klawe 1961; 3 Manzer 1965; 4 Patten, Rodman, and Waldron 1965; 5 Quast 1964; 6 Roedel 1948a.

CHUB MACKEREL

Scomber japonicus Houttuyn 1782

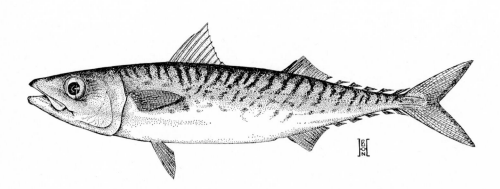

Scientific names from the Greek *scombros* (an ancient name for the common mackerel of Europe); and *japonicus* (of Japan).

The French name for this species is *maquereau blanc*.

Clemens and Wilby 1946 used the scientific name *Pneumatophorus diego* (Ayres 1856), and in 1961, *Pneumatophorus japonicus* (Houttuyn 1780) for the Pacific mackerel. The name used here is based on the opinions that the common mackerel of the northeast Pacific is the same as the chub or Spanish mackerel of the Atlantic and as the mackerel of the western Pacific.[11] These are placed in the same genus as the common mackerel of the Atlantic in agreement with the opinion that the main difference involving the presence of a gasbladder in the Pacific forms and chub mackerel is minor in view of the marked similarities,[11] and the oldest name is adopted.

Description   Body elongate, depth about 5 into standard length, spindle shaped, scarcely compressed, and tapered to a very fine caudal peduncle. Head about 4 into standard length, conical. Snout bluntly pointed. Mouth terminal, large, directed forward. Upper jaw to end of lachrymal (or suborbital) which is involved in mouth gape[1] extends to midpupil, maxillary to anterior part of eye. Teeth very fine, conical, in rows on jaws, and double rows on palatines and vomer. Interorbital space wide and arched, its width about 4.3 into length of head. Eye nearly round and rather large, its diameter about 5.5 into length of head, partly covered anteriorly and posteriorly by transparent adipose membranes. Opercles smooth. Gill membranes free of each other and the isthmus. Caudal peduncle least depth about 33 into standard length.

Fins   Dorsal (2), (VIII)IX to X — I, 12, moderately separated, the second followed by 5 or 6 finlets, the last finlet largest, spinous fin triangular. Caudal deeply forked, 2 subparallel scaly ridges at the base of the fin on either side. Anal II, 11, originating behind origin of rayed dorsal, followed by 5 or 6 rayed finlets increasing in size posteriorly. Pectorals small, subtriangular, about 20. Pelvics I, 5, thoracic. Spinous dorsal, pectoral, and pelvic fins recessed when depressed.

Gill Rakers   On first arch (38)41(43).[8]

Vertebrae   (29)30(31).[2]

Scales   Cycloid, small, about 210 to 220, deciduous. Lateral line canal, with minor undulations, slopes gently down from above pectoral fins to a point below dorsal finlets where it becomes level.

Colour   Metallic steel blue on dorsal surface, silvery below, a variable number of iridescent irregular black stripes diagonally across upper part of body and broken up below lateral line canal, 3 or more radiating lines behind each eye.

Size   The largest specimen recorded is 24.8 inches (63 cm) and about 6.3 pounds (2.9 kg).[14,15] Good-sized mackerel are considerably smaller, about 16 inches (40 cm).

Recognition   Chub mackerel are recognized by their streamlined spindlelike shape, the five or six rayed finlets behind the dorsal and anal fins, the substantial space between the rayed and spinous dorsal fins which is smaller than the insertion of the spinous dorsal, and the oblique stripes across the upper part of the body.

Life History   Spawning is not known to take place on the British Columbia coast but has been studied in California where it occurs near shore from late April to July at depths down to 50 fathoms (91.5 m). There may be more than one spawning per year by individual fish.[6] A female may produce over a million pelagic eggs.[12] These are 0.9 to 1.3 millimeters in diameter.[5,13] They hatch in about 3 days, depending on water temperature, producing larvae that are about 3 millimeters long.[5] Some mackerel mature in their second year and about half are mature at 13 inches (33 cm).[3] They may live for 9 or 10 years. Mackerel are gluttonous feeders, the diet consisting of a variety of crustaceans, squids, small fishes, such as sand lance, anchovy, etc., and *Velella*. In Asian waters mackerel are believed to leave the surface and lie inactive at depths throughout the winter months.[12] Mackerel are highly migratory, there is no basis for separating stocks of British Columbia and central Baja California,[17] and there is evidence of free interchange of individuals between Oregon and central Baja California.[7]

Distribution   From Banderas Bay and Mazatlan, Mexico, and the Gulf of California,[3,16] through Baja California, California, Washington,[19] British Columbia to southeast Alaska and the Gulf of Alaska.[18,20] In Asia waters from Sakhalin,[12] the Marine Territories of the USSR,[12] both coasts of Japan,[10] Korea,[3] Kwantung and as far south as Formosa.[13]

Fairly abundant off the west coast of Vancouver Island, sporadically, formerly mixed with schools of pilchards. Prince Rupert Harbour. On one occasion (1940) immature mackerel were fairly abundant in the Strait of Georgia,[9] and later there was stranding in the estuary of the Courtenay River.[4]

Utilization   Never consistent enough in availability to justify a commercial fishery

in British Columbia. A good food fish extensively used in California.

References   1 Allis 1903; 2 Clothier 1950; 3 Fitch 1958; 4 Foerster 1943; 5, 6 Fry 1936a, b; 7 Fry and Roedel 1949; 8 Godsil 1954; 9 Hart 1943a; 10 Matsubara 1955; 11 Matsui 1967; 12 Nikol'skii 1961; 13 Okada 1955; 14 Phillips 1937; 15, 16, 17 Roedel 1938b, 1948a, 1952; 18 Rounsefell and Dahlgren 1934; 19 Walker 1953; 20 Wilimovsky 1954.

ALBACORE

Thunnus alalunga (Bonnaterre 1788)

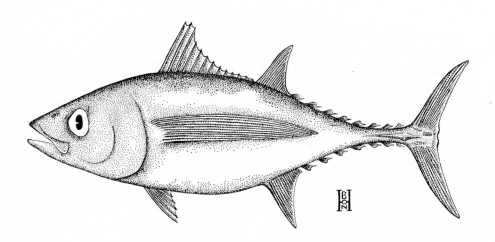

Scientific names from the old Greek *thunnos* (tuna or tunny); and the Sardinian Italian *ala* (wing) and *longus* (long — great pectoral fins).

The French name for this species is *germon*.

Clemens and Wilby 1946 and 1961 called this species *Thunnus alalunga* (Gmelin 1788).

Description   Body depth about 3.5 into standard length, fusiform, greatest depth

376

about middle of dorsal fin or slightly behind. Head length about 3.4 into standard length, smoothly conical. Mouth terminal, moderate in size, directed forward and slightly up. Upper jaw extends to anterior part of eye. Teeth small, conical, in jaws and on vomer; if present on shaft, minute, Interorbital space broad in a raised smooth arch. Eye diameter about 5.5 into length of head. Caudal peduncle with a strong lateral keel and secondary keels above and below it on either side, slender, its least depth about 38 into standard length. Gasbladder long and fairly wide, variable.

Fins   Dorsal (2), XIII or XIV — II, 13 or 14, first two spines longest and subequal, third nearly as long, and fourth about four-fifths length of third, depressible into a mid-dorsal groove; second fin about as high as first, short based; interspace between fins short; second followed by about 7 finlets, sometimes the first continuous with the second dorsal. Caudal broadly lunate, deep and slender. Anal II, 12 or 13, about same size and shape as second dorsal and originating below it, followed by about 7 or 8 finlets depending on interpretation. Pectorals very long and sabre shaped, curved downward, reaching beyond anal fin. Pelvics I, 5, thoracic, placed slightly in advance of pectorals.

Gill Rakers   On first arch (25)29(31).

Vertebrae   38.

Scales   Cycloid, moderate in size, corselet indistinct. Lateral line canal dipping downward at anterior end then sloping down to midside and nearly straight on posterior part of body.

Colour   Metallic steely blue on dorsal surface and sides, silvery below. Fins dark with metallic sheen, white posterior margins on some fins, especially caudal.

Size   Length to 49 inches (125 cm).[6] In an extensive study the largest fish was 53 inches fork length (134.6 cm).[5] Off the Canadian coast albacore infrequently exceed 98 centimeters, and ordinary large fish are about 90 centimeters total length.[10,12,20]

Recognition   Albacore is readily recognized off Canada as a mackerel-like fish with long sabrelike pectoral fins reaching beyond the anal fin.

Life History   During summer months, mainly July and August, albacore erratically occur along the offshore coasts of British Columbia,[6,17] and are available to British Columbia fishermen working off Washington and Oregon for a longer period and more consistently.[20] There is much circumstantial evidence that there is a northern migration during the fishing season and direct evidence from tagging of movements from Baja California to southern California. Movements may be as fast as 6 miles (11 km) per day. Albacore taken in the British Columbia fishery are all young immature fish in three or four size groups of uncertain age, but mainly in two size groups.[10,20,21] They appear to be part of the immature stock,[22] involved in a seasonal movement guided largely by the distribution of masses of warmer water. Areas of availability move northward with the onset of marine summer.[17] Catches are practically limited to areas of water temperature over 12.2 C (54 F) off Oregon to British Columbia, and are concentrated in areas between 14.4 to 16.1 C (58–61 F), especially along interfaces of warmer ocean water and cool water adjacent to the coast.[1] Observations by the Canadian fleet generally support this generalization,[3,22,26] although a few observations in 1946 and 1947 show best or good fishing at rather higher temperatures (to 18.3 C or 65 F) [2] Off Oregon northerly winds cause upwelling of cold bottom water inshore and albacore move rapidly offshore[14] at speeds as high as 15 miles (24 km) per day.[5] Spawning takes place from January to June south of and near the western part, between Hawaii and Japan, of the subtropical convergence.[5] There seems to be a single population through the temperate North Pacific,[9] with fish tagged off the Hawaiian Islands being recaptured off both Japan and North America,[19] although there is some evidence of isolation.[8] Young are widely dispersed after spawning in the tropical and subtropical waters of the North and South Pacific.[29] They have been found to be eaten by blue and striped marlin, *Makaira nigricans* and *Tetrapturus audax,* and wahoo, *Acanthocybium solanderi.*[29] Young grow at a rate of about 4 centimeters per month. Later growth slows to 13 to 7 centimeters per year.[5] Food of albacore taken by Canadian fishermen, or off Canada, shows a wide variety of marine animals, such as: pilchards, herring, anchovy, myctophids, saury, small rockfishes, other fishes, squid, and "red feed" (euphausiids).[11,20,27] On the central and northeast Pacific albacore feed night and day.[13] Judging from the success of fishing practices, albacore feed near the surface on active forage animals since they are taken best by dragging feathered lures near surface at relatively (to salmon trolling) high speeds, about 6 knots (11 km per hour). When albacore fishing is good it is extremely fast. So fishermen use barbless hooks and reel in lines very quickly, balancing any loss of fish against time lost in removing fish from the hooks. When albacore are hooked and boated, their reactions include a general increase in body temperature.[20] In the interest of conserving ice in the hold this necessitates a cooling off period in air. Similar rises in temperature are noted for other large pelagic fishes.[15] Along the west coast of North America albacore concentrate the radioactive isotopes of zinc and manganese, Zn^{65} and Mn^{54}.[23]

Distribution   Pelagic, oceanic, and highly migratory. In the Atlantic, Pacific, and Indian oceans. In the eastern Pacific from the Gulf of California and the Revilla-gigedo Islands off Mexico[5] (at least) to the Gulf of Alaska,[28] and offshore,[4,7,24] and through the intervening waters.[7,24,25] Off Japan.[16,18] Occurrence erratic through the northern part of its range.

Utilization   The albacore fishery out of British Columbia started about 1939 and in that year 284 thousand pounds (129 metric tons) were landed by trollers. In the following years production from the fishery fluctuated from zero to a peak in 1949 of 2231 thousand pounds (1010 metric tons). There was some support by government scouting activity. Since 1950 success diminished irregularly. The extent of a recent upturn in production is difficult to assess because the addition of purse seiners to the tuna fleet led to the inclusion in catches and records of bluefin and skipjack tunas. Total tuna landings in 1967 were 971 thousand pounds (441 metric tons). Most of the catch is frozen for subsequent canning although the fresh fish is excellent.

References   1 Alverson 1961; 2, 3 Bethune 1948, 1949; 4 Brock 1939; 5 Clemens 1961; 6 Clemens and Wilby 1961; 7 Cowan 1938; 8 Godsil 1948; 9 Godsil and Byers 1944; 10 Hart 1949a; 11 Hart and Barraclough 1948; 12 Hart and Pike 1948; 13 Iversen 1962; 14 Lane 1965; 15 Lindsey 1968; 16 Matsubara 1955; 17 Neave and Hanavan 1960; 18 Okada 1955; 19 Otsu 1960; 20, 21, 22 Partlo 1950, 1955a, b; 23 Pearcy and Osterberg 1968; 24 Samson 1940; 25, 26, 27 Scagel 1949a, b, c; 28 Wilimovsky 1954; 29 Yoshida 1965. See also Dung and Royce 1953, Ganssle and Clemens 1953, Hart 1942b, McHugh 1952.

BLUEFIN TUNA

Thunnus thynnus (Linnaeus 1758)

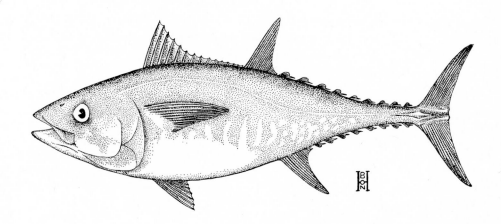

Scientific names from the old Greek *thunnos* (tuna or tunny) from *thuno* (rush) — two transliterations.

The French name for this species is *thon rouge*.

Recorded in Clemens and Wilby 1961 as *Thunnus saliens* Jordan and Evermann 1926.

Description   Body depth about 3.3 into standard length, fusiform, greatest depth about middle of first dorsal fin. Head length about 3.2 into standard length, smoothly conical. Mouth terminal, moderate in size, directed forward and slightly up. Upper jaw extends to anterior part of eye. Teeth small, conical, in 1 series in each jaw and minute on shaft of vomer. Interorbital space broad in a high smooth arch. Eye diameter about 8 into length of head. Caudal peduncle with a strong lateral keel on either side, and small keels above and below its posterior end, very slender, its least depth about 35 into standard length. Gasbladder usually present and small, often rudimentary.

Fins   Dorsal (2), XIII or **XIV** — I, 13, first fin highest anteriorly, declining evenly in height about through first 9 spines, then level and low, depressible into a mid-dorsal groove; second fin higher than first, higher than length of its own base which is short; interspace between fins short, second fin followed by about 8 finlets, sometimes the first continuous with second dorsal,[3] spaced evenly between it and caudal base. Caudal lunate, large. Anal I, 12, about same shape and size as second dorsal and placed behind it under first dorsal finlet, followed by about 7 or 8[3] ventral finlets. Pectoral length about 0.8 of length of head, not reaching beyond first dorsal. Pelvics I, 5, thoracic, under pectorals.

Gill Rakers   On first arch (32)35(39), (43 in Atlantic).

Vertebrae   38.

Scales   Cycloid, moderate in size. A corselet of modified scales extends back beyond the pectoral fin. Lateral line canal sloping down and back in an arch in anterior half of body, then straight along midside to caudal peduncle.

Colour   Dark steely blue above, silvery gray below with silvery spots behind and below pectoral fin, cheeks silvery, dorsal fins dusky, anal fin silvery gray tinged with yellow. Dorsal and anal finlets yellow. Pale vertical bars on young, tending to disappear with age.

379

Size   In the Atlantic, lengths of 14 feet (4.3 m) and 2000 pounds (910 kg) have been reported. In the Pacific 2.5 meters and 375 kilograms, and in the northeast Pacific over 7 feet (2.1 m) and 250 pounds (114 kg) are known.

Recognition   Recognized by the short to moderate pectoral fin extending only about as far as tenth to twelfth dorsal spine, the dorsal fins close together, the uniform steely blue on the dorsal surface, the absence of longitudinal stripes, the large silvery spots on the ventral surface, (not always apparent on large fish), and the yellowish finlets.

Life History   Eggs are 1.0 to 1.3 millimeters in diameter, with an oil globule, and are buoyant. Bluefin tuna grow rapidly and at a variety of rates. Off California the following lengths at age may be attained : 0, 51 to 69 centimeters; I, 54 to 92 centimeters; II, 77 to 112 centimeters; III, 100 to 128 centimeters; IV, 128 centimeters average; V, 142 centimeters average.[1] A tagged individual grew about 90 centimeters or 230 pounds (104 kg) in 62 months between tagging and recapture.[8] This fish migrated across the Pacific Ocean from near Cedros Island to south of Japan at 29.03 N, 137.42 E. Movements between California and Japan in both directions have been demonstrated and may be part of a regular migration pattern.[2] There may be northern movements in the marine summer. Bluefin tuna are known to feed on small schooling fishes such as sardine, jack mackerel, anchovy, and mackerel, and squid as they are available. They are known to be eaten by sperm whales.

Distribution   The bluefin tuna is herein considered to be distributed throughout the temperate and torrid zones all over the world,[5] although South Pacific and Atlantic species have been regarded as distinct.[4] In the eastern Pacific from at least as far south as Guadaloupe Island to the Gulf of Alaska (Kodiak Island[9]). Kuril Islands and Hokkaido.[7] Rare north of Point Conception, California. Only a few records well off southern and central British Columbia in summer.[6]

Utilization   An important sports and commercial fish in southern California, and elsewhere in the world where abundant. Now taken in moderate quantities by Canadian seiners working off the United States coast.

References   1 Bell 1963; 2 Clemens and Flittner 1969; 3 Godsil and Byers 1944; 4 Godsil and Holmberg 1950; 5 Matsubara 1955; 6 Neave 1959; 7 Okada 1955; 8 Orange and Fink 1963; 9 Radovich 1961. See also Ginsburg 1953.

The Stromateidae as used here is a grouping for convenience of fishes sometimes regarded as belonging to different families: Stromateidae, compressed fishes with falcate pectoral fins, forked tail, long dorsal and anal fins, and muscular tooth-lined pharynx; Centrolophidae, compressed fishes with rounded tail and pectoral fins, moderately long, low, upright fins, and toothed pharyngeal sacs; and Tetragonuridae, terete fishes with fringed mouth, doubly keeled caudal peduncle giving a squarish cross section. None of these kinds of fishes are common in British Columbia. Pacific pompano, medusafish, and squaretail.

MEDUSAFISH (Family Centrolophidae)

Icichthys lockingtoni Jordan and Gilbert 1880

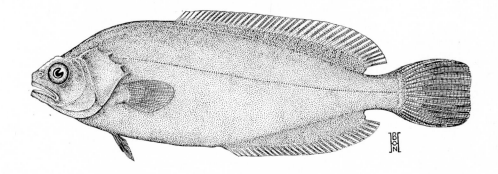

Scientific names from the Greek *eeko* (yield(ing) or flexible), and *ichthys* (fish); and W. N. Lockington, ichthyologist at the California Academy of Sciences.

Clemens and Wilby 1946, 1961 assigned the common name brown rudderfish to this species. It was at one time also called *Centrolophus californicus*.[4]

Description Body depth about 3 into standard length, compressed, pinched in along bases of dorsal and anal fins, with the dorsal constriction extending forward to the head, very limp and flexible. Head length about 4 into standard length, somewhat compressed, the whole dorsal surface a raised spongy mass. Mouth terminal, moderate in size, directed slightly upward. Upper jaw reaching a point below the middle of the pupil of the eye. Snout rounded. Teeth on jaws very fine but sharply pointed, needlelike teeth reported to be on pharyngeal plications. Interorbital space broad and poorly defined, its breadth 3 to 3.5 into length of head. Eye about 4.5 into length of head. Weak radiating striae on operculum, the stronger ones terminating at the edge in soft cartilaginous spines, fine hairlike processes along lower edge of operculum. Branchiostegals 5. Gill membranes separate and free from isthmus. Caudal peduncle compressed, its least depth 9 to 10 into standard length.

Fins   Dorsal (1), III, 34 to 39, spines weak, fin low anteriorly, highest at posterior end. Caudal rounded with a small notch, narrow. Anal III, 20 to 25, similar to dorsal. Pectorals about 19, small, rounded. Pelvics I, 5 thoracic, spine weak, fifth ray filamentous.

Scales   Cycloid, thin, deciduous, covering body and head. Small, 115 to 121 rows on midside. Lateral line canal nearly straight, short.

Colour   Bluish gray to brown, darker on scale pockets, fins dusky to black.

Size   Length to 8 inches (20 cm), 16 inches (41 cm) off California, 18 inches (46 cm) off Japan.[3]

Recognition   Notable for the limp, compressed, scaled body, the spongy top of the head, and the narrow tail.

Life History   Lives commensally in the bell of large jelly fishes,[4] or in the gastrointestinal cavity.[5] Young frequently observed near surface in California.[2] At all stages the skeleton is very poorly ossified.

Distribution   Baja California to the Gulf of Alaska and Japan. Observed near the surface but may be bathypelagic.

In Canada recorded from Sooke,[1] Esperanza Inlet of Vancouver Island and off Queen Charlotte Sound.

References   1 Cowan 1938; 2 Fitch 1952b; 3 Fitch and Lavenberg 1968; 4 Hobbs 1929; 5 Myers 1950.

PACIFIC POMPANO (FAMILY STROMATEIDAE)

Peprilus simillimus (Ayres 1860)

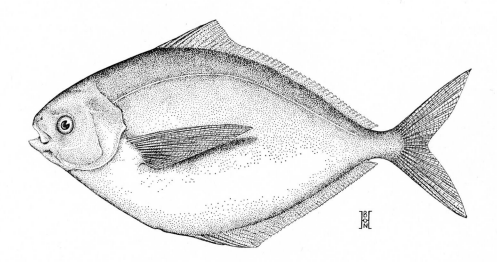

Scientific names from the Greek *peprilos* (an unknown fish); and the Latin *simillimus* (very similar to — *Rhombus,* a related genus).

Clemens and Wilby 1946 used the common name California pompano, and in 1961 used the scientific name *Palometa simillima.*

Description   Body short and very compressed, depth about 2 into standard length. Head compressed, rounded in profile, length about 4 into standard length. Mouth small, terminal, directed slightly upward. Upper jaw extending about two-thirds distance to anterior edge of orbit or 3.3 into length of head. Lower jaw included in upper. Teeth on jaws. Eyes about halfway down sides of head and interorbital space accordingly deeply domed and rounded. Eyes small, about 5 into length of head. Gill membranes united and free of isthmus. Caudal peduncle slender and short.

Fins   Dorsal (1), III, 45 to 47, long, low except at anterior end where longest rays are about 1.7 into length of head, membrane opaque and pigmented with only free ends of rays clearly evident. Caudal deeply and finely forked. Anal III, 39 to 44, similar in shape and texture to dorsal. Pectorals 20 to 22, long, nearly half as long again as head. Pelvics absent.[4]

Vertebrae   Usually 29 without urostyle.[3,4]

Scales   Cycloid, small. Lateral line canal starts high on sides of head and sweeps back in a grand arch following the dorsal profile of the body to a point almost below the end of the dorsal fin.

Colour   Brilliantly iridescent, green or blue above, silvery below. Dusky on fins.

Size   Length to 11 inches (28 cm).

Recognition   Recognizable by its very compressed body, long low dorsal and anal fins, and the absence of pelvic fins.

Life History   The centre of abundance appears to be in southern California

383

where it provides a minor fishery. It was especially abundant in California in 1947[2] and in that year was noted as abundant in Barkley Sound[5] and individuals seemed to remain and be caught there in subsequent years. Again abundant in 1951.

Distribution From Cedros Island in central Baja California[7] to Queen Charlotte Sound (Fitz Hugh Sound).

On both east and west coasts of Vancouver Island, and from Knight Inlet. Encountered in the Bellingham Bay to Eliza Island area of Washington State and in Puget Sound in years around 1959,[1] and subsequently.[6]

Utilization Never important in terms of total catch but a gourmet item in California through the fresh fish markets.

References 1 Batts 1960; 2 Bureau of Marine Fisheries, State of California 1949; 3 Clothier 1950; 4 Haedrich 1967; 5 Hart 1949c; 6 High 1966; 7 Roedel 1953b.

SMALLEYE SQUARETAIL (FAMILY TETRAGONURIDAE)

Tetragonurus cuvieri Risso 1810

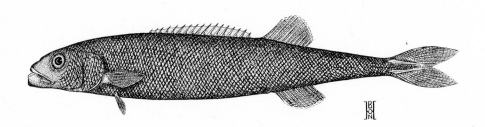

Scientific names from the Greek *tetragonos* (square) and *oura* (tail — cross section of caudal peduncle); and G. C. L. D. Cuvier 1769–1832, a founder of modern ichthyology.

Recorded by Clemens and Wilby 1961 as squaretail.

Description Body elongate, its depth about 6 into standard length, a little compressed. Head little compressed, its length about 5.3 into standard length. Snout blunt and rounded. Mouth terminal, rather large, directed forward. Upper jaw extending as far as anterior part of orbit but not to pupil, notched anteriorly. Lower jaw deeply notched anteriorly. Teeth conical, in upper jaw in a row, sparse on vomer and palatines. Teeth in lower jaw straplike, with oblique free ends, on the edge of a greatly broadened dentary. Lower jaw included. Interorbital space arched and wide, its width about 3.8 into length of head. Orbit rimmed with a series of specialized scales. Eye nearly round, moderate in size, its diameter about 5.3 into length of head.

Opercles fully scaled, upper part with scales extending beyond bony margin. Branchiostegals 5, opercular membranes free of each other and the isthmus. Caudal peduncle with 2 lateral converging keels on either side extending to base of caudal fin so that the cross section of the fin base is a square with the corners extended laterally, its least depth about 22 into standard length.

Fins   Dorsal (2), XV(XVIII)XXI — 12 to 15, spinous, low, and when relaxed fitting into a sharply incised depression. Caudal rather finely forked. Anal I, 11 to 13, behind rayed dorsal. Pectorals 14 to 17, small, low on body. Pelvics I, 5, thoracic, small.

Gill Rakers   About 14 to 17.

Vertebrae   About 52.

Scales   Ctenoid, fine ridges directed backward on each scale, the numbers of ridges generally related to the size of the fish, reaching at least 16. Scales on body arranged in evident sigmoid rows extending generally downward and forward, in concentric rows around eye, on preoperculum and adjacent areas, and in less definite vertical rows on the operculum, modified posteriorly to form prominent keels at the base of the tail fin. Absent from anterior parts of the head. Lateral line canal slightly arched upward at anterior end, then straight along the side of the body to the caudal peduncle. Scale rows to start of keels 98 to 103.

Colour   Dark brown, paler at base of tail and on head, otherwise almost uniform throughout.

Size   Greatest length recorded in the northeast Pacific 15 inches (38 cm), off New Zealand 25 inches (63.5 cm).

Recognition   Distinguished by its elongate subcylindrical body, the strikingly precise sigmoid rows of scales on the body, the converging ridges of scales at the base of the caudal fin, and the deep lower jaws.

Life History   Jellyfish parts are the only food found in squaretail stomachs. Jellyfish may be the main food and the arrangement of teeth and the digestive tract indicate a specialized diet. The species was originally described, quite vividly, as being poisonous,[6] the assumption being that toxins from jellyfish became incorporated in the fish flesh. Much later tests did not confirm that the fish is poisonous and it is suggested that the unwholesomeness may have been associated with maturing sexual products.[1]

Distribution   Recorded from the eastern and central North Atlantic, and the Mediterranean Sea. In the southwest Pacific (New Zealand and Australia), tropical mid-Pacific and off Japan.[3,4] In the eastern Pacific from the latitude of Cedros Island (Baja California)[2] through California and British Columbia,[5,8] south of the Aleutian Islands at about 45 N.[7] On the whole a fish of the near-surface layers,[3] but taken to at least 100 fathoms (183 m).[8]

References   1 Fitch 1952a; 2 Fitch and Lavenberg 1968; 3 Grey 1955; 4 Grinols 1965a; 5 Neave 1959; 6 Risso 1810; 7 Tononaka 1957; 8 Welander and Alverson 1954. See also Fitch 1951a.

FAMILY ICOSTEIDAE   RAGFISHES

The ragfishes have compressed bodies which are flaccid because the skeleton is largely gristle. Pelvic fins when present are thoracic. The one species present in British Columbia goes through such remarkable changes (like losing the pelvic fins) during development that it has been described as two species. The gasbladder is closed. Fins are without spines. The maxillary is not included in the upper border of the mouth. Most records of occurrence are from shallow water but the real centre of abundance for the species may be in deep water.

RAGFISH

Icosteus aenigmaticus Lockington 1880

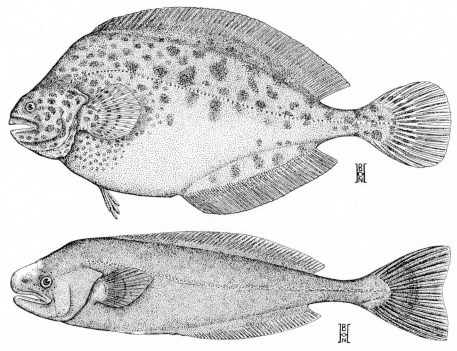

Juvenile *(top)*; Adult *(bottom)*.

Scientific names from the Greek *eeko* (yield) and *osteo* (bone — soft bones); and *aenigma* (plural *aenigmata* — puzzling).

In Clemens and Wilby 1946 this species was assigned the common name fantailed rag-fish. Also included in that volume was the so-called brown rag-fish *Acrotus willoughbyi* Bean 1887. This account follows Clemens and Wilby (1961) in accepting *Icosteus* as being the immature of *Acrotus* so that the older name, *Icosteus*, is used for both.

Description   Body depth about 2.6 into standard length, moderately compressed. Anterior profile steep, producing a

hump at the insertion of the dorsal fin. Head short, its length about 5 into standard length, somewhat compressed. Mouth terminal, rather small, directed slightly downward. Snout blunt. Upper jaw extending to a point just behind posterior margin of orbit. Teeth minute. Interorbital space wide, high, flat in the middle, about 2 into length of head. Eye small, diameter of the eyeball about 5 into length of head, eyeball partly obscured by surrounding membranes. Opercular membranes joined and free from isthmus. Caudal peduncle compressed, its least depth about 13 into standard length.[4]

Fins   Dorsal (1), 52 to 55, originating over posterior end of head. Caudal expanded and

386

rounded. Anal 34 to 40. Pectorals 20 to 21, rounded, pedunculate. Pelvics 5, abdominal in young, absent in adults.

Gill Rakers   On the first arch 15 to 17.

Scales   Absent from body generally. Skin tough. Along lateral line canal scales are gathered into clusters of small spines. On rays of vertical fins scales form numerous minute spicules. Lateral line canal gently arching upward at anterior end and then sweeping down smoothly to a point just anterior to the base of the caudal fin.

Colour   Brown and yellow irregularly blotched with faint purple, dusky on fins.

The foregoing description applies to the juvenile phase of this species which persists to a length of about 16 inches (40.6 cm). **Adults** differ in striking ways including: a generally less robust form, the absence of pelvic fins, having a forked tail, the presence of an overall chocolate colour.

Size   Length to 7 feet (2.1 m), or more.

Recognition   Noteworthy for the oval, extremely limp body and small eyes.

Life History   All that is known about the remarkable metamorphosis of this species from juvenile to adult is the change itself. Spawning is reported to take place both in summer[3,5] and in winter.[1] Eggs are clear, light amber in colour and it is assumed that because they are not adhesive they are pelagic. Fecundity is tentatively estimated at 293,000 for a 106-centimeter standard length specimen and 435,000 for a 136-centimeter specimen.[1] They eat small fishes and cephalopods and are eaten by sperm whales.[2]

Distribution   Northern Pacific Ocean from north and south California, Oregon, Washington,[3] British Columbia to southern Alaska,[8,9,10] and the Pacific coast of Japan. Pelagic or bathypelagic to 400 fathoms (732 m).[6]

In British Columbia from near Victoria, Barkley Sound and the Queen Charlotte Islands.[7]

References   1 Allen 1968; 2 Cowan 1938; 3 Crawford 1927a; 4 Fitch 1953; 5 Fitch and Lavenberg 1968; 6 Grinols 1965a; 7 Pritchard 1929; 8 Schultz 1930; 9 Schultz, Hart, and Gunderson 1932; 10 Wilimovsky 1954.

ORDER SCORPAENIFORMES

This order includes a wide range of families in which the suborbital bone is enlarged to form a suborbital stay extending down and back from the eye. It is occasionally apparent superficially, but its detection usually requires dissection. Pelvic fins are characteristically with one spine and five soft rays but are highly modified or absent in the Cyclopteridae.

FAMILY SCORPAENIDAE   SCORPIONFISHES

Scorpionfishes have the gill opening extending at least as far as the base of the lowest pectoral ray, the opening behind the fourth gill arch is much reduced or absent, and there are two opercular spines, and five preopercular spines. There is a suborbital stay. Off British Columbia two genera are represented. *Sebastolobus* is represented by two species and *Sebastes* by at least 35. *Sebastes* has replaced *Sebastodes* as used in Clemens and Wilby (1946 and 1961) as a result of studies of conventional morphological characters by Matsubara (1943) and McAllister (1961) and of biochemical analyses by Tsuyuki et al. (1968). All species have stout and moderately elongate bodies and are more or less laterally compressed. There is a single dorsal fin with 11 to 17 spines and 8 to 18 rays. The anal fin has three strong spines and five to nine rays. Pelvic fins are thoracic, each with one spine and five rays. The mouth is moderately large and terminal. Teeth are in patches on both jaws, vomer, and palatines. The gill membranes are separate from the isthmus, and the inner side of the opercle has an exposed pseudobranchial arch. There are seven branchiostegal rays. Various species are found from the intertidal zone to great depths (2800 m). *Sebastolobus* is oviparous, *Sebastes* ovoviviparous. *Sebastes* possesses a gasbladder which greatly expands when water pressure is quickly decreased by bringing the fish to the surface, often destroying them. *Sebastolobus* lacks a gasbladder. Many species are brilliantly coloured. All species are edible, and some are vigorously sought commercially. Scorpionfishes, rockfishes, and thornyheads.

388

KEY TO THE SCORPAENIDAE

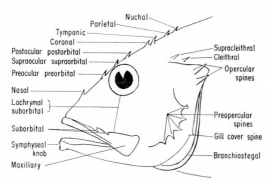

Head spines for a generalized rockfish.

	1	Dorsal fin spines 15 or 16(17); rays 8 to 10; vertebrae 28; sharp spiny ridge on side of head below eye .... Genus *Sebastolobus* 36
or	1	Dorsal fin spines usually 13((11, 12) 13(14)); rays 11 to 18; vertebrae 25 or 26; no continuous sharp ridge along side of head .... Genus *Sebastes* 2
	2	Anus anterior to anal fin by more than 1.1 orbit widths; colour olive-pink back and pink sides .... *Sebastes jordani,* Shortbelly rockfish, p. 423
or	2	Anus anterior to anal fin by less than 1.1 orbit widths 3
	3	Lower rim of orbit with 2 to 10 fine spines; colour red or reddish black .... *Sebastes aleutianus,* Rougheye rockfish, p. 394
or	3	Spines on lower rim of orbit 0 or 1 4
	4	Spines on top of head weak or absent; postocular, tympanic, coronal, and nuchal spines always absent 5
or	4	Spines on top of head moderate to strong; postocular and tympanic spines always present 12
	5	Upper jaw long, 2.3 to 2.9 orbit widths; extends beyond orbit 6
or	5	Upper jaw moderate, 1.5 to 2.3 orbit widths; does not extend posterior to orbit 7
	6	Gill rakers 28 to 31; lateral line canal pores 54 to 58; body red or olive-brown .... *Sebastes paucispinis,* Bocaccio, p. 435
or	6	Gill rakers 33 to 36; lateral line canal pores 44 to 49; body green or greenish black on back, silvery on sides .... *Sebastes brevispinis,* Silvergray rockfish, p. 405

389

| | 7 | Anal fin rays short, 1.0 to 1.3 orbit widths; colour pinkish red .... *Sebastes goodei*, Chilipepper, p. 420 |
| or | 7 | Anal rays moderate, 1.6 to 2.4 orbit widths .... 8 |

| | 8 | Posterior edge of anal fin slanting posteriorly .... 9 |
| or | 8 | Posterior edge of anal fin vertical or slanting anteriorly .... 10 |

| | 9 | Diagonal scale rows below lateral line canal 50 to 56; body colour bluish black .... *Sebastes mystinus*, Blue rockfish, p. 429 |
| or | 9 | Diagonal scale rows below lateral line canal 60 to 66; body colour brown .... *Sebastes entomelas*, Widow rockfish, p. 417 |

| | 10 | Peritoneum black; colour green and brown .... *Sebastes ciliatus*, Dusky rockfish, p. 409 |
| or | 10 | Peritoneum white .... 11 |

| | 11 | Posterior edge of anal fin slanted anteriorly; caudal peduncle deep, 2.8 to 3.2 into length of head; body colour black .... *Sebastes melanops*, Black rockfish, p. 426 |
| or | 11 | Posterior edge of anal fin vertical; caudal peduncle moderate, 3.2 to 3.4 into length of head; body colour green .... *Sebastes flavidus*, Yellowtail rockfish, p. 418 |

| | 12 | Supraocular spine present .... 13 |
| or | 12 | Supraocular spine absent .... 21 |

| | 13 | Peritoneum silver white .... 14 |
| or | 13 | Peritoneum silver gray with black dots, or black .... 16 |

| | 14 | Gill rakers 26 to 30; colour orange-yellow with black tips to fins .... *Sebastes ruberrimus*, Yelloweye rockfish, p. 442 |
| or | 14 | Gill rakers 35 to 45 .... 15 |

| | 15 | Scales on mandible rough; 2 sharp triangular spines on lower margin of suborbital bone; body colour vermilion mottled with gray .... *Sebastes miniatus*, Vermilion rockfish, p. 428 |
| or | 15 | Scales on mandible smooth; 1 sharp triangular spine on lower margin of suborbital bone; body colour orange and yellow mottled with gray .... *Sebastes pinniger*, Canary rockfish, p. 437 |

| | 16 | Lateral line canal pores less than 35 .... 17 |
| or | 16 | Lateral line canal pores more than 35 .... 18 |

	17	Second anal fin spine short, 7.3 to 12.4 into standard length; colour pink or orange-pink ....
		.... *Sebastes borealis,* Shortraker rockfish, p. 403
or	17	Second anal fin spine long 4.6 to 6.8 into standard length; colour rose-red or pink, and silvery .... *Sebastes aurora,* Aurora rockfish, p. 400
	18	Second anal fin spine longer than third, length 1.4 to 1.7 orbit widths .... *Sebastes helvomaculatus,* Rosethorn rockfish, p. 421
or	18	Second anal fin spine shorter than third, length 0.9 to 1.4 orbit widths 19
	19	Nuchal spines present or coalesced with parietal; body relatively deep at origin of ventral fins, 2.3 to 2.8 in standard length; 4 irregular, vertical, black bands on back and sides, surrounded by pink or orange; interior of mouth black .... *Sebastes crameri,* Darkblotched rockfish, p. 410
or	19	Nuchal spines absent 20
	20	Diagonal scale rows below lateral line canal 49 to 55; strong symphyseal knob; mouth colour pinkish; body colour bright red .... *Sebastes alutus,* Pacific ocean perch, p. 396
or	20	Diagonal scale rows below lateral line canal 57 to 67; weak symphyseal knob; mouth colour blotched with yellow and black; body colour red and yellow-orange with indistinct black bands across back .... *Sebastes reedi,* Yellowmouth rockfish, p. 440
	21	Interorbital space strongly concave 22
or	21	Interorbital space slightly convex to slightly concave, never strongly concave 23
	22	Lateral line canal pores 38 to 41; body colour black with yellow stripe from dorsal fin downward and posteriorly along lateral line .... *Sebastes nebulosus,* China rockfish, p. 431
or	22	Lateral line canal pores 43 to 50; body colour red to gray with 5 vertical dark bars .... *Sebastes nigrocinctus,* Tiger rockfish, p. 433
	23	Second anal spine length about equal to third 24
or	23	Second anal fin spine longer than third, usually by a quarter of an orbit width or more 30
	24	Peritoneum brown or black 25
or	24	Peritoneum silver-white 27
	25	Two strong spines on lower margin of suborbital bone; premaxillaries with prominent knobs extending anteriorly from jaw; body colour pink-red .... *Sebastes diploproa,* Splitnose rockfish, p. 412
or	25	Spines on lower margin of suborbital bone triangular or missing 26

26	Gill rakers 26 to 32; body white with broad red or pink vertical bands .... *Sebastes babcocki,* Redbanded rockfish, p. 401
or 26	Gill rakers 38 to 43; body red with 1 horizontal red or pink stripe along lateral line canal .... *Sebastes proriger,* Redstripe rockfish, p. 439

27	Spines usually absent on lower posterior edge of gill cover; vertical pink or red bars on body .... *Sebastes babcocki,* Redbanded rockfish, p. 401
or 27	Spines present on lower posterior edge of gill cover; no vertical bars on body 28

28	Lateral line canal pores 35 to 38; longest dorsal fin spine 4.1 to 4.5 into standard length; dorsal fin membranes deeply incised between spines; colour brown with light tan areas .... *Sebastes maliger,* Quillback rockfish, p. 424
or 28	Lateral line canal pores 39 to 49; longest dorsal fin spine 4.5 to 5.6 into standard length 29

29	Coronal spines usually present; body colour light brown, mottled with dark brown .... *Sebastes auriculatus,* Brown rockfish, p. 398
or 29	Coronal spines absent; body colour dark brown washed with copper-pink, and occasionally with yellow or cream blotches .... *Sebastes caurinus,* Copper rockfish, p. 407

30	Gill rakers on first arch less than 34 31
or 30	Gill rakers on first arch more than 34 33

31	Symphyseal knob weak or absent; body shape slender, depth at pelvic fins, 3.1 to 3.7 into standard length; depth at anal fin 4.4 to 5.2 into standard length; body colour pink with 4 horizontal, irregular green stripes .... *Sebastes elongatus,* Greenstriped rockfish, p. 414
or 31	Symphyseal knob strong; body shape moderate, depth at pelvic fins 2.7 to 3.2 into standard length; depth at anal fin 3.5 to 4.1 into standard length 32

32	Two strong sharp spines on lower margin of suborbital bone; spines present on lower posterior edge of gill cover; colour yellow-pink or silvery pink .... *Sebastes saxicola,* Stripetail rockfish, p. 444
or 32	Two triangular, blunt spines on lower margin of suborbital bone; spines usually absent from the lower posterior edge of gill cover; colour light red with irregular brown patches .... *Sebastes zacentrus,* Sharpchin rockfish, p. 450

33	Symphyseal knob strong; gill rakers 33 to 37 .... *Sebastes zacentrus,* Sharpchin rockfish, p. 450
or 33	Symphyseal knob weak or absent; gill rakers 36 to 45 34

34   No stripe along lateral line canal, diagonal scale rows below lateral line canal 40 to 45; body colour coppery red with indefinite broken cross bars or blotches; adults no longer than 16 cm .... *Sebastes emphaeus,* Puget Sound rockfish, p. 415

or   34   Stripe along all or part of lateral line canal; diagonal scale rows below lateral line canal 45 to 58 35

35   Pale pink stripe along posterior two-thirds of lateral line canal; pores along lateral line canal 42 to 52; body depth at origin of anal fin 3.8 to 4.2 into standard length .... *Sebastes variegatus,* Harlequin rockfish, p. 446

or   35   Brownish red or orange stripe along entire lateral line; pores on lateral line canal 39 to 41; body depth at origin of anal fin 4.2 to 4.4 into standard length; adults no longer than 19 cm .... *Sebastes wilsoni,* Pygmy rockfish, p. 448

36   Dorsal fin spines (15)16(17), the fourth or fifth longest, with length of longest spine about 3.8 into length of head; branchiostegals without scales; lining of gill cavity light except for a possible dusky blotch on inside of opercle; colour bright translucent (in life) red with some black on fins .... *Sebastolobus alascanus,* Shortpine thornyhead, p. 451

or   36   Dorsal fin spines usually 15(16), the third, or rarely the fourth longest, its length about 2.5 into length of head; branchiostegals usually but not always with scales; lining of gill cavity dark gray or black; colour red with some black on fins .... *Sebastolobus altivelis,* Longspine thornyhead, p. 453

ROUGHEYE ROCKFISH

Sebastes aleutianus (Jordan and Evermann 1898)

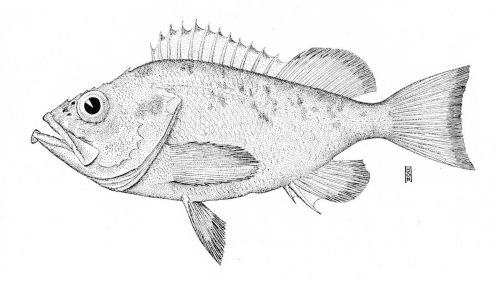

Scientific names from the Greek *sebastos* (magnificent); and *aleutianus* (the Aleutian Islands).

Scientific naming involves uncertainties. There is good evidence for the existence of physiological and/or biochemical distinctions among fish recognized under this name.[5]

Description   Body depth 2.7 to 3.0 into standard length. Compressed. Head length 2.5 to 2.7 into standard length, upper profile nearly straight. Mouth terminal, large, directed noticeably upward. Lower jaw projecting prominently. Upper jaw extending to midorbit. Symphyseal knob low, broad, projecting downward. Dentary elevation present in large specimens and not included in upper jaw when mouth closed. Eye diameter about 4.3 into length of head. Interorbital space at midorbit slightly convex to flat, frontal ridges between ocular ridges 4.6 to 5.5 into length of head. Caudal peduncle 10.0 to 11.8 into standard length.

Head Spines   Nasal, preocular, postocular, tympanic, parietal, coronal, and nuchal spines present, strong, and rather prostrate. Coronal spines may be absent and nuchal spines sometimes doubled. Parietal ridges strong and sometimes broken into points. Suborbital spines 2 or more. Preopercular spines strong, the lowermost sometimes multifid, the upper 2 to 4 sometimes directed backward. Opercular spines strong and sharp, the upper sometimes longer. Supracleithral and cleithral spines strong and occasionally bifid. Spines usually present on the lower edge of the gill cover.

Fins   Dorsal (1), XIII, 13 to 14(15), spinous portion moderately incised and notched. Caudal moderately indented. Anal III (6)7 to 8, second spine twice as thick as third, and in small specimens only reaching to its tip when the fin is depressed, posterior edge rounded. Pectorals 18 or 19, extending beyond tips of ventral, reaching anus in small specimens but not in large. Pelvics I, 5, thoracic.

Gill Rakers   On first gill arch 30 to 34.

Scales   Ctenoid, 47 to 55 diagonal rows below lateral line canal. Sometimes scales around edge of membrane surrounding eye. Pores in lateral line canal 29 to 34.[4]

Colour   Red or red-black on body. Vague dusky bars and spots may be present. Fins reddish with dark margins. Dusky blotch on operculum. Reddish lining in mouth and gill chambers. Peritoneum silver-gray with black dots.

Size   Length to 38 inches (97 cm).

Recognition   Recognizable by the 2 to 10 spines on the lower rim of the orbit.

Life History   Principal spawning period off British Columbia is April.[6]

Distribution   The species is known from central California to the Aleutian Islands at moderate depths from 50 to 400 fathoms (92–732 m).[1,3] Records of occurrence at depths of 1550 fathoms (2820 m) off Queen Charlotte Sound[2,3] may be based on *S. borealis*. Common in offshore waters. Rare inshore but the first British Columbia record is for Clio Channel.

References   1 Alverson, Pruter, and Ronholt 1964; 2 Bourne and Pope 1969; 3 Grinols 1965a; 4 Phillips 1957; 5 Tsuyki, Roberts, Lowes, Hadaway, and Westrheim 1968; 6 Westrheim, Harling, and Davenport 1968

PACIFIC OCEAN PERCH

Sebastes alutus (Gilbert 1890)

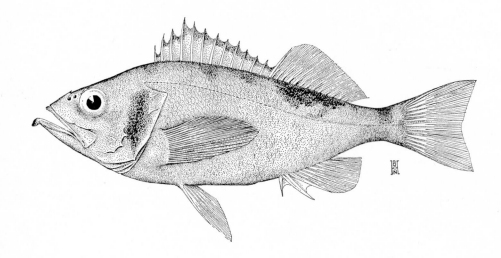

Scientific names from the Greek *sebastos* (magnificent); and *aloytos* (unwashed — speckled).

Called long-jawed rock-fish in Clemens and Wilby 1946 and longjaw rockfish in Clemens and Wilby 1961.

Description   Body depth 2.8 to 3.5 into standard length, compressed. Head 2.6 to 2.8 into standard length, upper profile nearly straight. Mouth terminal, large. Lower jaw projecting markedly. Upper jaw ending behind midorbit. Symphyseal knob very prominent, directed forward. Dentary elevation on lower jaw marked, mostly fitting into upper jaw. Eye diameter about 3.7 into length of head. Interorbital space at midorbits slightly convex to flat; width, medium, 4.6 to 4.9 into length of head.

Head Spines   Cranial spines small and weak in adult specimens. Nasal, preocular, supraocular, postocular, tympanic, and parietals usually present. Coronal and nuchal spines absent. A tympanic or supraocular spine may be absent. Parietal ridges low and thin. Preopercular spines strong, sharp, usually radially directed. Opercular spines strong, thin, and sharp, the uppermost usually larger. Suborbital bone with 2 sharply triangular spines, or rounded lobes. Supracleithral spine present and variable. Spines present on lower edge of gill covers.

Fins   Dorsal (1), XIII, 14 to 17, spinous portion moderately incised. Caudal with posterior margin indented. Anal III, 6 to 9, usually 8 or 9, free edge almost vertical, second spine usually but not always twice as thick as third, but not reaching its tip when the fin is depressed. Pectorals 18(17), tips extending to tips of pelvics and sometimes to anus. Pelvics I, 5, thoracic, tips sometimes extending to anus.

Gill Rakers   On first gill arch 30 to 38.

Vertebrae   26.

Scales   Ctenoid, 49 to 55 rows below lateral line canal (in California). Pores in lateral line canal 44 to 51.[8]

Colour   Bright carmine red, including fins, lighter on ventral surface with some silvering.

Some bright olive stippling on sides. Olive brown patches below dorsal fin and a dark blotch on the upper side of the caudal peduncle. Dark on lower lip, tip of mandible, margin of spinous dorsal, and lining of mouth. Peritoneum gray with black dots, or black.

Size   Length to 20 inches (51 cm).

Recognition   Notable for its prominent forward-directed symphyseal knob.

Life History   Pelagic juveniles were taken between 150 and 250 miles (280–260 km) off Nootka, B.C.[9] Juveniles may remain pelagic until the second or third year of life.[3] Young are born from January to March off southwest British Columbia[11] (later in northern waters) and probably in January and February off Oregon.[6] Off British Columbia 50 percent of the males are mature at 33 centimeters and 50 percent of the females at 35 centimeters.[12] Ocean perch are slow growing, and probably reach a maximum age of about 30 years.[10] Males grow more slowly and have shorter lives. Natural mortality was estimated to be 32 percent annually off Oregon in 1949–52. Fecundity is about 31,000 at 32.4 centimeters and 7 years of age, and 305,000 at 43.6 centimeters and 20 years. Ocean perch are eaten by halibut and albacore.

Distribution   Mainly offshore from southern California to the Bering Sea at depths from the surface to 350 fathoms (640 m)[5,10] mainly below 70 fathoms (128 m).[1] Most fishing is between 90 and 160 fathoms (165–290 m).[2] *S. paucispinosus* (*sic*) of the Asian coast[7] has been synonymized with *S. alutus*[4] extending the range in the western Pacific to northern Honshu Island, Japan. Generally distributed throughout coastal British Columbia waters and abundant offshore.

Utilization   The Pacific ocean perch is the most important species of rockfish harvested in the northeast Pacific.[2] Recent Canadian landings (1968–70) averaged about 33 million pounds (15,000 metric tons) annually. Its predominance is partly a result of market conditions but is also based on abundance, especially in deep water. The product is filleted.

References   I Alverson 1960; 2 Alverson, Pruter, and Ronholt 1964; 3 Alverson and Westrheim 1959; 4 Barsukov 1964; 5 Grinols 1965a; 6 Hitz 1962; 7 Matsubara 1955; 8 Phillips 1957; 9 Taylor 1968; 10, 11 Westrheim 1958, 1970; 12 Westrheim, Harling, and Davenport 1968. See also Barsukov 1963, Matsubara 1943, Westrheim, Davenport, Harling, Smith, and Wowchuk 1969.

BROWN ROCKFISH

Sebastes auriculatus Girard 1854

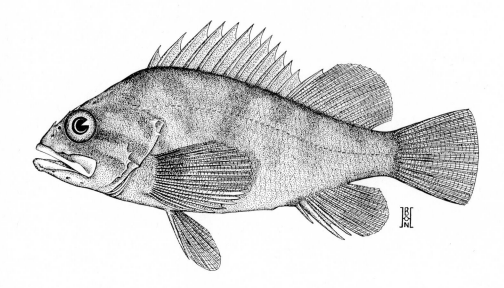

Scientific names from the Greek *sebastos* (magnificent); and the Latin *auriculatus* (eared).

This fish was recorded as brown rockfish *Sebastodes dallii* (Eigenmann and Beeson 1894) in Clemens and Wilby 1946 and as *Sebastodes auriculatus* (Girard 1854) in Clemens and Wilby 1961.

Description　　Body depth 2.7 to 2.8 into standard length, compressed. Head 2.5 to 2.7 into standard length. Mouth terminal, rather large. Lower jaw slightly longer than upper. Upper jaw extends beyond posterior margin of eye. Symphyseal knob present or absent. Eye moderate, diameter 4.5 to 5.1 into length of head. Interorbital space at midorbit 4.9 to 5.8 into length of head, flat or slightly convex. Least depth of caudal peduncle 8.5 to 9.4 into standard length.

Head Spines　　Nasal, preocular, postocular, tympanic, parietal, and coronals (usually, (0–2)[3]) present, moderately strong, rather prostrate. Nu-

chals present. Supraoculars absent. Parietal ridges strong and thin, sometimes irregular on edge. Five preopercular spines strong, occasionally bifid, usually radially directed but occasionally the upper 2 to 4 are directed backward. Two opercular spines strong and sharp. Cleithral and supracleithral spines strong and sharp, supracleithral sometimes doubled. A small lobe followed by a larger subtriangular spine on suborbital bone. Spine on lower edge of gill cover.

Fins　　Dorsal (1), XIII (12)13(15), rather weakly notched, and deeply incised. Caudal rounded. Anal III, (6)7(8), second spine about twice as thick as third and reaching or nearly reaching its tip when fin depressed, posterior margin rounded. Pectorals (15)18, extending about to tips of pelvics but not reaching anus. Pelvics I, 5, thoracic.

Gill Rakers　　On first gill arch 25 to 30.

Scales　　Ctenoid, rather large, 45 to 52 diagonal rows below lateral line canal. Lateral line canal slopes downward. Pores on lateral line canal 42 to 49.

398

Colour   Light brown mottled with dark brown, vague dark bars across back, dark blotches on upper portion of operculum, dusky pink on fins and lower part of head. Peritoneum silvery white.

Size   Length to 20.5 inches (52 cm).

Recognition   Noteworthy for the strong prostrate coronal spine(s) (usually), barely convex interorbital space, and 2 shades of brown in body colour with pink or yellowish lower part of head.

Life History   Egg yolks are clear before ovulation.[3] Females produce about 52,000 young at a length of 31.1 centimeters and 339,000 at 47.7 centimeters. Most in Puget Sound are carrying young in May,[2] and they probably give birth in June.[1]

Distribution   Baja California[4] to southeastern Alaska.[5] Not commonly observed in British Columbia but probably widely, if sparsely, distributed in shallow water. Well known in Puget Sound.[2]

References   1 DeLacy and Dryfoos 1962; 2 DeLacy, Hitz, and Dryfoos 1964; 3 Hitz and DeLacy 1961; 4 Phillips 1957; 5 Wilimovsky 1954.

AURORA ROCKFISH

Sebastes aurora (Gilbert 1890)

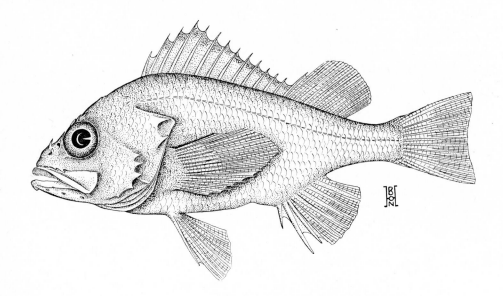

Scientific names from the Greek *sebastos* (magnificent); and the Latin *aurora* (dawn — colouring).

Description   Body depth 2.6 to 3.2 into standard length, compressed. Head length 2.4 to 2.6 into standard length, upper profile moderately convex. Mouth terminal, moderate in size. Jaws about equal. Lower jaw with small symphyseal knob and a small dentary elevation. Upper jaw extending to posterior part of eye. Premaxillaries not meeting at jaw line, leaving 2 moderate lobes. Interorbital space at midorbit flat or concave, a low median groove and rounded frontal ridges, its width 5.2 to 6.7 into length of head. Eye large, its diameter 3.2 to 4.1 into length of head. Caudal peduncle compressed, its least depth 9.6 to 11.8 into standard length.

Head Spines   Nasal, preocular, supraocular, postocular, tympanic, parietal, and nuchals

present, strong, and sharp. Coronal spine usually absent but 1 or both may be present. Parietal ridges thin and moderately high. Five preopercular spines strong and sharp, upper 2 largest, may be radially directed, or upper 2 may be directed backward. Supracleithral and cleithral spines present but may be weak (or doubled). Two triangular spines on lower edge of suborbital bone, may be bifid or trifid. Usually no spine on gill cover.

Fins   Dorsal (1), XIII, (12)13(14), moderately notched and incised. Caudal truncate. Anal III, (5)6, second spine little thicker than third, its end reaching to tip of third or beyond when the fin is depressed, its posterior edge rounded. Pectorals (16)17 or 18, long, reaching beyond origin of anal fin and tip of pelvics. Pelvics I, 5, thoracic.

Gill Rakers   On first gill arch 24 to 28.

Scales   Ctenoid, large, deciduous, 41 to 50 diagonal rows below lateral line canal. Lateral line canal sloping down, pores 27 to 31. Fatty swellings at anterior ends of bases of dorsal and anal fins.

Colour   Rose-red and pink on dorsal surface, silvery on sides and ventral surface. Lining of mouth and gill cover red. Peritoneum black or silver gray with black dots.

Size   Length to 15 inches (38 cm).

Recognition   Noteworthy for the small projecting lobes in the upper jaw and for the presence of supraocular and nuchal spines.

Distribution   From San Diego[4] through Oregon[3] to southern British Columbia. Off British Columbia, 30 miles (48 km) southwest of Amphitrite Point in 230 fathoms (421 m), 48.47 N, 126.35 W.[5] It is reported as deep as 325 fathoms (595 m)[2] and as most abundant between 200 and 300 fathoms (366–550 m).[1]

References   1 Alverson, Pruter, and Ronholt 1964; 2 Grinols 1965a; 3 Heyamoto and Hitz 1962; 4 Phillips 1957; 5 Westrheim 1968.

REDBANDED ROCKFISH

Sebastes babcocki (Thompson 1915)

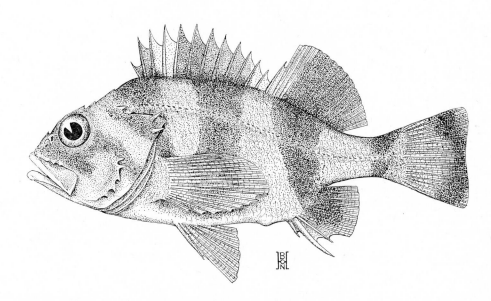

Scientific names from the Greek *sebastos* (magnificent); and John Pease Babcock, enlightened fishery administrator in California and British Columbia.

This species was recorded in Clemens and Wilby 1961 as flag rockfish *Sebastodes rubrivinctus* (Jordan and Gilbert 1880). *Sebastes rubrivinctus* has been shown to be a different species so far not recorded north of San Francisco (about 38 N).[6,7]

Description   Body depth 2.6 to 2.8 into standard length. Head with upper profile nearly straight or slightly concave, its length 2.5 to 2.9 into standard length. Mouth terminal. Maxillary extending to midorbit or rear of orbit. Symphyseal knob low. Dentary elevation absent or much reduced. Interorbital space flat to moderately concave with narrow median groove between low frontal ridges, its width 4.5 to 7.2 into length of head, and more than 1.7 times width of lachrymal.[7] Orbit width 3.6 to 4.3 into length of head. Caudal peduncle about 9.8 to 11.3 into standard length.

Head Spines   Nasal, preocular, postocular, and parietal spines present. Tympanics usually present. Nuchals occasionally present. Spines moderately strong and rather prostrate. Supraocular, coronal, and occasionally nuchals absent. Preopercular spines strong and sharp with upper 2 frequently longer and directed backward, the lower 3 directed downward. Opercular spines strong and sharp with upper sometimes longer. Suborbital bone carries 2 triangular spines, the posterior one sometimes multifid. Supracleithral and cleithral spines present and strong. Usually there are no spines on the free edges of the gill covers.

Fins   Dorsal (1), XIII, (13)14(15), moderately notched, rather strongly indented in spinous portion. Caudal with posterior margin almost straight. Anal III, 6 or 7, posterior edge rounded or sloping slightly backward, second spine usually twice as thick as third. Pectorals (17)19(20). Pelvics I, 5. Tips of pectorals extend beyond tips of pelvics.

Gill Rakers   Rakers on first gill arch usually 30 or 31.

Scales   Ctenoid, on mandible and branchiostegals.[2]

Colour   Light pink to white with 4 broad vertical dark red bands on head, body (2), and caudal peduncle, becoming faded in large specimens. The first band extends from the occiput region downward and backward across the upper portion of the gill cover to the base of the pectoral fin; the second runs more or less straight downward.[7] Peritoneum variable from silvery white to black or blotched.

Size   Length to 25 inches (64 cm).

Recognition   Supraocular spine missing. Gill rakers 30 to 31. Body white or pink with vertical dark red bands. Lower 3 preopercular spines directed downward. Branchiostegals with scales. Interorbital space more than 1.7 times width of lachrymal bone.

Life History   Off Oregon probably gives birth to young in April and May,[4] and off British Columbia in April.[9,10] Fifty percent of males are mature at 38 centimeters and females at 42 centimeters off British Columbia.[9]

Distribution   San Diego[7] to near Kodiak Island, Alaska, as far north as 60.02 N, and west to Amchitka Island in the Aleutians at 220 fathoms (402 m).[1,3] Uncommon south of San Francisco. Off British Columbia in open waters from the west coast of Vancouver Island to Dixon Entrance, Queen Charlotte Sound, Hecate Strait.[8] Found at 50 to 240 fathoms (92–439).[5]

References   1 Best and Eldridge 1969; 2 Harling, Davenport, Smith, and Wowchuk 1970; 3 Heyamoto and Hitz 1962; 4 Hitz 1962; 5, 6 Phillips 1957, personal communication; 7 Rosenblatt and Chen 1972; 8 Westrheim 1965; 9 Westrheim, Harling, and Davenport 1968; 10 Westrheim, Harling, Davenport, and Smith 1968. See also Ketchen 1954.

SHORTRAKER ROCKFISH

Sebastes borealis Barsukov 1970

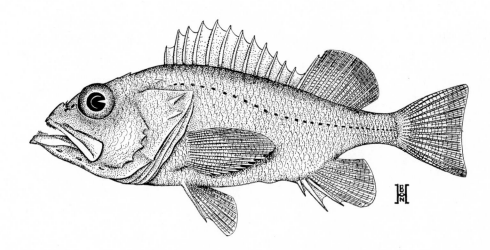

Scientific names from the Greek *sebastos* (magnificent); and the Latin *borealis* (northern).

Clemens and Wilby 1946 called this species *Sebastodes introniger* (Gilbert 1890), the black-throated rock-fish. Clemens and Wilby 1961 identified it with *Sebastodes aleutianus,* the rougheye rockfish of Jordan and Evermann 1898. Re-examination of available specimens using new information obtained from hemoglobin electropherograms shows that a hitherto unrecognized species has created confusion and that probably *Sebastes introniger* and *Sebastes melanostomus* are synonyms and that this species does not occur off the Canadian coast.[2,3]

Late in 1970 Tsuyuki and Westrheim described a new species as *Sebastes caenaematicus.*[3] However, earlier in 1970, Barsukov[1] working independently in the USSR published a description of what is tentatively (pending comparative electropherograms) regarded as the same species, and named it *Sebastes borealis*. That name is currently accepted.

Description   Body depth 2.6 to 3.1 into standard length, compressed. Head 2.3 to 2.7 into standard length, profile nearly straight, pointed. Mouth terminal, fairly large, directed noticeably upward. Lower jaw projecting. Upper jaw extends beyond midorbit. Symphyseal knob small. Small dentary elevation. Interorbital space flat or slightly concave, its width 5.0 to 6.5 into length of head. Orbit 3.2 to 5.0 into length of head. Caudal peduncle compressed, its least depth about 13 into standard length.

Head Spines   Nasal, preocular, supraocular, coronal, parietal, and nuchal present, moderate to weak. Parietal ridges moderate. Spines 0 or 1 on lower rim of orbit. Preopercular spines pointed, upper 2 close together. Two opercular spines, moderately strong and sharp. Two lobes on lower margin of suborbital bone. Cleithral and supracleithral spines moderate. One to three spines on lower edge of gill cover.

Fins   Dorsal (1), XIII, 13, moderately notched, membrane moderately incised, longest spine 2.5 to 3.5 into length of head, longest ray 2.2 to 2.8 into length of head. Caudal fin moderately indented. Anal III, 7, second spine thickest, not extending as far as third in depressed fin, posterior profile rounded, sometimes with a slight anterior slope. Pectorals 17 to 20, reaching tips of pelvics, usually reaching anus. Pelvics I, 5, thoracic.

Gill Rakers   On first gill arch 27 to 31.

Vertebrae   About 26.

Scales   Ctenoid, 36 to 46 diagonal rows below lateral line canal. Pores in lateral line canal 28 to 32. Lateral line canal sloping downward about to point above anus, then straight to base of caudal, dark.

Colour   Pink with vague vertical red bands, or orange-pink. Fins reddish, pelvics and pectorals sometimes edged with black. Mouth and gill cavities usually red with black blotches; gill cavities occasionally black with red blotches. Peritoneum silver gray with black dots.

Size   Length to 36 inches (91 cm).

Recognition   Noteworthy for its pink or orange-pink colour, not more than one spine on suborbital rim, relatively short gill rakers on the first arch, red or red-black lining in mouth, silver-gray peritoneum with black dots, and pink-black lining to gill chamber, and one or more spines on lower edge of gill cover.

Distribution   Off Vancouver Island and southeastern Alaska.

References   1 Barsukov 1970; 2 Tsuyuki, Roberts, Lowes, Hadaway, and Westrheim 1968; 3 Tsuyuki and Westrheim 1970. See also Barrett and Moser 1966, Westrheim and Tsuyuki 1972.

SILVERGRAY ROCKFISH

Sebastes brevispinis (Bean 1883)

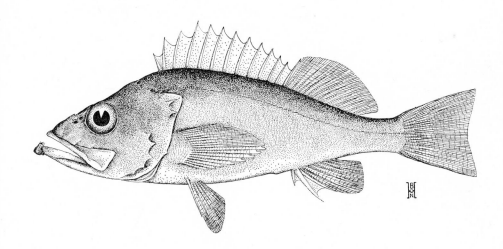

Scientific names from the Greek *sebastos* (magnificent); and from the Latin *brevis* (short) and *spinus* (spine).

Description Body depth usually 3.0 to 3.2 into standard length. Head elongate, pointed, upper profile moderately sloping, straight from upper jaw to posterior end of parietals, its length 2.6 to 2.8 into standard length. Mouth terminal, large. Lower jaw projecting far beyond upper profile of head, its length 5.0 to 5.5 into standard length. Symphyseal knob large. Interorbital space at midorbit moderately convex, broad, its width 3.7 to 5.0 into length of head. Caudal peduncle 10.6 to 11.5 into standard length.

Head Spines Nasal, preocular, parietal, all weak, others usually absent. Supracleithrals and cleithrals strong. Two long sharp operculars with the upper larger. Five preopercular spines, the second larger, lower 1 or 2 sometimes reduced. Suborbital usually with a small lobe on lower surface followed by a single or multifid spine. No spines on lower edge of gill cover.

Fins Dorsal (1), XIII, 15 to 17, moderately notched, spinous portion moderately incised. Caudal fin indented. Anal III, 7, posterior edge nearly vertical; tip of second ray usually, but not always, failing to reach tip of third in depressed fin. Pectorals 16 to 18, 9 to 11 rays unbranched, extending beyond tips of pelvics but not as far as anus. Pelvics I, 5, thoracic.

Gill Rakers On first gill arch 33 to 36.

Scales Weakly ctenoid, in oblique rows below lateral line canal 58 to 70. Pores in lateral line canal 44 to 53.

Colour Dark gray or olive on back, silver on sides, and abruptly white ventrally. Lips blackened. Ventral surface and paired fins tinged with pink and red. Peritoneum white with numerous black dots giving silver-gray appearance.

Size Length to 28 inches (71 cm).

Recognition Distinguished by the large mouth with the maxillary extending posterior to the orbit, and the lateral line canal pores 44 to 49. Fresh specimens are green or gray on the back and silvery on the sides.

Life History   Off Oregon the young are probably not released until late spring or summer.[2] Off Washington young are released in June.[1]

Distribution   From near Santa Barbara Island, southern California,[4] to the Bering Sea. In the open coast regions off the west coast of Vancouver Island and Queen Charlotte Sound,[3,5] and from inside waters. From the surface to 200 fathoms (366 m).

Utilization   Common in commercial catches, amounting to as much as 30 percent of the total rockfish landed excluding ocean perch.

References   1 DeLacy and Dryfoos 1962; 2 Hitz 1962; 3 Hitz, Johnson, and Pruter 1961; 4 Strachan 1965; 5 Westrheim 1964.

COPPER ROCKFISH

Sebastes caurinus Richardson 1845

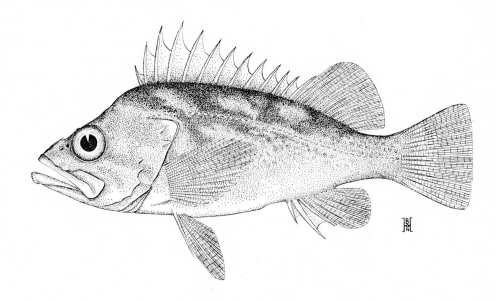

Scientific names from the Greek *sebastos* (magnificent); and the Latin *caurinus* (northwest).

Description   Body depth 2.5 to 2.8 into standard length, compressed. Head length 2.5 to 2.8 into standard length, profile about straight above bluntly bulbous snout. Mouth terminal, large. Lower jaw projects beyond upper but does not enter dorsal profile. Upper jaw extends to about posterior part of eye. Symphyseal knob absent or small. No patch of teeth at point of lower jaw. Interorbital space smoothly concave, its width 5.4 to 6.3 into length of head. Eye diameter 4.2 to 5.2 into length of head. Caudal peduncle compressed, comparatively deep, its least depth 8.1 to 9.0 into standard length.

Head Spines   Nasal, preocular, postocular, tympanic, and parietal present, thick, and prostrate.

Supraocular, coronal, and nuchal spines absent. Parietal ridges moderately developed and rounded. Preopercular spines triangular and blunt, directed backward, sometimes broadened and divided. Both opercular spines short and blunt, sometimes divided. Lower edge of suborbital bone usually with a small lobe followed by a larger triangular projection. Cleithral and supracleithral spines strong and sharp. Spine at lower edge of gill cover.

Fins   Dorsal (1), XIII, (11,12)13(14), moderately incised and notched. Caudal rounded. Anal III, (5)6, second spine about twice as thick as third, and reaching about as far when the fin is depressed, free margin of fin almost vertical or rounded. Pectorals (16)17(18), tips reach tips of pelvics and may or may not extend as far as or beyond anus. Pelvics I, 5, thoracic.

Gill Rakers   On first gill arch 26 to 32.

Scales   Ctenoid, diagonal rows below lateral line canal 39 to 45.

Colour Variable. Dark or olive brown washed with copper-pink and occasionally splashed with dull yellow. Two yellow or light bands radiating posteriorly from eyes. Sometimes orange on chin or yellow on cheeks. A light blotch often on midside. Fins all copper-black. Peritoneum white.

Size Length to 21.5 inches (55 cm).[6]

Recognition Notable for the dark fins, the coppery coloration, and the deep caudal peduncle.

Life History The yolks in copper rockfish ova have been found to clear quickly immediately before ovulation.[4] In Washington most females are carrying embryos in April.[1] Fecundity compared with length is about: 25 centimeters, 20,000; 34 centimeters, 215,000; 51 centimeters, 600,000; and 47 centimeters, 640,000.[1,3] The species is commonly taken on rocky reefs in shallow waters of the Strait of Georgia by otter trawls and handlines, and is filleted for use. Young have been found at the surface around flotsam in Queen Charlotte Sound.[2]

Distribution From Monterey, California,[5] to the Gulf of Alaska at Day Harbor, Blying Sound and Port Dick.[8] Washington and Oregon.[7] Common in many shallow water areas throughout British Columbia.

References 1 DeLacy, Hitz, and Dryfoos 1964; 2 Hitz 1961; 3, 4 Hitz and DeLacy 1960, 1965; 5, 6 Phillips personal communications; 7 Schultz and DeLacy 1936; 8 Westrheim 1966a.

DUSKY ROCKFISH

Sebastes ciliatus (Tilesius 1810)

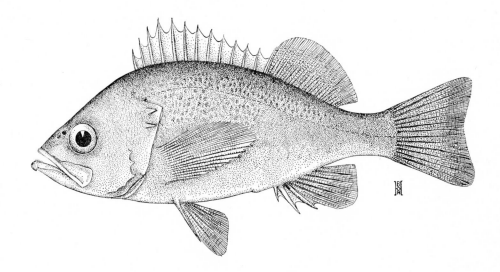

Scientific names from the Greek *sebastos* (magnificent); and the Latin *ciliatus* (eyelash).

Description Body depth about 2.6 into standard length, compressed. Head length about 2.8 into standard length, dorsal profile almost straight. Mouth terminal, large. Lower jaw projecting and in dorsal profile of head. Upper jaw extending to posterior edge of pupil. Symphyseal knob evident. No dentary elevation. Eye diameter about 4.2 into length of head. Interorbital space convex, smooth, its width about 3.9 into length of head. Caudal peduncle compressed, its least depth about 9.4 into standard length.

Head Spines Nasal weak. Parietals very weak. Parietal ridges barely discernible. Preopercular spines all 5 triangular, directed radially downward. Operculars flattened and moderately developed. Cleithrals and supracleithrals developed and sharp. Spine on lower margin of gill cover. Other spines absent.

Fins Dorsal (1), XIII, 15, moderately incised and notched. Caudal slightly indented. Anal III, 8, second spine more than twice as thick as third but its tip fails to reach tip of third when fin is depressed, posterior edge nearly vertical or slanting slightly forward. Pectorals 18, reaching about to tip of pelvics but neither reaching anus. Pelvics I, 5 thoracic.

Gill Rakers On first gill arch about 35.

Scales Ctenoid, about 54 rows below lateral line canal. Pores in lateral line canal about 48.

Colour Gray brown, with brown spots on dorsal surface, becoming light gray below. Pectoral fins, ventral fins, and lower jaw tinged with pink. Brown streaks radiating posteriorly from eye. Dusky to black on all fins. Peritoneum black.

Size Length to 16 inches (41 cm).

Recognition Distinguished by convex interorbital space, green and brown

409

body, moderate symphyseal knob, black peritoneum, posterior profile of anal fin vertical or slanted anteriorly.

Distribution   From Dixon Entrance, British Columbia, at 54.13 N, 132.42 W[3] (not Neah Bay, Washington[3]), through southeast Alaska, and Gulf of Alaska to Bering Sea.[4] Uncertainly off Kamchatka.[2]

Taken at 84 to 88 fathoms (154–161 m) in Dixon Entrance, and between 100 and 149 fathoms (183–273 m) in the Gulf of Alaska.[1]

References   1 Alverson, Pruter, and Ronholt 1964; 2 Barsukov 1964; 3 Westrheim 1968; 4 Wilimovsky 1954.

DARKBLOTCHED ROCKFISH

Sebastes crameri (Jordan 1896)

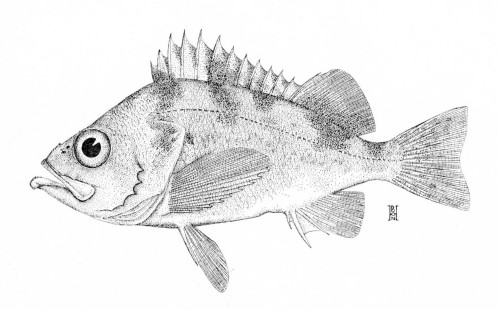

Scientific names from the Greek *sebastos* (magnificent); and Frank Cramer, a student of the group.

Called blackblotched rockfish, *Sebastodes crameri,* in Clemens and Wilby 1961.

Description   Body depth 2.3 to 2.8 into standard length, compressed. Head 2.4 to 2.7 into standard length, upper profile nearly straight with bulge over eyes. Mouth terminal, large. Lower jaw projecting beyond

410

upper. Upper jaw extending to midorbit or beyond. Symphyseal knob moderately well developed and directed downwards. Dentary elevation prominent only in larger specimens, not completely included in snout when jaws closed. Eye diameter about 3.8 into length of head. Interorbital space at midorbit 3.7 to 4.3 into length of head, moderate to slightly convex. Caudal peduncle about 10 into standard length.

Head Spines   Nasal, preocular, supraocular, postocular, tympanic, and nuchal all present, small, and rather prostrate. Nuchal and parietal spines may be coalesced. Coronal spine absent. Parietal ridges moderately high and thin. Preopercular spines with upper 3 largest. Two opercular spines, long and sharp. Two triangular spines on lower margin of the suborbital bone, the rear one sometimes double. Cleithral and supracleithral spines strong. Spine present on lower margin of gill cover.

Fins   Dorsal (1), XIII, 12(13 to 14), spinous portion moderately incised and notched. Caudal moderately indented. Anal III, 5 to 7, second spine about twice as thick as third but not reaching its tip when the fin is depressed, posterior profile nearly vertical. Pectorals, 18 to 20, tip usually reaching beyond tips of pelvics and as far as anus. Pelvics I, 5 thoracic.

Gill Rakers   On first gill arch 29 to 34.

Scales   Ctenoid, 48 to 62 diagonal rows below lateral line canal. Pores on lateral line canal 40 to 50.

Colour   Pinkish with 3 or 4 dark patches along back under spinous dorsal, under the rayed dorsal, and on caudal peduncle. Young may be washed with light yellow-green. Peritoneum brown with black dots to black.

Size   Length to 22.5 inches (57 cm).

Recognition   Noteworthy as a pinkish or orange rockfish with three to five dorsal dark blotches on back and with a deep body.

Life History   Spawning of young off British Columbia takes place primarily in February.[5] Pelagic young are food for albacore.[2]

Distribution   Southern California (Point Dume) to the Bering Sea at depths from 16 to 300 fathoms[3,4] (29–550 m). Offshore and in Juan de Fuca Strait, and Haro Strait. Most abundant in the deeper part of its depth range.[1]

References   1 Alverson, Pruter, and Ronholt 1964; 2 Alverson and Welander 1952; 3 Grinols 1965a; 4 Phillips 1957; 5 Westrheim, Harling, and Davenport 1968.

SPLITNOSE ROCKFISH

Sebastes diploproa (Gilbert 1890)

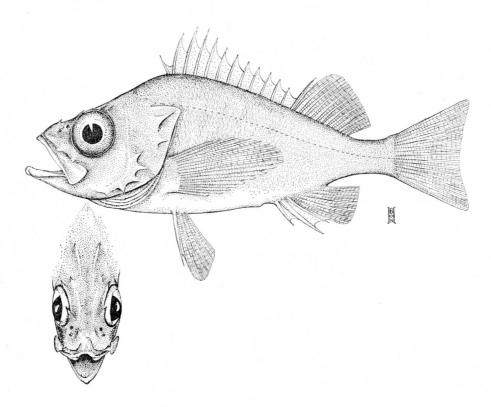

Scientific names from the Greek *sebastos* (magnificent); and *diploos* (double) and *prora* (prow).

Description Body depth 2.6 to 2.8 into standard length, compressed. Head 2.4 to 2.7 into standard length, upper profile essentially straight. Mouth terminal, moderate. Lower jaw slightly longer. Upper jaw extending about to midorbit. The front ends of the premaxillary bones are expanded into raised dentigerous lobes widely separated to receive the single large dentigerous lobe at the symphysis of the lower jaw. Symphyseal knob small and directed downward. Eye large, diameter about 3.2 into length

of head. Interorbital space at midorbit 5.0 to 6.1 into length of head; usually a low median groove with low frontal ridges on either side which may be as high as the ocular ridges. Caudal peduncle depth about 11 or 12 into standard length.

Head Spines Nasal, preocular, postocular, tympanic, and parietals present, strong and sharp. Tympanics occasionally missing. Supraocular, coronal, and nuchal spines absent. Parietal ridges high and thin. Five preopercular spines strong and sharp, often with the top 2 or 3 strongest. Two opercular spines long, thin and sharp, the upper usually longer. Two strong spines present on the subocular bone. Cleithral moderately strong, supracleithral usually weak. Spine usually present on lower edge of gill cover (not on specimen illustrated).

Fins   Dorsal (1), XIII, (11)12 to 13(14), moderately notched and incised. Caudal moderately indented. Anal III, 6 to 7(8), second spine usually twice as thick as the third with its tip reaching about to the tip of the third when the fin is depressed, posterior edge vertical or slightly rounded. Pectorals (17)18(19), extending beyond tips of pelvics and reaching the anus or beyond. Pelvics I, 5, thoracic.

Gill Rakers   On first gill arch 32 to 37.

Scales   Ctenoid, moderate in size in 53 to 57 diagonal rows below lateral line canal. Lateral line canal slopes downward. Pores on lateral line canal 33 to 43.

Colour   Uniform rose-red to pink on dorsal surface, silvered ventrally. Sometimes sparsely spotted with dark or with dark bar behind pectoral fin. Rose coloured in mouth and gill cavity. Peritoneum black.

Size   Length to 18 inches (46 cm).

Recognition   Prominent dentigerous lobes on premaxillary bones at tip of jaw accommodating dentigerous lobe of lower jaw. Presence of suborbital and nuchal spines.

Life History   Young are born in late spring off British Columbia and Oregon[4,7] at a length of about 5.2 millimeters.[2] Fecundity is about 14,000 at 7.5 inches (19 cm) length and 255,000 at 14.5 inches (37 cm). Off California 50 percent are mature at 8.25 inches (21 cm), or 5 years of age[5,6] whereas off British Columbia 50 percent of males and females are mature at 27 centimeters.[8]

Distribution   From Baja California near San Martin Island and Los Coronados Island to southeast Alaska (Prince William Sound) and the Alaskan Peninsula and the intervening regions at depths of 50 to 316 fathoms (91–578 m).[1,3,5] British Columbia records are from the Strait of Georgia and the west coast of Vancouver Island.

References   1 Alverson, Pruter, and Ronholt 1964; 2 DeLacy, Hitz, and Dryfoos 1964; 3 Grinols 1965a; 4 Hitz 1962; 5, 6 Phillips 1957, 1964; 7 Westrheim, Harling, and Davenport 1968; 8 Westrheim, Harling, Davenport, and Smith 1968.

GREENSTRIPED ROCKFISH

Sebastes elongatus Ayres 1859

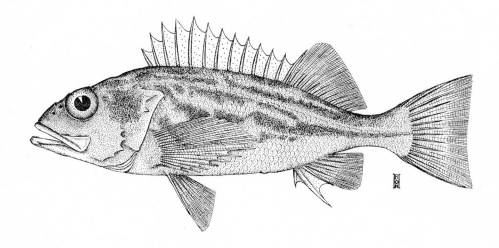

Scientific names from the Greek *sebastos* (magnificent); and the Latin *elongatus* (elongate).

Description   Body rather elongate, depth 3.1 to 3.7 into standard length, compressed. Head about 2.6 into standard length, upper profile arched. Mouth terminal, moderate. Lower jaw projecting beyond upper, but not entering dorsal profile. Upper jaw extending about to posterior edge of pupil of eye. Symphyseal knob rudimentary. Dentary elevation present but not as a distinctly raised patch. Eye moderate, diameter 3.2 to 4.0 into length of head. Interorbital space at midorbit 7.0 to 8.1 into length of head, slightly concave, with a slight median groove and low frontal ridges sometimes evident. Caudal peduncle slender, 11.4 to 13.4 into standard length.

Head Spines   Nasal, preocular, postocular, tympanic, and parietals present and moderately strong. Supraocular, coronal, and nuchal spines absent. Parietal ridges moderately high and thin. The 5 preopercular spines are directed radially or

backward with the upper 2 usually longest. Two opercular spines moderately strong and sharp. No real spines along edge of suborbital. Cleithral and supracleithral spines moderately strong. Spine along lower edge of the gill cover.

Fins   Dorsal (1), XIII, (12)13(14), spinous portion moderately notched and incised. Caudal almost truncate. Anal III, 6, second spine about twice as thick as third and when fin depressed its tip extends beyond that of third, the posterior edge is almost vertical. Pectorals 16 to 17(18), tips usually extending beyond tips of pelvics and usually reaching anus. Pelvics I, 5, thoracic.

Gill Rakers   On first gill arch 28 to 33.

Scales   Ctenoid, 42 to 55 rows below lateral line canal. Pores in lateral line canal 40 to 45.

Colour   Dorsal third of body pink with 2 green stripes on either side of lateral line canal frequently broken into blocks. Green on head and fins but none on lower part of body and head. Peritoneum gray with black dots.

Size   Length to 15 inches (38 cm).

Recognition   Distinguished by its slender form, green horizontal stripes and the absence of real spines on suborbital bone.

Life History   Young are probably born in late spring or early summer off Oregon,[3] Washington,[5] and British Columbia.[7,8] Newly released larvae are about 5 millimeters in length.[2,8]

Distribution   From Baja California (Cedros Island)[4] to the Gulf of Alaska (Green Island, 60.15 N, 147.27 W[6]). Most commonly encountered between depths of 50 and 200 fathoms (91–366 m), in both inshore and offshore waters.[1] Fairly common in the Strait of Georgia.

References   1 Alverson, Pruter, and Ronholt 1964; 2 DeLacy, Hitz, and Dryfoos 1964; 3 Hitz 1962; 4 Phillips 1957; 5 Smith 1936; 6 Westrheim 1966a; 7 Westrheim, Harling, and Davenport 1968; 8 Westrheim, Harling, Davenport, and Smith 1968.

PUGET SOUND ROCKFISH

Sebastes emphaeus (Starks 1911)

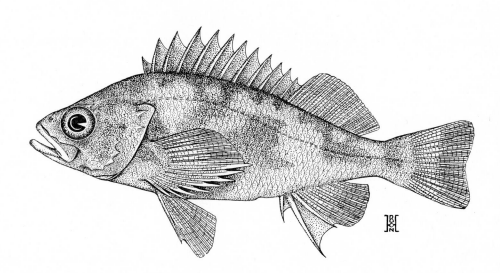

Scientific names from the Greek *sebastos* (magnificent); and *emphaeus* (display).

Description   Body depth about 3.2 into standard length, compressed. Head length about 3 into standard length. Mouth

415

terminal, fairly large, directed forward and upward. Lower jaw projecting moderately. Upper jaw extends to midorbit or a little beyond. Symphyseal knobs and dentary elevation not noticeably developed. Interorbital space about 4 into length of head, somewhat convex between orbital ridges. Eye diameter about 3 into length of head. Caudal peduncle least depth about 11 into standard length.

Head Spines Nasal, preocular, postocular, tympanic, and parietal spines present, moderate to weak, with exception of nasal which is depressed. Supraocular, coronal, and nuchal spines absent. Parietal and frontal ridges, moderately developed. Of the 5 preopercular spines the upper 4 are moderately developed and directed backward, the lowest spine is reduced. Two opercular spines sharp and moderately developed. Cleithral and supracleithral spines appear to be moderately developed in small individuals. Other spines not evident in small specimens examined.

Fins Dorsal (1), XIII, 14 or 15, little indented and notched. Caudal weakly forked. Anal III, 7, second spine extending beyond tip of third when fin is depressed, thicker than third but not twice as thick, posterior edge rounded and sloping slightly backward. Pectorals about 17, reaching beyond tip of pelvic but not as far as anus. Pelvics I, 5, thoracic, not reaching anus except in small specimens.

Gill Rakers On first gill arch 41 to 45, slender.

Scales Ctenoid, 41 to 46 along or above lateral line canal. Lateral line canal irregular, approximately paralleling dorsal profile.

Colour Copper-red with indefinite, broken, greenish-brown cross-bars or blotches. Greenish bands run back from eyes. Spinous dorsal dark green with bright red toward tips of spines, outer part of soft dorsal bright red, the base almost black. Pectorals, pelvics, and anal clear brilliant light red.[2]

Size Length to 6 inches (15 cm).

Recognition Notable for the copper-red body with greenish-brown bars and blotches, dark or black peritoneum, convex interorbital space between frontal ridges, dorsal fin weakly indented and incised, second ray of anal fin only moderately thicker than third but longer, and anal fin rounded.

Distribution Known mainly from deep water in the Puget Sound–San Juan area of the State of Washington.[1,2,3] There is a tentative Canadian record.

References 1 DeLacy, Dryfoos, and Miller 1963; 2 Hitz 1965; 3 Starks 1911.

WIDOW ROCKFISH

Sebastes entomelas (Jordan and Gilbert 1880)

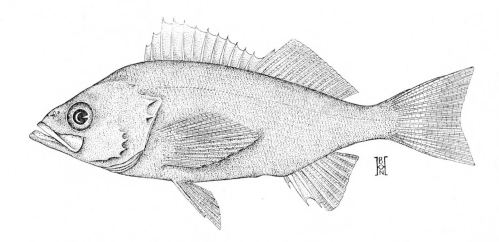

Scientific names from the Greek *sebastos* (magnificent); and *entos* (within) and *melas* (black).

Description   Body depth 2.7 to 3.3 into standard length. Dorsal and ventral profiles evenly curved. Head relatively short, its length 3.0 to 3.2 into standard length, upper profile almost straight. Mouth terminal, large. Jaws almost even or lower projecting slightly. Upper jaw ending just before midorbit. Symphyseal knob absent. Eye 3.5 to 4.5 into length of head. Interorbital space at midorbit highly convex, broad, its width 3.3 to 4.1 into length of head. Caudal peduncle 10.5 to 11.9 into standard length.

Head Spines   Absent or weakly represented by tips of nasals, preoculars, or parietals in adults. No spines on lower edge of suborbital bone. Preopercular and opercular spines moderately developed. Moderate supracleithral and cleithral spines, the latter broad. No spines, or small spines, on the edge of gill cover.

Fins   Dorsal (1), XIII, 14 to 16, moderately notched, spinous portion with membranes moderately incised and low. Caudal fin indented. Anal III, 8 to 10, posterior edge sloping strongly posteriorly. When the fin is depressed the second spine fails to reach as far as the tip of the third in larger specimens. Second spine barely thicker than third. Pectorals 17(18) (8 to 10 unbranched). Pelvics I, 5, thoracic. Tips of pectorals reaching beyond tips of pelvics but not as far as anus.[5]

Gill Rakers   On first gill arch 35 to 37.

Scales   Strongly ctenoid, in oblique rows below lateral line canal 58 to 66. Pores along lateral line canal 52 to 58.

Colour   Grayish black to brown on dorsal surface, paler below, and with some vague yellowish mottling on back. Single dark spots on operculum and suboperculum. A dark streak extends down and back from midorbit. Fins dusky, anal with blotched white bar paralleling the free edge. Peritoneum black or silver gray with black dots.
Young specimens under 10 inches are lighter in colour and have vague streaks of orange. In young under 8 inches (20 cm) cranial spines are sometimes present and second spine may reach tip of third in depressed anal fin.

Size   Length to 21 inches (53 cm).

Recognition Convex interorbital space with spines weak or absent. Symphyseal knob absent. Posterior edge of anal fin slanting posteriorly. Diagonal rows of scales below lateral line 60 to 66. Colour washed-out brown flecked with yellow.

Life History In California 50 percent are mature at 12.75 inches (32.4 cm) in length or 4 years old. At 12.5 inches (31.8 cm) females produce about 55,000 young, at 20 inches (50.8 cm) about 900,000. Off Oregon young are produced mainly in January and February.[1,2,6] Mainly a plankton feeder in California, off Oregon about half the food is smallfin lanternfish.[4]

Distribution Todos Santos Bay, Baja California, to southeast Alaska. In British Columbia taken at Rivers Inlet, Queen Charlotte Sound, and the west coast of Vancouver Island. Found in depths of 50 to 200 fathoms (91–366 m).[3,6]

References 1 Hitz 1962; 2 Hitz, Johnson, and Pruter 1961; 3 McAllister and Westrheim 1965; 4 Pereyra, Pearcy, and Carvey 1969; 5, 6 Phillips 1957, 1964.

YELLOWTAIL ROCKFISH

Sebastes flavidus (Ayres 1862)

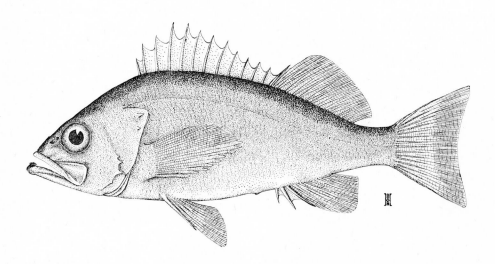

Scientific names from the Greek *sebastos* (magnificent); and the Latin *flavus* (yellow).

Description Body depth 2.7 to 2.9 into standard length. Anterior dorsal profiles gently curved, streamlined. Head 2.7 to 2.9

into standard length. Mouth terminal, large. Lower jaw projecting beyond upper strongly but not entering upper profile of head. Upper jaw extending nearly to posterior edge of orbit. Symphyseal knob small and projecting downward. Dentary elevation moderately developed. Snout sharply pointed. Eye diameter 3.6 to 4.5 into length of head. Interorbital space at midorbit 3.7 to 4.3 into length of head, strongly and evenly convex. Caudal peduncle 9.0 to 9.6 into standard length.

Head Spines   Spines on top of head obsolete except for weak nasals. Parietals ridges weak. Five preopercular spines only moderately strong and sharp, all radially directed or with the upper 2 directed backward. Two opercular spines, moderately strong, thin and sharp. On gill cover spines weak or absent. Cleithral spine weak. Supracleithral weak or entirely absent.

Fins   Dorsal (1), XIII, 14 to 15(16), moderately notched and incised. Caudal nearly truncate but slightly forked. Anal III, (7)8(9), second spine barely thicker than third and its tip not approaching that of third when the fin is depressed, posterior margin of fin nearly vertical. Pectorals (17)18(19), tips about reaching tips of pelvics but not extending to anus. Pelvics I, 5, thoracic.

Gill Rakers   On first gill arch 34 to 39.

Scales   Ctenoid, 55 to 60 diagonal rows below lateral line canal. Pores in lateral line canal 49 to 55.

Colour   Olive green, vaguely streaked and mottled with brown. Dusky green with yellow on fins including tip of caudal fin. Young prominently speckled with brown; with a black blotch on the posterior part of the caudal fin. Peritoneum silvery white, young with black speckling.

Size   Length to 26 inches (66 cm).

Recognition   Convex interorbital space with spines weak or absent. Prominent symphyseal knob. Posterior edge of anal fin vertical. Body colour green or green-brown.

Life History   Young are born in January and February off Oregon[4] and March off British Columbia[10] at a length of about 4.5 millimeters.[2] In California 50 percent are mature at 13 inches (33 cm) or 5 years. Twelve-inch (30.5-cm) fish produce about 50,000 young and 19- to 21-inch (48.3–53.3-cm) fish up to 633,000 young.[7] Forms schools off bottom.[9] Found to eat in one locality mainly smallfin lanternfish with lesser quantities of crustaceans and squid.[5]

Distribution   San Diego, California[6] to the Gulf of Alaska,[6] Kodiak and Admiralty Island.[8] Recorded from the surface to 300 fathoms.[1,3] In British Columbia generally distributed in water of suitable depth in the Strait of Georgia, Queen Charlotte Sound, and off the west coast of Vancouver Island, and taken on a variety of gear.

References   1 Alverson, Pruter, and Ronholt 1964; 2 DeLacy, Hitz, and Dryfoos 1964; 3 Grinols 1965a; 4 Hitz 1962; 5 Pereyra, Pearcy, and Carvey 1969; 6, 7 Phillips 1957, 1964; 8 Westrheim 1966b; 9 Vancouver Public Aquarium 1969; 10 Westrheim, Harling, and Davenport 1968.

CHILIPEPPER

Sebastes goodei (Eigenmann and Eigenmann 1890)

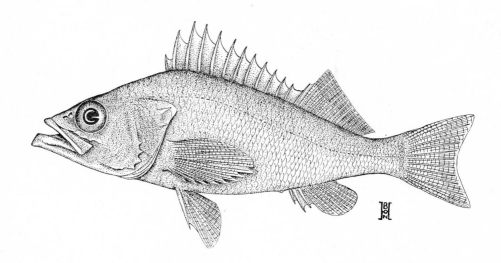

Scientific names from the Greek *se-bastos* (magnificent); and Dr G. B. Goode, U.S. ichthyologist.

Description   Body depth 3.3 to 3.5 into standard length. Head with an almost straight dorsal profile, its length 2.7 to 2.9 into standard length. Mouth moderate, maxillary reaching midorbit. Symphyseal knob moderately strong, sharp, forward projecting, upper surface in dorsal profile of head. No raised patch of teeth at tip of lower jaw. Interorbital space strongly convex with slight flattening next to orbits, its width 3.7 to 4.0 into length of head. Orbit width 4.0 to 4.4 into length of head. Caudal peduncle slender, 11.4 to 12.5 into standard length.

Head Spines   On cranium obsolete in adult fish. Preopercular spines moderately strong and sharp, second and third from top usually longest. Opercular spines moderately long and sharp. Supracleithral spine weak, almost obsolete, the cleithral moderately strong. Spines on lower edge of suborbital may be present or absent — usually present on specimens less than 10 inches. There is no spine on the edge of the gill cover.

Fins   Dorsal (1), XIII, (13)14, strongly indented, moderately incised. Caudal moderately indented. Anal III, 8(9), all spines short, free edge slanted posteriorly, second spine barely thicker than third and not reaching its tip when the fin is depressed. Pectorals (16)17(18) with (7)8(9) unbranched. Pelvics I, 5. Tips of pectorals reach beyond tips of pelvics but do not reach anus.

Gill Rakers   On first gill arch 34 to 39.

Scales   Diagonal rows below lateral line canal 60 to 77. Pores along lateral line canal 50 to 57.[1]

Colour   Body pinkish red. Fins pink. Peritoneum silvery white; with black dots in small specimens.
Young have light olive on back. Nasal, prefrontal, or parietal spines may be weakly present. Under 10 inches small sharp spines usually present on lower edge of suborbital.

Size   Reaches length of 22 inches (56 cm).

Recognition   In colour and slender form resembles Pacific ocean perch from which it may be distinguished by the absence of cranial spines in adults, by having a white peritoneum, and by smaller scales (60–77 rows below lateral line canal — as against 49–55). Anal fin low, its longest ray 0.7 to 1.0 into width of orbit.

Life History   Half of the males are mature at 11.5 inches (29 cm) in length, half the females at 12 inches (30 cm) or 4 years old. At 12 inches females produce about 29,000 young at a birth, at 20.5 to 22 inches (52–56 cm) some 538,000. In California feeds on red feed like euphausiids and small fishes like anchovies, lanternfish, and young hake.[2,3]

Distribution   Magdalena Bay, Baja California, to Cape Scott, northwest coast of Vancouver Island (50.39 N, 128.39 W) at depths to 180 fathoms (330 m). There is only one record from British Columbia.[4]

References   1, 2, 3 Phillips 1957, 1964, personal communication; 4 Westrheim 1965.

ROSETHORN ROCKFISH

Sebastes helvomaculatus Ayres 1859

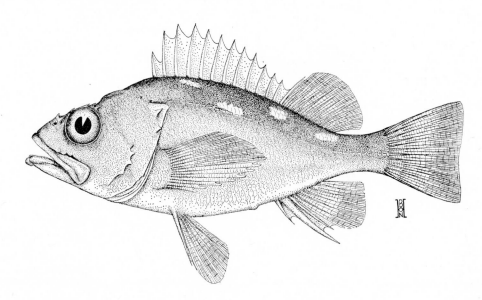

Scientific names from the Greek *sebastos* (magnificent); and the Latin *helvanicus* (light yellow) and *maculatus* (spotted).

An aberrant specimen of this species was identified as *Sebastodes rosaceus* and so recorded in Clemens and Wilby 1961.

S. rosaceus is now dropped from the Canadian list.

Description   Body depth 2.8 to 3.1 into standard length. Head with upper profile slightly convex, 2.4 to 2.5 into standard length. Mouth terminal and moderate, premaxillary separated into 2 toothed lobes. Maxillary extending to midorbital or rear of pupil. Moderately strong downward projecting symphyseal knob. No obvious dentary elevation. Interorbital space strongly concave with median groove and low frontal ridges, 7.0 to 8.1 into length of head. Caudal peduncle 10.8 to 12.2 into standard length.

Head Spines   Nasal, preocular, supraocular, postocular, tympanic, and parietal spines present, strong, and sharp. Coronal spines absent and nuchal spines usually absent. Occasionally a supraocular or preocular spine is bifid. Parietal ridges high and thin. Preopercular spines moderately strong and sharp, usually radially directed and evenly spaced. Opercular spines moderately strong and sharp. Supracleithral and cleithral spines strong. Lower margin of suborbital bone occasionally with 2 triangular spines, more frequently with a triangular spine, and a small projection anteriorly. The lower edge of the gill cover may or may not have a spine.

Fins   Dorsal (1), XIII, (12)13(14), moderately high, notched, and incised. Caudal slightly indented. Anal III, 6(7), posterior edge almost vertical. Pectorals (15)16 to 17(18) with (6)7 to 8 unbranched. Pelvics I, 5. Tips of pectorals extend beyond tips of pelvics and to anus or beyond.

Gill Rakers   On first gill arch 28 to 33.

Scales   Ctenoid, 42 to 48 diagonal rows below lateral line canal. Pores along lateral line canal 34 to 41.

Colour   Orange-yellow with light olivaceous mottling on back. Four or five clear white blotches bordered or tinged with light pink or orange on the upper part of the body. A dusky area on operculum. Fins pink with some yellow-green. Peritoneum black, or gray with black dots.

Size   Reaches 13 inches (33 cm).

Recognition   Distinguished in Canada by its markedly concave interorbital space and characteristic colour pattern.

Distribution   From Guadaloupe Island, Baja California, to Gulf of Alaska, 65 miles (105 km) east of St. Elias, and east of Sitkina Island at 56.21 N, 152.21 W (Nishimoto 1970). British Columbia records are from Queen Charlotte Sound, off Vancouver Island (Esteban Deep). It is recorded at depths from 50 to 300 fathoms (92–550 m).

References   Alverson, Pruter, and Ronholt 1964; Heyamoto and Hitz 1962; Phillips 1957; Westrheim 1965.

SHORTBELLY ROCKFISH

Sebastes jordani (Gilbert 1893)

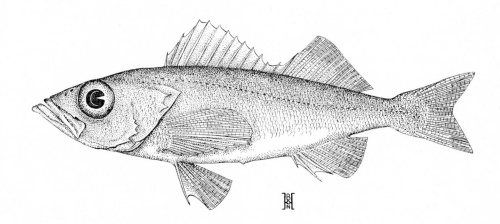

Scientific names from the Greek *sebastos* (magnificent); and David Starr Jordan, eminent U.S. ichthyologist and educator.

Description   Body elongate, depth 3.7 to 4.1 into standard length. Head moderate, upper profile slightly convex, 2.6 to 3.0 into standard length. Mouth terminal, moderate. Lower jaw slightly projecting. Upper jaw ending at or before midorbit. Symphyseal knob small, sharp, forward projecting. Eye diameter 3.1 to 3.9 into length of head. Interorbital space at midorbit flat or slightly convex, broad, 4.3 to 5.1 into length of head. Caudal peduncle rather slender, 11.4 to 14.1 into standard length.

Head Spines   Cranial spines weak; nasal and parietals always present; preocular, postocular, and tympanics may be present weakly. Supraocular, coronals, and nuchals are always absent. Preopercular spines small and sharp with second and third from the top stronger, lowest sometimes not discernible. Opercular spines short, thin, and sharp. Suborbital bone with usually 2 small spines present, the rearmost directed backward. Supracleithral and cleithral spines absent or much reduced. Spines on the lower edge of the gill cover absent.

Fins   Dorsal (1), XIII or XIV, 13 to 16, deeply notched, membrane of spinous portion slightly incised. Caudal with posterior margin deeply indented. Anal III (8)9 to 10(11), free edge slanted posteriorly, the second spine barely thicker than the third, the tip of the second spine not reaching the tip of the third when the fin is depressed. Pectorals 19 to 21(22), 12 to 15 unbranched. Tips of the pectoral fins extend slightly beyond the tips of the pelvics to the anus.

Gill Rakers   On the first gill arch 41 to 46 (42–47 in California).

Scales   Ctenoid, 65 diagonal rows below lateral line canal (in California). Pores along lateral line canal (52)53 to 58(59).[1]

Colour   Olive-pink dorsally, light pink on sides. Fins same colour as adjacent body parts. Peritoneum silver gray with black dots, or black.

Size   Length to 12 inches (30.5 cm).

Recognition   Anus located midway between the origins of the anal and pelvic fins.

Life History   A few fish are mature at 6 inches (15 cm) long and 50 percent at **6.5 inches** (16.5 cm) or 3 years old. Seven-inch (17.8-cm) females produce about 7000 young at birth, 12-inch (30.5-cm) individuals 50,000.[2]

Distribution   The range is from Ensenada, Baja California, to the west coast of Vancouver Island (La Pérouse Bank).[4] At depths to 150 fathoms (275 m) in California, at 110 fathoms (201 m) off Washington.[3]

References   1, 2 Phillips 1957, 1964; 3 Welander and Alverson 1954; 4 Westrheim and Pletcher 1966.

QUILLBACK ROCKFISH

Sebastes maliger (Jordan and Gilbert 1880)

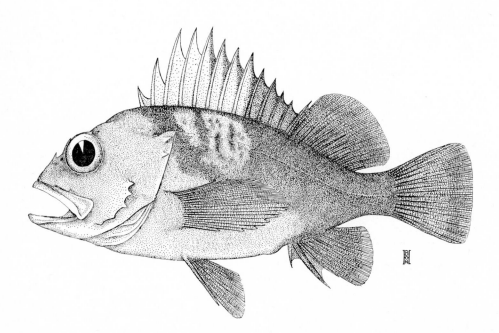

Scientific names from the Greek *sebastos* (magnificent); and the Latin *malus* (mast) and *gero* (bear).

Clemens and Wilby 1946 called this species *Sebastodes maliger,* orange-spotted rock-fish.

Description   Body depth 2.5 to 2.7 into standard length, compressed. Head 2.4 to 2.6 into standard length, upper profile weakly convex, with bulge over eyes. Mouth terminal, large. Upper jaw slightly projecting, extending to about midorbit. Symphyseal

424

knob may be weakly present. No raised patch of teeth at tip of lower jaw. Interorbital space concave, a marked median trough, interorbital width 5.5 to 6.6 into length of head. Eye diameter about 3.9 to 4.6 into length of head. Caudal peduncle compressed, its least depth 8.8 to 9.3 into standard length.

Head Spines   Nasal, preocular, postocular, tympanic and parietal present, strong and somewhat prostrate, tympanic not always well developed. Nuchal and coronal absent, and supraocular usually absent. Parietal ridges strong and thin, usually irregular on top. Preopercular spines short, thick, radially directed. Opercular spines moderately well developed and usually sharp. Spines on lower edge of suborbital bone weak, if present. Cleithral and supracleithral spines present, may be embedded. Spines present on lower edge of gill cover.

Fins   Dorsal (1), XIII, (12)13 or 14, moderately notched, spinous portion very high and deeply incised. Caudal rounded. Anal III, (6)7, second spine twice as thick as third, its tip may or may not reach tip of third in depressed fin, free edge rounded and nearly vertical. Pectorals (16) 17(18), tip extending to end of pelvics, and to anus or beyond, lower rays exserted and thickened. Pelvics I, 5, thoracic.

Gill Rakers   On first gill arch 30 to 33.

Scales   Ctenoid, 39 to 45 rows below lateral line canal. Pores on lateral line canal 35 to 43.

Colour   Brown with yellow or light tan areas on anterior part of body especially, in vague bands over back through spinous dorsal and over occiput. Paler below. Orange brown spotting on lower anterior part of body and head. Fins all dark except for yellow streak through spinous dorsal. Peritoneum silvery white.

Size   Length to 24 inches (61 cm).

Recognition   Notable for the high, deeply incised spinous dorsal fin, and the brown and yellow body colour, with brown speckling on the lower anterior portion.

Distribution   Central California (Point Sur[4]) to southeast Alaska[2,3] or Gulf of Alaska.[5] In the northern part of its range the quillback rockfish tends to be a fish of the inlets and shallow rockpiles,[1,2] taken to 150 fathoms (275 m) off California.[2] In Canada taken as a sport fish and to a moderate extent for commercial filleting.

References   1 Alverson, Pruter, and Ronholt 1964; 2 Grinols 1965a; 3, 4 Phillips 1957, personal communication; 5 Wilimovsky 1954.

BLACK ROCKFISH

Sebastes melanops Girard 1856

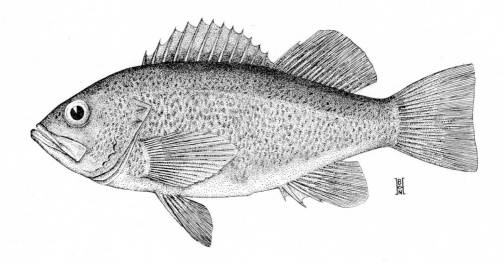

Scientific names from the Greek *sebastos* (magnificent); and *melas* (black) and *ops* (face).

Sometimes referred to by British Columbia fishermen as black bass.

Description   Body depth 2.7 to 3.1 into standard length, compressed. Head length, 2.7 to about 2.9 into standard length, upper profile almost straight. Mouth terminal, large. Lower jaw projecting to upper profile of head. Upper jaw ending below posterior part of eye. Symphyseal knob absent or vestigial. Dentary elevation small and not as a distinct patch. Eye diameter 3.7 to 4.3 into length of head. Interorbital space at midorbit strongly convex, notably smooth and broad, 3.9 to 4.4 into length of head. Caudal peduncle deep, about 8.0 to 9.2 into standard length.

Head Spines   Tips of nasals weakly present. Other spines obsolete although weak preoculars or postoculars may be present. Five preoper-

cular spines radially directed or with upper 2 directed backward. Two opercular spines strong and sharp, the upper often longer. No spines on suborbital bone. Cleithral spine weak, supracleithral usually absent. Usually no spine on lower edge of gill cover.

Fins   Dorsal (1), XIII (13)14 to 15(16), moderately incised. Caudal with posterior margin indented. Anal III (7)8(9), rounded at lower corner, posterior edge sloping forward, second ray only slightly thicker than third and its top not reaching the top of the third when the fin is depressed. Pectorals 18 to 19(20), tips of pectoral usually reaching about to tips of pelvics but not to anus. Pelvics I, 5, thoracic.

Gill Rakers   On first gill arch, 33 to 39.

Scales   Ctenoid, 50 to 55 rows below lateral line canal. Pores in lateral line canal 46 to 53.

Colour   Black on back, becoming gray mottled with black on the sides. Almost white along belly. Dark on posterior portion of spinous dorsal fin. All fins dark. Young specimens gray with brown spotting and mottling. Peritoneum silvery white, sometimes with dark flecks.

Size   Length to 23.25 inches (59 cm).

Recognition   Convex interorbital space with spines weak or absent. Weak symphyseal knob. Posterior edge of anal fin slanted anteriorly. Caudal peduncle deep, 2.8 to 3.2 into length of head. Body colour gray black.

Life History   Young are born off British Columbia, mainly in April.[5] Forms schools off bottom.[4]

Distribution   Southern California (San Miguel Island)[3] to the Gulf of Alaska[6] and intervening states. Found from the surface to 200 fathoms (366 m), most common in the 100 to 150 fathom (183–274 m) zone.[1] Widely distributed along the coast of British Columbia and found among rocks where it is taken on handlines. A spent female was taken in a surface gillnet over 2700 fathoms (5000 m) far from shore in February.[2]

References   1 Alverson, Pruter, and Ronholt 1964; 2 Dunn and Hitz 1969; 3 Phillips 1957; 4 Vancouver Public Aquarium 1969; 5 Westrheim, Harling, and Davenport 1968; 6 Wilimovsky 1954.

VERMILION ROCKFISH

Sebastes miniatus (Jordan and Gilbert 1880)

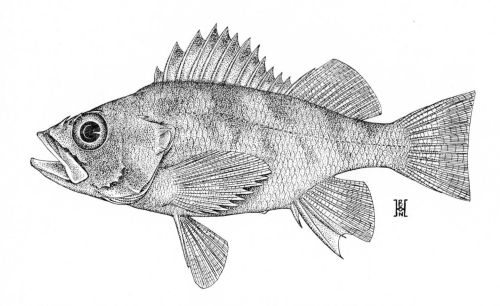

Scientific names from the Greek *sebastos* (magnificent); and the Latin *miniatus* (vermilion).

Description   Body depth 2.6 to 2.9 into standard length. Head 2.6 to 2.7 into standard length, upper profile gently curved. Mouth terminal, moderate in size, directed forward and upward. Lower jaw protruding. Upper jaw extending beyond midorbit in larger specimens. Symphyseal knob low and broad, extending downward. Small dentigerous lobe at symphysis of lower jaw. Interorbital space convex, flattened near orbit, nearly flat in small specimens, its width about 4.5 into length of head. Eye diameter 3.2 to 4.5 into length of head. Caudal peduncle compressed, deep, its least depth 7.5 to 10.4 into standard length.

Head Spines   Nasal, preocular, supraocular, postocular, tympanic, and parietal present. Nuchals occasionally present. Coronals absent. Parietal ridges low and thin. Five preopercular spines strong and sharp, second and third from top usually longer, may be radially directed, or upper 2 or 3 may be directed backward. Two preopercular spines strong and sharp. Two strong, sharp spines on suborbital bone. Cleithral and supracleithral spines strong and sharp. Spines present or absent on lower margin of gill cover.

Fins   Dorsal (1), XIII, (13)14(15), moderately notched and incised. Caudal slightly indented. Anal III, 7, second spine only slightly thicker than third, its tip reaching tip of third in depressed fin only in small specimens; tip of fin rounded, upper part of posterior edge slanting forward and up. Pectorals (16, 17)18, tip reaching tip of pelvics, and may (or may not) extend as far as anus. Pelvics I, 5, thoracic.

Gill Rakers   On first gill arch 35 to 43.

428

Scales   Ctenoid, rather large, diagonal rows below lateral line canal 45 to 48, on maxillary and mandible. Lateral line canal arches up anteriorly and then slopes down to caudal peduncle. Pores in lateral line canal 40 to 47.

Colour   Vermilion, dark red dorsally mottled with gray on sides, paler red ventrally, fins red. Indefinite darker markings across dorsal part of body and head. Mouth red. Three obscure orange stripes radiate from eyes. Specimens under about 30 centimeters (12 inches) long, uniform dark red with fins edged in black. Peritoneum silver white in larger specimens.

Size   Length to 36 inches (91 cm)[2] or 30 inches (76 cm).[4]

Recognition   Noteworthy for vermilion red coloration, red mouth, scales on maxillary and mandible, and deep caudal peduncle.

Distribution   From San Benito Island, Baja California, through California, Oregon, and Washington[3,5] to central Vancouver Island, occurring mainly at depths from 100 to 150 fathoms (183–274 m).[1,3] British Columbia records from Clayoquot Sound near Flores Island at 30 fathoms (55 m) and the Strait of Georgia, (probably) near Deep Bay.

References   1 Alverson, Pruter, and Ronholt 1964; 2 Clemens and Wilby 1961; 3 Grinols 1965a; 4 Phillips 1957; 5 Schultz and DeLacy 1936.

BLUE ROCKFISH

Sebastes mystinus (Jordan and Gilbert 1880)

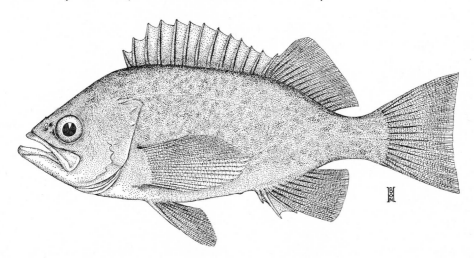

Scientific names from the Greek *sebastos* (magnificent); and *mystas* (priest).

Clemens and Wilby 1946 listed this species as priest-fish, *Sebastodes mystinus.*

Description   Body depth about 2.7 to 2.9 into standard length, compressed. Head length 3.0 to 3.1 into standard length, upper profile nearly straight. Mouth terminal,

429

large, directed forward and upward. Lower jaw projecting. Upper jaw extending to midorbit or posterior part of pupil. Symphyseal knob absent or vestigial. No dentary elevation at tip of lower jaw. Eye diameter 4.1 to 4.9 into length of head. Interorbital space at midorbit strongly and evenly convex, very broad, 3.2 to 3.5 into length of head. Caudal peduncle 8.9 to 9.6 into standard length.

Head Spines   Tips of nasal spines are weakly present, and occasionally minute preopercular spines are present. Other spines usually obsolete. Parietal ridges weakly developed. Five preopercular spines moderately strong and sharp, the upper 4 usually directed backward, but occasionally radially directed. Two opercular spines short and sharp. On suborbital bone occasionally a triangular spine present. Cleithral spine moderately strong, supracleithral weak or absent. Small spine present on the lower posterior edge of the gill cover.

Fins   Dorsal (1), XIII, 15 to 16(17), spinous part somewhat excised, and moderately indented. Caudal fin indented. Anal III, 8 to 9 (10), posterior edge sloping backward, second spine only slightly thicker than third, its tip failing to reach tip of third when the fin is depressed. Pectorals (16)17 to 18, tips of the pectorals usually extending as far as tips of the pelvics, usually but not always failing to extend to the anus. Pelvics I, 5, thoracic.

Gill Rakers   On first gill arch 33 to 38.

Scales   Ctenoid, 50 to 56 diagonal rows below lateral line canal. Pores in lateral line canal 49 to 56.

Colour   Bluish black, mottled with paler colour on sides and belly. Dusky to black on all fins.

Young under about 5 inches (12.7 cm) are gray overlaid with irregular reddish streaks and with fine black flecks over the body.

Peritoneum variable with size, light in small and large individuals, black between lengths of about 9 to 13 inches (23–33 cm).

Size   Length to 21 inches (53 cm).

Recognition   Convex interorbital space with spines weak or absent. Symphyseal knob weak. Posterior edge of anal fin slanted posteriorly. Caudal peduncle deep, 2.9 to 3.1 into length of head. Body colour bluish black.

Life History   In California young are released from November to January. Males mature younger, in their third and fourth years, females in their fourth and fifth years, recruitment to the fishery is in the fifth to seventh years. Fecundity may reach 524,000.[5] Food consists of tunicates, jellyfish, and fishes.[2]

Distribution   From San Tomas, Baja California to the Bering Sea[4,6] and intervening areas. It occurs from the surface to 300 fathoms (550 m) but is most commonly encountered from 100 to 300 fathoms (183–550 m). It is not frequently encountered in British Columbia.[1,3]

References   1 Alverson, Pruter, and Ronholt 1964; 2 Gotshall, Smith, and Holbert 1965; 3 Grinols 1965a; 4 Phillips 1957; 5 Wales 1952; 6 Wilimovsky 1954.

430

CHINA ROCKFISH

Sebastes nebulosus Ayres 1854

Scientific names from the Greek *sebastos* (magnificent); and the Latin *nebulosus* (clouded).

Clemens and Wilby 1946 listed this species as yellow-striped rock-fish, *Sebastodes nebulosus* (Ayres 1854). In 1961 the common name was spelled yellowstripe rockfish.

Description　Body depth 2.4 to 2.6 into standard length, compressed. Head 2.4 to 2.5 into standard length, dorsal profile almost straight but obscured by heavy spines. Mouth terminal, large. Jaws almost equal in length. Upper jaw extends to posterior part of eye. No dentary elevation. Symphyseal knob, if present, low and downward projecting. Eye diameter 3.7 to 4.7 into length of head. Interorbital space about flat between the much-elevated spiny ridges above orbits, its width about 6.4 to 7.7 into length of head. Caudal peduncle compressed, its least depth 9.2 to 9.6 into standard length.

Head Spines　Nasal, preocular, postocular, tympanic, parietal present, thick, and high, encased in thick skin. Supraocular, coronal, and nuchal spines absent. Parietal ridges high and thick. Five preopercular spines short and thick, lower 2 often reduced, usually radially directed, but all may be directed backward. Opercular spines both triangular. Two rounded and/or triangular spines on lower margin of each suborbital bone. Cleithral and supracleithral spines strong and sharp. Small spines may be present at lower edges of gill covers.

Fins　Dorsal (1), XIII 13(14), spinous, moderately notched and strongly incised. Caudal rounded. Anal III, (6)7(8), second spine about twice as thick as third and extending beyond tip of third when fin is depressed, free margin of fin rounded and tending backward. Pectorals (17) 18(19), tips extending beyond tips of pelvics and usually beyond anus. Pelvics I, 5, thoracic.

Gill Rakers　On first gill arch 27 to 31.

431

Scales   Ctenoid, rows below lateral line canal 43 to 48. Pores in lateral line canal, 37 to 48.

Colour   Blue-black mottled with yellow or white, more white below. A broad irregular yellow stripe sloping downward from dorsal fin at the third spine to lateral line canal and posteriorly to base of caudal. Fins blue-black. Peritoneum pale.

Size   Length to 17 inches (43 cm),[3] to 12 inches (30.5 cm) in Canada.

Recognition   Interorbital space strongly concave. Supraocular spines absent. Lateral line canal pores 38 to 41. Body colour black with a broad yellow stripe from spinous dorsal fin downward and posteriorly along lateral line canal.

Distribution   Cape Buchon in central California[2] to southeastern Alaska.[4] In British Columbia the species occurs in both inside and outside waters at depths down to 69 fathoms (126 m). However, it is most commonly taken at less than 50 fathoms (92 m).[1] Evidently remains close to home crevices and takes shelter when disturbed.

References   1 Alverson, Pruter, and Ronholt 1964; 2, 3 Phillips 1957, 1967b; 4 Wilimovsky 1954.

432

TIGER ROCKFISH

Sebastes nigrocinctus Ayres 1859

Scientific names from the Greek *sebastos* (magnificent); and the Latin *niger* (black), and *cinctus* (belt).

Clemens and Wilby 1946 called this species banded rock-fish, and in 1961, black-banded rockfish, *Sebastodes nigrocinctus*.

Description   Body depth 2.4 to 2.6 into standard length, compressed. Head length 2.5 to 2.6 into standard length, upper profile nearly straight. Mouth terminal, large. Lower jaw projecting beyond upper. Upper jaw extending about to midorbit. Snout blunt and straight. A low flat symphyseal knob sometimes present. No raised patch of teeth at tip of lower jaw. Interorbital space concave, divided by spiny ridges, its width 7.0 to 8.1 into length of head. Eye diameter 4.2 to 4.8 into length of head. Caudal peduncle compressed, its least depth 8.9 to 10.1 into standard length.

Head Spines   Nasal, preocular, postocular, tympanic, coronal and nuchals present, thick and coarse, sometimes divided into several points. Parietal ridges high and thick, edges usually irregular. Preopercular spines coarse and blunt, radially directed, upper 2 longest. Both opercular spines long and sharp. Lower margin of suborbital bone with a small lobe anteriorly followed by a large triangular spine. Cleithral and supracleithral spines strong and sharp. No spines on lower margins of gill covers.

Fins   Dorsal (1), XIII, (13)14(15), moderately incised, weakly notched. Caudal rounded. Anal III, (6)7, second spine at least twice as thick as third, its tip nearly reaching or reaching tip of third when fin is depressed, posterior edge rounded. Pectorals (18)19(20), tips reaching to or beyond tips of pelvics and usually as far as anus. Pelvics I, 5, thoracic.

Gill Rakers   On first gill arch 27 to 31.[4]

Scales   Ctenoid, diagonal rows below lateral line canal 44 to 53. Pores on lateral line canal 41 to 50.

Colour   Shades of pink, gray, or rose, most frequently light red, with 5 black or red bars vertically across body, 2 black or red bars radiating posteriorly from eyes; in young individuals, tips of ventral and anal fins darkened. Peritoneum white.

Size   Length to 24 inches (61 cm).

Recognition   Interorbital space strongly concave. Supraocular spines absent. Lateral line canal pores 43 to 50. Body colour red or pink with 5 black or dark red vertical bands.

Life History   The tiger rockfish is a solitary fish frequenting crevices and caves, where it sometimes lies on its side. As a result it is infrequently captured on moving gear and is probably more abundant than superficially evident. They are taken on setlines at depths between 30 and 150 fathoms (55–275 m). Many were killed in 1958 by the explosion to demolish Ripple Rock in Discovery Passage. Territorial behaviour is marked and tiger rockfish are aggressive in defending a home crevice. When disturbed they become darker in colour. These and other colour changes induced by changes in lighting, etc., take place very quickly.[5] The young have been found sheltering among gooseneck barnacles on a covered glass fishing float 7.5 miles (12 km) north northwest of Triangle Island.[2]

Distribution   Point Buchon, central California to southeastern Alaska.[1,3] In British Columbia most commonly observed in the Strait of Georgia at depths down to 150 fathoms (275 m).

References   1 Grinols 1965a; 2 Hitz 1961; 3, 4 Phillips 1957, personal communication; 5 Vancouver Public Aquarium Staff 1969.

Description of Colour Illustrations

(on following pages)

Lingcod

Grunt sculpin

Pacific halibut

Coastal cutthroat trout

Rainbow trout

Pacific herring

Striped seaperch

Kelp greenling

Surf smelt

Pink salmon, fresh-run female

Pink salmon, spawning male

Pink salmon, spawning female

Chum salmon, sea-run

Chum salmon, spawning male

Chum salmon, spawning female

Coho salmon, fresh-run male

Coho salmon, spawning male

Coho salmon, spawning female

Sockeye salmon, fresh-run

Sockeye salmon, spawning male

Sockeye salmon, spawning female

Chinook salmon, fresh-run male

Chinook salmon, spawning male

Chinook salmon, spawning female

BOCACCIO

Sebastes paucispinis Ayres 1854

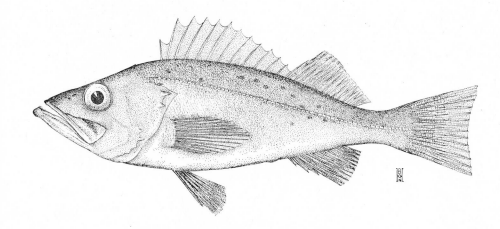

Scientific names from the Greek *sebastos* (magnificent); and the Latin *pauci* (few) and *spinus* (spine).

Bocaccio means large mouth.

Description   Body depth 3.4 to 4.1 into standard length, compressed. Head 2.6 to 2.8 into standard length, upper profile concave from snout to occiput. Mouth terminal, very large, directed forward and up. Upper jaw extending beyond posterior margin of orbit. Tip of lower jaw thickened but no real symphyseal knob present. Lower jaw projecting markedly and entering dorsal profile. Interorbital space evenly convex, its width 4.2 to 4.8 into length of head. Eye diameter 4.6 to 5.1 into length of head. Caudal peduncle compressed, its least depth 10.9 to 12.2 into standard length.

Head Spines   Cranial spines generally absent, although nasals and parietals sometimes show. Parietal ridges weakly developed. Preopercular spines strong, thin, sharp, radially directed, upper 3 best developed. Two opercular spines moderately strong, thin, and sharp, the upper longer. Small spines on lower margin of suborbital bone present only in small specimens. Cleithral and supracleithral spines present, supracleithral not strong. No spine on lower margin of gill cover.

Fins   Dorsal (1), XIII, 14(13–15), moderately incised, and deeply notched. Caudal slightly indented. Anal III, 9(8–10), second spine hardly thicker than third, its tip not reaching tip of third when fin depressed, posterior edge slightly rounded and nearly vertical with a slight posterior slant. Pectorals 15(16), extending beyond tips of pelvic but not reaching anus. Pelvics I, 5, thoracic.

Gill Rakers   On first gill arch 28 to 31.

Scales   Ctenoid, 72 to 90 rows below lateral line canal. Pores along lateral line canal 54 to 58.[3]

Colour   Light olive brown, copper brown, or brick red dorsally, silvery red or pink on sides, small brown spots on sides most noticeable in small specimens. Bright red and golden orange[1] individuals are sometimes found. Peritoneum silvery white, sometimes with black dots, which are numerous in individuals under 25 centimeters.

Size   Length to 36 inches (91 cm).

435

Recognition   Head profile concave. Interorbital space convex with spines weak or absent. Very large mouth with greatly projecting lower jaw. Lateral line canal pores 54 to 58. Body colour reddish or olive brown.

Life History   Bocaccio start maturing in California at about 14 inches (35.6 cm) long or 3 years old, and 50 percent are mature at 16.5 inches (41.9 cm) or 4 years. They reach an age of about 30 years. Bocaccio are ovoviviparous. Females 15 inches (38.1 cm) in length produce about 20,000 young in a batch; a 30.5-inch (77.5-cm) individual produces about 2,300,000.[4] In California females become pregnant in October, and in November give birth to hatched, yolkless, larvae 4 to 6 millimeters long with well-developed eyes, jaws, and pectoral fins. Physiological preparation for a second brood follows immediately and it is born in March. Newly released larvae occupy the upper mixed layer of water, transform into juveniles at about 30 millimeters standard length and move into shallow water for their first year.[2] Off British Columbia adults are found most commonly at depths below 40 fathoms, where they eat small fishes. Bocaccio are well regarded as sport fish in the Howe Sound area but are not sought as a commercial fish in Canada. In southern California it is an important commercial species.

Distribution   From Sacramento Reef, Baja California, to the Gulf of Alaska, off Kruzof Island[6] and Kodiak Island.[5] Through coastal British Columbia but most abundant in the southern part.

References   1 Davenport 1966; 2 Moser 1967; 3, 4, 5, Phillips 1957, 1964, personal communication; 6 Westrheim 1966b.

CANARY ROCKFISH

Sebastes pinniger (Gill 1864)

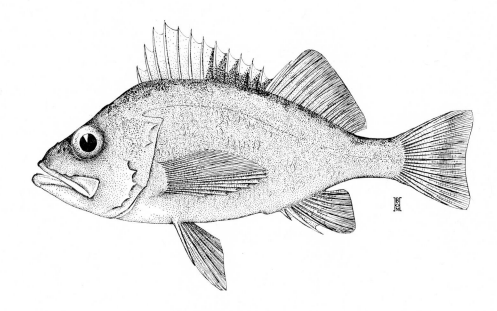

Scientific names from the Greek *sebastos* (magnificent); and the Latin *pinna* (fin) and *gero* (bear).

Assigned the common name orange rockfish in Clemens and Wilby 1961, spelled orange rock-fish in 1946.

Description   Body depth about 2.7 to 3.3 into standard length, compressed. Head 2.7 to 2.8 into standard length, snout curved downward but rest of dorsal profile straight. Mouth terminal, large. Lower jaw projecting but not extending beyond upper profile of head. Upper jaw reaches to a point under posterior part of eye. Symphyseal knob present but inconspicuous. Dentary elevation present on lower jaw. Eye diameter 3.8 to 4.3 into length of head. Interorbital space at midorbit, strongly convex, flattened near orbits, less convex in small specimens, 3.8 to 4.3 into length of head. Caudal peduncle 8.3 to 9.2 into standard length.

Head Spines   Nasal, preocular, supraocular, postocular, tympanic, and parietals all present but small. Coronal and nuchal spines absent. Parietal ridges low and thin. Five preopercular spines long and thin, the second and third from the top usually longer, usually radially directed. Opercular spine both long and sharp, the upper often longer. On the lower margin of the suborbital bone a small lobe followed posteriorly by a larger, sharply triangular spine. Cleithral and supracleithral spines both strong. Spine sometimes present on the posterior edge of the gill cover.

Fins   Dorsal (1), XIII, 14 or 15, spinous portion moderately incised, rather strongly notched. Caudal strongly indented. Anal III, 7, posterior edge almost vertical with an anterior slant, second spine only a little thicker than third, its tip fails to reach tip of third spine. Pectorals 17(18), tips extend about to tips of pelvics and both usually reach anus. Pelvics I, 5, thoracic.

Gill Rakers   On first gill arch 41 to 45.

Scales   Ctenoid. Diagonal rows of scales below lateral line canal, 43 to 50. Pores in lateral line canal 39 to 43.

Colour   Gray mottled with orange or orange mottled with yellow giving a predominantly clear orange impression, paler below. Bright orange on all fin membranes, dark blotch on posterior part of spinous dorsal. Peritoneum white; smaller individuals with black dots on white.

Size   Length to 30 inches (76 cm).

Recognition   Notable for its orange colour with three bright orange stripes across the head, dark blotch on posterior end of spinous dorsal, scales on under side of lower jaw smooth to touch.

Life History   Off British Columbia gives birth to young in January[7] or later.[2] In California about 50 percent of the population is mature at 14 inches (35.6 cm) and 5 or 6 years of age. Nineteen-inch (48.3-cm) fish carry 260,000 young and 21- to 26-inch (53.3–66-cm) fish about 1,900,000.[4]

Distribution   Baja California[3,5] to southeast Alaska (56.16 N, 134.07 W)[6] and the intervening areas. Encountered at depths of 50 to 100 fathoms but the species occurs nearly to 200 fathoms (366 m).[1] Fairly common at suitable depths on hard bottom in British Columbia.

References   1 Alverson, Pruter, and Ronholt 1964; 2 Clemens and Wilby 1961; 3, 4 Phillips 1957, 1964; 5 Roedel 1948b; 6 Westrheim 1966b; 7 Westrheim, Harling, and Davenport 1968.

REDSTRIPE ROCKFISH

Sebastes proriger (Jordan and Gilbert 1880)

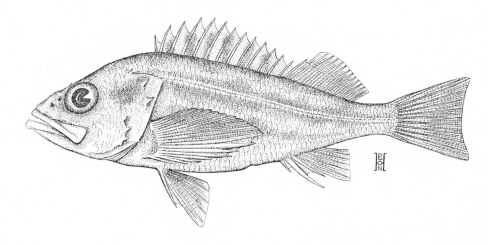

Scientific names from the Greek *sebastos* (magnificent); and the Latin *prora* (bow) and *gero* (bear).

Description   Body depth 3.3 to 3.6 into standard length, compressed. Head length 2.9 to 3.1 into standard length, upper profile barely convex. Mouth terminal, large, directed forward. Lower jaw projecting well beyond upper which extends to midpupil. Symphyseal knob strong and directed forward. Dentary elevation usually present with teeth at end outside snout when mouth closed. Eye diameter about 3.7 into length of head. Interorbital space at midorbit slightly concave, its width 4.1 to 4.3 into length of head. Caudal peduncle compressed, its least depth about 12 into standard length.

Head Spines   Nasal, preocular, postocular, tympanic, and parietal spines present but sometimes obscure. Supraocular, coronal, and nuchal spines absent. Parietal ridges moderately high and thin. Five preopercular spines moderately strong and sharp, directed backward, the second and third usually longest. Two opercular spines moderately long and sharp. Cleithral and supracleithral spines moderately well developed. Two rather large projections usually present on lower margin of suborbital bone. Spine present on lower margin of gill cover.

Fins   Dorsal (1), XIII, (13)14 or 15, spinous portion moderately incised and weakly notched. Caudal moderately indented or not indented. Anal III, (6)7, second ray twice as thick as third and reaches its tip when fin is depressed, posterior edge of fin nearly vertical, or slanted posteriorly. Pectorals (16)17(18), tips reaching beyond pelvics and easily reaching anus. Pelvics I, 5, thoracic.

Gill Rakers   On first gill arch 36 to 43.

Scales   Ctenoid, 55 to 60 rows below lateral line canal. Pores on lateral line canal 47 to 53.

Colour   Pale red, mottled with olive dorsally and flushed with yellow on lower sides. Lateral line canal in a clear light red band. Olive stripes radiating from eyes. Dusky on top of lower jaw. Fins red, dorsal and caudal with some light green, lower fins with some yellow. Peritoneum black or dark brown.

Size   Length to 20 inches (51 cm),[4] 2 feet (61 cm) has been reported.

Recognition   Supraocular spine absent. Symphyseal knob moderate. Clear red stripe running full length of lateral line canal.

Distribution   Southern California (San Diego) through Oregon,[1] Washington,[2] British Columbia, and Alaska to the Bering Sea.[1,3,5] At depths ranging from 50 to 200 fathoms (92–366 m). Generally distributed in coastal British Columbia.

References   1 Alverson, Pruter, and Ronholt 1964; 2 DeLacy, Dryfoos, and Miller 1963; 3 Grinols 1965a; 4 Phillips 1957; 5 Wilimovsky 1954.

YELLOWMOUTH ROCKFISH

Sebastes reedi (Westrheim and Tsuyuki 1967)

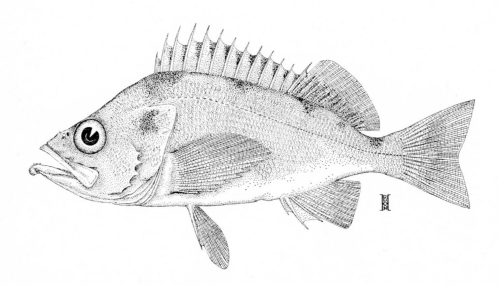

Scientific names from the Greek *sebastos* (magnificent); and *G. B. Reed,* Fisheries Research Board of Canada research vessel, for Dr G. B. Reed, Chairman of the Board, and educator.

Description   Body depth 2.6 to 3.9 into standard length, moderately compressed. Head pointed with profile nearly straight, its length 2.6 to 2.9 into standard length. Orbit 3.5 to 4.4 into length of head, not included in profile. Mouth terminal, large. Upper jaw 5.3 to 6.5 into standard length. Symphyseal knob moderate, projecting forward. Dentary elevation of lower jaw partly included in snout when jaws

440

closed. Posterior end of maxillary under rear of pupil. Bony interorbital width 3.8 to 4.8 into length of head, flat to slightly convex. Caudal peduncle sometimes slender, 9.7 to 13.9 into standard length.

Head Spines   On top of head moderate to weak, nasal, preocular, supraocular (usually), postocular, tympanic, and parietal present. Coronals and nuchals absent. Parietal ridges low, thin. Lower margin of suborbital bone with 2 triangular lobes with weak to moderate teeth on each. Five preopercular spines radially directed, lowermost blunt. Two opercular spines moderately strong and sharp. Supracleithral and cleithral spines moderate. Strong spines present on lower margin of the gill cover.

Fins   Dorsal (1), XIII, 14 or 15, moderately notched, membranes on spinous portion moderately incised. Caudal fin moderately indented. Anal III, 7 or 8, second spine thicker than third, just failing to meet tip of third when fin is depressed. Pectoral fins (18)19(20), unbranched rays (7)9 to 11(12–13). Pelvics I, 5. Tips of pectorals extend beyond tips of pelvics, occasionally reaching anus.

Gill Rakers   On first gill arch (30)31 to 35(36).

Scales   Diagonal rows below lateral line canal (57–58)59 to 66(67). Pores along lateral line canal (47–48)49 to 54(55).

Colour   Below about 16 inches (41 cm) total length, red intermingled with black blotches on dorsal surface. Larger specimens, red intermingled with yellow-orange. Three indistinct black bands across top of head anterior and posterior to orbit, and across parietals. Vague black blotches on back and nape, midspinous dorsal, and caudal peduncle. Dark red on both jaws. Along lateral line canal distinct pink. Mouth pinkish white with black and yellow blotches. Peritoneum silver gray with black dots.

Size   Reaches a length of 21.2 inches (54 cm).

Recognition   Marked by yellow and black blotches in mouth with 57 to 67 diagonal rows of scales below lateral line canal, 30 to 36 gill rakers on first arch, 47 to 55 pores along lateral line canal, and a moderate symphyseal knob. Nuchal spines and vertical dark bands across the body are missing. There is a supraocular spine or usually two.

Life History   No females were mature at less than 33 centimeters (9 years old), or males at less than 31 centimeters (or 9 years old).[2] Young are born in April at a size of 6 millimeters.[1] Ages as high as 34 years were encountered. There is considerable segregation of sizes on different fishing grounds.

Distribution   The yellowmouth rockfish has been taken from off Cape Blanco, Oregon to Sitka, Alaska, at depths of 77 to 200 fathoms (141–366 m). As the species is newly described, it is likely that the range will be extended with easier recognition and reporting. British Columbia records are from Rennell Sound, Queen Charlotte Islands, Queen Charlotte Sound, and the west coast of Vancouver Island.

Utilization   Although substantial aggregations of yellowmouth rockfish have been encountered, they were all on rough bottom where only large foreign trawlers have successfully fished.

References   1 Westrheim, Harling, Davenport, and Smith 1968; 2 Westrheim and Tsuyuki 1967.

YELLOWEYE ROCKFISH

Sebastes ruberrimus (Cramer 1895)

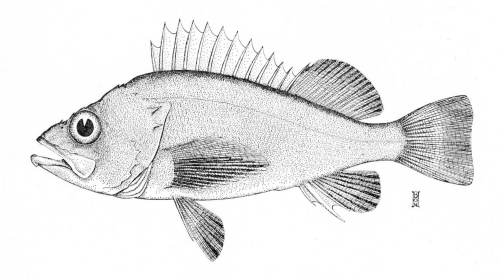

Scientific names from the Greek *sebastos* (magnificent); and the Latin *ruberrimus* (very red).

Clemens and Wilby 1946, 1961 used the locally well-established common name red snapper *Sebastodes ruberrimus* for this species. Unfortunately that common name is reserved for another species.

Description Body depth 2.4 to 3.0 into standard length, compressed. Head 2.4 to 2.5 into standard length, upper profile almost straight. Mouth terminal, large. Upper jaw extending to posterior part of eye. Lower jaw somewhat projecting. Symphyseal knob broad, low, rounded. No raised patch of teeth at tip of lower jaw. Interorbital space concave, its width 5.7 to 7.0 into length of head. Eye diameter 4.3 to 5.1 into length of head. Caudal peduncle compressed, its least depth 9.2 to 10.5 into standard length.

Head Spines Nasal, preocular, supraocular, postocular, tympanic, and parietal present; nuchal and coronals present or absent. In large individuals, roughnesses on spines makes their identification difficult. Parietal ridges strong and high, smooth in young, rough in adults. Preopercular spines short and thick, sometimes divided at tips. Opercular spines short, thick, sharp, sometimes bifid. Cleithral and supracleithral spines strong and sometimes bifid. Lower margin of suborbital bone usually with a small lobe followed by a larger triangular projection. Weak spine present on lower margin of gill cover.

Fins Dorsal (1), XIII, (13,14)15(16), moderately incised and notched. Caudal rounded. Anal III, (5,6)7(8), second spine twice as thick as third, its tip in the depressed fin may reach almost to tip of third spine, or slightly beyond, posterior edge of fin rounded or vertical. Pectorals (18)19(20), tips reaching beyond tips of pelvics but not as far as anus. Pelvics I, 5, thoracic.

Gill Rakers On first gill arch 26 to 30.

Scales Ctenoid, 45 to 50 rows below lateral line canal. Pores on lateral line canal 39 to 46.[9]

Colour Orange-yellow washed with pink on back and sides, paler below, fins pink, usually black on tips, and in very large specimens black mottling around head. Peritoneum white with black dots.

Young are differently and so characteristically coloured that they were meticulously described as a new species, *Sebastodes bilineata* Welander and Alverson (1954), subsequently corrected by Hubbs. In the young, over a rather dark background, there is a light stripe along the whole lateral line canal to the base of the caudal fin where the stripe divides at right angles to surround the caudal peduncle; a second light stripe extends below it from ahead of the eye to below the rayed part of the dorsal fin.[7,10] They have been taken by diving between 20 and 30 meters.

Size Length to 36 inches (91 cm).

Recognition Ocular and parietal ridges high and rugose. Supraocular spine present. Gill rakers 26 to 30. Eye brilliant yellow.

Life History Fecundity of a 19.5-pound (8.9-kg) specimen was 2,700,000.[6] In Washington young are born in June.[3,4] Yelloweye rockfish are generally distributed at depths between 25 and 300 fathoms (46–550 m). They are caught by most kinds of fishing gear but ordinarily are not common in trawl catches.[1] They are taken often on setlines, and, as they are destroyed by pressure change when brought to the surface, great wastage resulted when they were not used. They are well regarded as a source of market fillets. Yelloweye rockfish are taken on live or dead herring bait, halibut jigs, and are known to eat crustaceans and lingcod spawn.

Distribution Ensenada, Baja California,[8] through California, Oregon, and British Columbia[2,5] to the Gulf of Alaska.[11] Common throughout coastal British Columbia around reefs in both inside and outside waters.

References 1 Alverson, Pruter, and Ronholt 1964; 2 Barsukov 1964; 3 DeLacy and Dryfoos 1962; 4 DeLacy, Hitz, and Dryfoos 1964; 5 Grinols 1965a; 6 Hart 1942c; 7 Hubbs 1959; 8, 9 Phillips 1957, personal communication; 10 Welander and Alverson 1954; 11 Wilimovsky 1954.

STRIPETAIL ROCKFISH

Sebastes saxicola (Gilbert 1890)

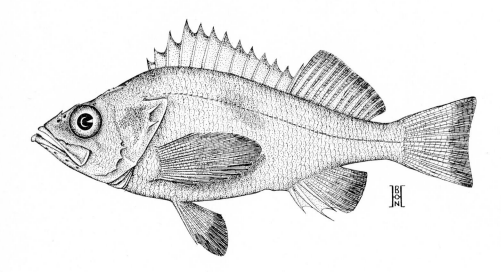

Scientific names from the Greek *sebastos* (magnificent); and the Latin *saxum* (rock) and *colo* (inhabit).

Referred to as the olive-backed rockfish in Clemens and Wilby 1946.

Description   Body depth 2.9 to 3.2 into standard length. Head 2.5 to 2.8 into standard length, dorsal profile entered by eyes, drooping slightly at snout. Mouth terminal, moderate in size. Lower jaw projecting and entering profile of head. Upper jaw extends to point under midorbit of eye or rear of pupil. Symphyseal knob prominent and directed forward. A raised patch of teeth at the tip of the lower jaw is present in large specimens and is not completely included by snout when the jaws are closed, inconspicuous in small fish. Interorbital space flat or slightly concave, usually with a narrow median groove, its width 4.7 to 5.3 into length of head. Eye large, diameter 2.9 to 3.2 into length of head. Caudal peduncle 10.1 to 12.1 into standard length.

Head Spines   Nasal, preocular, postocular, tympanic, and parietals present, moderately strong and sharp. Supraocular, coronal, and nuchal spines absent, except that a nuchal spine is sometimes present. Parietal ridges moderately high and rounded. Five preopercular spines thin and sharp, usually radially directed, second from top usually strongest. Two opercular spines thin and sharp. Lower margin of the suborbital bone with 2 strong, sharply triangular spines directed posteriorly. Cleithral and supracleithral present, cleithral sometimes double. Spines present along the lower edge of the gill cover.

Fins   Dorsal (1), XIII, (12)13(14), moderately incised and notched. Caudal moderately indented. Anal III, (5,6)7(8), posterior edge directed somewhat backward, second spine twice as thick as third with its tip projecting beyond tip of third when the fin is depressed. Free edge nearly vertical or with a slight posterior slant. Pectorals (15)16(17), their tips extending beyond tips of pelvics or nearly so, and nearly reaching or reaching anus, in young, tips may extend beyond anus. Pelvics I, 5, thoracic.

Gill Rakers   On first gill arch 31 to 34.

444

Scales   Ctenoid. Diagonal rows below lateral line canal 43 to 53. Pores in lateral line canal 36 to 42.

Colour   Pink tinged with yellow, with vague darker blotches along the back. Silvery pink ventrally. Caudal fin with green streaks on membranes. Peritoneum black.

Size   Length to 13.5 inches (34 cm).

Recognition   Supraocular spine absent. Second anal fin spine reaching beyond third in depressed fin. Two strong, sharp, hooked spines on lower margin of suborbital bone.

Life History   Young about 4.3 millimeters in length[2] are released mainly in February in British Columbia[7] and January and February off Oregon.[4] In California, some mature at 2 years of age and 5 inches (127 mm) in length; half the males are mature at 5.75 inches (146 mm) and half the females at 6.75 inches (171 mm) at 4 years of age. Females produce about 15,000 young at 7 inches (178 mm) and 200,000 at 12.5 inches (318 mm).[6]

Distribution   Taken from Sebastian Viscaino Bay in Baja California to southeastern Alaska.[5] It is encountered at depths from 230 fathoms to 25 fathoms (421–46 m),[1,3] but most commonly below 100 fathoms (183 m).[1] In British Columbia both offshore and in the Strait of Georgia.

References   1 Alverson, Pruter, and Ronholt 1964; 2 DeLacy, Hitz, and Dryfoos 1964; 3 Grinols 1965a; 4 Hitz 1962; 5, 6 Phillips 1957, 1964; 7 Westrheim, Harling, and Davenport 1968.

HARLEQUIN ROCKFISH

Sebastes variegatus Quast 1971

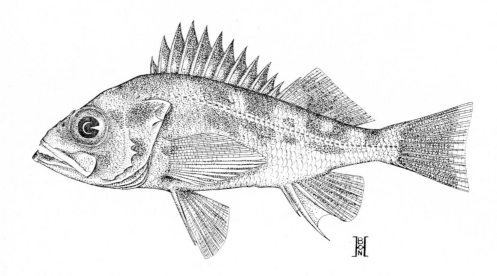

Scientific names from the Greek *sebastos* (magnificent); and the Latin *variegatus* (marked with different patches of colour).

Description   Body rather slender, its depth about 3.3 into standard length, compressed, flattened laterally near head. Head length about 2.9 into standard length, dorsal profile generally smooth and slightly concave. Mouth terminal, moderate in size, directed forward and upward. Lower jaw projects and enters dorsal profile of head. Upper jaw extends about to midorbit. Teeth in anterior part of lower jaw larger than others, in a narrowly divided tuft. Symphyseal knob weakly developed or absent. Eye large, orbit about 3.4 into length of head. Interorbital space flat to convex with cranial ridges seldom entering profile, width at midorbit about 4.8 into length of head. Caudal peduncle depth about 11 into standard length.

Head Spines   Nasal, preocular, postocular, tympanic, and parietals present. Occasionally a nuchal present. Other cranial spines absent. Parietal ridges well developed. Five preopercular spines, the upper 3 long and slightly divergent, the lower 2 broadly triangular and strong, the second from top longest. Two opercular spines well developed and slightly divergent. No real spines on subocular bone but 2 blunt prominences on suborbitals. Cleithral and supracleithrals well developed. Occasionally a spine on lower edge of gill cover.

Fins   Dorsal (1), XIII, (13)14 to 15, moderately notched and strongly incised. Caudal moderately indented. Anal III, (6)7, second spine thicker than third and its tip when the fin is depressed extends beyond the third by about one-sixth of its length, its posterior edge sloping backward. Pectorals (17)18(19), reaches nearly to anus. Pelvics I, 5, thoracic, tip reaches about to anus.

Gill Rakers   On first gill arch 36 to 40(41),

Vertebrae   About 26.

446

Scales   Mostly ctenoid but less toothed, or smooth, on belly, chest, and isthmus, covering body and mostly all head and fin rays. Scale rows below lateral line canal (46)47 to 57(58). Pores on lateral line canal (42)43 to 51(52).

Colour   Base colour light pink to red masked by an irregular pattern of darker pigment. Three dark masses on sides, below or on dorsal fin interrupted by an unpigmented band along lateral line canal, a smaller black mass ends at the lateral line canal on the upper part of the caudal peduncle. Upper part of head with broad dark bands radiating back from eye. Outer part of spinous dorsal black, rest the base colour of body. Rayed dorsal interspersed with pink and dark with an intrusion of black body pigment near base, with a pink edge. Anal fin pink with dark streaks between second and third spines. Pectorals pink, the colour obscured distally by dusky markings. Pelvics same shade as adjacent body. Peritoneum dark brown to jet black.

Size   Total length to 12.5 inches (32.4 cm).

Recognition   Supraocular spines absent. Symphyseal knob weak. Second anal fin spine longer than third. Clear band extending along posterior two-thirds of lateral line canal.

Distribution   From Goose Island Bank, Queen Charlotte Sound, to Unimak Pass, Aleutian Islands, at moderate depths.

References   Quast 1971.

PYGMY ROCKFISH

Sebastes wilsoni (Gilbert 1915)

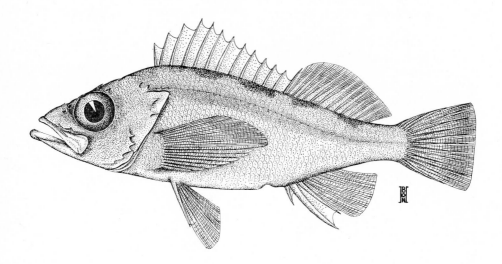

Scientific names from the Greek *sebastos* (magnificent); and Charles Branch Wilson, productive student of crustacean parasites of fishes.

Clemens and Wilby 1946 called this species Wilson's rock-fish *Sebastodes wilsoni*.

Description   Body depth 3.4 to 3.7 into standard length, compressed. Head length 2.7 to 2.9 into standard length, profile slightly arched. Mouth terminal, large, directed forward and upward. Lower jaw projects beyond upper jaw but does not enter dorsal profile, upper jaw extends about to midorbit. A small downward-projecting symphyseal knob may or may not be present. No obviously raised patch of teeth at end of lower jaw. Interorbital space flat or flat and slightly depressed, its width 4.7 to 5.8 into length of head. Eye diameter 3.0 to 3.1 into length of head. Caudal peduncle compressed, its least depth 11.3 to 12.4 into standard length.

Head Spines   Nasals, preoculars, postoculars, tympanics, and parietals all moderately strong. Supraoculars, coronals, and nuchals absent. Parietal ridges moderately high and thin. Five preopercular spines moderately strong and sharp, radially directed, or the upper 3 spines may be directed backward. Both opercular spines long and sharp. No spines on the edge of the suborbital bone but there may be small projections. Supracleithral and cleithral spines strong, the cleithral occasionally doubled. No spines on edge of gill cover.

Fins   Dorsal (1), XIII, 13 or 14, moderately incised and little notched. Caudal truncate or slightly rounded. Anal III, 6(7), the second spine not quite twice as thick as third, more strongly curved, and in the depressed fin extending beyond third by about one-quarter width of orbit, its posterior edge almost vertical with a slight posterior slant. Pectorals (16)17, tips extending beyond tips of pelvics, which in turn reach about to anus. Pelvics I, 5, thoracic.

Gill Rakers   On first gill arch 38 to 43.

Scales   Ctenoid, diagonal rows below lateral line canal 45 to 50. Pores along lateral line canal 37 to 44.[5]

448

Colour   Very pale brown flushed with clear red, 4 dark vague blotches along either side of dorsal fin and extending on fin, a brownish-red stripe below lateral line canal. Peritoneum black.

Size   Length to 8.25 inches (21 cm).

Recognition   Supraocular spine absent. Second anal spine longer than third. Gill rakers 36 to 41. Lateral line canal pores 39 to 41. Body colour red on back and sides, silver below lateral line canal. A marked delineation between dorsal and ventral coloration extending posteriorly from a point midway between the lateral line canal and the base of the pectoral fin to the lateral line canal at the caudal peduncle.

Distribution   Offshore in the eastern Pacific at depths from near surface to 150 fathoms (274 m)[1,3] from Point San Louis, central California[6] to southeastern Alaska.[1] In British Columbia reported from Swiftsure Bank, between Sydney Inlet and Esteban Point, off Quatsino Sound, and northern Hecate Strait at 53.40 N, 131.30 W.[4]

References   1 Alverson, Pruter, and Ronholt 1964; 2 Gilbert 1915; 3 Grinols 1965a; 4 Harling 1966; 5, 6 Phillips 1957 personal communication.

SHARPCHIN ROCKFISH

Sebastes zacentrus (Gilbert 1890)

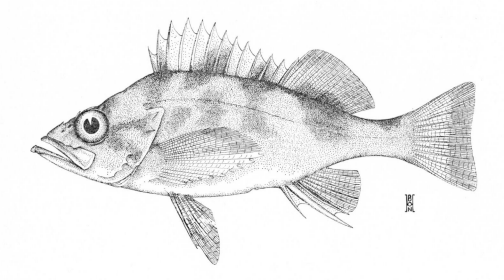

Scientific names from the Greek *se-bastos* (magnificent); and *za* (very) and *kentron* (spine).

This species was referred to as big-eyed rock-fish *Sebastodes zacentrus*, in Clemens and Wilby 1946.

Description   Body depth 2.7 to 3.2 into standard length. Head with upper profile straight, its length 2.7 to 2.8 into standard length. Mouth terminal, moderate in size. Maxillary extends to midorbit or rear of pupil. Strong symphyseal knob extending mainly forward. Raised patch of teeth on tip of lower jaw tends to fit outside snout. Interorbital space variable but nearly flat, its width 4.5 to 5.6 into length of head. Eye diameter in length of head 2.9 to 3.4. Caudal peduncle 10.3 to 11.0 into standard length.

Head Spines   Nasal, preocular, postocular, tympanic, and parietal spines all present, strong,

and sharp. Supraocular, coronal, and nuchal spines usually absent. Parietal ridges moderately high and thin. Preopercular spines sharp, the upper 2 or 3 sometimes directed backward. Both opercular spines sharp, well developed. Supracleithral and cleithral spines both moderately strong. Lower margin of suborbital bone with 2 moderate, bluntly triangular spines, the posterior one sometimes bifid; a short ridge above these makes a shelf beneath each nostril. Lower edge of gill cover usually without spines.

Fins   Dorsal (1), XIII, (13)14 to 15, only slightly notched, moderately incised. Caudal slightly to moderately indented. Anal III, 7(8), posterior edge almost vertical, second spine twice as thick as third in large fish and extending beyond it in the depressed fin. Pectorals 17(18), with 8(9) unbranched. Pelvics I, 5, thoracic. Tips of pectorals extend to tips of pelvics, reaching anus in small specimens but not in larger fish.

Gill Rakers   On first gill arch 31 to 37.

Scales   Ctenoid, 43 to 50 diagonal rows below lateral line canal (in California). The number is higher in Gulf of Alaska specimens (45–59). Pores along lateral line canal 39 to 45.

Colour   Light red with (or without) vague dark brown irregular patches on back. Yellow-red on sides. Usually a forked dark bar extends backward from the rear of the orbit. Peritoneum black.

Size   Length reaches 13 inches (33 cm).

Recognition   Supraocular spine absent. Second anal fin spine longer than third.

Suborbital bone forms shelf below nostrils. (Very similar to *Sebastes variegatus*.)

Distribution   San Diego, California,[3] to the Gulf of Alaska off Sanak Islands 54.13 N, 161.37 W.[1] In British Columbia it is recorded from Burrard Inlet, Hardy Bay, Hope Island, Cape Scott, and Dixon Entrance.[2,4]

References   1 Alverson, Pruter, and Ronholt 1964; 2 Hitz, Johnson, and Pruter 1961; 3 Phillips 1957; 4 Westrheim 1965.

SHORTSPINE THORNYHEAD

Sebastolobus alascanus Bean 1890

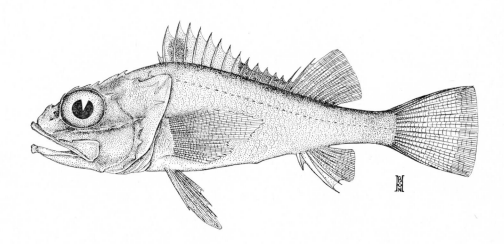

Scientific names from the Greek *sebastos* (magnificent) and *lobos* (lobe — of pectoral fin); and Alaska.

Clemens and Wilby 1961 called this species spinycheek rockfish which in 1946 they spelled spiny-cheeked rock-fish. It has

also been called shortspine channel rockfish.

Description   Body elongate, depth 3.6 to 4.3 into standard length. Head length 2.2 to 2.5 into standard length, upper

451

profile convex. Mouth terminal, large. Jaws about even. Upper jaw extending about to posterior rim of orbit. Median notch in premaxillaries leaving a notch as seen either from in front or above. Symphyseal knob small, rather sharp, and directed downward. Eye large, oval, its length 2.9 to 3.7 into length of head. Interorbital space at mid-orbits narrow, 9.1 to 10.8 into length of head, strongly and evenly concave. Caudal peduncle relatively long and slender, its least depth 10.2 to 12.5 into standard length.

Head Spines   Nasal, preocular, supraocular, postocular, tympanic, parietal, and nuchal spines present, strong, and sharp. Spines coalesced into sharp ridges. Coronal spine absent. Five preopercular spines strong and sharp with the uppermost longest and sharpest, sometimes seemingly doubled by proximity of the last spine of the spiny suborbital ridge. Preopercular spines radially directed. Two long, strong opercular spines. Cleithral and supracleithral spines strong. Lower margin of the postorbital bone with 2 triangular spines, the anterior one directed outward and the posterior one directed down. No spine on the lower edge of the gill cover.

Fins   Dorsal (1), (XV)XVI(XVII), 8 or 9, deeply notched and incised, the fourth or fifth spine longest with the longest spine about 3.8 into length of head. Caudal slightly rounded. Anal III, (4)5; the second spine twice as thick as the third but, with the fin depressed, barely reaching its tip or extending beyond it by one-quarter orbit; posterior edge truncate or nearly so, and almost vertical. Pectorals 22 or 23, tip extending well beyond tip of pelvics and about even with the anus, the lower 6 or 7 rays are exserted and flattened, constituting a recognizable section of the fin. Pelvics I, 5, thoracic, the spine and anterior rays coalesced to form a massive appendage.

Gill Rakers   On first gill arch 18 to 23.

Scales   Ctenoid, moderate in size, in 35 to 46 diagonal rows below the lateral line canal, none on branchiostegal membranes. Lateral line canal slopes downward. Pores along lateral line canal 29 to 33.[4]

Colour   Brilliant red (translucent in life) with some black on fins, usually 1 or 2 black blotches on membrane of spinous dorsal. Peritoneum white with black dots, darker in small specimens.

Size   Length to 29.4 inches (75 cm).

Recognition   Notable for the strong spiny ridges on the head, the pectoral fin in two sections, the broadly notched and incised dorsal fin with more than 13 spines and with the fourth or fifth ray longest.

Life History   Oviparous. Eggs, presumably of *S. alascanus,* float in masses of various sizes and shapes. Frequently the masses are bilobed with the lobes 6 inches (15 cm) to 2 feet (61 cm) in length, consisting of hollow conical sheaths containing a single layer of eggs in a gelatinous matrix. The masses are transparent and not readily observed in the daylight but may be seen under artificial lights. Eggs are 1.2 to 1.4 millimeters in diameter with a 0.2 millimeter oil globule. They move freely in the matrix. Complete hatching time is unknown but is more than 10 days. Three-day-old larvae are about 3 millimeters long. Both eggs and larvae float to the surface in sea water.[3]

Distribution   From Baja California[6] to the Bering Sea as far as the Commander Islands, through southern and northern California, Oregon, Washington, and Alaska.[2] Reported from the Okhotsk Sea[5] but not known from off the Asian mainland.[1] The species favours quite deep water, 50 to 800 fathoms (92–1460 m), but less deep than *S. altivelis.* It is common off British Columbia in waters of suitable depth, including those of Juan de Fuca Strait, Strait of Georgia, and Queen Charlotte Sound.

References   1 Barsukov 1964; 2 Grinols 1965a; 3 Pearcy 1962; 4 Phillips 1957; 5 Shmidt 1950; 6 Wilimovsky 1954. See also Hubbs 1926b.

LONGSPINE THORNYHEAD

Sebastolobus altivelis Gilbert 1893

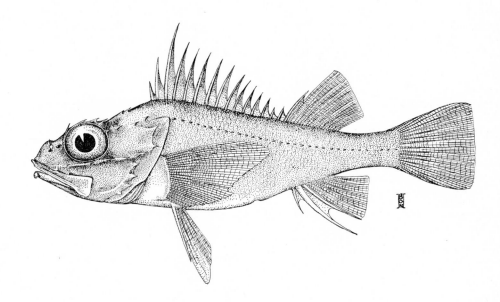

Scientific names from the Greek *sebastos* (magnificent) and *lobos* (lobe — of pectoral fin); and the Latin *altus* (high) and *velum* (sail — dorsal fin).

Description   Body elongate, depth 3.4 to 4.1 into standard length. Head length 2.3 to 2.5 into standard length, upper profile convex. Mouth terminal, large. Upper jaw overhanging lower jaw, extending about to rear of pupil. Median notch in premaxillaries leaving a notch as seen from either in front or above. Symphyseal knob small and directed forward. Eye large, oval, its length 2.8 to 3.2 into length of head. Interorbital space at midorbit 8.5 to 11.1 into length of head, strongly concave, low frontal ridges on either side of median groove. Caudal peduncle least depth 8.7 to 11.3 into standard length.

Head Spines   Nasal, preocular, supraocular, postocular, tympanic, parietal, and nuchal spines present and sharp, directed backwards, some in continuous ridges. Coronal absent. Five preopercular spines strong and sharp, radially directed. Two opercular spines, long, strong, and sharp. Cleithral and supracleithral spines well developed and sharp. Lower margin of suborbital with 2 triangular spines. Well-developed suborbital ridges with sharp spines, the last in line with the upper preopercular spine. No spine on lower edge of gill cover.

Fins   Dorsal (1), XV(XVI) 8 to 9(10), deeply and broadly notched and incised, the third spine longest and its length about 2.5 into length of head. Caudal barely rounded. Anal III, (4)5(6); the second spine about twice as thick as third, its tip reaching beyond tip of third about to end of soft rays when the fin is depressed; the posterior edge truncate, vertical or sloping slightly posteriorly. Pectorals 22 to 24, extending well beyond tips of pelvics and reaching anus, lower 6 to 7 rays expanded and lengthened to form a recognizable lobe. Pelvics I, 5, thoracic, spine and first 3 rays stoutly joined to form a strong unit.

Gill Rakers   On first gill arch 21 to 26.

453

Scales   Ctenoid, large, in 32 to 38 diagonal rows below lateral line canal. Usually on branchiostegal membranes. Lateral line canal sloping down to caudal peduncle. Pores along lateral line canal 28 to 32. A flaplike cirrus on nares opening.

Colour   Red with some black on fins, black on membrane of spinous dorsal. Peritoneum white with black dots, black in small specimens.

Size   Length to 15 inches (38 cm).

Recognition   Noteworthy for the strong spiny ridge along the suborbital bone, the lobed pectoral fin, the broadly notched dorsal fin with more than 13 spines and a long third spine.

Life History   Oviparous. Some males are mature at 252 millimeters and all at 282 millimeters. Practically all females are mature at 270 millimeters but few much under that length. Off Point Reyes, California, a ripe and running female was recorded on March 17 from 385 fathoms (705 m).

Distribution   From Cape San Lucas, Baja California to the Aleutian Islands at depths from 370 to 1600 meters.[2,3] Common at temperatures of 4.4 to 7.8 C[1] and from (110–199) to 958 fathoms ((200–365) to 1750 m).[2] Off the British Columbia shore from southern Vancouver Island to the Queen Charlotte Islands.[4]

References   1 Barsukov 1964; 2 Grinols 1965a; 3 Phillips 1957; 4 Westrheim 1968. See also Best 1964.

FAMILY ANOPLOPOMATIDAE   SABLEFISHES

The Anoplopomatidae includes two genera from the North Pacific. One species is of moderate size, the other large. They are stream-lined fishes with two dorsal fins and one lateral line canal. The gill membranes are attached to the isthmus. There are no scales on the branchiostegals, and no cirri or ridges on the head. There is a large slit behind the last gill arch. Pelvic fins are thoracic and have one spine and five soft rays. Both species frequent deep water as adults but may be found near surface as juveniles. *Anoplopoma* is a prized commercial species. Skilfish and sablefish or blackcod.

KEY TO THE ANOPLOPOMATIDAE

1   Body slender; spines in dorsal fin 17 to 22; interspace between dorsal fins more than twice diameter of eye; anal fin with 15 to 19 rays, its origin below that of second dorsal fin ....
.... *Anoplopoma fimbria,* Sablefish, p. 455

or 1   Body stout; spines in dorsal fin 12 to 14; interspace between dorsal fins about equal to diameter of eye, or less; anal fin with 11 to 14 rays; its origin posterior to that of second dorsal fin ....
.... *Erilepis zonifer,* Skilfish, p. 458

SABLEFISH

Anoplopoma fimbria (Pallas 1811)

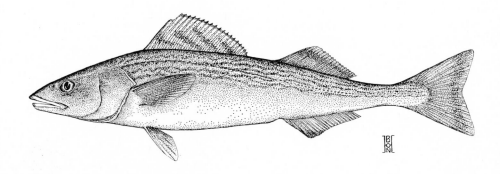

Scientific names from the Greek *anoplis* (unarmed) and *poma* (operculum); and the Latin *fimbria* (fringe).

It seems unlikely that the AFS Committee name sablefish will win acceptance with the Canadian fishing industry. The present name blackcod may well remain current.

Description   Body rather elongate, about 4.5 into standard length and only slightly compressed, the general impression is one of sleekness. Head about 3.5 into standard length, conical. Mouth terminal, moderate, directed slightly upward, lower jaw included. Maxillary narrow, reaching to point below pupil of eye. Teeth fine and in patches, on jaws, vomer, and palatines. Eye small, about 6.5 into length of head. Gill membranes united and joined to isthmus. Caudal peduncle about 21 into standard length, only slightly deeper than length of eye.

455

Fins Dorsal (2), XIX to XXVII, — I, 16 to 20, well separated, interspace twice diameter of eye or more. Caudal prominently forked. Anal III, 15 to 19, mirroring second dorsal. Counts are for British Columbia specimens and differ slightly for other areas. Spines on dorsal and anal fins are frequently embedded and difficult to determine.[24] Pelvics I, 5, thoracic.

Gill Rakers 62 to 65.

Vertebrae 63.3 (British Columbia).

Scales Weakly ctenoid, small, elongate, covering body and head. Lateral line canal moderately high, following dorsal contour to caudal peduncle where it is at midside.

Colour Slaty black or greenish gray on dorsal surface, somewhat reticulate. Light gray on ventral surface. Pale on outer margins of all fins except spinous dorsal which has narrow black margin. Black lining on operculum. "The blackest fish on the dock." Young fish (to 2 feet or 61 cm) much lighter, at about a foot, often green with dark bars on dorsal surface. At 5 inches (127 mm) dark on back as in adult except for light blue along sides.[15] Calico and yellow variants reported from California.[22] Young have relatively large pectoral fins.[9]

Size Length to 40 inches (1 m), (Clemens and Wilby) or 126 pounds (57 kg) (head on, eviscerated).[5]

Recognition Identified by having two medium-sized, almost equal dorsal fins well separated, fine teeth in patches, and more than 15 spines in first dorsal fin.

Life History Spawning apparently in January and February. In February a ripe female observed off Cape St. James at 137 fathoms (250 m). Eggs are pelagic, presumably smooth, without an oil globule, diameter between 2.05 and 2.10 millimeters.[28] Postlarvae about 1 inch long (25 mm) have been found at the surface in May, 100 to 185 miles (161–312 km) off the coast of Oregon. Great schools of juveniles occasionally come into inshore harbours like Nootka and at Monterey.[10] A weight of 1.5 or 2 pounds is reached at 2 to 3 years.[6] At 20 inches (51 cm) fish grow about one pound (454 grams) per year. At the age of 5 years off Oregon male sablefish average 57 centimeters and females 60 centimeters in length.[25] Some tagging records[12] and racial studies based on meristic characters indicate several more or less separate divisions of the stock along the west coast of North America[23,24] but tagging results show extensive migrations,[16,26] and no evident interruption in growth rate by migrations of 2100 to 2700 miles (3400–4300 km) in 6 or 7 years.[21] In captivity sablefish are indiscriminate feeders. They have been observed to feed actively on saury and blue lanternfish attracted to lights on a ship.[14] Other observations indicate food as crustaceans, worms, and small fishes.

Distribution Cedros Island, Baja California through the intervening offshore waters to Alaska, the Bering Sea,[5,13] Pribilof Islands,[3] Kamchatka,[6] and off Hokkaido, Japan.[19,20] Adults in commercial quantities are most abundant in water deeper than 200 fathoms[2] and down to 500 fathoms (366–915 m).[8] Partly grown individuals are commonly encountered in shallower water including the Strait of Georgia, Puget Sound, and Juan de Fuca Strait.[11] Evidently sablefish move into very deep water during the winter months.[1]

Utilization The sablefish is highly regarded as a fish for smoking in Canada and most of the product is used in this way. Fish are caught mainly by longlining and by trawling in deep water. In millions of pounds (454 metric tons), the annual Canadian catch in recent years has been:[17,18]

1931–35	0.6
1936–40	1.0
1941–45	1.9
1946–50	1.9
1951–55	1.4
1956–60	0.8
1961–65	0.8
1966	1.4
1967	0.9
1968	0.9
1969	0.8
1970	0.5

The Canadian catch is only a small part of the total. The United States landings were about six times the Canadian (in 1967). They were greatly exceeded by Japanese catches. USSR landings from the northern part of the range (Bering Sea) were reported as 38 million pounds (17,000 metric tons) in 1967.[5]

The livers are sources of oil rich in vitamins A and D.[4] In California most of the catch is sold fresh.[27]

It appears that off the southern part of British Columbia where trawlers and longliners combine in exploitation of sable-fish, the stock is being definitely overfished. Elsewhere further from market the fishery is in better condition.[7,18]

The sablefish reacts well to being confined and as it is a valuable species may lend itself to profitable culture.

References   1 Alverson 1960; 2 Alverson, Pruter, and Ronholt 1964; 3 Andriashev 1937; 4 Bailey, Carter, and Swain 1952; 5 Bell personal communication; 6 Bell and Gharrett 1945; 7 Bell and Pruter 1958; 8 Bourne and Pope 1969; 9 Brock 1940; 10 Cox 1948; 11 DeLacy, Dryfoos, and Miller 1963; 12 Edson 1954; 13 Grinols 1965a; 14 Grinols and Gill 1968; 15 Heyamoto 1962; 16 Holmberg and Jones 1954; 17 Ketchen and Forrester 1954; 18 Larkin and Ricker 1964; 19 Matsubara 1955; 20 Nikol'skii 1961; 21 Pasquale 1964; 22, 23 Phillips 1952; 1958a; 24 Phillips, Clothier, and Fry 1954; 25, 26 Pruter 1954, 1959; 27 Roedel 1953b; 28 Thompson 1941; The Pacific Marine Commission in 1954 distributed as Bulletin 3 a compilation of reports on the Pacific sablefish with statistical tables and fishing surveys.

SKILFISH

Erilepis zonifer (Lockington 1880)

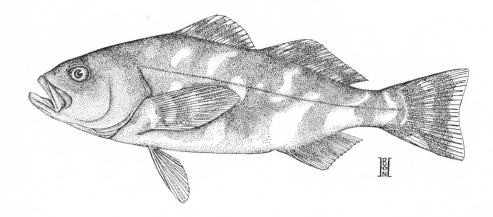

Scientific names from the Greek *eri* (very) and *lepis* (scaley); and the Latin *zona* (zone) and *fero* (to bear).

Description Body depth 3 to 4 into standard length, moderately compressed. Mouth terminal, moderate in size, directed slightly upward with the lower jaw protruding slightly. Upper jaw reaching about to point below posterior edge of eye. Snout blunt, about 3.5 into length of head. Teeth sharp, conical in 2 rows in lower jaw and in a band, broadest medially in the upper. Interorbital space broad, raised, flat, its width about 2.5 into length of head. Eye drop-shaped with narrow portion forward, its long diameter 5.5 to 6.1 into length of head. Gill membranes attached to isthmus. Branchiostegals 6, covered with scales. Caudal peduncle moderate and compressed, its least depth 3.5 into length of head.

Fins Dorsal (2), XII to XIV — I to II, 15 to 17, 2 fins separated by about two-thirds long axis of eye. Spines in rayed part may be buried and difficult to find. When depressed the spinous dorsal is retracted into a shallow groove. Caudal shallowly forked. Anal III, 11 to 14 (here again it may be difficult to find all the spines), origin posterior to origin of rayed dorsal, but fin not extending as far back. Pectorals 17, rounded. Pelvics I, 5, thoracic.

Scales Ctenoid, covering body, head, and inner ends of fin rays on all soft-rayed fins. Lateral line canal almost straight. Oblique rows of scales above lateral line canal 122 to 134.

Colour In young, backs and most of sides grayish blue or green with striking blotches and intrusions from the pale midventral line of light colour. Similar barring on all fins. Very variable, in the aquarium darker at night. In general darkens with age so that on older fish back and dorsal parts of sides are uniformly almost black, with soiled white on margin of scales.[9]

Size Reaches at least 5 feet 10 inches (178 cm) and 200 pounds (91 kg)[6] but may get much larger.

Recognition Two dorsal fins placed closely together, the absence of spines on the head, and scales on the rayed fins.

Life History   The young of this characteristically deepwater fish are on occasion encountered in numbers near the surface. They have been observed repeatedly and captured by angling at the offshore weather station.[5] They thrive in captivity. In the Vancouver Public Aquarium one grew from 16 to 30 inches (40–76 cm) in 2.5 years and another from 10 to 40 inches (25–102 cm) in 10 years.[9]

Distribution   In deep water from central California (Monterey Bay, Moss Landing[5]) through Washington, British Columbia and Alaska,[1,7,8] and offshore[3] to the Kuril Islands, Kamchatka, Hokkaido,[4] and central Honshu.[2,7]

References   1 Grinols 1965a; 2 Matsubara 1955; 3 Neave 1959; 4 Okada 1955; 5, 6 Phillips 1966, 1967a; 7, 8 Thompson 1916, 1917a; 9 Vancouver Public Aquarium 1969.

FAMILY HEXAGRAMMIDAE   GREENLINGS

The Hexagrammidae is a small family of moderate-sized and moderately elongate fishes of the North Pacific. There are a suborbital stay and six branchiostegal rays. The posterior nostril is reduced or absent. Teeth are small and the gill membranes joined except in *Ophiodon* where canine teeth are prominent and the gill membranes are separated. There is a large slit behind the last gill arch. Pelvic fins are thoracic. Several species have multiple lateral line canals on each side. They are common bottom fishes of shallow water, although *Ophiodon* sometimes goes to considerable depths. *Ophiodon* is a commercially important species but the others, although reputed to be of good flavour, are not marketed commercially. *Zaniolepis* is sometimes assigned to the separate family Zaniolepidae because of its comblike scales, the unperforated scales in the lateral line canal, the difference in the number of suborbital bones, the arrangement of the supports for the anterior dorsal fin spine, and in other ways. Greenlings and lingcod.

KEY TO THE HEXAGRAMMIDAE

1   One lateral line canal on each side of body 5

or 1   More than 1 lateral line canal on each side of body ....
.... Genus *Hexagrammos* 2

2   Lateral line canals on each side of body 4 ....
.... *Hexagrammos octogrammus,* Masked greenling, p. 464

or 2   Lateral line canals on each side of the body 5 3

3   Multifid cirrus above each eye prominent; another cirrus, very small, in a slight depression midway between middle of front of eye and origin of dorsal fin; short stout spine closely applied to first ray of anal fin ....
.... *Hexagrammos decagrammus,* Kelp greenling, p. 461

or 3   Multifid cirrus above each eye present; no cirrus near occiput; no spine before anal fin 4

4   **Cirrus above eye small,** its length less than half diameter of eye; caudal peduncle slender, its depth 3 or more into length of head; first lateral line canal short, not extending beyond spinous portion of dorsal fin; fourth lateral line canal short, not extending beyond middle of pelvic fin; caudal fin slightly indented ....
.... *Hexagrammos stelleri,* Whitespotted greenling, p. 466

or 4   Cirrus above eye large, slender, densely fringed, its length equal to or longer than diameter of eye; caudal peduncle stout, its depth about 2 into length of head; first lateral line canal long, extending beyond middle of rayed portion of dorsal fin; fourth lateral line canal long, extending to about middle of anal fin; caudal fin slightly rounded ....
.... *Hexagrammos lagocephalus,* Rock greenling, p. 463

5   Maxillary not reaching anterior margin of eye; vertical dark bars on sides of body and caudal fin ....
.... *Oxylebius pictus,* Painted greenling, p. 470

or 5   Maxillary reaching point well behind anterior margin of eye; no distinct bars on sides of body 6

6   Anterior spines of dorsal fin elongate, the second to nearly half length of body; teeth on jaws small ....
.... *Zaniolepis latipinnis,* Longspine combfish, p. 471

or 6   Anterior spines of dorsal fin not elongate; teeth on jaws enlarged, canine
.... *Ophiodon elongatus,* Lingcod, p. 467

KELP GREENLING

Hexagrammos decagrammus (Pallas 1810)

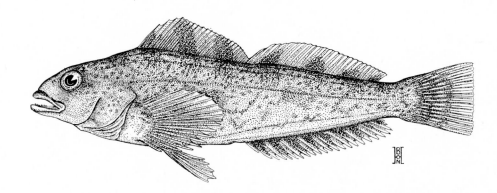

Scientific names from the Greek *hex* (six) and *gramma* (line); and *deca* (ten) and *gramma* (line).

The species was recorded by Clemens and Wilby 1946 as *Chiropsis decagrammus* (Pallas). An early name used by J. K. Lord 1866 was chirus.

Description   Body elongate, its depth about 4 into standard length, rather chunky, and only moderately compressed. Head conical, somewhat compressed, its length about 3.6 into standard length. Mouth terminal, small, directed forward. Upper jaw just about reaching point below anterior margin of the orbit. Snout bluntly rounded. Lips thick. Teeth moderate, in rows on sides of jaws and patches at the tip. Interorbital space gently rounded, its width about 5 into length of head, slightly less than the length of the eye which is deeper than long. Opercular membrane broadly joined and free of isthmus. Branchiostegals 6. Caudal peduncle compressed, its least depth 10.5 into standard length.

Fins   Dorsal (1), XXI or XXII, 24, strongly notched, caudal broadly rounded or truncate. Anal I, 23 to 24, the spine closely applied to first ray. Pectorals 19, rays flattened, membrane between rays deeply incised, especially those between the last 7. Pelvics I, 5, thoracic, rays flattened.

Scales   Small, ctenoid, covering body and upper part of head. Lateral line canals 5 on each side: (1) from occipital region close to dorsal fin ending at point below middle of rayed portion, (2) from occipital region to base of caudal fin, (3) from immediately above opercle to base of caudal fin, (4) from edge of gill opening near pectoral fin passing above pelvic and terminating near end of anal fin, and (5) from isthmus as a single line branching a little beyond halfway from pelvic insertion to anus and passing along side of anal fin to base of caudal. A cirrus above and behind each eye, lying back flat when not erected. Another pair of cirri on occiput between anterior edge of eye and insertion of dorsal in a slight pit. These cirri are small and difficult to make out (not shown in drawing).

Colour   Variable in pattern and hue. In male, brownish olive, often tinged with blue or copper. Blue spots on head and anterior part of body, each surrounded by a reddish brown ring of small spots, mottled brown on dorsal fin, dusky blue on pelvic and anal fins, brown to black on pectoral fins spotted with white giving appearance of transverse bars. At spawning time all the blue concentrated at the head and tends to disappear from the rest of the body. In female, from light

461

brown with small reddish spots to light blue with rows of round orange spots, red to orange on dorsal fin, clouded with blue, orange or pale yellow on pectoral fins without markings. In both sexes an ocellus at the posterior end of the rayed portion of the dorsal fin.

Size   Length to 21 inches (53 cm).

Recognition   Distinguished by the two pairs of cirri, the single small spine at the front of the anal fin, and the ocellus on the posterior portion of the dorsal fin. (Note colour illustration, Plate III.)

Life History   Spawning takes place in October and November when pale blue eggs are laid in large masses. The food consists of worms, crustaceans, and small fishes. In late spring in the southern Strait of Georgia the food of young individuals 17 to 60 millimeters (0.6–1.4 inches) taken at the surface is mainly copepods with some amphipods and other crustaceans, *Oiko-pleura,* and young fishes, especially walleye pollock.[1,2,3,4,5] Small kelp greenling, 1 to 3 inches (25–76 mm) in length are commonly taken on the high seas in the Gulf of Alaska. It is commonly found in the stomachs of steelhead and salmons.

Distribution   From southern California (San Pedro, Los Angeles Harbor, and Santa Monica Bay)[6] to southeastern Alaska and through the Aleutian Islands.[7] Found abundantly along rocky shores throughout coastal British Columbia.

Utilization   The flesh is very palatable but is seldom brought to market by commercial fisheries.

References   1, 2, 3 Barraclough 1967a, b, c; 4, 5 Robinson, Barraclough, and Fulton 1968a, b; 6 Roedel 1953b; 7 Wilimovsky 1964.

ROCK GREENLING

Hexagrammos lagocephalus (Pallas 1810)

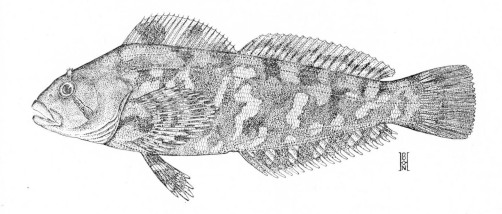

Scientific names from the Greek *hex* (six) and *gramma* (line); and *lagos* (hare) and *cephelos* (head).

Clemens and Wilby in 1946 called this species *Lebius superciliosus* (Pallas), the fringed greenling. In 1961 the scientific name *Hexagrammos superciliosus* (Pallas 1810) was used.[2]

Description Body depth elongate, about 3.7 into standard length, moderately compressed, stout posteriorly. Head, short and bluntly conical, length about 4 into standard length. Mouth terminal, small, directed forward. Upper jaw reaching anterior edge of orbit. Snout curving downward. Lips thick. Teeth small and conical, in rows on sides of jaws, and patches anteriorly. Interorbital space somewhat bowed, and moderate, its width about 3.8 into length of head. Eye rather small, a little longer than wide, its length about 5 into length of head. Opercular membranes broadly joined and free from isthmus. Branchiostegals 6. Caudal peduncle compressed, its least depth about 10 into standard length.

Fins Dorsal (1), XX or XXI, 23 or 24, barely joined. Caudal flatly rounded. Anal 21 or 22, distinctly emarginate throughout. Pectorals 19, lower 7 rays emarginate. Scales on rays of central part of fin for about one-quarter of the length. Pelvics I, 5, thoracic.

Scales Rather small, ctenoid, covering body and top of head, cycloid on cheeks and opercles. Lateral line canals 5 on each side: (1) from occipital region close to dorsal fin ending below middle of rayed portion of dorsal, (2) from occipital region to base of caudal fin, (3) from immediately above opercle to base of caudal fin, (4) from gill opening below pectoral above pelvic to a point above posterior half of anal fin, and (5) median from isthmus to point behind the pelvic fins where it branches, coming close to the fourth lateral line canal and near the anus, and then passing close to the anal fin as far as the base of the caudal fin. A large pinnate cirrus over each eye. A row of pores along lower jaw.

Colour Extremely variable. Ground colour usually dark green or brown with coarse red or light blotches running down and back, 2 lines of red radiating back and down from the eye. A prominent dark spot above the angle of the operculum. Bars of dark colour on spinous dorsal, anal, pectoral, and pelvic fins, and mottling on caudal and rayed dorsal.

463

Size   Length to 24 inches (61 cm).

Recognition   Noted for the large cirri over the eyes and the dark spot above the base of each eye.

Life History   A 66-millimeter (2.6-inch) specimen from Saanich Inlet was found to have eaten euphausiids.[1]

Distribution   Southern California (where it is not common) to the Bering Sea[3] and Kuril Islands. Generally distributed throughout coastal British Columbia, including the west coast of Vancouver Island, the Queen Charlotte Islands, and the Strait of Georgia.

References   1 Barraclough, Robinson, and Fulton 1968; 2 Quast 1965; 3 Roedel 1953b.

MASKED GREENLING

Hexagrammos octogrammus (Pallas 1811)

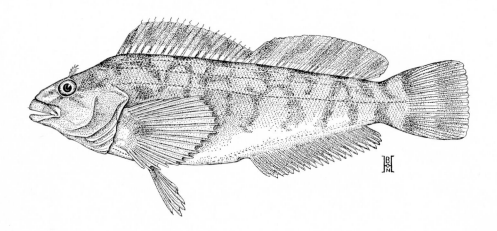

Scientific names from the Greek *hex* (six) and *gramma* (line); and *octo* (eight) and *gramma* (line).

Description   Body elongate, its depth about 4.0 into standard length, generally stout anteriorly and little compressed. Head conical, slightly compressed, its length about 3.9 into standard length. Mouth terminal, small, directed forward. Upper jaw not quite reaching anterior margin of orbit. Snout rounded. Lips thick. A line of small pores under lower jaw. Teeth moderate in size, in rows in both jaws, and smaller in patches in anterior roof of mouth behind main row. Interorbital space slightly raised, almost flat near midline, gently rounded, its width about 5.0 into length of head. Eye oval, its length about 5.7 into length of head. Opercular membranes widely joined at isthmus. Branchiostegals 6. Caudal peduncle compressed, its least depth about 10.5 into standard length.

Fins   Dorsal (1), (XVII)XIX(XX), 22 to 25, moderately notched. Caudal rounded with a suggestion of 2 lobes. Anal 22 to 25. Pectorals (18)19, rays flattened, membranes between rays moderately incised, deeply so between the last 6 rays. Pelvics I, 5, thoracic.

Scales   Small, ctenoid, covering body and dorsal part of head, leaving bare snout and lower part of head except for small patches of scales behind the tips of the maxillary, on the bases of pectoral and caudal fins. Lateral line canals 4 on each side: (1) close on either side of dorsal fin from first spine to about fifth to last ray, (2) close below and parallel to the last line from anterior to the dorsal origin to the base of the caudal fin, (3) from the top of the gill opening above midside to the base of the caudal fin, and (4) from the throat as a single median line to a point beyond the pelvic insertion where it divides, extending on either side of the anal fin to near the end of the caudal peduncle. A flat, black, pinnate cirrus is over each eye and lies back when not erected.

Colour   Variable, green-brown, paler below; dark saddles and spots along dorsal midline, some extending beyond the midlateral line: a few black flecks on the sides, and darker spots on the sides behind the upper edge of the gill cover. In highly coloured individuals the outer parts of the dorsal and anal fins are dark, the anal almost black with a pale margin, and the pelvic fins dark. In others black pigment is confined to diagonal bands across the fins.

Size   Reaches a length of at least 11 inches (28 cm).

Recognition   Notable for the smallish mouth and teeth, the single large cirrus over the eye, and the four lateral line canals.

Distribution   Northern British Columbia, through southeastern Alaska[2] and Gulf of Alaska to the Okhotsk Sea.[3] Known from British Columbia only as young. Four specimens under 2 inches (51 cm) in length were collected at Qlawdzeet Anchorage, Stephens Island (54.12 N, 130.42 W) in northern British Columbia. Ray and spine counts agree with those for specimens obtained in Alaska.[1]

References   1 Peden 1971; 2 Quast 1968; 3 Wilimovsky 1954.

WHITESPOTTED GREENLING

Hexagrammos stelleri Tilesius 1809

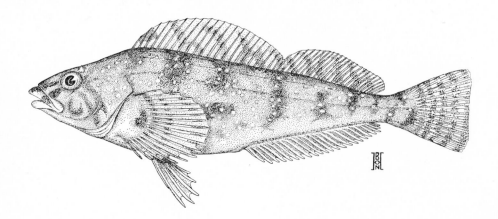

Scientific names from the Greek *hex* (six) and *gramma* (line); and G. W. Steller, naturalist with C. J. Bering's voyage of discovery.

Description   Body elongate, its depth about 4.5 into standard length, compressed. Head short, rather compressed, conical, its length about 3.7 into standard length. Mouth terminal, small, directed forward. Upper jaw not reaching anterior margin of the orbit. Snout gently curving downward to upper jaw. Lips thick. Teeth small, conical, in rows along jaws but in patches inside tips of jaws. Interorbital space raised above edge of orbit but flat, its width about 4.2 into length of head. Eye longer than deep, its length about 5 into length of head. Opercular membrane broadly joined at base and free of isthmus. Branchiostegals 6. Caudal peduncle compressed, its least depth about 14 into standard length.

Fins   Dorsal (1), XXII to XXV, 19 to 24, moderately notched. Caudal slightly forked. Anal 23 to 25, slightly emarginate. Pectorals 19, emarginate, especially so between last 6 rays. Pelvics I, 5, thoracic, all rays flattened and fleshy.

Scales   Small, ctenoid on body and top of head, cycloid on cheeks and opercle, behind eye, and about midline. Lateral line canals 5 on each side: (1) from occipital region close to dorsal fin to point below midpoint of spinous part, (2) occipital region to base of caudal fin, (3) from immediately above opercle to caudal fin, (4) from gill opening below pectoral fin to point above pelvic fin, and (5) from isthmus to behind origin of pelvics, then branching and continuing on either side of the anal fin to the base of the caudal. A moderately large pinnate cirrus which fits backward flat against the head above and behind the eye when not erected. There is a row of small pores on the lower jaw and preopercle.

Colour   Variable. Light brown to green, sometimes tinged with pale red, barred or blotched with dusky, rather small white spots conspicuous on body. Anal fin yellowish. Dark bars or rows of dark spots on all fins but pelvics.

Size   Length to 16 inches (41 cm).

Recognition   Recognizable by the white spots on the sides, the short first and fourth lateral line canals and the slender caudal peduncle.

466

Life History   The food consists of worms, crustaceans, and small fishes. In Saanich Inlet young, up to 60 millimeters (2.5 inches), were found to be eating such crustaceans as copepods (mainly), amphipods, decapod larvae, ostracods, and barnacle larvae, with fish eggs, and *Oikopleura*.[1,2] The eggs are blue. Spawning occurs in April. Young grow quickly, from 30 to 40 millimeters in May to 90 to 120 millimeters in August.[4]

Distribution   Northern California (where it is uncommon)[7] through Washington,[3] British Columbia, the Aleutian Islands[10] to the Bering Sea,[9] Kamchatka,[6] Tatar Strait, Hokkaido,[8] and Peter the Great Bay.[5]

Generally distributed through coastal British Columbia along rocky shores.

Utilization   The flesh is of good quality but is seldom handled commercially.

References   1 Barraclough and Fulton 1968; 2 Barraclough, Robinson, and Fulton 1968; 3 DeLacy, Dryfoos, and Miller 1963; 4 Lamb personal communication; 5 Matsubara 1955; 6 Popov 1933; 7 Roedel 1953b; 8 Shmidt 1950; 9, 10 Wilimovsky 1954, 1964.

LINGCOD

Ophiodon elongatus Girard 1854

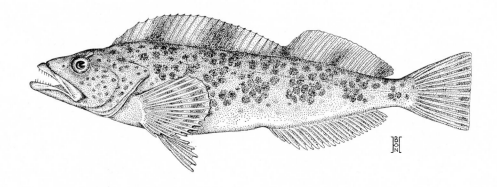

Scientific names ,from the Greek *ophis* (snake) and *odons* (tooth); and the Latin *elongatus* (elongate).

Description   Body depth around 4.5 into standard length, variable, tapering toward caudal peduncle. Head large, conical, depressed, its length about 3 into standard length. Mouth terminal, large with great gape, directed slightly upward. Maxillary extending beyond posterior part of eye. Lower jaw projecting. Teeth large, canine. Eye oval, rather small, length about 6 into length of head. Gill membranes briefly united anteriorly, free from isthmus. Anal papilla on male.

Spines   Preopercular spines 4 to 5.

Fins   Dorsal (1), XXIV to XXVII, 21 to 24, moderately notched, base long, moderately high, spinous part slightly incised. Caudal truncate. Anal III, 21 to 24, base moderately long, spines in adults buried in flesh, the third closely applied to the first ray. Pectorals much expanded. Pelvics I, 5, thoracic.

Vertebrae   55 to 57, mean of 12, 56.[15]

Scales   Cycloid, small, covering body and head. Lateral line canal rather high along body, dropping to midside on the caudal peduncle, pores in its length 154 to 180. Large dark multifid cirrus over each eye.

Colour   Very variable. Bold darker mottling on many shades of brown, gray, or green on back and sides, depending on environment. Paler below. Some, usually smaller, individuals are strongly green with the colour permeating the flesh.

Size   Length to 5 feet (152 cm).

Recognition   Recognizable by its single moderately and once-notched long dorsal fin, large mouth, large teeth, thoracic pelvic fins, and small smooth scales covering body and on the head. (Note colour illustration, Plate I.)

Life History   Spawning takes place from December to March. Females deposit their eggs in crevices or under rocks in shallow water, sometimes in the intertidal zone. The eggs vary around 3.5 millimeters in diameter when water hardened and have tough membranous shells. They adhere strongly to each other and to rocks so that they produce large thick masses up to 30 pounds (13.6 kg) and 2.5 feet (76 cm) of pinkish opalescent eggs. The male guards the eggs against intruders and fans them

with his large pectoral fins. Hatching is progressive with the eggs on the outside of the mass hatching first. The newly hatched young are 7 to 10 millimeters long, they have a bright yellow oil globule near the liver, and blue eyes. They sink to the bottom in strong light. The yolk sac is absorbed in about 10 days. After a few weeks' growth, the young fish are attracted to lights at night. Occasionally they are taken in beach seines on sandy beaches.[29] During April lingcod 0.5 to 2 inches (13–49 mm) long are generally and abundantly distributed through the low salinity water influenced by the Fraser River discharge (including Saanich Inlet) where the food is almost entirely copepods. In May they are less abundant and by July they are no longer encountered.[6,7,8,9,10,25,26] At 1 year of age they average about 10.5 inches (27 cm) in length and by the end of their second year average size in the Strait of Georgia is about 18.5 inches (47 cm).[11,17,20] Later growth in males is at a rate of about 2.7 inches or 1.7 pounds (6.9 cm or 0.8 kg) per year, and for females 3.1 inches or 2.7 pounds (7.9 cm or 1.2 kg). Females reach 36 inches (91 cm) at 10 to 14 years. Males seldom exceed 36 inches.[12] One tagged fish grew 11 pounds in 12 years between tagging and recapture.[4] Males reach maturity at 18 to 20 inches (46–51 cm), females at 27.5 to 30 inches (70–76 cm). Newly maturing females produce (60,000)100,000 to 150,000 eggs. Large females 40 inches (102 cm) in length may produce as many as 500,000 eggs.[3,21,28]

Lingcod show two patterns of movement. Some individuals are obviously quite sedentary, making few, if any, movements. Tagged fish are recaptured at the place of release after years of freedom.[13,19,21] However, there are obviously migratory populations also. Lingcod tagged and returned after being handlined on reefs tended to be returned by handline fishermen. Those tagged from trawl catches tended to be returned by trawlers.

Lingcod are voracious feeders on fishes, including herring and sand lance, when available, and a variety of bottom forms

468

such as flounders, hake, walleye pollock, cod, and rockfishes. They also eat Crustacea and octopus, and are definitely cannibalistic. Juveniles feed extensively on copepods and other small crustaceans.

Distribution   From Ensenada, Baja California[16,27] to Kodiak Island and the Shumagin Islands south of the Alaska Peninsula, well distributed along the coast, from the surface to 230 fathoms (421 m).[18] Most common south of Cape Spencer (Alaska) through British Columbia in the upper 50 fathoms (92 m).[2] Reports of occurrence in the Bering Sea have not been substantiated.

Utilization   The lingcod is highly esteemed as a fresh fish. It supports two well-established fisheries whose catches are supplemented by less productive fishing methods. The traditional handline fishery with a spreader bar from live-well boats produced about six million pounds of fish annually through the efforts of moderately capitalized individualists. They worked mainly in the sheltered waters of the Strait of Georgia and its approaches.[29] Catches were held alive, unfed, until ready for sale, when the fish were slaughtered and shipped immediately as a high grade product. During the late 1940's the more efficient otter trawlers began making substantial landings for the most part with fish dressed and iced immediately on capture. Otter trawlers worked mainly off the west coast of Vancouver Island and in more exposed parts of the coast. Lingcod are taken to smaller extents by longlines, sunken gillnets, and sports gear. The total commercial landings in millions of pounds (454 metric tons) are shown in the following tabulation:[23]

1931–35	6.6
1936–40	7.0
1941–45	8.4
1946–50	8.3
1951–55	5.2
1956–60	6.2
1961–65	4.7
1966	5.0
1967	5.0
1968	6.3
1969	5.0
1970	4.6

Catches reach a peak during the spring months.[1] The livers are a rich source of vitamin A.[5]

Because of the importance of the fishery and conflicts of interest, the lingcod fishery has been examined by biologists. In some areas large numbers of young lingcod are taken in winter trawling operations but this probably does not affect the production of larger fish.[22] Because of fish habits, handlines and trawlers are not in competition at any one time.[13] However, in the Strait of Georgia little advantage in production and considerable loss in efficiency would result from increasing the rate of fishing,[14] and the lingcod population off the south coast of Vancouver Island is probably over fished.[24]

References   1 Alverson 1960; 2 Alverson, Pruter, and Ronholt 1964; 3, 4 Anon 1935b, 1954b; 5 Bailey, Carter, and Swain 1952; 6, 7, 8 Barraclough 1967a, b, c; 9, 10 Barraclough and Fulton 1967, 1968; 11, 12, 13, 14 Chatwin 1954, 1965a, b, 1958; 15 Clothier 1950; 16 Fitch 1949; 17 Forrester 1969b; 18 Grinols 1965a; 19, 20, 21, Hart 1943b, c, 1967; 22 Ketchen 1950a; 23 Larkin and Ricker 1964; 24 Reeves 1966; 25, 26 Robinson, Barraclough, and Fulton 1968a, b; 27 Roedel 1948b; 28 Wendler 1953; 29 Wilby 1937. See also Fraser 1916b.

PAINTED GREENLING

Oxylebius pictus Gill 1862

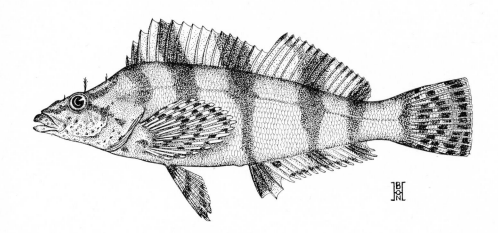

Scientific names from the Greek *oxys* (sharp) and *lepys* (kettle — fish); and the Latin *pictus* (picture).

Description   Body rather elongate, depth about 3.5 into standard length, compressed. Head with snout drawn out, head length about 3 into standard length, compressed. Mouth terminal, small, directed forward. Upper jaw about 3.3 into length of head, not reaching anterior margin of the eye. Lips fleshy, the upper lip well separated from the nasals. Teeth fine. Interorbital space narrow and flat, its width about 7 into length of head. Eye diameter about 5 into length of head. Nostrils single. Gill membranes broadly united and free of isthmus. Branchiostegals 6. Caudal peduncle compressed, its length about 9 into standard length.

Fins   Dorsal (1), XVI, 14 to 16, only slightly notched but the rayed part rather higher than spinous part. Caudal gently rounded. Anal III or IV, 12 or 13, notched between spinous and rayed parts, well incised. Pectorals 15, membrane between lower rays moderately incised. Pelvics I, 5, thoracic.

Scales   Ctenoid, except on cheek where they are cycloid, on head as far as interorbital, moderate, about 76 along midside. Lateral line canal almost straight. Cirri, 2 pairs branched and erect, the larger on the supraorbital, the smaller on the occipital.

Colour   Variable, often golden to tan or gray, prominently marked with about 7 vertical dark reddish brown bars which continue on dorsal and anal fins. Three dark lines radiating from eye, 1 forward to snout, the other 2 diverging backwards. Lines of large dark spots on pelvic fins and tail fin and coarse dark speckling on throat and lower part of head. Some individuals are so dark generally that the dark bars are scarcely distinguishable and have small white flecks indiscriminately over the body.

Size   Length to 10 inches (25 cm).

Recognition   Distinguished by the elongate pointed head with two pairs of cirri, the single lateral line canal, the notched anal fin, and the dark firmly outlined vertical bars crossing the body and unpaired fins.

470

Life History   Infrequently encountered as it does not take bait and lives in sheltered areas. In the aquarium it is observed to hang vertically on steep rock faces confirming observation in nature.[3]

Distribution   Southern California to Queen Charlotte Islands. In British Columbia recorded from Saanich Inlet,[1,2] Departure Bay, Howe Sound, Burrard Inlet, English Bay, Lagoon Bay, and Carmichael Passage of Moresby Island.

References   1 Barraclough, Robinson, and Fulton 1968b; 2 Jordan and Gilbert 1881; 3 Starks 1911.

LONGSPINE COMBFISH

Zaniolepis latipinnis Girard 1857

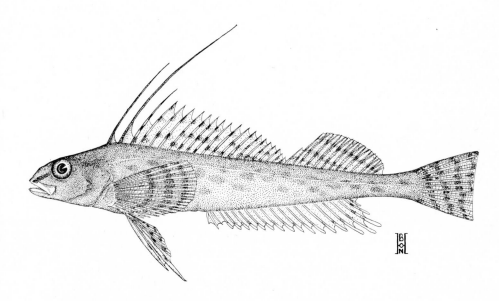

Scientific names from the Greek *zanion* (comb) and *lepis* (scale); and the Latin *latus* (broad) and *pinna* (fin).

Clemens and Wilby 1946 used longspined greenling as the common name for the species.

Description   Body elongate, depth about 5.5 or 6 into standard length, compressed, tapering evenly from immediately behind head to caudal peduncle. Head about 4.5 or 5 into body length, blunt, moderately compressed. Mouth terminal, moderate in size, directed slightly upward, lower jaw included. Snout short. Upper jaw about reaching anterior edge of pupil. Teeth small on jaws and vomer. Interorbital space flat and its width about 5.5 into length of head.

471

Eye large, its length about same as snout and about 3.8 into length of head. Gill membrane fused anteriorly but not connected to isthmus. Branchiostegals 6. Caudal peduncle drawn out and slender, its least depth about 18 into standard length.

Spines   A pair of sharp, low spines on the nasals. Three or four sharp spines directed backward from the lower part of the preoperculum.

Fins   Dorsal (1), XX or XXI — I, 11 or 12, fins joined by membrane and really one fin, but *extremely deeply notched*. Membrane between first and second spine practically non existent, between the second and third very low, and between the third and fourth and thereafter strongly indented. The second spine very long, about twice as long as head. First and third spines also long. Caudal end straight or very slightly forked. Anal III, 16 or 17, slightly notched between spined and rayed parts, rayed parts indented, strongly so at posterior end of fin. Pectorals about 14. Pelvics I, 5, thoracic, spine strong, first 2 rays much elongated, extending beyond anus.

Vertebrae   40 or 41.[1]

Scales   Very small, ctenoid, well seated, covering head except snout. Lateral line canal somewhat high following dorsal contour of the body throughout its length. A few filamentous cirri are on anterior end of sides in a few specimens.

Colour   Olive green to light yellowish brown, dark spots on the body and dark bars or spots on all the fins. Dark streak from front of eye to tip of snout.

Size   Length to 12 inches (30.5 cm).

Recognition   Noteworthy for the long, excessively incised rays in the spinous dorsal, the long broad development of the first rays of the pelvic fin with the first supported by a strong spine, the fine, firmly attached scales, and the long taper of the slender body down to a shallow caudal peduncle. Cirri over the eye are absent or much reduced.

Distribution   Southern California to Vancouver Island. Canadian records for Alberni, Victoria, Saanich Inlet, Nanaimo, Nanoose Bay and Fanny Bay.[2]

References   1 Clothier 1950; 2 Fannin 1898.

FAMILY COTTIDAE

SCULPINS

The Cottidae is a large circumboreal family of bottom dwelling fishes displaying a wide variety of forms. The bodies of most species are stout anteriorly tapering off to rather narrow caudal peduncles, but some are generally slender. They range from small to moderate size. There are six branchiostegal rays in most but *Psychrolutes* has seven and by some is regarded as belonging to a separate family. There is a suborbital stay. Eyes are usually large and placed high on the head. Scales may nearly cover the body, be in rows or patches, or be absent except for the lateral line canal. In some species scales are thickened or otherwise modified. Most species have cirri, some in great numbers. There are spinous and rayed sections of the dorsal fin, usually but not always separated. There are no spines in the anal fin. Pectoral fins are expanded and fanlike. Pelvic fins are small, thoracic, and consist of one spine and two to five soft rays, or in one species are completely absent. Most species are in shallow water and cottids may be abundant in the intertidal zone; some occur in moderately deep water; and several species are well established in fresh water far from the sea. A general name for the family is sculpins but there may be special names for striking common species.

KEY TO THE COTTIDAE

1   Pelvic fins absent .... *Ascelichthys rhodorus,* Rosylip sculpin, p. 484

or   1   Pelvic fins present 2

2   Pectoral fins united along ventral edges ....
                          Synchirus gilli, Manacled sculpin, p. 542

or   2   Pectoral fins separate 3

3   Length of head about half standard length ....
                   Rhamphocottus richardsoni, Grunt sculpin, p. 538

or   3   Length of head less than half standard length 4

4   Body not rising abruptly behind head; caudal fin symmetrical or nearly so; generally lacking the combination of characters below 6

or   4   Body rising steeply from occiput to dorsal origin; spinous dorsal fin with membrane to end of spines and higher than rayed fin (in *N. oculofasciatus* very steeply and very much higher); scales as minute spines embedded in papillae; 2 lower preopercular spines present, but reduced; diagonal bar running down and backward through eye ....
                                 Genus *Nautichthys* 5

5   Dorsal fin with 27 to 30 soft rays; lateral line canal pores 41 to 45; spinous dorsal height more than twice length of its base; caudal fin more developed dorsally .... *Nautichthys oculofasciatus,* Sailfin sculpin, p. 522

or   5   Dorsal fin with 19 to 21 soft rays; lateral line canal pores 35 to 38; spinous dorsal height less than length of base; caudal fin nearly symmetrically developed .... *Nautichthys robustus,* Smallsail sculpin, p. 525

6   Head very broad and depressed, covered with high, blunt, bony projections; mouth very large and directed strongly and obliquely upward; spinous part of dorsal fin deeply incised between spines; large fleshy pennantlike flaps near tips of spines ...... *Hemitripterus bolini,* Bigmouth sculpin, p. 505

or   6   Head, mouth, and dorsal fin not so modified 7

7   Body robust, or slender, or more or less tadpolelike, not deep and compressed; no large cirri on snout and lower jaw 9

or   7   Body deep and moderately compressed; long slender cirri on snout and lower jaw .... Genus *Blepsias* 8

8   Spinous dorsal fin notched between third and sixth spines; smooth silvery white spots below lateral line canal on anterior part of body, and light spots on dorsal fins ....
                     Blepsias cirrhosus, Silverspotted sculpin, p. 489

or   8   Spinous dorsal fin with membrane moderately incised, but not notched; body and fins without prominent bare light spots ....
                         Blepsias bilobus, Crested sculpin, p. 487

	9	Scales or pores on lateral line canal more than 25 10
or	9	Scales or pores on lateral line canal less than 25 39

	10	Dorsal fins 2, the first spinous, the second rayed 13
or	10	Dorsal fin 1, notched between spinous and rayed parts, and the spinous part separately notched 11

	11	Gill membranes free of isthmus, scales deeply embedded and not readily visible; pelvic fins with 1 spine and 5 soft rays .... *Scorpaenichthys marmoratus,* Cabezon, p. 540
or	11	Gill membranes fused to isthmus; bands of scales above and below lateral line canal; pelvic fins with 1 spine and 4 soft rays .... Genus *Hemilepidotus* 12

	12	Bands of scales between dorsal fin and lateral line canal with 6 or 7 rows at the widest part; gill membranes widely joined to the isthmus .... *Hemilepidotus spinosus,* Brown Irish lord, p. 504
or	12	Bands of scales between dorsal fin and lateral line canal with only 4 rows at the widest part; gill membranes narrowly joined to the isthmus .... *Hemilepidotus hemilepidotus,* Red Irish lord, p. 502

	13	Gill membranes free of isthmus or narrowly joined to isthmus with a posterior free fold 14
or	13	Gill membranes broadly joined to isthmus 38

	14	Characters combined of slender conical fish with prominent row of hooked spines close to dorsal fin; no protuberance between nasal spines; and lower pectoral rays exserted for more than half their length .... *Paricelinus hopliticus,* Thornback sculpin, p. 532
or	14	Some or all of the above characters absent 15

	15	Spines in first dorsal fin more than 16; pelvic fin with 1 spine and 5 soft rays .... *Jordania zonope,* Longfin sculpin, p. 516
or	15	Spines in first dorsal fin fewer than 13; pelvic fin with 1 spine and 4 soft rays 16

	16	Upper preopercular spine antlerlike with 3 to 6 upwardly directed free spinules 17
or	16	Upper preopercular spine not antlerlike (except in *Artedius fenestralis),* covered with skin, may be simple, bifid, or trifid 22

	17	Scales completely covering body between dorsal fin and lateral line canal .... *Chitonotus pugetensis,* Roughback sculpin, p. 491
or	17	Scales between dorsal fins and lateral line canal in a band, mostly 2 scales wide .... Genus *Icelinus* 18

474

18   Dorsal fin with first 2 spines greatly elongate, and free of connecting membranes for outer third of length 19

or 18   Dorsal fin with first 2 spines about same length as succeeding spines 20

19   Upper posterior angle of orbit with 2 distinct spines; no cirri on nasal spine; rows of scales on back not reaching to end of base of dorsal fin .... *Icelinus tenuis,* Spotfin sculpin, p. 513

or 19   Upper posterior angle of orbit without spines; long cirrus at base of nasal spine; row of scales along back reaches to end of rayed dorsal fin .... *Icelinus filamentosus,* Threadfin sculpin, p. 510

20   Scale rows beside dorsal fin ending anterior to end of base of rayed dorsal .... *Icelinus burchami,* Dusky sculpin, p. 508

or 20   One of 2 scale rows beside dorsal fin extending beyond base of rayed dorsal 21

21   Prominent blunt protuberance between nasal spines .... *Icelinus oculatus,* Frogmouth sculpin, p. 511

or 21   No protuberance between nasal spines ....*Icelinus borealis*, Northern sculpin, p. 507

22   Scales absent or reduced to mere prickles all over body, or scattered over body embedded in fleshy papillae 23

or 22   Scales in a single row, or in bands above lateral line canal, or completely covering area above lateral line canal; scales not reduced to prickles irregularly scattered over body embedded in fleshy papillae 24

23   Scales on body widely scattered in fleshy papillae, head broad and depressed .... *Myoxocephalus polyacanthocephalus,* Great sculpin, p. 521

or 23   Scales absent or reduced to mere prickles, head not broad and depressed 33

24   Scales in 1 row, or 4 rows, above lateral line canal or completely covering area above lateral line canal 28

or 24   Scales in a wide band, 7 to 10 rows in width above lateral line canal .... Genus *Artedius* 25

25   Bands of scales on sides of body meeting behind rayed dorsal fin 26

or 25   Bands of scales on sides of body not reaching beyond end of rayed dorsal fin; no scales on head .... *Artedius lateralis,* Smoothhead sculpin, p. 481

477

PADDED SCULPIN

Artedius fenestralis Jordan and Gilbert 1882

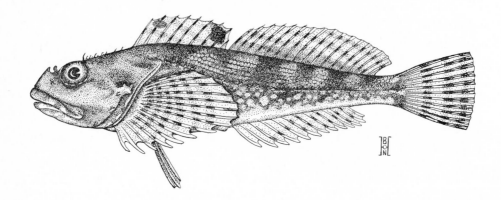

Scientific names from Petrus Artedi, early ichthyologist associated with Linnaeus; and the Latin *fenestralis* (with a window).

Description   Body elongate, its depth about 4 into standard length, deepest at spinous dorsal, arching down to blunt snout and tapering to caudal peduncle, barely compressed at deepest part, moderately compressed posteriorly. Head length about 2.9 into standard length, depressed. Mouth terminal, moderate in size, directed slightly upward. Upper jaw extending to posterior part of eye. Lips moderately thickened. Teeth mostly small and in bands on jaws, vomer, and palatines, a few larger teeth in both jaws. Interorbital space concave, its least width about 8 into length of head. Eye subelliptical, its length about 5.5 into length of head. Opercular membranes broadly united and free of isthmus. Caudal peduncle compressed. Anus at anal insertion. Anal papilla small and conical.

Spines   Nasal short and stout. Preopercular, 3, the upper flattened, with 2 secondary spines directed upward and 1 pointed back, the others small and inconspicuous. All covered with skin.

Fins   Dorsal (2), VIII to IX — 16 to 18; distinctly separated, the rayed portion somewhat higher. Caudal almost truncate. Anal 12 to 14, emarginate. Pectorals about 15, lower 7 emarginate, and lower 6 thickened. Pelvics I, 3, thoracic, reaching anus.

Scales   Weakly ctenoid, in fleshy padlike papillae, in about 9 or more rows in width diagonally in widest part, extending back nearly to caudal fin and meeting over caudal peduncle. Scales around posterior part of orbits and extending backward from orbits in irregular patches. A few thin scales on upper part of operculum. Lateral line canal curving downward toward caudal peduncle, scales 35 to 37, small and deeply embedded. Cirri on anterior nares, posterior end of maxillary. Several pairs of moderately large and varied cirri on top of head behind interorbital space, smaller single cirri on remainder of top of head, and 3 on each preopercular free edge. A series of single or double cirri along lateral line from head to a point below end of first third of rayed dorsal.

Colour   Very variable, orange, yellow, light green, occasionally cream on the dorsal surface, cream to pale brown on ventral surface, 4 green, brown or dark saddles across the body over the spinous dorsal, 2 at the rayed dorsal, and 1 at the caudal peduncle, light spots on body irregularly scattered, dark bars on fins except pelvics. In males 2 dark spots on spinous dorsal,

478

the posterior prominent, the anterior smaller and less distinctly defined. During breeding season the body in males becomes dusky to almost black, particularly the lower part, other colours are intensified, the dark marks on the spinous dorsal become joined by 3 bands of colour, dusky, pale blue, and golden yellow.

Size   Length to 5.5 inches (14 cm).

Recognition   Noted for the flattened skin-covered preopercular spine with three (or two) points, the stellate scales on the head, the dorsal bands of scales in fleshy, padlike papillae meeting behind the rayed dorsal fin, and the embedded lateral line canal scales.

Life History   Spawning occurs from January to March, females depositing salm-on-coloured eggs. Shrimps and small fishes are included in the food.

Distribution   Northern California, Washington,[1] and the Gulf of Alaska at northwest Unalaska Island and the northwest shore of the Alaska peninsula.[3,4] In British Columbia abundant in the Strait of Georgia and Burrard Inlet where it is common at Lumberman's Arch in December.[2] Recorded from the west coast of Vancouver Island at Ucluelet and Tofino, and Drew Harbour. Taken at depths down to 30 fathoms (55 m).

References   1 DeLacy, Dryfoos, and Miller 1963; 2 Lamb 1969; 3, 4 Wilimovsky 1954, 1964.

SCALYHEAD SCULPIN

Artedius harringtoni (Starks 1896)

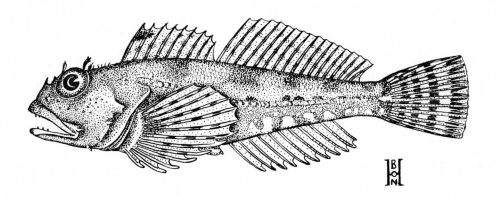

Scientific names from Petrus Artedi, an early ichthyologist associated with Linnaeus; and **Mark W. Harrington**, President of the University of Washington.

Referred to as the plumose sculpin in Clemens and Wilby 1946.

479

Description   Body elongate, depth about 3.8 into standard length, deepest under spinous dorsal fin, barely compressed near head, more so posteriorly. Head length about 25 into standard length, depressed. Mouth terminal, moderate in size, directed slightly upward. Upper jaw extending to posterior part of pupil, barely overhanging lower jaw. Snout in profile and from above, a blunt wedge. Lips thick. Teeth in jaws, conical, in bands, some enlarged and sharp (possibly limited to males); on vomer; and on anterior end of palatines only. Interorbital space concave, its width about 10 into length of head. Eye moderate in size, longer than wide, its length about 4.4 into length of head. Gill membranes broadly joined and free of isthmus. Caudal peduncle depth about 11 into standard length, compressed. Anus close to anal fin. Anal papilla in mature males large, cylindrical, with small conical tubular filament asymmetrically placed at the tip, in immature males, small and conical.

Spines   Nasal well developed and stout; preopercular 2, the upper sturdy, flattened or bifid; the lower minute. All covered by skin.

Fins   Dorsal (2), IX or X — 16 to 18, the parts barely but distinctly separate, each fin outline about parallel to dorsal surface, the rayed portion definitely low, caudal rounded. Anal 10 to 14. Pectorals about 13, all rays thick and exserted, the lower most so. Pelvics I, 3, thoracic, the tips reaching or almost reaching anus.

Scales   Ctenoid, in broad bands on upper part of body, 8 to 10 rows in width diagonally at widest part, extending backwards from about second dorsal ray to behind the dorsal fin on caudal peduncle, in longitudinal series 38 to 51, not approaching lateral line canal; a scale at the base of each dorsal soft ray; irregularly on top of head and operculum; scales in axillae behind bases of pectoral fins. Lateral line canal sloping downward through anterior half of fish and then level at midside to base of tail fin, scales 35 to 39. Cirri: on posterior end of maxillary, supraocular (in male), large multifid cirri over anterior and posterior margins of eye, followed by a third smaller cirrus (smaller in female), several pairs of long filamentous cirri on top of head. Long filamentous cirri on lateral line canal approximately between centres of spinous and rayed sections of dorsal fins.

Colour   In male brownish olive on dorsal surface and dusky cream on ventral surface, 5 to 7 dark saddles across the back, various sizes of light spots on lower part of the body confluent into ventral colour, brilliant orange-yellow on ventral surface of the head in adults, inside of mouth purple-red spots on a light violet background, radiating red bars around eye. Conspicuous white spot at base of caudal fin. In females colour generally similar but with white to pink or red on pelvic and anal fins. Brown spots on rays of dorsal fins, caudal, and pectoral fins arranged so as to give banded appearance. A prominent spot, bright red in life, near the tips of the first 2 dorsal spines.

Size   Length to 4 inches (10 cm).

Recognition   Noteworthy for the flattened bifid preopercular spine covered with skin, the band of scales along the upper part of the body meeting its fellow above the caudal peduncle, and a few enlarged teeth in each jaw.

Life History   Encountered at moderate depths. Sexual dimorphism is marked in this species and, the male was at one time described as *Pterygiocottus macouni*.[1] Very territorial, with males displaying as though to intimidate intruders.

Distribution   From southern California (in the region of upwelling cold water south of Monterey and at San Miguel Island) through Washington,[2,4] British Columbia and southeastern Alaska[5] to Kodiak Island, Alaska.[3] In British Columbia, from the southern Strait of Georgia (Nanaimo, Burrard Inlet, English Bay), the west coast of Vancouver Island at Ucluelet, Bute Inlet, and the Queen Charlotte Islands. Frequently found on rocky reefs and pilings between 5 and 11 meters.[4]

References   1 Bean and Weed 1920; 2 DeLacy, Dryfoos, and Miller 1963; 3 Hubbard and Reeder 1965; 4 Lamb personal communication; 5 Quast 1968.

SMOOTHHEAD SCULPIN

Artedius lateralis (Girard 1854)

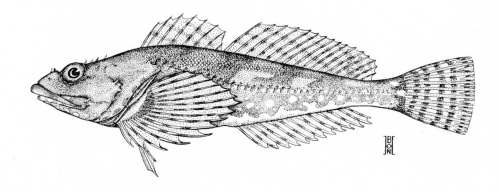

Scientific names from Petrus Artedi, early ichthyologist associated with Linnaeus; and the Latin *lateralis* (of the side — related to scale arrangement).

Referred to as the round-nosed sculpin in Clemens and Wilby 1946.

Description   Body elongate, its depth about 4 into standard length, deepest under spinous dorsal, dorsal profile arching down to caudal peduncle, abdominal deepening prominent, compressed. Head length about 2.6 into standard length, depressed. Mouth terminal, moderate in size, directed slightly upward. Upper jaw extending to posterior part of eye, overhanging lower jaw. Snout bluntly pointed in lateral profile and narrowly rounded from above. Lips thick. Teeth moderate in size, in bands on both jaws and on vomer and palatines. Interorbital space almost flat and rather wide, its width about 10 into length of head. Eye rather small, and almost round, its length about 4 into length of head. Gill membranes broadly fused and free of isthmus. Caudal peduncle compressed, about 13 into standard length. Anal papilla small and bluntly conical. Anus immediately anterior to anal fin.

Spines   Nasal blunt and low. Preopercular, 1 only, biramous, blunt, and moderate in size. Both sets of spines covered with skin.

Fins   Dorsal (2), VII to X — 15 or 17, barely joined by a low membrane, rayed portion slightly higher, rays and spines prominent at margin but not exserted. Caudal rounded. Anal 12 to 14. Pectorals about 14, the lower 8 thickened and exserted. Pelvics I, 3, thoracic, extending only a little more than half distance to anus from insertions.

Vertebrae   In California 32(31) in 12 specimens.[2]

Scales   Weakly ctenoid, in a band up to 7 or 8 scales wide in diagonal rows between the lateral line canal and dorsal insertion but separated from them, extending from about spine III to the third to last ray, 24 to 31 diagonal rows. No scales on head. Lateral line canal, 35 to 36 scales, arching down along edge of appressed pectoral fin to midside and then straight, scales embedded. Nasal cirrus small and multifid; at posterior tip of maxillary 3 stout simple cirri; at top of head numerous filamentous cirri arranged irregularly in about 3 transverse rows; usually up to 4 on the preopercle, the upper (when present) above the spine, and the others close to the edge of the bone; sometimes 1 at the top of the gill opening, and another near the upper posterior angle of the opercular flap. A row of cirri along the anterior end of the lateral line canal to a point about below the first third of the rayed dorsal, in various shapes as filaments or flaps, often paired.

Colour   Olive green to dark brown on dorsal surface, cream to faint green on the ventral surface, about 6 irregular dark saddles across the back. Numerous pale spots on lower part of the body and head. Conspicuous dark bars on all fins except pelvics. In male small black spots on membrane of spinous dorsal between first and second spines; duskiness pronounced in breeding season. Colour adapted to environment.

Size   Length to 5 inches (12.7 cm).

Recognition   Noted for the single bifid skin-covered preopercular spine, the narrow band of scales separated from both the lateral line canal and the dorsal insertion and not extending as far as the last dorsal ray, and the embedded scales of the lateral line canal.

Life History   Common along the Canadian coast in tide pools and shallow water. Spawning occurs in February. The small cherry-red eggs are deposited in a mass in a protected location among rocks and hatch in about 16 days. Summer spawnings are recorded from the Seattle area.

Distribution   From northern Baja California through Washington[3] and southeastern Alaska[6] to Kodiak Island, Alaska.[4] The species is generally distributed in shallow water in British Columbia, to 13 meters.[1,5]

References   1 Bean and Weed 1920; 2 Clothier 1950; 3 DeLacy, Dryfoos, and Miller 1963; 4 Hubbard and Reeder 1965; 5 Osgood 1901; 6 Quast 1968.

PUGET SOUND SCULPIN

Artedius meanyi (Jordan and Starks 1895)

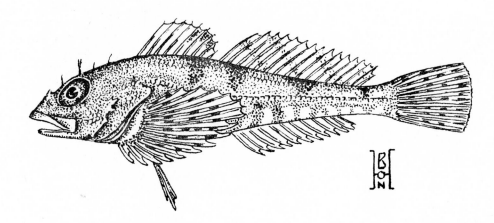

Scientific names from Petrus Artedi, an early ichthyologist associated with Linnaeus; and Professor E. S. Meany of the University of Washington.

Description   Body rather elongate, depth about 3.5 into standard length, depth greatest at origin of dorsal fin, tapered evenly to caudal peduncle. Cross section at thickest place round or slightly depressed. Head length about 2.5 into standard length. Mouth terminal, moderate in size, directed forward. Upper jaw extending to posterior part of pupil, about 2.2 into length of head. Lips rather thick. Upper profile of head arching to rather blunt (about 45°) angle at upper jaw. Interorbital space flat between orbits and narrow, about 12 into length of head. Eye large, oval, its length about 4 into length of head. Gill membranes broadly united and free of isthmus. Caudal peduncle moderately compressed, its depth about 13 into standard length.

Spines   Nasal well developed and sharp, directed backward. Preopercular 4, the upper one large and bifid, the other 3 diminishing in size in order downward.

Fins   Dorsal (2), X — 15 or 16, separated by about diameter of pupil, rayed portion higher. Caudal bluntly rounded with central rays not necessarily longest. Anal 11 or 12, origin below origin of rayed dorsal. Pectorals 15 or 16, reaching to about fifth ray of anal. Pelvics I, 3, reaching about to anus.

Scales   On sides above lateral line canal continuous with scales on head. Scales on top of head, opercle, suborbital, snout, cheek above maxillary, margins of interorbital space, and 4 or 5 rows on the upper surface of the eye. Lateral line canal curved slightly downward, 36 to 38 scales. A long fingerlike cirrus on the preorbital and a 3-branched cirrus half as long as eye on the postorbital. One cirrus above and in front of the corner of the gill opening. A series of cirri along the posterior part of the suborbital stay, and a cirrus at the end of each dorsal spine. Other smaller cirri on eyeball, near spines on gill cover, and along the lateral line canal.

Colour   Green to cream with darker indefinite saddles along the back and vermiculations ventrally. Dorsal, caudal, and pectoral fins edged or lightly streaked with brown.

Size   Length to 2 inches (5.1 cm).

Recognition   Recognizable in Canada by the (nearly) complete squamation above the lateral line canal with scales on the cheek and snout, the well-developed slender preorbital tentacle, and the large trifid postorbital cirrus.

Distribution   From Port Orchard, Puget Sound, to Queen Charlotte Sound at 51.09 N, 127.55.5 W, and off Graham Island at 53.52 N, 133.19 W at 82 meters (NMC 67-346) (Peden 1972 personal communication). Sooke and Howe Sound in southern British Columbia.[2,3] Probably more common than indicated by the few specimens in collections.

References   1 Jordan and Starks 1895; 2 McAllister personal communication; 3 Rosenblatt and Wilkie 1963.

ROSYLIP SCULPIN

Ascelichthys rhodorus Jordan and Gilbert 1880

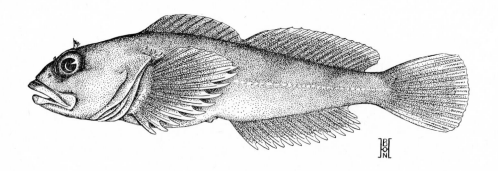

Scientific names from the Greek *a* (without), *scelos* (leg), and *ichthys* (fish — no pelvic fins); and *rodor* (rose) and *oros* (margin).

Description   Body rather elongate, its depth about 3.6 into standard length, slightly compressed at the anterior end, more so posteriorly. Notable constriction between the anus and the anal insertion. Head large, depressed, its length about 2.7 into standard length. Mouth terminal, large, directed forward. Upper jaw extends to posterior edge of pupil, overhanging lower jaw. Lips thick. Teeth fine and pointed, in bands on jaws, vomer, and palatines. Interorbital space nearly flat, moderately wide, about 3 into length of eye. Eye oval, its length about 4 into length of head. Opercular membranes joined and free from isthmus. Caudal peduncle compressed, its least depth about 10 into standard length. Anal papilla small and conical.

Spines   Only 1 preopercular spine evident, stout, hooked upward, and covered with skin.

Fins   Dorsal (1), VII to X, 17 to 20, deeply notched, spinous part about half height of rayed part, spines weak. Caudal well rounded. Anal 13 to 16, emarginate. Pectorals 17, rounded, 7 lower rays markedly exserted. Pelvics absent.

Scales   No scales. Skin smooth. Lateral line canal slopes downward from above pectoral fin base to midside over anal fin, pores 34 to 38. Cirri, a palmate multifid cirrus on head behind and beside each eye, a cluster of 5 to 9 filamentous cirri above the insertion of each pectoral fin.

Colour   Dark olive brown to slaty above. Yellowish gray on abdomen, shading into cinnamon under pectoral fin. Lateral line canal lighter. Margins of rayed dorsal, caudal, and pectoral fins lighter.

Size   Length to 4.5 inches (11.4 cm).

Recognition   Noted for its smooth skin, the low spinous dorsal, absence of pelvic fins, and the single hooked preopercular spine.

Distribution   Northern California to southeast Alaska. British Columbia records include those from Victoria, west coast of Vancouver Island, Strait of Georgia. A common tidepool fish found under rocks at low tide.

SPINYNOSE SCULPIN

Asemichthys taylori Gilbert 1912

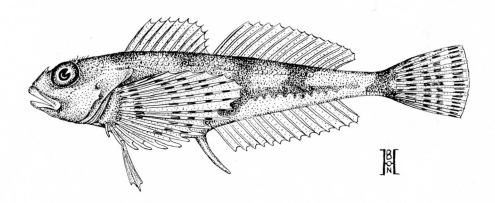

Scientific names from the Greek *a* (negative), *sem* (sign), and *ichthys* (fish); and the Reverend G. W. Taylor, Curator and first Director of the then Biological Board of Canada's (Pacific) Biological Station at Nanaimo, British Columbia.

Recorded under the common name Taylor's sculpin by Clemens and Wilby 1946, and in 1961 as *Radulinus taylori*.

Description   Body elongate, depth about 5 into standard length, greatest depth

485

close behind pectoral fin, tapering evenly back to caudal peduncle. Only slightly compressed. Head length about 3.5 into standard length, deepest at eyes. Mouth terminal, inferior, moderate in size, and directed forward. Upper jaw extending about to point below anterior margin of the eye. Lips rather thick. Snout sloping abruptly. Interorbital space concave, its width about 4 into length of head. Eye large, oval, its length about 4 into length of head. Gill membranes broadly united and free of isthmus. Caudal peduncle notably compressed only at base of caudal fin, its depth about 15 into standard length. Anal papilla elongate and conical.

Spines　Nasal, strong, sharp, and curved backward. Preopercular 3, the upper 2 small and flat and the lowest barely perceptible, all covered with skin.

Fins　Dorsal (2), X or XI — 15 or 16, the rayed portion slightly higher. Caudal bluntly rounded. Anal 15 or 16, origin below that of the rayed dorsal. Pectorals 16 or 17, its longest ray reaching about to third or fourth ray of anal fin, the lower 10 or 11 rays thickened, slightly exserted. Pelvics I, 3, thoracic.

Scales　Above lateral line canal in 1 to 4 rows from head to about third to last soft dorsal ray. On occipital, interorbital space, and around eyes. Lateral line canal sloping down slightly from anterior end, then straight, 34 to 36 spinous plates with slight keels forming a rough ridge. Cirri slender and filamentous in a broken row below lateral line canal between centres of 2 dorsal fins. A short cirrus on the posterior margin of the orbital rim. A row of minute spinous projections on the upper anterior margin of the eyeball.

Colour　Olive brown on dorsal surface, lighter ventrally. Four dark saddles across body. Brown bars on pectoral and caudal fins.

Size　Length to 2.25 inches (5.7 cm).

Recognition　Noteworthy for the scales on the top of the head and around the eyes, the strong curved nasal spines, the high lateral line canal with slightly keeled scales, and the long pectoral fins.

Distribution　From the southern Strait of Georgia to Tasu Harbour, Queen Charlotte Islands. It seems likely that further exploration will extend the range of this inconspicuous little sculpin.

References　Gilbert 1912; Wilby 1936b.

CRESTED SCULPIN

Blepsias bilobus Cuvier 1829

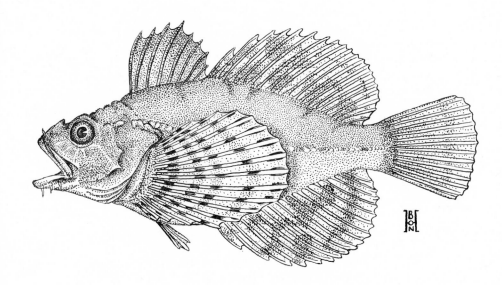

Scientific names from the Greek *blepo* (look — an old fish name); and the Latin *bi* (two) and *lobus* (lobe — two dorsal fins, each smoothly contoured).

The crested sculpin was recorded as *Histiocottus bilobus* (Cuvier and Valenciennes 1829) by Clemens and Wilby 1946.

Description   Body depth about 2.6 into standard length, compressed. Head about 2.7 into standard length, somewhat compressed. Snout bluntly rounded. Top of head fairly flat in both planes. Mouth terminal, moderate in size, directed forward and up. Upper jaw extends about to anterior part of pupil. Teeth small, pointed, and weak in jaws, vomer, and palatines. Interorbital space nearly flat, its width about 2.4 into length of head, thickening at upper rims of orbits. Eye diameter about 5 into length of head, the rim of the orbit barely entering dorsal profile of head. Gill membranes united and free of isthmus. Caudal

peduncle moderate and compressed, its least depth about 14 into standard length. Anus about one-fifth of distance from pelvic insertion to anal origin. Anal papilla small and rounded.

Spines   Nasal recumbent and weak, directed backward. Four preopercular spines, the second longest, strongest, and sharpest, the lower 2 much reduced. Moderate ridges on frontal, occipital, supraocular, and postocular much thickened.

Fins   Dorsal (2), VIII or IX — 21 or 22, spinous part with somewhat exserted spines but no indenting, rayed portion high. Caudal rounded. Anal 18 to 20. Pectorals 16, long, extending a third of distance along anal fin, free ends of rays expanded. Pelvics I, 3, thoracic, short.

Scales   Ctenoid, reduced to small plates, each with a minute spine embedded in a fleshy papilla, covering all of body and upper part and sides of head, on bases of fin rays. Lateral line canal descending gradually from behind eye through anterior half of body and then straight along midside to base of caudal. Pores along lateral line canal about 52. Cirri moderately large, simple cirri on either side of snout and on upper jaw, 3 under each lower jaw. Minute cirri at end of each maxillary bone.

Colour   Olive green on dorsal surface, paler below, 4 or 5 faint dusky blotches across body, dusky bars on rayed dorsal, pectoral, and caudal fins.

Size   Length to 10 inches (25 cm).

Recognition   Recognized by the compressed body, the moderate cirri on snout and lower jaw, the spinous dorsal without an indentation, the general distribution of closely packed scales within papillae over the whole body.

Distribution   From northern British Columbia through southern Alaska and the Aleutian Islands (Krenitzen Islands[3]), the Bering Sea,[1,4] the Commander Islands, Kamchatka and Terpenija Bay to Toyama Bay.[1,2] British Columbia records from Dean Channel at Cascade Inlet, Bella Bella, and Bella Coola, are the southern limits of the known range.

References   1 Matsubara 1955; 2 Shmidt 1950; 3, 4 Wilimovsky 1954, 1964.

SILVERSPOTTED SCULPIN

Blepsias cirrhosus (Pallas 1811)

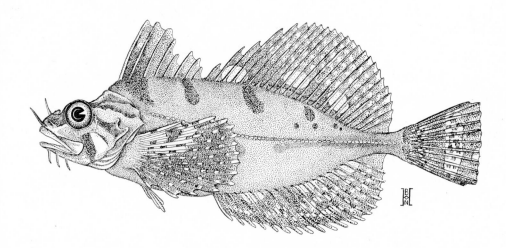

Scientific names from the Greek *blepo* (look — an old fish name); and the Latin *cirrhosus* (bearing cirri).

Called silver spot in Clemens and Wilby 1946.

Description   Body depth about 3.5 (3.3–4.3) into standard length, compressed. Head about 3.5 into standard length, concave in upper profile (between orbits). Mouth terminal, moderate in size, directed forward and up. Jaws about even. Upper jaw extends about to posterior end of pupil. Teeth small, conical, in bands on jaws, sparse on vomer, on palatines. Interorbital space concave in both planes with high, thick supraorbital ridges and evident parietal and median ridges, its width about 3.5 into length of head. Eyes round and prominent, diameter about 3.8 into length of head. Gill membranes fused and free of isthmus. Caudal peduncle slender and compressed, its least depth about 17 into standard length. Anus about one-third of distance from pelvic insertion to anal origin. Anal papilla small and rounded.

Spines   Nasal blunt, directed backward and inward. Four preopercular spines, all blunt and skin covered, the second one largest, the lower 2 much reduced. Much thickened frontal, occipital, and postorbital ridges.

Fins   Dorsal (2), VI to IX — 20 to 25, barely separated, spinous portion indented at fifth spine, lobes of membrane at tips of first few (4) spines, rayed portion high. Caudal rounded. Anal 18 to 21. Pectorals 12, low on body, reaching beyond anal origin. Pelvics I, 3, thoracic, short.

Scales   Ctenoid, reduced to small plates, each with a minute spine embedded in a fleshy papilla, covering body except for patches along posterior part of lateral line canal, caudal peduncle, small spots below the lateral line canal and much of the space covered by the pectoral fin; in patches on lower part of head. Lateral line canal descending in a waving line from the top of the operculum to about end of pectoral fin and then straight along midside to base of caudal fin. Pores 43 to 57. Cirri long, slender, simple, and substantial, 1 pair on snout, ordinarily lying back above maxillary, 1 single erect median cirrus on snout, 3 pairs under lower jaw. Small cirri on nasal spines, above eyes, and on throat.

Colour   Light olive brown or green above, white to coppery yellow on ventral surface, dark marks on upper part of body forming vague saddles. Reddish on sides behind head. White spots below lateral line canal anteriorly; 3 black bars radiating from each eye; and 1 joining eyes. Brown to black with large clear areas on all fins except pelvics. Inside of mouth blue.

Size   Length to 7.5 inches (19 cm).

Recognition   Noteworthy for its compressed body, the indented spinous dorsal fin, the prominent cirri on snout and lower jaw, and the general distribution of closely packed scales embedded within cirri on the body, missing the area under the pectoral fins and around the posterior part of the lateral line canal.

Life History   Eggs are reported to be clear light brown or blue. They are attached to rocks in shallow water. In Puget Sound females are ripening eggs in early February.

Distribution   From northern California where it is not common[1] to the Aleutian Islands[6] and Bering Sea.[5] Reports from Asian waters[3,4] south to Tsuruga, Japan, are probably based on another subspecies.[2] In shallow water of weedy bays and down to 20 fathoms (37 m). Not uncommon in southern British Columbia both in the Strait of Georgia and off the open coasts.

References   1 Bolin 1944; 2 Matsubara 1955; 3 Popov 1933; 4 Watanabe 1960; 5, 6 Wilimovsky 1954, 1964.

ROUGHBACK SCULPIN

Chitonotus pugetensis (Steindachner 1877)

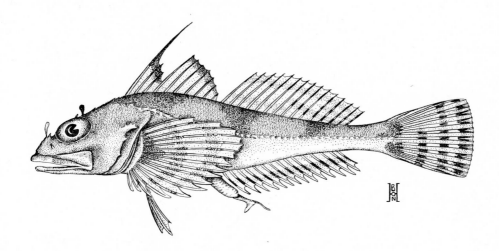

Scientific names from the Greek *chiton* (tunic) and *notos* (back); and Puget (Sound).

Description Body elongate, its depth about 5.1 into standard length, compressed, deepest at dorsal origin and tapered evenly to caudal peduncle. Head length about 2.8 into standard length, about as broad as deep. Mouth terminal, large, directed forward. Upper jaw extending nearly to posterior edge of orbit, overhanging lower jaw. Snout bluntly rounded in both planes. Lips somewhat thickened. Teeth small, conical, on jaws, vomer and palatines in bands, tending to be in rows around edges of vomer and palatines. Interorbital space narrow and concave, its width about 16 into length of head. Eye moderate in size, oval, its length about 3.7 into length of head. Opercular membranes broadly joined and free of isthmus. Caudal peduncle about 16 into standard length, moderately compressed. Anal papilla very large and thick, narrower near end, with a curved tip.

Spines Nasal short, sharp, erect, supraorbital above and behind eye, double spine on parietal. Four pairs of preopercular spines, the upper largest and antlerlike with 3 secondary upward directed spines; the second close to it and strong, directed backward and down; and the remaining 2 well developed and sharp, directed down and downward and forward, in order.

Fins Dorsal (2), X or XI — 14 to 17, joined if at all only by a low membrane. Spinous dorsal deeply emarginate between rays 3 and 4 with spine lengths ranked in order as 1, 4 (etc.) 2, 3. Spinous fin from the fourth spine and all rayed fins slightly emarginate. Caudal fin large and barely rounded. Anal 14 to 17, emarginate. Pectorals about 16, emarginate. Pelvics I, 3, thoracic, reaching to anus or beyond.

Vertebrae 34 or 35 in 16 California specimens.[2]

Scales Ctenoid, rough and large, almost covering body above the lateral line canal and the head above a line joining largest preopercular spine and the lower rim of the orbit. Lateral line canal sloping down to about the tip of the pectorals and then straight, 36 to 39 scales. Cirri on nasal, eyeball, and postocular, all broad and paddlelike.

491

Colour   Dark grayish green to brown with a series of usually 4 dark brown saddles along dorsal surface. Lighter below lateral line canal and creamy white below pectoral fins, sometimes behind pectoral base. Very dark margins on both sections of spinous dorsal. Dark margins on rayed dorsal. Light margins outside a dark band on anal. Brown pigment on spines, in bands on rayed dorsal and caudal fins. A brilliant red blotch below lateral line canal under rayed dorsal fin, especially in breeding season. During actual courtship males become very dark on fins and head.[4]

Size   Length to 9 inches (23 cm).

Recognition   Recognizable for the deep emargination of the spinous dorsal between the third and fourth spines and by having the upper part of the head and body almost covered by rough, ctenoid scales.

Life History   In the aquarium, this species buries itself in the sand.[4] Its food in nature consists to a large extent of shrimps and other crustaceans. Eggs are salmon coloured.

Distribution   From Baja California and southern California to Washington[3] and to northern British Columbia. In British Columbia it is fairly common in the southern Strait of Georgia. Recorded from Port Simpson in northern British Columbia and Ucluelet on the west coast of Vancouver Island.[1] Most common at depths less than 40 fathoms (73 m).

References   1 Bean and Weed 1920; 2 Clothier 1950; 3 DeLacy, Dryfoos, and Miller 1963; 4 Lamb personal communication; 5 Vancouver Public Aquarium 1969.

SHARPNOSE SCULPIN

Clinocottus acuticeps (Gilbert 1895)

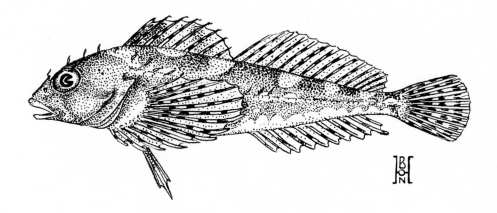

Scientific names from *Clinus* and *Cottus* (two genera of small fishes); and the Latin *acutis* (sharp) and *ceps* (head).

Description　Body rather elongate, its depth about 4.2 into standard length, slightly compressed. Head rather depressed and small, its length about 3.5 into standard length. Mouth terminal, moderate in size, directed forward. Snout rather sharp. Lips thickened, especially the upper. Upper jaw extending to anterior part of eye. Teeth in fine bands on jaws. Interorbital space concave, its width about 5.5 into length of head. Eye round, its length about 4.3 into length of head. Gill membranes joined and free of isthmus. Caudal peduncle compressed, its least depth about 17 into standard length. Anal papilla flattened so that the long axis is across the fish, with a triple distal end. Anus about one-third distance from pelvic insertion to anal origin.

Spines　Nasal small, conical, directed backward. Preopercular, 1, small, curving upward and in. Both blunt and skin covered.

Fins　Dorsal (2), VII to IX — 14 to 16, low, the 2 parts barely separated. Caudal rounded. Anal 10 to 13, origin below third ray of dorsal, next to last ray longest. Pectorals about 13, large. Pelvics I, 3, thoracic.

Scales　No scales. Lateral line canal high anteriorly, decurved, and then straight to caudal peduncle. Cirri simple, 1 on inside of each nasal spine, 1 on upper part of each eyeball, 1 pair above and behind eyes, 2 or 3 pairs between them and the occiput along the two sides of the head, 1 on the end of each maxillary, 2 on the edge of each preopercular bone, 2 at the upper corner of the opercular opening, along the lateral line canal in a row for about two-thirds of its length, and at the ends of each dorsal fin spine.

Colour　Green to light brown on dorsal surface varying with surroundings, whitish to cream on ventral surface. Irregular dark band on each side of body, extended to form about 6 saddles across the back, variously blotched with light colours between the saddles, along the lateral line canal, and toward the ventral surface. Three dark bands radiating from eyes. Dark area between first and third spines of dorsal fin.

Size　Length to 2 inches (5.1 cm).

493

Recognition   Notable for the acute snout, the single spine on each preoperculum tending to turn inward, the cirrus on each eyeball, and the dark area at the anterior end of the dorsal fin.

Life History   The eggs are brown and rather large, about 1 millimeter in diameter. Breeding was observed on July 4 at Eagle Point, San Juan Islands. A female taken at the north end of Wiers Beach contained free eggs on April 28.

Distribution   Northern California, Washington[1] to the Aleutian Islands[3] and Bering Sea.[2] Generally distributed in shallow water throughout coastal British Columbia.

References   1 DeLacy, Dryfoos, and Miller 1963; 2, 3 Wilimovsky 1954, 1964.

CALICO SCULPIN

Clinocottus embryum (Jordan and Starks 1895)

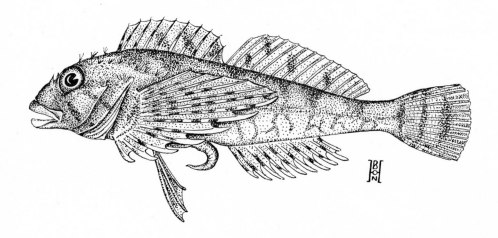

Scientific names from *Clinus* and *Cottus* (two genera of small fishes); and the Greek *en* (in) and *bryon* (seamoss).

Clemens and Wilby 1946 recorded this species as the mossy sculpin.

Description   Body rather elongate, its depth about 4 into standard length, slightly compressed. Head rather depressed and small, its length 3.5 to 4 into standard length, possibly larger in males than in females. Mouth terminal, moderate in size, directed forward. Snout steep. Upper jaw extending to anterior margin of the pupil. Lips thickened, especially the upper. Teeth fine, in bands in jaws. Interorbital space concave, its width about 7 into length of head. Eye almost round, its length about

494

4.3 into length of head. Gill membranes joined and free of isthmus. Caudal peduncle compressed, its least depth about 13 into standard length. Anal papilla large, tubular, curved forward. Anus about halfway between pelvic insertion and dorsal origin.

Spines   Nasal small, blunt, skin covered, almost erect. Preopercular 1, small, blunt, skin covered.

Fins   Dorsal (2), almost contiguous, VIII to X — 14 to 17. Caudal barely rounded. Anal 9 to 12, short, starting and ending within limits of rayed dorsal, deeply incised. Pectorals large, extending to about third ray of anal, about 13, lower 5 rays thickened and exserted. Pelvics I, 3, thoracic.

Scales   No scales. Lateral line canal sloping down and back anteriorly and then straight to base of caudal fin, Cirri: prominent, usually multifid, cirri along first third of lateral line canal, the row continuing on head to upper posterior rim of orbits, on nasal and preopercular spines; on midline of head and clustering at upper angle of gill opening.

Colour   Light olive green to pink or rich maroon on dorsal surface, paler below. About 6 dark brownish green saddles across back and vertical dark vermiculations below lateral line canal extending almost to anal fin. Dark bands extending down and back from eye. Brown to orange bars on all fins except pelvics.

Size   Length to 2.75 inches (7 cm).

Recognition   Noted for the single blunt preopercular spine, the multifid cirri along lateral line canal and on head, the forward position of the anus, and the narrow snout.

Distribution   Recorded from Baja California. From northern California (from areas of upwelling south of Monterey) to Washington[1] and the Bering Sea[2] through the Aleutian Islands.[3] In British Columbia records are from both coasts of Vancouver Island, and it is probably not uncommon in rocky inshore areas.

References   1 DeLacy, Dryfoos, and Miller 1963; 2, 3 Wilimovsky 1954, 1964.

MOSSHEAD SCULPIN

Clinocottus globiceps (Girard 1857)

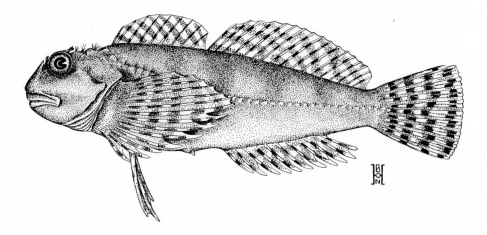

Scientific names from *Clinus* and *Cottus* (two genera of small fishes); and the Latin *globus* (globe) and *ceps* (head).

Clemens and Wilby 1946 used the common name globe-headed sculpin for this species.

Description   Body elongate, somewhat compressed anteriorly, more so farther back, depth about 3.5 into standard length. Head short, broad, blunt, its length about 3.8 into standard length. Mouth terminal, moderate, directed forward, slightly overhung by the thickened upper lip and steep snout. Teeth fine, in bands on jaws. Interorbital space narrow and concave, its width about 2 into length of eye. Eye round, its length about 4.3 into length of head. Gill membranes joined and free of isthmus. Caudal peduncle compressed, its least depth about 17 into standard length. Anal papilla stout, conical, ending in horn. Anus about two-thirds distance from insertion of pelvic fins to origin of anal fin.

Spines   Nasal spine blunt, directed backward and up. Preopercular spine blunt, directed backward, both spines covered with skin.

Fins   Dorsal (2), IX or X — 15 to 17, spinous portion lower. Caudal rounded. Anal 10 to 12, membranes greatly excised, origin below anterior third of rayed dorsal. Pectorals 14, the lower 8 rays thickened and 6 or 7 excised, large and rounded. Pelvics I, 3, thoracic.

Scales   Scales absent. Lateral line canal starts above pelvic fin insertions and dips to midside where it continues to caudal peduncle, 34 to 40 pores. Multifid cirri along first third of lateral line canal. Dense rows of multifid cirri on upper part of head, occasionally cirri on maxillaries of large specimens.

Colour   Olive to reddish brown on dorsal surface, about 6 dark blotches across body. Fins heavily banded with dark brown or black. Colour varies with habitat and may be bright.

Size   Length to 7.5 inches (19 cm).

Recognition   Notable for the blunt head, the single, blunt, skin-covered preopercular spine, the dense multifid cirri on the anterior part of the lateral line canal and in rows on the head.

496

in tide pools. It will rest almost completely out of water on rocks.[1]

References   1 Lamb personal communication.

SPINYHEAD SCULPIN

Dasycottus setiger Bean 1890

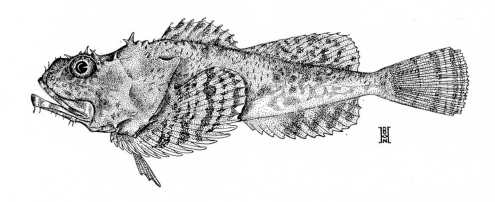

Scientific names from the Greek *dasys* (rough or warty) and *Cottus* (a kind of sculpin); and the Latin *seto* (bristle) and *gero* (to bear).

Description   Body elongate, depth about 4.3 into standard length, slightly depressed anteriorly, tapered. Head length about 2.3 into standard length, depressed. Mouth terminal, large, directed forward and up. Lower jaw protruding. Upper jaw extending to posterior edge of pupil. Snout broad, with a broad bump anterior to eyes. Teeth fine, in broken rows or patches on jaws and palatines. Interorbital space wide, about 4 into length of head, concave in both planes. Eye oval, its length about 4.4 into

length of head. Opercular membranes united and connected to isthmus so as to leave a broad free fold. Caudal peduncle somewhat compressed, its least depth about 15 into standard length. Anus about two-thirds distance from pelvic insertion to anal origin. Anal papilla small and rounded.

Spines   Numerous and stout. Preopercular spines 4, unbranched, low on head, 2 lower directed straight down or forward, the upper 2 directed backward. Four spines variously directed above or around eyes. Occipital spine largest and may be doubled. Cleithral and frontal spines strong.

Fins   Dorsal (2), IX or X — 13 to 15, low, with all boundaries vague from encroachment of

497

loose skin. Caudal slightly rounded. Anal 13 or 14. Pectorals 23, large with broad base carried forward. Pelvics I, 3, thoracic.

Scales   Skin very loose. Scales ctenoid, few, in 2 broken rows along upper side, and on nape, each scale with numerous prickles, and most with 1 or more cirri. Lateral line canal slightly descending and then straight, difficult to see, pores 13 to 16. Cirri numerous and moderate in size, scattered over upper part of body and head, on lateral line canal pores and tips of spines of dorsal fin; in a line on caudal fin; and small on eyeballs.

Colour   Gray with chocolate brown spots on dorsal surface, brownish white on ventral surface, darker posteriorly, 5 or 6 darker saddles across the body, black specks on all fins, dark bars on all fins but pelvics.

Size   Length to 9 inches (23 cm).

Recognition   Distinguished by the large head with upright, variously directed blunt, sturdy spines, the loose skin, and the rows of spiny scales on either side of the spinous dorsal. With the heavy spines and dispersed cirri a very shaggy-appearing fish.

Distribution   From Washington[2] to the Aleutian Islands[6] and Bering Sea[5], Avachina Gulf at 96 to 134 m and 0.2 to 2 C,[1] Kamchatka, Okhotsk Sea, Sakhalin,[3] Hokkaido, and Honshu.[4] In British Columbia common at moderate depths 10 to 60 fathoms (18–110 m) where in the Strait of Georgia it is taken by shrimp trawlers.

References   1 Andriashev 1937; 2 DeLacy, Dryfoos, and Miller 1963; 3 Shmidt 1950; 4 Watanabe 1960; 5, 6 Wilimovsky 1954, 1964.

498

BUFFALO SCULPIN

Enophrys bison (Girard 1854)

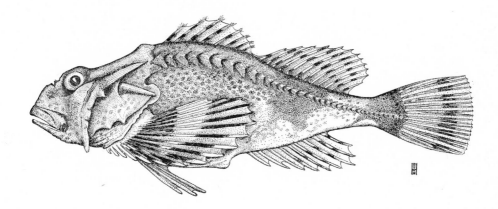

Scientific names from the Greek *en* (on) and *ophrys* (eyebrow — supraocular ridges); and *bison* (North American buffalo).

Description Body depth 3.2 (2.8–3.7) into standard length, stout anteriorly, about circular in cross section anteriorly, tapered to caudal peduncle. Head large, its length 2.2 (2.0–2.4) into standard length, broad, dorsal profile convex. Snout blunt. Mouth terminal, moderate in size, directed forward. Lower jaw shallow, closing inside upper jaw. Upper jaw extending beyond midpupil. Teeth fine and sharp on pads in jaws and vomer. Interorbital space narrow, concave, its width about 7.3 into length of head. Eye length about 5 into length of head. Gill membranes broadly fused to the isthmus without any free fold. Caudal peduncle moderately compressed, its least depth 13 (11.8–14.0) into standard length. Anus close to origin of anal fin. No anal papilla.

Spines Nasal sharp on small specimens, in larger ones, broad, blunt, rather rough. Pre-orbital, supraocular, parietal, and nuchal ridges on top of head. Preopercular with 4 spines, the upper greatly elongated, its length about 2.8 into head length, its base serrate anteriorly, the lower 3 spines well developed but much shorter, the lowest stoutest of the 4, flattened, and directed downward. Two sharp spines on edge of operculum. Supracleithral spine at upper angle of gill slit.

Fins Dorsal (2), (VII)VIII(IX) — (10) 12(13). Caudal broadly rounded. Anal (8)9. Pectorals (16)17(18). Pelvics I, 3, thoracic.

Scales Ctenoid, restricted to lateral line canal. Lateral line canal high, following dorsal contour, 30 to 35 rough bony plates without keels. One or more cirri on end of maxillary. Small specimens have simple cirri at ends of dorsal spines; in larger individuals these become tufts, apparently extending with growth along the tops of the spines from before backward, eventually reaching all (but possibly the last spine), invading the free edges of the intervening membranes, and becoming abundant on the anterior edge of the first spine.[2]

Colour Dorsal surface variable, green-black, brown, or occasionally white with black mottling, body crossed by 3 dark saddles. Top of head may be pink. Ventral surface ivory or white.

Dorsal, caudal, and pectoral fins heavily marked with dark brown or black spotting or bars. May have orange on caudal. Spots on anal fin few, absent on pelvics.

Size   Length to 12 inches (30.5 cm).

Recognition   Identified by the preopercular spines; the uppermost long, directed out, up, and back, and the lowest large, flattened and directed downward, the gill membranes fused to the isthmus without a free fold, and the high lateral line canal with large raised plates.

Life History   Spawns in February and March depositing orange-brown eggs in small clusters. In southern British Columbia young have reached about 11 millimeters in length by June.[1] Food of larger individuals is recorded as including shrimps, crabs, amphipods, mussels, and young fishes such as herring, salmon, seaperches, and sand lance, and sea lettuce, *Ulva*. When the fish is disturbed the gill cover is expanded, displaying the great spines and thus presenting a very formidable appearance.

Distribution   From Monterey, California, to the Gulf of Alaska and Kodiak Island. Commonly taken on beaches throughout British Columbia.

References   1 Robinson, Barraclough, and Fulton 1968a; 2 Sandercock and Wilimovsky 1968.

SOFT SCULPIN

Gilbertidia sigalutes (Jordan and Starks 1895)

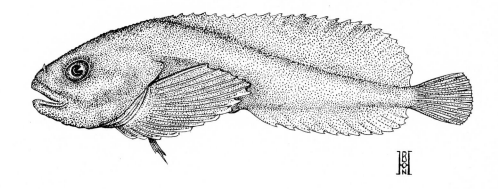

Scientific names from C. H. Gilbert, distinguished U.S. ichthyologist and fishery scientist; and the Greek *sig* (quiet) and *lutes* (bather).

Description Body elongate, depth about 3.5 into standard length, deepest at head, tapered quite evenly to caudal peduncle. Head large, compressed, its length about 2.5 to 3.0 into standard length. Mouth terminal, rather large, directed slightly upward. Upper jaw barely reaching anterior edge of orbit, its length about 2.4 into length of head. Lower jaw very little projecting. Teeth small, conical, in bands in both jaws. Interorbital space convex and wide, its width about 3 into length of head. Eyes small, oval, its length about 8 into length of head. Gill membranes broadly joined to isthmus. Branchiostegals about 13. Caudal peduncle compressed, its depth about 10 into standard length. Anus immediately in front of anal fin. A small anal papilla. No evident spines on head.

Fins Dorsal (1), XXII — 15 (about 37 total), continuous, spinous and rayed parts about equal in height, elevated posteriorly, all covered with skin so that spines and rays cannot be distinguished with certainty without dissection.[6] Somewhat emarginate. Caudal well rounded. Anal 14 or 15, high posteriorly. Pectorals 17 or 18, extending beyond anus, lower rays thickened, fanned out in life. Pelvics I, 3, thoracic, partly attached to body.

Gill Rakers Around 13.

Scales No scales. Lateral line canal indistinct. Skin smooth, very loose on body. Papillae in a single row along midside and on anterior part of head. Semitransparent. Pores on lateral line canal and around mouth large and vague, largest toward posterior end.

Colour Variable, changing rapidly. Translucent pink to gray or brown on dorsal surface, lighter on fins. Pectoral fins pale or bright orange, and fanned out. Some dark spots on fins and vague darker markings on body. Sometimes spotted. Eyes orange.

Size Length to 3.25 inches (8.3 cm).

Recognition Distinguished by its loose skin, general tadpolelike appearance,

501

anus immediately in front of anal fin, and low anterior portion of the dorsal fin.

Life History   Individuals from 5 to 40 millimeters are taken in plankton in the Fraser River plume in April and May and were found to be eating copepods, amphipods, euphausiids, ostracods, decapod larvae, pteropods, fish larvae and eggs, and phytoplankton.[1,2,3,7] A specimen was found in the stomach of a lancetfish taken on a trolling spoon at about 30 fathoms (55 m) off Quatsino Sound.[4] In Puget Sound it has been found in sponges. Spawning takes place in British Columbia in late July.

Distribution   Washington[5,8] to southeast Alaska[9] and the Aleutian Chain. In British Columbia in the southern Strait of Georgia from the surface to depths of 123 fathoms (225 m).

References   1, 2   Barraclough 1967b, c; 3 Barraclough and Fulton 1967; 4 Carl and Wilby 1945; 5 DeLacy, Dryfoos, and Miller 1963; 6 Moffett 1970; 7 Robinson, Barraclough, and Fulton 1968a; 8 Welander and Alverson 1954; 9 Wilimovsky 1954.

RED IRISH LORD

Hemilepidotus hemilepidotus (Tilesius 1810)

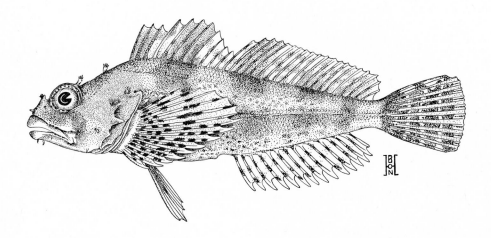

Scientific names from the Greek *hemi* (half) and *lepidotus* (scaled).

Description   Body elongate, depth about 3.7 into standard length, compressed.

Head large, depressed, its length about 2.7 into standard length. Mouth terminal, rather large, directed forward. Upper jaw extending to midpupil. Snout blunt and rounded. Lips thick. Teeth fine and sharp in rows on jaws,

502

palatines, and vomer. Interorbital space strongly concave and narrow, its width a little more than half length of eye and about 7 into length of head. Orbit elevated. Eye oval, its length about 4 into length of head. Opercular membranes broadly united so as to leave a moderate fold free from the isthmus. Caudal peduncle compressed, its least depth about 13 into standard length. Anal papilla small and rounded.

Spines Nasal large, stout, sharp, and covered with skin. Preoperculars 4, the upper 2 long, sharp, and directed backward, the lower 2 less prominent, blunt, and directed back and down. A well-developed cleithral spine above base of pectoral fin.

Fins Dorsal (1), (X)XI(XII), (18)19(20), moderate notches in the spinous part after the third spine, and between the spinous and rayed parts, emarginate. Caudal bluntly rounded. Anal (13)15(16), emarginate, all below rayed dorsal. Pectorals (15)16(17), lower 8 or 9 rays exserted, large. Pelvics I, 4, thoracic, reaching anus, rather larger in males.

Vertebrae 35.[4]

Scales Cycloid, many on raised papillae, in 2 bands, the upper with 4 scale rows surrounding the dorsal fin but not touching it, the other with a single row above the lateral line canal and up to 9 rows below it, widest above the origin of the anal fin, not touching the lateral line canal anteriorly, a triangular patch of scales under the pectoral fin. Lateral line canal sloping gently down and then straight to the base of the caudal fin, 59 to 69 scales. Cirri: 1 on each nasal spine, broad and branched, above eye a large flattened branched cirrus on edge of orbit and a smaller one medial to it, a pair of palmate cirri on the occiput, on the lower part of the lachrymal bone 4 cirri in a group and 2 separate cirri. A multifid cirrus on the upper part of each operculum, small barbel-like cirri under the lower jaw near 2 pores there, 2 small cirri on each side of the lower jaw, a broad cirrus on the end of the maxillary, 2 small cirri on the lower edge of each preoperculum, and small simple cirri singly or in pairs in broken line along the anterior end of the lateral line.

Colour Variable, predominately red, sometimes brilliant red, with brown, white, and black mottling and spotting all over. There are 4 irregular dark saddles across the back. The caudal fin has the rays darker, sometimes with vertical light bars. In some large males the pelvic fins (including the bases of the pectorals) become darkly spotted; in the pectoral axils light bars or spots make striking contrasts.[4]

Size Length to 20 inches (51 cm).

Recognition Noteworthy for having the single dorsal fin in three steps, a band of scales not more than four or five scales wide surrounding the dorsal fin, and the gill membranes united and narrowly joined to the isthmus.

Life History The red Irish lord spawns masses of tough pink eggs in conspicuous masses in shallow water or the intertidal zone. Spawning in southern British Columbia is in March. In April in southern British Columbia young are about three-quarters of an inch (16–22 mm) long and are found to be eating copepods.[1,2] The food of adults includes crabs, barnacles, and mussels.

Distribution From central California (Mussel Point) through Oregon, Washington,[3] British Columbia, Alaska, and the Aleutian Islands,[7] the Bering Sea,[6] Pribilof Islands, Saint Paul Island, Commander Islands to Kamchatka (Petropavlosk[5]). Common along the inside coast in British Columbia.

References 1, 2 Barraclough 1967a, b; 3 DeLacy, Dryfoos, and Miller 1963; 4 Peden 1964; 5 Popov 1933; 6, 7 Wilimovsky 1954, 1964.

503

BROWN IRISH LORD

Hemilepidotus spinosus (Ayres 1855)

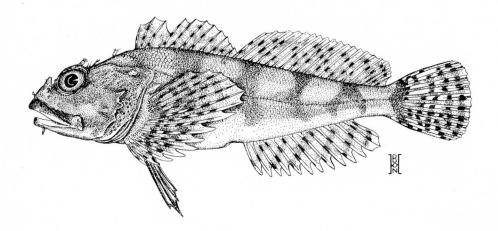

Scientific names from the Greek *hemi* (half) and *lepidotus* (scaled); and the Latin *spinosus* (spiny).

Description   Body elongate, compressed, its depth 4.6 into standard length. Head massive, depressed, its length about 2.7 into standard length. Mouth terminal, moderate in size, directed forward. Upper jaw extending almost to midpupil, overlaps lower jaw. Snout blunt and round. Lips thick. Teeth small and sharp, in bands on jaws, and rows on palatines and head of vomer. Interorbital space strongly concave, and narrow, its width about half length of eye. Orbit elevated. Eye oval, its length about 4 into length of head. Opercular membranes united and fused to the isthmus so that there is no free fold. Caudal peduncle compressed, its least depth about 14 into standard length. Anal papilla small and rounded.

Spines   Nasal rounded, blunt, covered with skin. Preoperculars 4, the upper 3 grouped together and stout, the lowest small and sharp. Two cleithral spines above base of pectoral fin.

Fins   Dorsal, (1) XI, 18 to 20, third spine shortened, deeply notched between third and fourth spines, and between spinous and rayed portions. Caudal rounded. Anal 14 to 16, emarginate except around last 4 rays. Pectorals 14 to 16, lower 7 or 8 rays thickened and emarginate. Pelvics I, 4, almost reaching anus.

Vertebrae   35.[2]

Scales   Ctenoid, small, in 2 bands, the upper band 6 to 8 scales wide on either side of the mid-dorsal line, the other around and below the lateral line canal consisting also of 6 to 8 rows. A small patch of scales behind base of pectoral fin. Lateral line canal slopes gently down to a level a little below midside, lateral line canal pores on body about 63. Cirri: on nasal spines, 1 small on each; above orbit 1 pair, multifid and large; on top of head, 2 small pairs; a large pair on nape; 1 on each operculum and preoperculum; 1 on end of each maxillary; 1 pair below lower jaw; small cirri below suborbital ridges.

Colour   Brown, often tinged with red on dorsal surface, mottled, and barred with 4 dark saddles over dorsal surface.

Size   Length to 10 inches (25 cm).

504

Recognition   Noteworthy for having scales in dorsal and lateral bands about 6 to 8 scales wide, notched spinous dorsal fin, gill membranes joining and uniting with isthmus leaving no free fold.

Life History   Adults not common in inside waters of British Columbia although young, one-third to one-half inch long (8–13 mm), have been taken in the Strait of Georgia and found to eat bryozoan larvae, amphipods, and copepods.[1] Post-larvae were taken at about 51 N, 130 W in the entrance to Queen Charlotte Sound.[3]

Distribution   Santa Barbara Island, California, to Puffin Island, 50 miles (81 km) south of Sitka, Alaska, British Columbia,[1] Bering Sea. Canadian records from Sooke, Ucluelet, Bajo Point, Sidney Inlet, Nootka Island, Ououkinsh Inlet, Brooks Peninsula, Cape Scott, and Rose Harbour. To 240 feet (73 m).[2]

References   1 Barraclough 1967a; 2, 3 Peden 1964, 1966c.

BIGMOUTH SCULPIN

Hemitripterus bolini (Myers 1934)

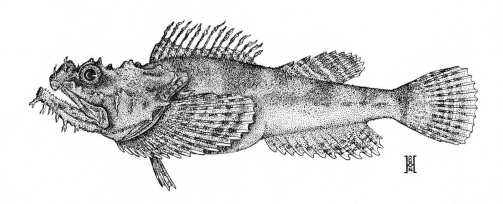

Scientific names from the Greek *hemi* (half), *treis* (three), and *pteron* (fin); and R. L. Bolin, U.S. ichthyologist.

Description   Body elongate, depth about 5 into standard length, depressed and flabby immediately behind head, relatively slender posteriorly. Head large, its length about 2.3 into standard length, low, depressed. Mouth terminal, extremely large, directed mostly forward. Upper jaw extending well behind posterior margin of eye. Lower jaw greatly protruding. Snout with a prominent knob. Teeth large and pointed, in several rows, on jaws, palatines, and vomer, larger on lower jaw and directed

505

inward, largest of all on palatines. Interorbital space markedly concave in both planes, bounded by knob on snout, ridges around and behind orbits, and nuchal spines and ridges, crossed by a low ridge joining posterior rims of orbits, its width about 3 into length of head. Eye round, its diameter about 6.4 into length of head, in a raised orbit. Opercular membranes broadly joined with a wide free flap. Caudal peduncle moderately compressed, its least depth about 12 into standard length. Anus about midway between pelvic insertions and anal origin. Anal papilla small.

Spines   Nasal spines small and sharp, between them a rounded knob. A ridge, almost continuous from anterior edge of orbit, with large blunt elevations corresponding to preocular, supraocular, postocular, coronal, parietal, and nuchal spines. Additional blunt suborbital, tympanic, and cleithral spines. Two small blunt spines below eye. Four preopercular spines, the upper 2 longest and pointed, the lower 2 blunt, the lowest reduced to a low triangle.

Fins   Dorsal (2), XIII or XIV — 11 or 12, spinous portion deeply incised (for about two-thirds the length of the spines), ragged cirruslike pennants on all spines, fourth and fifth spines shorter than third and sixth, rayed dorsal with rays slightly exserted, opaque. Caudal rounded, rays somewhat exserted. Anal 13, rays somewhat exserted. Pectorals 20 to 23, with a long base and the lower rays originating forward, with the last ray under the end of the maxillary. Pelvics I, 3, thoracic.

Scales   Ctenoid, in the form of spiny prickles or tubercles embedded in skin. Scattered on rays and spine of fins at bases. Lateral line canal vague, almost straight along midside, about 40 to 42 pores. Cirri large and numerous, mainly on head including the following positions: upper lip, 2 pairs; premaxillaries, large; preoculars, small; small on upper part of the eyeball; median

between nuchal spines, and between postocular spines; in a cluster between parietal and tympanic spines, several along suborbital ridge; near posterior end of the operculum and close to edge of operculum posterior to highest preopercular spine; 2 at end of maxillary; a series of 10 or more large cirri along and under lower jaw. One on body behind end of operculum; ragged filamentous cirri on free sides and tips of dorsal spines. A number of smaller cirri on head and pectoral fin.

Colour   Mottled gray or brown above, paler below. Four or 5 vague darker saddles across back; 2 tan stripes across head; red below anterior part of spinous dorsal; mottled red brown on membranes of spinous dorsal fin, lighter between fifth and eighth spines; chestnut brown on rayed dorsal with pale gray marbling; on pectorals alternating bands of yellow brown, light grey, and dark brown; light grey with fine black speckling and orange patches on anal fin; on caudal fin dark reddish brown with fine vertical stripes of gray brown.

Size   Length to 27 inches (69 cm).

Recognition   Notable for the large, flat, wide head with a huge mouth and protruding lower jaw, the numerous blunt spines, the raised orbits, and the greatly exserted spines of the dorsal fin.

Distribution   From northern British Columbia through southeastern Alaska[1,3] to the Bering Sea.[2] The most southerly records for the species are from British Columbia near Hakai Pass at about 51.15 N, 129 W, 118 fathoms (208 m), and off Reef Island at 53.11 N, 131 W, 67 fathoms (125 m).

References   1 Schultz, Hart, and Gunderson 1932; 2, 3 Wilimovsky 1954, 1964.

NORTHERN SCULPIN

Icelinus borealis Gilbert 1895

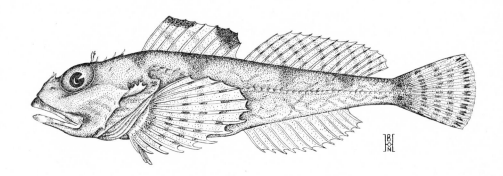

Scientific names from the Greek *Hicelos* (god of sleep — quiescent lurking fish); and the Latin *borealis* (northern).

The common name comb sculpin was used in Clemens and Wilby 1961.

Description   Body elongate, its depth about 4.5 to 5 into standard length, gently arched to robust caudal peduncle. Head compressed, its length about 2.7 into standard length. Mouth terminal, rather large, directed forward. Upper jaw extending to midarea of pupil. Teeth small and conical in pads or bands in jaws, vomer, and palatines. Interorbital space narrow and rather concave, its width about 15 into length of head. Eye large, oval, its length about 3.2 into length of head. Gill membranes broadly fused, and free of isthmus. Caudal peduncle only slightly compressed, its depth about 15 into standard length. Anus about five-sixths of distance between insertion of pelvic fins and origin of anal fin. Anal papilla small, short, conical.

Spines   Nasal stout and quite erect. Preoperculars 3, the uppermost antlerlike with 3 to 6 sharp points directed upward, the others simple and stout, the lower strong and directed downward.

Fins   Dorsal (2), IX or X — 15 to 17, well separated, spinous section not emarginate. Caudal well rounded. Anal 12 to 14. Pectorals 15 to 17, lower rays only slightly thickened, tip reaching beyond anus. Pelvics I, 2, thoracic, short, frequently curved.[1]

Scales   Ctenoid. A double uninterrupted row of scales from below dorsal origin to midway in rayed dorsal (lower) and upper part of caudal peduncle (upper). Lateral line canal arching, sloping gently down, scales rough, 37 to 40. Cirri: at base of nasal spines moderately large and simple, supraocular, large and bifid, at least 2 other pairs on head, along lateral line canal filamentous, cirri associated with lower preopercular spines. Mucous pits on lower jaw with large median one at symphysis. Anal papilla small and conical.

Colour   Dark olive gray or brown on dorsal surface, lighter below. Dark saddles, usually 4, across body. Fine brown bars on head and all fins except anal. Black spots on the fringe of the dorsal fin darker in males.

Size   Length to 4 inches (10.2 cm).

Recognition   Recognizable by the regular outline of the spinous dorsal, the antlerlike upper preopercular spine, the strong downward directed lower preopercular spine, and the double row of scales along the upper side.

Distribution   Found from Washington[2] through British Columbia to the Bering Sea[3] and the Aleutian Islands (Attu and Unalaska)[4] at depths from 10 to 121 fathoms (18–222 m).[3] In British Columbia commonly taken off the south and west coasts of Vancouver Island and in the **Strait** of Georgia and Burrard Inlet at 5 to **25** fathoms (9 to 46 m) where shrimps were found constituting a considerable amount of the food.

References   1 Bolin 1936b; 2 DeLacy, Dryfoos, and Miller 1963; 3 Grinols 1965a; 4 Wilimovsky 1964.

DUSKY SCULPIN

Icelinus burchami Evermann and Goldsborough 1907

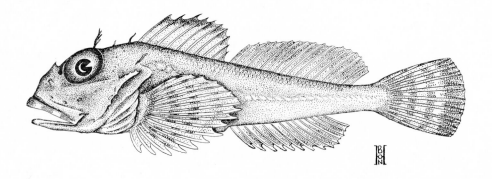

Scientific names from the Greek *Hicelos* (god of sleep — quiescent lurking fish); and James S. Burcham, U.S. Bureau of Fisheries.

Description   Body depth about 4.5 into standard length, deepest at nape, tapering sharply at first and then more gradually to caudal peduncle. Head rather large, its length about 2.6 into standard length. Mouth terminal, low, moderate in size, directed nearly straight forward. Upper jaw length about 2.2 into length of head, extending to posterior edge of pupil. Lower jaw barely included. Interorbital space flat, median ridge very faint, its width about 7 into length of head. Occipital ridges not pronounced with intervening space flat. Eye moderate, ovate, its length about 3.2 into length of head. Gill membranes broadly joined and free of isthmus. Caudal peduncle compressed, its depth about 12 or 13 into standard length. Anal papilla small.

Spines   Nasal spine present and stout. Dorsal preopercular spine strong, directed upward,

508

sharp, its length about 1.5 in orbit, 3 sharp secondary spines directed upward on its upper surface. Lower edge of preopercle with 3 short, stout, triangular spines, the upper 2 directed backward and downward, the lowest is longest and sharpest, directed downward and forward. Opercular spine flat and obscure. No spines at upper posterior angle of orbit, post-temporal, nor on subopercle.

Fins   Dorsal (2), IX or X — 16 to 18, well separated, the longest spine about 2.8 into length of head, the longest ray about 3 into length of head. Caudal narrowly rounded. Anal, 12 to 14, longest ray about 3 into length of head. Pectorals 18 or 19, in 2 sections, free edge at upper end entire, lower part with membrane excised. Pelvics I, 2, thoracic, very small, extending one-fifth to one-sixth of distance to anal origin.

Scales   Two rows of ctenoid scales extend along upper part of side from fifth to seventh dorsal spine to fourth to last ray, with upper row continuing to next to last ray. Lateral line canal with 35 to 39 scales. Rest of body without scales. Anterior pores of mandibular series opening separately on either side of symphysis. Pores on head very large. Supraorbital cirrus flat and bifid, about as long as pupil of eye. A slender simple cirrus on middle of fronto-parietal ridge, another with 2 branched tips at posterior end of ridge, a small inconspicuous one on suborbital stay, one just in front of upper end of gill opening, a small simple cirrus and a long slender one on the base of opercular flap, and a small white filament near tip of maxillary. Cirri developed at the tips of dorsal spines. No nasal cirri.

Colour   Preserved specimens yellowish brown with small light spots and dark irregular blotches. Dorsal, caudal, anal, and pectoral fins dark, blotched with white.[1,2,3]

Size   Length to 5 inches (12.7 cm).

Recognition   Noteworthy for absence of spines at upper posterior angle of orbit, on post-temporal, and on subopercle. Very large pores on head. Ribbonlike postorbital cirrus with an expanded branching tip. Incomplete double band of scales on upper part of side. Very small pelvic fins.

Distribution   Southern California. California at 310 fathoms (570 m) to southeast Alaska (Loring), at 134 fathoms (245 m).[4,5] British Columbia records from the southern Strait of Georgia, Passage Island.

References   1 Barraclough and Butler 1965; 2 Bolin 1936b; 3 Evermann and Goldsborough 1907; 4 Grinols 1965a; 5 Wilimovsky 1954.

THREADFIN SCULPIN

Icelinus filamentosus Gilbert 1890

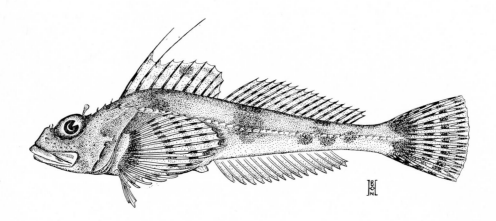

Scientific names from the Greek *Hicelos* (god of sleep — quiescent lurking fish); and the Latin *filamentum* (thread).

Clemens and Wilby 1961 use the common name filamented sculpin for this species.

Description   Body elongate, depth about 4.4 into standard length, dorsal profile rather bowed, somewhat compressed. Head length about 2.5 into standard length, about as deep as wide. Mouth terminal, moderate, directed forward. Upper jaw extends about to middle of pupil, overhanging lower. Lips rather thick. Snout bluntly rounded in both planes. Teeth fine, conical, in bands on jaws and patches on vomer and palatines. Interorbital space narrow, concave, its width about 9 into length of head. Eye rather large, elliptical, its length about 2.3 into length of head. Opercular membranes broadly joined and free of isthmus. Caudal peduncle compressed, its depth about 17 into standard length. Anal papilla short, stout, and conical.

Spines   Nasal well developed and sharp, directed backward. Frontal rather weak. Parietal well developed, both directed backward. Preopercular 4, the uppermost strongly developed and antlerlike with 2 (or more) strong secondary spines directed up; the second close to it, triangular, directed upward; and the lower 2 finer and directed down.

Fins   Dorsal (2), IX to XI — 15 to 18, distinctly separated, the first 2 spines elongated and delicate, free at ends, the second longer, the outline of the remainder of both dorsal fins little incised. Caudal fanned out and bluntly rounded. Anal 13 to 15, anterior rays thickened and exserted. Pectorals about 17, the lower 8 thickened and exserted. Pelvics I, 2, small, thoracic, extending about one-third distance to anal origin.

Vertebrae   34 or 35.[1]

Scales   Ctenoid. On upper part of body in 2 rows close to dorsal fins from around seventh spine to end of rayed section, 27 to 33, in row. On lateral line canal 36 to 39. Flaplike cirri above nostrils, a large multifid cirrus on the supraocular, cirri on top of head between preoperculum and dorsal insertion. Others reported from tip of maxillary, preopercle and cheek, and along lateral line canal.

Colour   Olive green to light brown on dorsal surface, creamy yellow to light brown on ventral surface, 4 dark saddles across back, bars of dark blotches on all fins except pelvics and anal. Sometimes dusky along margin of anal fin. Males sometimes variously blotched with orange to red. Silvery areas anterior to and behind base of pectoral fin.

Size   Length to 10.6 inches (26.9 cm).

Recognition   Recognized by the 2 elongated filamentous first dorsal rays, the second being longer, and the scale rows extending to the posterior end of the rayed dorsal fin. Long median pore under lower jaw.

Life History   The food is reported to consist of various crustaceans, including shrimps and isopods.

Distribution   From southern California, Point Loma through Washington to British Columbia, and possibly Alaska.[2,3]

In British Columbia from the southern Strait of Georgia, Porlier Pass, Active Pass, Burrard Inlet at 20 to 40 fathoms (37–73 m) Malaspina Inlet, and the west coast of Vancouver Island off Esteban Point at 60 fathoms (110 m).

References   1 Clothier 1950; 2 DeLacy, Dryfoos, and Miller 1963; 3 Grinols 1965a.

FROGMOUTH SCULPIN

Icelinus oculatus Gilbert 1891

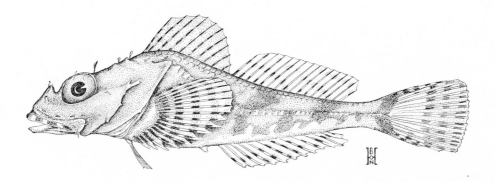

Scientific names from the Greek *Hicelos* (god of sleep — quiescent lurking fish); and the Latin *oculatus* (large eyed).

Description   Body depth about 4.2 into standard length, stout and subcylindrical anteriorly, compressed and slender behind. Head length about 2.5 into standard length, moderately convex in profile. Mouth terminal, large, directed forward. Upper jaw extending beyond centre of pupil. Lips thin and snout fairly acute in profile. Lower jaw

511

closes inside upper. A prominence on snout between nasal spines enters strongly into profile. Teeth in bands on jaws, vomer, and palatines, minute in jaws, slightly larger on roof of mouth. Interorbital space narrow, concave, its width about 15 into length of head. Eye large, oval, length about 4 into length of head. Opercular membranes joined and free of isthmus. Caudal peduncle about 16 into standard length, compressed. Anus close to anal fin. Anal papilla bluntly conical.

Spines   Nasal small, sharp, hooked backward weakly. Preopercular spines 4, the upper much the largest with 2 or 3 upward-directed spinules, the lower spines broad blunt triangles, the second close to the first. Occipital spines, procumbent.

Fins   Dorsal (2), X — 16 or 17. Caudal almost truncate. Anal 13 or 14. Pectorals 17, lower 8 rays exserted. Pelvics I, 2, thoracic, small.

Scales   Ctenoid, rather large, restricted to a double row close to dorsal fins, continued as short single rows on caudal peduncle. Lateral line canal about 38, rough, gently decurved and then straight. Cirri: on nasal simple; on postorbital large with expanded tips; filamentous near occi-pital spine, on top of head, on suborbital stay, near third preopercular spine, on tip of gill cover, and at upper end of gill opening; single and paired cirri at posterior end of maxillary; an irregular row (5–8) of filamentous cirri along lateral line canal; 2 slender cirri on upper part of eyeball.

Colour   Pale brown, 3 dark saddles across back, finer and paler markings below lateral line canal. Faint barring on dorsal, anal, and caudal fins, stronger on pectoral fins. Fleshy base of caudal dark, but rays and membrane near base notably clear.

Size   Length to 7 inches (17.8 cm).

Recognition   Noteworthy for its large mouth and eyes, thin lips, double rows of scales close to dorsal fins and continuing for about four scales as single rows on the caudal peduncle.

Distribution   A rare species known from off San Diego, California,[1] to Pendrell Sound, Redondo Islands, British Columbia.[2]

References   1 Bolin 1944; 2 McPhail 1969.

SPOTFIN SCULPIN

Icelinus tenuis Gilbert 1890

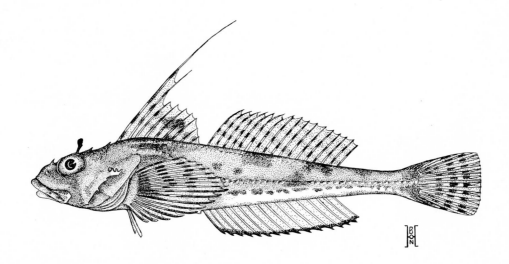

Scientific names from the Greek *Hicelos* (god of sleep — quiescent lurking fish); and the Latin *tenuis* (slender).

Clemens and Wilby 1961 used the common name lesser filamented sculpin for this species.

Description   Body elongate, greatest depth about 5.5 to 6.0 into standard length, tapering evenly from widest point behind head to caudal peduncle, nearly cylindrical. Head about 3 into standard length, somewhat depressed. Mouth terminal, moderate, directed forward. Upper jaw overhanging lower, extending almost to anterior edge of pupil. Snout blunt in profile and bluntly rounded from above. Lips thick. Teeth conical, in bands on both jaws, vomer, and palatines. Interorbital space concave, rather narrow, its least width about 13 into length of head. Eye moderate, oval, its length about 4 into length of head. Gill membranes broadly joined and free of isthmus. Caudal peduncle, almost cylindrical, its diameter

about 17 into standard length. Anus two-thirds distance from insertion of pelvic fins to origin of anal. Anal papilla small, conical.

Spines   Nasal, moderate in size, curved backward, sharp. Postocular spines well developed, directed backward, sharp. Preopercular spines 4, the upper antlerlike, with 3 to 5 sharp upward directed secondary spines; second and third spines small, the second quite close to the upper large spine.

Fins   Dorsal (2), IX to XI — 16 to 19, the first spine much elongated to almost half body length, the second also elongated but less so. Spinous dorsal emarginate, rayed part entire. Caudal bluntly rounded. Anal 13 to 17, almost entire. Pectorals about 17 with the lower 9 thickened and exserted. Pelvics I, 2, thoracic.

Vertebrae   About 37.

Scales   Ctenoid, on upper part of body in 2 rows close to dorsal fins from about middle of spinous fin to below fourth or fifth ray of rayed fin, 9 to 15 in each row. Lateral line canal curved down sharply over pectoral fin and then straight to near end of caudal peduncle. One pair moderate flaplike cirri between nasal spines and nostril, large multifid supraocular cirri over each eye. Slender, filamentous cirri elsewhere on head. Sparse small cirri on lateral line canal.

Colour   Light brown on dorsal surface variously blotched with orange, creamy white on ventral surface, dusky blotches along and below lateral line canal, and 4 darker saddles over back and upper side from nape to caudal peduncle. Silvery area between gill opening and pectoral base. Brown bars on dorsal, caudal, and pectoral fins, dark edge on anal. The male has a prominent dark spot near the end of the sixth spine on the dorsal fin.

Size   Length to 5.5 inches (14 cm).

Recognition   Distinguished by the elongated first spine, distinctly longer than the second and the flowing contour of the dorsal profile of the head.

Distribution   From San Benito Island in Baja California through Washington[1] to northern British Columbia[3] and possibly Alaska.[2] Known depth range in California 18 to 204 fathoms (33–373 m), in British Columbia 20 to 70 fathoms (37–128 m). British Columbia records from off Bowen Island and False Narrows in the southern Strait of Georgia and Tasu Sound, Queen Charlotte Islands.

References   1 DeLacy, Dryfoos, and Miller 1963; 2 Grinols 1965a; 3 Wilby 1936b.

THORNY SCULPIN

Icelus spiniger Gilbert 1895

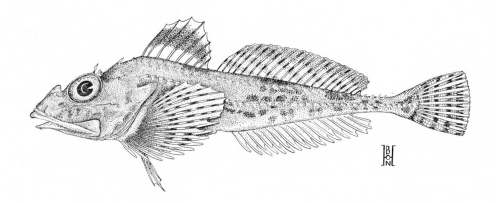

Scientific names from *Hicelos* (son of Hypnos, Greek god of sleep — quiescent lurking fish); and the Latin *spinus* (spine) and *gero* (bear).

Description   Body elongate, its depth about 6 into standard length, moderately robust and subcylindrical immediately behind head, slender and compressed posteriorly. Head large, wedgelike in profile, its length about 3 into standard length. Mouth terminal, large, directed forward. Lower jaw included in upper. Upper jaw barely extends beyond pupil of eye. End of maxillary with top turned partly outward rather than vertical. Teeth extremely small, in pads on jaws, vomer, and palatines. Interorbital space concave and narrow, its width about 14 into length of head. Eye oval, large, its length about 3.4 into length of head. Opercular membranes joined and free of isthmus. Caudal peduncle rather long and only moderately compressed, its least depth about 20 into standard length. Anus about three-quarters of distance from pelvic fins to anal fin origin. Anal papilla small and thick.

Spines   Nasals short and sharp on either side of a median hump on snout. Four preoper-cular spines, the uppermost bifid, the 2 upper spines larger and directed dorsally, the lower 2 directed down. Supraorbital spines small and in a cluster of 3 over each orbit. Occipital spines strong and directed backward. Two recognizable spines on prominent suborbital ridge.

Fins   Dorsal (2), VIII(IX) — 20 or 21. Caudal rounded. Anal 15 to 17, insertion below space within that of rayed dorsal. Pectorals (18) 19, rounded, reaching anus, lower rays exserted. Pelvics I, 3, thoracic.

Scales   Ctenoid, in a single row above the lateral line canal from nape (in line with occipital spine) to caudal, each with a large, thornlike spine, 28 to 37, and a similar row below lateral line canal from head to caudal base. A few scattered scales in axil of pectoral fin. Lateral line canal bending down from anterior end, then straight along midside, 41 to 44. No scales on head. One simple supraocular cirrus.

Colour   Brownish on upper surface, paler below. Four dark saddles across back. Dark bands on both dorsals, caudal, and pectorals; other fins plain.

Size   Length to 7.5 inches (19 cm).

Recognition   Distinguished by the rows of large thornlike spines from the head

515

to the tail, the short-based, high, spinous dorsal, and a blunt protuberance between the two nasal spines.

Distribution   From northern British Columbia to the Bering Sea,[2] and westward to Semisopochnoi Island,[3] in the western Bering Sea, Okhotsk Sea, and south to Japan (possibly as subspecies). Known from British Columbia only from one specimen caught northwest of Cape Knox, Queen Charlotte Islands at 54.37 N, 133.55 W, by N. Bourne, D. B. Quayle, and J. Scoggan.[1]

References   1 Barraclough 1971; 2, 3 Wilimovsky 1954, 1964.

LONGFIN SCULPIN

Jordania zonope Starks 1895

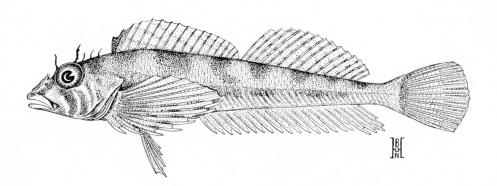

Scientific names from David Starr Jordan, eminent U.S. ichthyologist; and the Greek *zone* (zone) and *ope* (window).

Description   Body elongate, slender, and tapered, depth about 5.8 into standard length, deepest at base of pectoral fins. Head small, depressed, its length about 3.8 into standard length. Mouth terminal, small, directed forward. Upper jaw barely reaching anterior margin of eye. Lips thickened. Teeth fine, conical, in bands on jaws and vomer. Interorbital space concave, its width about 3 into length of eye. Eye oval, its length about 3 into length of head. Opercular membranes joined and free of isthmus. Caudal peduncle compressed, its least depth about 18 into standard length. Anal papilla small and conical.

Spines   Nasal long, sharp, curved backward. Preopercular 2, the upper fine, the lower well developed and directed upward.

Fins   Dorsal (2), XVII or XVIII — 15 to 17, barely separated, with entire outlines, and similar in size and shape. Caudal rounded. Anal 22 to 24, originating below posterior third of dorsal, long based, rather low with posterior 4

516

rays somewhat lengthened, all rays exserted. Pectorals about 14 with lower 7 thickened, and lower 6 much exserted. Pelvics I, 5, thoracic.

Scales   Strongly ctenoid, covering body above lateral line canal, irregularly fused; below lateral line canal generally fused to form serrate ridges directed down and back. Lateral line canal with about 48 to 50 scale rows, sloping gently downward. Cirri: 2 small cirri on either side of each nasal spine, long cirri above anterior edges of eyes and very large ones just behind midpoints of eyes. Three pairs of long slender cirri along top of head.

Colour   Olive green generously marked with red. Six or 7 dark saddles across back and another series of dark spots along midside. Oblique dark bands across dorsal and pectoral fins, wide dark, and narrow light sinuous bands on head.

Size   Length to 5 inches (12.7 cm).

Recognition   Recognized by the slender body, the long spinous dorsal and anal fins, the serrate oblique plates on the lower sides of the body, and the pelvic fins with 1 spine and 5 rays.

Life History   Breeding was observed in October. During breeding both sexes, and especially the male, darkened in colour. Several clusters of 20 to 30 eggs were released. The fish are active and highly territorial in behaviour.[1]

Distribution   Central California, Washington,[2] to Barkley Sound, British Columbia. Found in Jervis Inlet, Sooke. In the Vancouver Public Aquarium it is noted that this species frequently hangs vertically on rock faces.[3] This explains why it was rarely encountered by collectors before they began the general use of scuba diving. It is now commonly encountered and collected in Juan de Fuca Strait and the Strait of Georgia by scuba divers at depths of 2 to 18 meters.[4]

References   1 Lamb personal communication; 2 Schultz 1930; 3 Vancouver Public Aquarium 1969; 4 Wilkie 1963.

PACIFIC STAGHORN SCULPIN

Leptocottus armatus Girard 1854

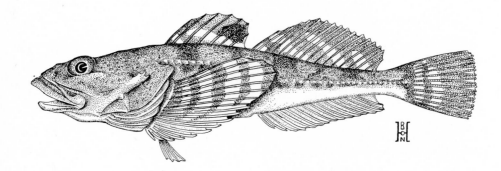

Scientific names from the Greek *leptos* (slender) and *Cottus* (a sculpin); and the Latin *armatus* (armed).

Clemens and Wilby 1961 used the common name staghorn sculpin, and in 1946 the common name cabezon.

Description   Body elongate, its depth about 5 to 5.5 into standard length, subcylindrical in cross section anteriorly, somewhat compressed posteriorly. Head large, its length about 2.6 into standard length, broad and much depressed. Mouth terminal, moderate in size, directed forward, the lower jaw included in the upper. Snout rather pointed in profile. Upper jaw extends about to posterior margin of pupil. Teeth fine, sharp, in bands on both jaws, vomer, and palatines. Interorbital space broadly concave, its width about 6 into length of head. Eye oval, its length about 5.6 into length of head. Opercular membranes fused to isthmus with no free fold. Caudal peduncle compressed, its least depth about 18 into standard length. Anal papilla small and conical.

Spines   No nasal spine, but there is a low median bump on the snout. Preopercular spines 3, the upper large and strong with 3 sharp secondary spines directed upward and a smaller one recurved, the lower spines well developed but simple, less sharp, and less prominent.

Fins   Dorsal (2), VI to VIII — 15 to 20. Caudal rounded. Anal 15 to 20. Pectorals about 19. Pelvics I, 4, thoracic.

Scales   No scales or cirri. Pores on lateral line canal 37 to 42. Lateral line canal almost straight.

Colour   Grayed olive to green with some yellow on dorsal surface. Orange-yellow to white below. Creamy yellow with green or dark bars on fins except pelvics and anal. Orange on margin with large dark spot on posterior portion of spinous dorsal fin.

Size   Length to 18 inches (46 cm).

Recognition   Recognized by the scaleless body, the prominent antlerlike preopercular spines, the dark spot on the posterior part of the spinous dorsal fin, and the strong markings on the body.

Life History   Spawning takes place in February. A voracious feeder. Food is mainly invertebrates, and the Pacific staghorn sculpin in turn is eaten by water fowl. The species is observed to bury itself, all but the eyes, in bottom sand.[2] When stressed it may produce a very low-pitched humming sound and/or expands its gill covers to give a very formidable appearance.

Distribution   From northern Baja California[1] to the Gulf of Alaska.[3] Very abundant throughout British Columbia in tide pools and at moderate depths. Penetrates lower portions of coastal streams.

References   1 Roedel 1948b; 2 Vancouver Public Aquarium 1969; 3 Wilimovsky 1954.

BLACKFIN SCULPIN

Malacocottus kincaidi Gilbert and Thompson 1905

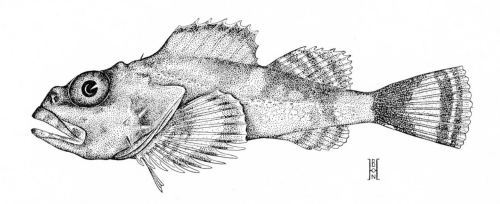

Scientific names from the Greek *malaco* (soft) and *Cottus* (a sculpin); and Professor Trevor Kincaid, of the University of Washington.

Description   Body rather elongate, its depth about 3.5 into standard length, slightly compressed. Head massive and depressed, its length about 2.4 into standard length, dorsal profile strongly arched to a blunt snout. Mouth terminal, large, directed slightly upward. Upper jaw extending to point below anterior part of pupil. Teeth small and conical, in bands on upper and lower jaws. Interorbital space moderately concave, about 6.5 into length of head. Eye large, about 4 into length of head. Gill membranes united and joined to isthmus at centre. Caudal peduncle compressed, its depth about 12 into standard length. Anus about two-thirds distance from insertion of pelvic fin to origin of anal fin.

519

Spines   Nasals low and blunt, barely perceptible under skin. Four preoperculars; the second largest with a branch at the base; the lowest blunt and poorly marked.

Fins   Dorsal (2), VIII or IX — 14 or 15, spines weak. Caudal bluntly rounded. Anal 11 or 12. Pectorals about 21, large, emarginate, the inner surface joined to the body by a fold of skin. Pelvics I, 3, thoracic, small.

Scales   Absent. Lateral line canal slightly curved down and then straight, 14 or 15 pores, large pores under lower jaw and many on head and body. A pair of large multifid cirri on anterior nasal openings, 2 pairs of filamentous cirri on side of occipital region, filamentous cirri on upper part of eyeball, numerous fine protuberances around upper jaw, and on upper part of eye, simple cirri at ends of dorsal spines.

Colour   Gray to light brown dorsally, lighter below with fine dark speckling. Several irregular brown blotches on dorsal surface, and light spots on sides. Narrow light bands on margins of all fins (except pelvic) with darker band below. Light bands on rayed dorsal, caudal, and pectoral fins. In mature males, margins of dorsal fins golden in breeding season.

Size   Length to 8 inches (20 cm).

Recognition   Noteworthy for its thin loose skin, gill membranes attached to the isthmus, light margins to fins outside dark bands.

Distribution   Recorded from Washington[1] to Alaska off Bird Island. Reported from Japan.[3] In British Columbia in the Strait of Georgia at depths from 15 to 65 fathoms (27–119 m). Burrard Inlet. Drury Inlet. Off the Queen Charlotte Islands in midwater at depths between 90 and 275 meters over depths of 1830 to 2200 meters.[2]

References   1 DeLacy, Dryfoos, and Miller 1963; 2 Taylor 1967b; 3 Watanabe 1958.

GREAT SCULPIN

Myoxocephalus polyacanthocephalus (Pallas 1811)

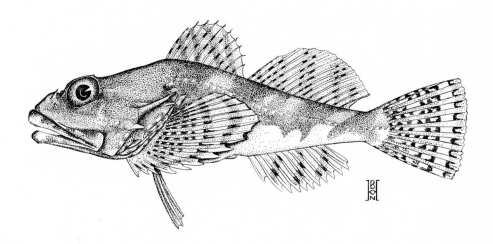

Scientific names from the Greek *myoxos* (dormouse) and *cephale* (head); and *poly* (many), *acantha* (spine), and *cephale* (head).

Description   Body depth about 3.9 into standard length, sharply tapered in both planes, almost cylindrical at head, compressed posteriorly. Head very large, its length about 2.1 into standard length, depressed. Mouth terminal, rather large, directed forward, overhung by thickened upper lip. Lower jaw extends almost to posterior margin of eye. Snout bluntly pointed. Teeth fine, in bands on jaws, palatines, and vomer. Interorbital space moderately concave, its width about 8.5 into length of head. Eye oval, its length about 5 into length of head. Opercular membranes united and attached to the isthmus so as to leave a broad free fold. Caudal peduncle compressed, its least depth about 13 into standard length. Anal papilla small and rounded.

Spines   Nasal short and blunt. Preoperculars 3, the uppermost very long, straight, stout, sharp, and directed back, out, and up; the second close to it, smaller, and covered with flesh; the lowest inconspicuous and directed downward. Well-developed opercular and cleithral spines.

Fins   Dorsal (2), IX or X — 13 to 16, rayed portion somewhat higher. Caudal slightly rounded. Anal 11 to 13, shorter than rayed dorsal in base. Pectorals about 15, lower rays most exserted. Pelvics I, 3, almost reaching anus.

Scales   Much reduced and embedded in fleshy papillae, most noticeable on head. Lateral line canal sloping down to caudal peduncle, and then straight back, about 35 lateral line canal pores. A minute cirrus above and behind each orbit, and papillae on the end of each dorsal spine.

Colour   Deep olive on dorsal surface with 4 dark saddles across back. Ventral surface pale. Brown bars running downward on relaxed unpaired and pectoral fins.

Size   Length to 2 feet 6 inches (76 cm). Larger individuals have been mentioned.

Recognition   Noteworthy for the long, straight, smooth, uppermost opercular spine and the scales embedded in fleshy papillae on the head.

Distribution   Washington[1] through British Columbia and Alaska to the Bering Sea,[3,6] including many of the Aleutian Islands,[7] and to Kamchatka[4] and Hokkaido.[5] Common at moderate depths through coastal British Columbia. In winter it is taken off

beaches in Burrard Inlet.[2] Food includes small fishes.

References   1 DeLacy, Dryfoos, and Miller 1963; 2 Lamb personal communication; 3 Matsubara 1955; 4 Popov 1933; 5 Watanabe 1960; 6, 7 Wilimovsky 1954, 1964.

SAILFIN SCULPIN

Nautichthys oculofasciatus (Girard 1857)

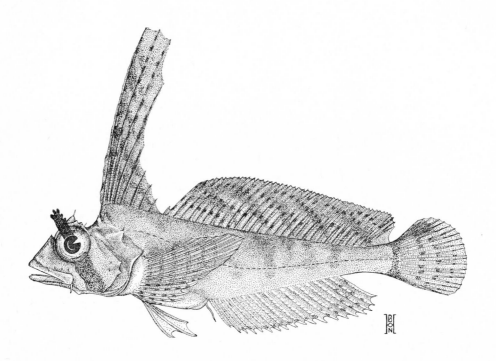

Scientific names from the Greek *nautys* (sailor) and *ichthys* (fish — sail-like fin); and the Latin *oculus* (eye) and *fasciatus* (banded).

Clemens and Wilby 1946 called this species sailor-fish, *Nautichthys oculo-fasciatus.*

Description   Body elongate, its depth about 4.1 into standard length, compressed. Head length about 3.1 into standard length, posterior part with a marked dorsal transverse furrow. Mouth terminal, moderate in size, directed almost forward. Upper jaw extending beyond centre of pupil, enclosing lower jaw. Snout steep and head consequently blunt in profile. Upper margin of orbit strongly entering profile of head. Teeth fine, in patches on jaws, vomer, and palatines. Interorbital space very concave between high orbital rims, its width about 7 or 8 into length of head. Eye large, its diameter about 3.2 into length of head. Opercular membranes fused to isthmus. Caudal peduncle short, compressed, its least depth about 14 into standard length. Anus about one-third distance from pelvic insertion to anal insertion. Anal papilla very slender, with anus surrounded in an oval fleshy fold.

Spines   Nasal spine well developed, its outer edge continuing profile of snout, sharp. On upper posterior rim of orbit 3 or 4 blunt spines in line with strong blunt flattened spines on fronto-parietal ridge. A groove on top of head between rows of spines. A large postemporal spine above gill opening. Preopercular spines 3, all blunt and skin covered, the top one largest.

Fins   Dorsal (2), VIII or IX — 27 to 30, the 2 fins practically joined by membrane, spinous fin, almost as high as snout to anus length, with 4 long weak spines, originating abruptly at, or overhanging, depression at posterior end of head, rayed fin long and moderately high. Caudal rounded and directed upward. Anal 18 to 20, relatively long, rays moderately exserted. Pectorals 13 or 14, placed low, lower 5 rays thickened and moderately exserted, tip of fin extending well beyond anal insertion. Pelvics I, 3, thoracic.

Scales   Reduced ctenoid, in form of small slender spines embedded in papillae, covering most of body and head except axils of paired fins, a narrow band extending back from the anus on either side of the anal fin, and the end of the snout and along the mid-dorsal line of the head, present on soft rays of dorsal, caudal, pectoral, and pelvic fins nearly to the tips. Lateral line canal in a flattened sigmoid curve from posttemporal spine to base of caudal, pores 41 to 45. Cirri: a large dark flattened cirrus on upper part

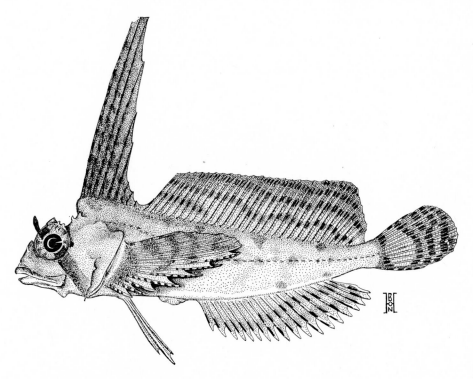

of each eyeball, in a series with 3 or 4 smaller cirri; smaller cirri usually on maxillary, tips and bases of postorbital spines and other spines on top of head, near nasal spines, along suborbital stay, and along edge of preoperculum.[2]

Colour   Variable, gray above with dark markings and obscure dusky bands, paler below. Spinous dorsal darker. Other fins, except pelvics, diagonally streaked with darker. Sometimes red flecks on rayed dorsal and on eyes. A very distinct black band running diagonally down and back through the eye.

A recognizable variant of the species occurs in Knight Inlet, British Columbia. In it, as shown in the illustration, the first dorsal is dominated by spines II, III, I rather than the first 4 spines. The whole fin is frail and when removed from fluid appears more like a mast than a sail.

Size   Length to 8 inches (20 cm)

Recognition   Identified by the long and nearly equal four or five spines in the dorsal fin, the striking diagonal band through the eye, the long dark cirrus on the eyeball, the depressed occiput, and the upturned caudal fin.

Life History   The sailfish sculpin is evidently nocturnal. It swims mainly with the long spinous dorsal fin and occasionally may be observed hanging upside down from the roof of a crevice with the long fin extending in front of the head. Eggs are orange in colour and are deposited in late winter or spring. Young, about 1 inch (23 mm), were taken in May off the outlet of the Fraser River. The food includes crustaceans.[4,6] The species is reported to avoid freezing temperatures.[1]

Distribution   Reported from near Point Sal, San Louis Obispo County, California, to Kodiak Island,[3] Alaska,[7] Bering Sea, northeast of St. Lawrence Island, Anadyr Gulf, and Cape Navarin, Okhotsk Sea, Aniva Bay, and Moneron Island in the north Sea of Japan.[5] Records of occurrences in the Bering Sea are probably in error because of accepted records based on *Nautichthys pribilovius.* Found throughout coastal southern British Columbia and frequently taken in shrimp trawls at depths down to 60 fathoms (110 m). There is little doubt that it will be found commonly in northern British Columbia with further exploration.

References   1 Andriashev 1937; 2 Bolin 1944; 3 Hubbard and Reeder 1965; 4 Lamb personal communication; 5 Matsubara 1955; 6 Robinson, Barraclough, and Fulton 1968a; 7 Wilimovsky 1954.

SMALLSAIL SCULPIN

Nautichthys robustus Peden 1970

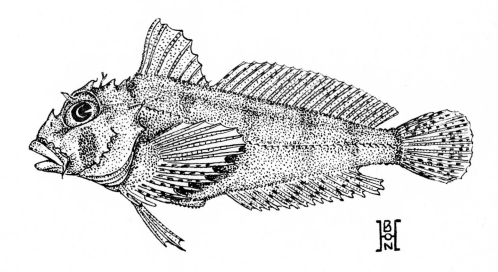

Scientific names from the Greek *nautys* (sailor) and *ichthys* (fish); and the Latin *robustus* (sturdy).

Description   Body rather elongate, its depth about 3.5 into standard length, robust and barely compressed anteriorly, strongly compressed posteriorly. Head length about 3 into standard length, slightly compressed. Mouth terminal, small, directed a little upward. Upper jaw extending to anterior part of eye, and a little longer than lower jaw. Snout steep and short. Upper margin of orbit projects well above upper profile of head. Teeth on jaws, vomer, and palatines. Interorbital space concave between high orbital rims, about 6.5 into length of head. Eye large, diameter about 3.2 into length of head. Opercular membranes fused to isthmus. Caudal peduncle compressed, its least depth about 13 into standard length. Anus close to anal fin. Anal papilla bulbous.

Spines   Nasal sharp and strong. Broad-pointed postorbital spines with small protuberances posterior to bases. Broad pointed spines in line on posterior part of occiput joined to postocular by ridges. Small spines in post-temporal region. Occiput deeply concave between ridges. Preopercular spines 3, the upper largest but all blunt and reduced.

Fins   Dorsal (2), (VII)VIII — (19)20(21), spinous part short with anterior spines longest. Caudal slightly rounded. Anal 14 or 15. Pectorals 14 to 15(16), rounded, lower 8 rays exserted, middle rays lengthened reaching anal insertion. Pelvics I, 2, thoracic, reaching anus.

Scales   Ctenoid, minute, in form of strong prickles encased in fleshy papillae; covering body except under pectoral fin, and head except snout, lips, and branchiostegals; on rays of unpaired and pectoral fins. Lateral line canal curves slightly upward in midbody, about 36 pores. Cirri: large multifid cirrus on upper part of eye; simple cirri near tips of head spines; large cirri behind postorbital spines and posterior tips of maxillae, about 6 tuberclelike cirri along postorbital margin.

Colour   Pale brown, lighter ventrally. Dark band through eye. Eye and its cirrus black. Dorsal fins speckled, with spinous fin darker. Usually 4 dark saddles across back, and dark band at base of caudal fin. Posterior edge of caudal darker.

Size   Length to 2.5 inches (6.4 cm).

Recognition   Recognizable by having a combination of: gill membranes fused to isthmus, strong longitudinal depression in occiput, scales embedded in papillae covering body except in axilla, moderate-sized spinous dorsal, second dorsal with fewer than 22 rays, and black band through eye.

Distribution   From off the Washington coast at 48.12 N, 122.49 W at 73 meters (Albatross Station 2865, September 6, 1888, USNM 127026 (Peden 1972 personal communication)) to Naden Harbour, Queen Charlotte Islands, and Attu Island, Alaska. A newly described species with its distribution still inadequately known.

References   Peden 1970.

TIDEPOOL SCULPIN

Oligocottus maculosus Girard 1856

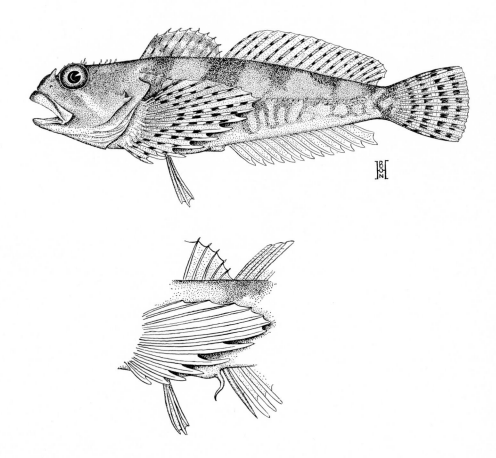

Scientific names from the Greek *oligo* (few) and *Cottus* (a genus of sculpins); and the Latin *macula* (spot).

Description   Body elongate, its depth about 4 into standard length, compressed. Head somewhat depressed, its length about 3 into standard length. Snout blunt in profile. Mouth terminal, moderate in size, directed forward and somewhat dorsally. Upper jaw extending to midpupil.

Teeth fine, in bands on jaws. Interorbital space concave, its width about 6 into length of head. Eye almost round, its diameter about 4 into length of head. Gill membranes united and free of isthmus. Caudal peduncle compressed, its least depth about 12 into standard length. Anal papilla long, slender, usually curved forward.

Spines   Nasal thick, blunt, skin covered, sometimes double. Preopercular 1, bifid, with 1 branch directed upward and the other back.

527

Fins   Dorsal (2), VIII or IX — 16 to 18. Caudal rounded. Anal 12 to 14, usually originating below posterior end of dorsal insertion, in males first 3 or 4 rays much thickened, slightly lengthened and membranes between them deeply incised. Pectorals about 14, lower 6 or 7 rays exserted. Pelvics I, 3, thoracic.

Scales   Scales absent. Lateral line canal high anteriorly, decurved, and then straight, pores 34 to 39. Cirri singly or in pairs along anterior half of lateral line canal, in 2 rows on head between rear of orbit and occiput. Small cirri at end of each maxillary, about 5 along edge of preopercle, and 1 at upper angle of operculum. Fleshy cirri near tips of anterior dorsal spines.

Colour   Reddish brown, green, or crimson on dorsal surface, white to cream tinged with green or blue ventrally. Five irregular dark saddles across back. Light spot at base of caudal fin. Fins, except pelvics, mottled and/or barred. Black spot at base of anterior membranes of spinous dorsal. In males a small orange spot on outer anterior margin of spinous dorsal. Colouring varies with environment.

Size   Length to 3.5 inches (8.9 cm).

Recognition   Notable for the forked single preopercular spine, the sparse cirri along the top of the head, and the enlarged three or four rays at the anterior end of the anal fin in the male.

Life History   The species is very abundant in tide pools around rocky shores. Observations on spawning in the Vancouver Public Aquarium showed males to clasp females with a pectoral fin and fertilize pale green eggs as they were deposited on a rock. Courting males appear to prefer females with distended abdomens as with eggs or food. The part played by the enlarged anal rays is not recorded. Age group 0 appears in late June in Canada and Alaska and by the end of the year is from 16 to 34 millimeters long. Age group I reached 40 millimeters or more. In Puget Sound growth during the 0-year is about the same or a little faster. Females reach maturity at about 1 year.[1] Tidepool sculpins show a definite tendency to return to their home pool if moved.[3]

Distribution   From northern California to the Bering Sea, the Kuril Islands, and the Okhotsk Sea.[2,4,5] Generally distributed in coastal British Columbia.

References   1 Atkinson 1939; 2 DeLacy, Dryfoos, and Miller 1963; 3 Eastman 1962; 4 Watanabe 1958; 5 Wilimovsky 1954.

SADDLEBACK SCULPIN

Oligocottus rimensis (Greeley 1901)

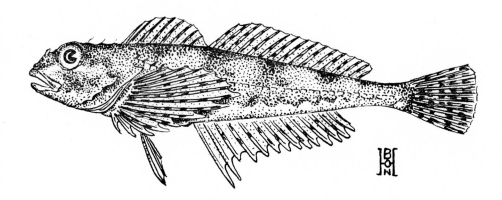

Scientific names from the Greek *oligo* (few) and *Cottus* (a genus of sculpins); and *rimensis* (cleft sword — possibly referring to the first two separated anal fin rays).

Clemens and Wilby 1946 recorded this species as the prickly sculpin.

Description   Body elongate, its depth about 5 into standard length, compressed. Head length 3 to 3.5 into standard length, slightly depressed. Snout blunt. Mouth terminal, moderate in size, directed forward and somewhat dorsally. Upper jaw extending to anterior part of pupil. Teeth fine, sharp, in bands on jaws. Interorbital space concave and narrow, its width about 6 into length of head. Eye almost round, its diameter about 4 into length of head, lower part light in colour. Gill membranes united and free of isthmus. Caudal peduncle compressed, its least depth about 15 into standard length. Anal papilla small and slender, usually curved forward.

Spines   Nasal spine broad, weak, sharp, curved backward. Four preopercular spines are all small and decrease in size from above downward, all blunt and covered with skin, the upper one simple and curved upward.

Fins   Dorsal (2), VIII to X — 16 to 19. Caudal barely rounded. Anal 13 to 15, originating below posterior part of spinous dorsal, first 2 rays in male greatly lengthened, about the same cross section, with the intervening membrane deeply incised. Pectorals about 13, very large, and rounded. Pelvics I, 3, thoracic.

Scales   Ctenoid, reduced to separated prickles, on most of body but not observed on head. Lateral line canal sloping down anteriorly and then straight to the end of the caudal peduncle, pores 35 to 41. Cirri along anterior half of lateral line canal filamentous, a spaced-out row of 4 filamentous cirri extending back along top of head from above each orbit. Small cirri on ends of maxillaries and median to nasal spine.

Colour   Light olive green or reddish brown on dorsal surface, shading into pale yellow or green below. Five irregular dark blotches across back with pale blue borders. Dark reticulations on sides. Faint green or brown bars on rayed dorsal, caudal, anal, and pectoral fins. Young often very brightly coloured.

Size   Length to 2 inches (5.1 cm).

529

Recognition   Distinguished by the blunt profile of the snout, the blunt preopercular spines with the uppermost simple and curved up, and by having the scales reduced to prickles over the whole body.

Distribution   From Baja California to Vancouver Island. Recorded from British Columbia in the southern part of the Strait of Georgia, Juan de Fuca Strait, and Barkley Sound.

FLUFFY SCULPIN

Oligocottus snyderi Greeley 1901

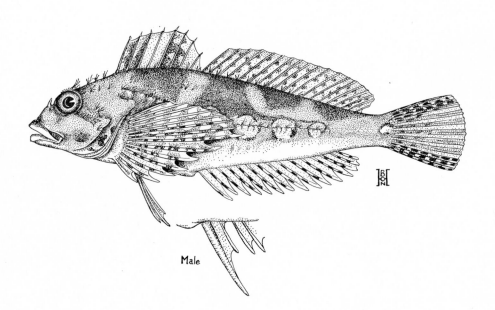

Male

Scientific names from the Greek *oligo* (few) and *Cottus* (a genus of sculpins); and John Otterbein Snyder, U.S. ichthyologist.

Description   Body elongate, its depth about 3.3 into standard length, compressed. Head length about 3.2 into standard length, slightly depressed. Mouth terminal, moderate in size, directed forward. Upper jaw extending to anterior edge of pupil. Teeth fine, in bands on jaws, and a patch on the vomer. Interorbital space strongly concave and moderately narrow, its width about 6 into length of head. Eye oval, its length about 4 into length of head. Gill membranes united and free of isthmus. Caudal peduncle compressed, its least depth about 11 into standard length. Anal papilla slender and conical.

530

Spines   Nasal broad, weak, blunt, and skin covered. Preoperculars 1, blunt and skin covered, divided at end.

Fins   Dorsal (2), VII to IX — 17 to 20. Caudal rounded. Anal 12 to 15, emarginate, its origin below spinous dorsal, in males the first ray is much enlarged and the membrane between the second normal-sized ray and the third is almost missing, the enlarged ray is prehensile and is used to clasp the lower abdomen of the female closely during copulation.[2] Pectorals about 14, lower 6 rays exserted. Pelvics I, 3, thoracic.

Scales   Scales absent. Lateral line canal high anteriorly, gradually sloping down, and then straight to the end of the caudal peduncle, pores 36 to 39. Cirri in rows of clusters: (1) along the anterior three-quarters of the lateral line canal, (2) beside the dorsal fins between the approximate centres of the 2 parts and (3) along a short row between (1) and (2). Clusters of cirri on top of head and behind rims of orbits. Filamentous cirri at tips of dorsal spines, on nasal and preopercular spines, and on edges of preopercular and opercular bones.

Colour   Bright, most often green or light reddish brown but frequently pink or lavender, 4 to 6 dark saddles across back, on sides dark circles and other markings, darkened bands on all fins but pelvics. Patterns may be less obvious in males. Colour changes with environment.

Size   Length to 3.25 inches (8.3 cm).

Recognition   Noted for its forked preopercular spine, the three rows of clustered cirri on either side of the body, and the single enlarged anal ray in males.

Distribution   From Baja California and southern California to the Queen Charlotte Islands (Skidegate Inlet) and southeastern Alaska near Sitka.[3] Most of the British Columbia records are from the outer coasts, Ucluelet, Clayoquot and Kyuquot sounds. San Juan Islands in Washington.[1]

References   1 DeLacy, Dryfoos, and Miller 1963; 2 Morris 1956; 3 Quast 1968.

THORNBACK SCULPIN

Paricelinus hopliticus Eigenmann and Eigenmann 1889

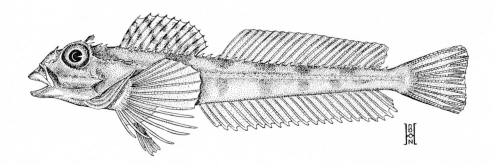

Scientific names from the Greek *para* (near) and *Icelinus* (a genus of sculpins); and *hopliticus* (armed).

Description   Body elongate, its depth about 6.5 into standard length, slightly compressed anteriorly, more so posteriorly. Head length about 3.9 into standard length. Mouth terminal, small, directed forward. Jaws about even. Upper jaw not reaching anterior edge of orbit. Teeth small, sharp, conical, in broad bands on jaws, vomer, and palatines. Interorbital space very narrow and strongly concave, its width about 7.5 into length of head. Eye oval, its length about 4 into head length. Gill membranes united and free of isthmus. Caudal peduncle compressed and slender, its least depth about 20 into standard length. Anus close to origin of anal fin.

Spines   Nasal strong and sharp, curved backward. Postocular spine stout and directed backward. Parietal spines, 2 on each side, stout and strong, all these spines in line. Preopercular spines 3, the upper 2 strong, sharp, directed backward, and close together. The lowest spine smaller. Two small spines behind orbit in line with a strong post-temporal spine on side of head. Two series of serrations, one along the suborbital ridge and another arching around the edge of the upper half of the orbit and entering profile.

Fins   Dorsal (2), XII or XIII, 19, rayed part not emarginate. Caudal almost truncate. Anal 23, emarginate, markedly longer than rayed dorsal. Pectorals 15, lower 6 rays lengthened and much exserted. Pelvics I, 5, thoracic, extending past anus.[2]

Scales   Ctenoid, numerous, each scale with a fine spine embedded in a soft papilla, covering the entire body and the upper posterior part of the head to the nasal spines, except for small tracts under pectoral and pelvic fins and along base of anal fin. A prominent row of about 35 much enlarged scales with sharp backward-directed hooklike spines on either side of the dorsal fin. Lateral line canal almost straight with enlarged scales with somewhat enlarged spines, about 44. Cirri: a large flattened postorbital cirrus, a relatively large flattened cirrus on cheek immediately behind end of maxillary. Other cirri occasionally seen on lower margin of suborbital stay, on maxillary, on posterior end of suborbital stay, at base of opercular flap, and 2 or 3 along margin of the preoperculum.[1,2]

Colour   Light olive green with 4 to 6 poorly defined brownish cross bands, sides below lateral line canal with 7 or 8 dusky purplish blotches. Yellow-brown flecks along lateral line canal, a distinct series of small blue spots below it. Lower surface light gray. Spinous dorsal olive green with yellow-brown bars. Rayed dorsal, caudal, and upper part of pectoral transparent with brown rays. Pelvics tipped with yellow.

Size   Length to 7 inches (18 cm).

Recognition   Noteworthy for the longitudinal series of scales beside dorsal fin, each bearing a prominent recurved spine, the greatly exserted pectoral rays, the anal fin definitely longer than the rayed dorsal.

Distribution   From southern California (off San Diego) to northern British Columbia. The only Canadian record is from about 53.12 N, 130.16 W near Banks Island. Found on rocky bottom between 48 and 100 fathoms (88–183 m). Rare.

References   1 Barraclough and Ketchen 1963; 2 Bolin 1944.

TADPOLE SCULPIN

Psychrolutes paradoxus Günther 1861

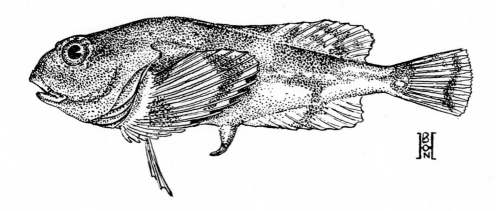

Scientific names from the Greek *psychrolutes* (one who bathes in cold water); and *paradoxos* (unaccountable).

Description   Body depth about 3.5 into standard length, stout forward, tapered toward tail, almost round in cross section immediately behind head, compressed posteriorly. Head large, its length about 2.5 into standard length, depressed. Mouth terminal, moderate in size, directed forward and up. Upper jaw extends to upper part of the eye.

Teeth fine, conical, in several rows on jaws. Interorbital space ill-defined, broadly concave, its width approximately 4 into length of head. Eye length about 3.7 into length of head. Gill membranes fused to the isthmus. Caudal peduncle compressed, its least depth immediately behind the anal fin, about 12 into standard length. Anus about midway between origin of pelvics and anal fin. Anal papilla large, conical, pointed, directed forward.

Spines   Absent.

533

Fins   Dorsal (1), X to XII — 12 to 17, spinous portion and anterior part of rayed portion very low, all buried in a ridge of opaque skin and rays not readily counted without dissection, posterior part of rayed fin higher. Caudal rounded. Anal 12 to 14, rays hidden in skin, relatively high and truncated posteriorly, mirroring rayed dorsal. Pectorals 20 to 23. Pelvics I, 3, thoracic.

Scales   Scales absent. Lateral line canal straight, indistinct, about 10 well-spaced pores. Papillae small and scattered over body and upper part of eyeball in ill-defined rows. A soft knob on upper anterior rim of orbit. Body jellylike so that freshly caught fish appear dead.

Colour   Gray to light brown on dorsal surface, creamy white on ventral surface, black bands and light blotches across back. Irregular pale orange, pink, and yellow markings on pectoral fins in addition to a strong dark bar two-thirds of the way to the tip. Dark vertical bars on caudal fin.

Size   Length to 2.3 inches (5.8 cm).

Recognition   Recognizable by the large smooth head giving a tadpolelike appearance, the anus midway between pelvic and anal fins, the small papillae on the body, the low spinous portion of the dorsal fin, and the strong dark bar on the pectoral fin.

Life History   In southern British Columbia young tadpole sculpins between 12 and 22 millimeters long occur in plankton in low salinity water near the outlet of the Fraser River in April and to a less extent in May. They were found to be eating barnacle larvae, copepods, and amphipods.[1,2,8] The eggs are about 1.4 millimeters in diameter. It favours water at low temperatures (but above freezing).

Distribution   From Puget Sound[3,6] to Adak Island[11] and the Bering Sea[10] to the Kuril Islands[4] to Etorofu,[9] Kamchatka,[7] Okhotsk Sea,[6,9] and north Sea of Japan.[5,6] At moderate depths from 30 to 120 fathoms (55–220 m). Generally distributed through British Columbia coastal waters, occasionally taken by trawling off West Vancouver at 18 to 22 fathoms (33–40 m), and by beach seining.

References   1, 2 Barraclough 1967a, b; 3 DeLacy, Dryfoos, and Miller 1963; 4 Grinols 1965a; 5 Jordan and Starks 1904; 6 Matsubara 1955; 7 Popov 1933; 8 Robinson, Barraclough, and Fulton 1968a; 9 Shmidt 1950; 10, 11 Wilimovsky 1954, 1964.

SLIM SCULPIN

Radulinus asprellus Gilbert 1890

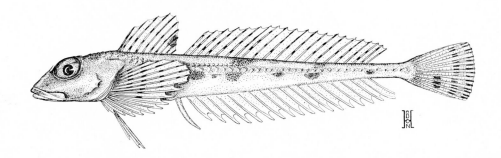

Scientific names from the Latin *radula* (scraper); and *asper* (rough) and *ella* (diminutive).

Clemens and Wilby 1946 called this species darter sculpin. This name is now assigned to *R. boleoides*.

Description   Body very elongate, depth about 8 into standard length, terete or depressed. Head length about 4.3 into standard length, fairly blunt and convex in profile. Mouth terminal, moderate in size, directed forward. Upper jaw extending to anterior edge of pupil, barely including lower jaw. Teeth small, conical, in bands on jaws and vomer. Interorbital space flat, very narrow, its width almost 20 into length of head. Eye large, oval, its length about 3.3 into length of head. Gill membranes united and joined to isthmus so as to leave a broad free fold. Caudal peduncle slender and cylindrical, its least depth about 40 into standard length. Anus close to anal fin insertion. Anal papilla slender and long.

Spines   Nasal long and slender, directed backward. Preoperculars 4, the upper well developed and sharp, the second triangular, with a sharp point, and the lower 2 reduced in large individuals to rounded protuberances.

Fins   Dorsal (2), (IX)X(XI) — 20 to 23, the spinous portion rounded. Caudal shallowly rounded. Anal (21)23(25). Pectorals (17)18(20), lower 10 rays exserted but not thickened. Pelvics I, 3, thoracic.

Scales   Ctenoid, small, in a row originating in the interorbital space, extending around the posterior margins of the eyes and continuing back, with about 25 scales above the lateral line canal, as far as the middle of the rayed dorsal fin; in a band across the anterior edge of snout. Lateral line canal follows dorsal contour above midside with 38 to 41 large keeled scales. Cirri few and not evident.

Colour   Dorsally olive green, blotched with orange bars, 3 or 4 indistinct dark saddles, diffuse dark spots along lateral line canal. Dark streak extending forward and down from eye. Dorsal, caudal, and upper pectoral fins faintly barred with reddish brown on rays. Margin of anal creamy white. Dark blotch on posterior margin of rayed dorsal.

Size   Length to 6 inches (15.2 cm),[2] or about 5 inches (12.7 cm).[1]

Recognition   Noted for its slender terete body, long slender nasal spines, scales across the end of the jaw, single row of scales above lateral line canal extending from inside of orbit to middle of second dorsal fin.

Distribution   From Coronado Islands, southern California, through Oregon, Washington, and British Columbia to Alaska.[3] At depths of 10 to 70 fathoms (18–128 m) in British Columbia and to 155 fathoms (284 m) in California. A common fish throughout coastal British Columbia at moderate depths. Taken in shrimp trawls.

References   1 Bolin 1944; 2 Clemens and Wilby 1961; 3 Grinols 1965a.

DARTER SCULPIN

Radulinus boleoides Gilbert 1898

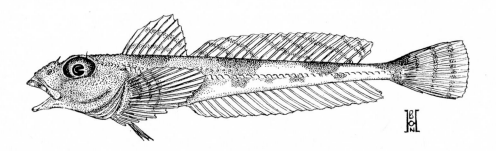

Scientific names from the Latin *radula* (scraper); and the Greek *boleo* (dart) and *oid* (like — a dart(er), a group of slender freshwater fishes).

Description   Body slender and very elongate, its depth about 10 into standard length, almost round in cross section throughout. Head length about 4 into standard length, profile convexly bowed but snout longer than eye length. Mouth terminal, small, directed forward. Upper jaw barely extends to anterior part of eye. Lower jaw closes inside upper. Teeth minute on jaws, vomer, and anterior ends of palatines. Interorbital space flat and narrow, its width about 15 into length of head. Eye oval, its length about 3.5 into length of head. Gill

membranes united below isthmus, joined to it at its tip. Caudal peduncle slender and round in cross section, its least depth about 30 into standard length. Anus about two-thirds distance from pelvic base to anal origin. Anal papilla a large slender cone.

Spines   Nasal spines sharp and stout but weakly attached. Preopercular spines with dorsal one evident, medium in size, and sharp, below it a broad triangle, followed by inconspicuous flutings in the margin of the bone.

Fins   Dorsal (2), X — 21, the spinous portion short and relatively high, the rayed portion long. Caudal rounded. Anal 21 to 23, long and moderate in height. Pectorals 19 to 20, lower rays barely exserted. Pelvics I, 3, thoracic, small (less than 1.2 times pectoral base).

Scales   Ctenoid: on body in a single row above anterior part of lateral line canal but not in contact with it, under pectoral fin; on head scattered, in front of eye, in bands across interorbital space and behind eyes, on operculum and on occiput. Lateral line canal almost straight along and above midside, 39 to 40 pores. A small cirrus on upper posterior part of each eyeball, and another pair sometimes detectable on either side of occiput.[1]

Colour   Olive gray with 4 wide brown saddles with darkened boundaries across the back, small dark blotches along middle of sides, throat and belly silvery, other ventral surfaces white. Both dorsal fins, caudal, and upper part of pectorals faintly barred with brownish. Pelvics and anal colourless.

Size   Length to about 5.5 inches (14 cm).

Recognition   Noteworthy for its slender rounded form, single exposed preopercular spine, only one cirrus evident and it on the eyeball, and short pelvic fin.

Distribution   From Santa Catalina Island, California to off Langara Island of the Queen Charlotte group about 54.12 N, 133.00 W (specimen in British Columbia Provincial Museum) (Peden 1972 personal communication). The only other Canadian record is from 2 miles (3 km) off Cape James, Hope Island at the entrance to Queen Charlotte Strait.[2] Found at depths of 65 to 80 fathoms (119–146 m).

References   1 Bolin 1944; 2 McPhail 1969.

GRUNT SCULPIN

Rhamphocottus richardsoni Günther 1874

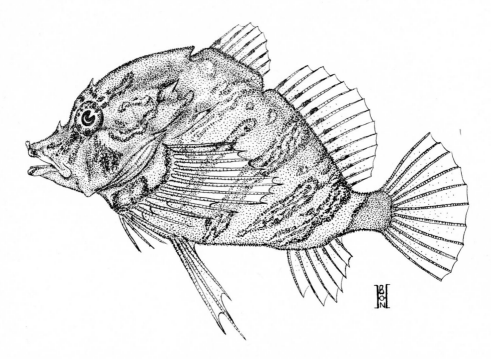

Scientific names from the Greek *rhamphos* (snout) and *Cottus* (a genus of sculpin); and John Richardson, naturalist and explorer.

Clemens and Wilby 1946 used the common name grunt-fish for this species.

Description   Body short, its depth about 2.1 into standard length, compressed. Head massive, its length about 1.8 into standard length, flattened on top, 2 prominent, rounded, fronto-parietal ridges extending along top from anterior edge of orbit to nape, terminating in a stout, blunt spine. Mouth terminal, small, directed forward. Snout narrow and rounded. Upper jaw not extending halfway to posterior edge of orbit, includes lower jaw. Lips thick. Teeth small, conical, in rows on jaws, sometimes on

vomer and palatines. Interorbital space broad, raised, concave, its width about 3.8 into length of head. Eye oval, its length about 6 into length of head. Gill membranes joined to isthmus so as to leave only a small gill opening. Caudal peduncle compressed, its least depth about 9 into standard length. Anus about three-quarters of distance from pelvic insertion to anal insertion. Anal papilla short and conical.

Spines   Nasal stout, curving backward. Postocular stout, sharp, directed backward. Nuchal blunt. Cleithral and supracleithral at upper edges of gill slit, well developed and sharp. Clavicular very stout and sharp. Preopercular strong and sharp.

Fins   Dorsal (2), VII or VIII — 12 or 13, spinous portion small with weak spines and recessible into a groove, a notch between the 2 fins. Caudal well rounded. Anal 6 or 7, small, placed well back. Pectorals 15 or 16, lower 8 thickened and greatly exserted. Pelvics I, 3, insertion about halfway between pectoral insertion and anus.

Scales   Reduced to minute plates bearing stiff multifid spines, each embedded in an erect fleshy papilla; covering body, head, and on bases of dorsal, anal, pectoral, and pelvic fin rays and on first dorsal spine; minute on eyeball, in 4 or 5 rows on upper part. Lateral line canal high anteriorly following dorsal contour from head and through anterior two-thirds of rayed dorsal, about 25 pores obscured by scale papillae. A small movable flaplike cirrus on the upper lip of large individuals, not always displayed.

Colour   On dorsal surface creamy yellow barred with dark brown streaks passing downward and forward; creamy to lemon yellow or pale red on ventral surface, creamy brown on head with dark brown blotches, dark streaks radiating from eyes and extending on cornea; bright red on caudal peduncle at base of caudal; clear coral red margined with crimson on rayed dorsal, pectoral, anal, and caudal fins; orange on exserted rays of pectoral fins and on pelvic fins; black spots on spinous dorsal fin and near base of rayed dorsal.

Size   Length to 3 inches (7.6 cm).

Recognition   Readily identified by the short stout form and the large head with heavy blunt ridges, the long snout, and the greatly exserted lower rays of the pectoral fin. (Note colour illustration, Plate I.)

Life History   Young grunt sculpins 14 to 18 millimeters long have been taken in the low-salinity water off the outlet of the Fraser River in late April, May, and June. They were found to be eating copepods, amphipods, decapod and barnacle larvae, and fish larvae, including walleye pollock.[1,2,3,5] Older individuals also eat crustaceans. The grunt sculpin is common along the whole coast in tide pools and shallow water, usually along rocky shores, but it occurs also on sandy beaches, and it has been taken in trawls down to a depth of 90 fathoms (165 m). It swims with its head high or crawls over rocks and seaweed on its long pectoral fin rays. The common name comes from the half grunting, half hissing sound made when the fish is removed from water. Yellow to orange eggs are produced in winter.

Distribution   From Santa Barbara, California,[4] to the Bering Sea.[6] Generally distributed through coastal British Columbia.

References   1, 2, 3 Barraclough 1967a, b, c; 4 Phillips 1958b; 5 Robinson, Barraclough, and Fulton 1968a; 6 Wilimovsky 1954.

CABEZON

Scorpaenichthys marmoratus (Ayres 1854)

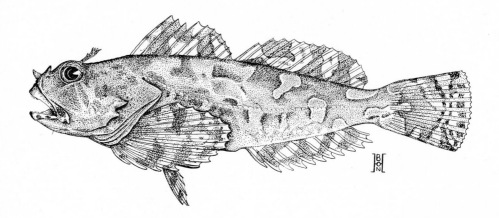

Scientific names from the Greek *scorpaena* (a related species) and *ichthys* (fish); and the Latin *marmoratus* (marbled).

Clemens and Wilby 1946 called this species giant marbled sculpin.

Description   Body elongate, its depth about 3.4 into standard length, compressed. Head length about 2.9 into standard length, depressed. Mouth terminal, rather large, directed forward. Snout steep and blunt. Upper jaw extending to anterior part of pupil. Lips thickened. Teeth small, in bands on jaws, palatines, and vomer. Interorbital space concave, its width about 5.4 into length of head. Eye oval, entering profile, its length about 5 into length of head. Opercular membranes broadly fused, free of isthmus. Caudal peduncle compressed, its least depth about 10 or 11 into standard length. Anal papilla small.

Spines   Nasals stout, blunt, skin covered, directed partly backward in front of each eye. Preopercles 3, blunt and skin covered, the ventral one reduced, the upper 2 stout and directed backward.

Fins   Dorsal (1), extremely indented, (VIII) XI(XII), 15 to 18, the first 3 or 4 spines exserted, successively smaller, the last of the series followed by a more excised fin membrane and a longer spine, emarginate. Caudal barely rounded. Anal 11 to 13, all excised, and all under the rayed part of the dorsal fin. Pectorals 15, lower 6 to 8 moderately exserted and thickened. Pelvics I, 5, thoracic.

Vertebrae   About 35 (10 counts in California).[2]

Scales   So deeply embedded as to appear absent. Lateral line canal sloping down and back from anterior end, then straight to the end of the caudal peduncle. Pores 71 to 88. Cirri: a large triangular median flap that folds down on the premaxillaries, a large cirrus — lance shaped with branches along one edge — above the posterior margin of each orbit, and a small fleshy flap at the end of each maxillary.

Colour   Olive green to brown or gray, mottled with large paler areas frequently edged with darker shades of the general body colour. Colour variable, changing through a wide range with the environment. Juveniles are frequently reddish in base colour.

540

Size   Length to 30 inches (76 cm). Weight to 25 or 30 pounds (11–14 kg).[7]

Recognition   Noted for the flaplike cirrus on the snout, the form of the spinous part of the dorsal fin with the anterior spines exserted and becoming progressively shorter to a minimum at the third or fourth spine, the marbled colour pattern, and the pelvic fins with a spine and five rays.

Life History   Spawning takes place in British Columbia from January through March. The eggs are stuck prominently on rocks where, because of their greenish colour, they are evident. In California eggs are produced in several batches. A female 43 centimeters long may produce a batch of 49,000 eggs, a 65-centimeter specimen 95,000 eggs.[4] The eggs are unwholesome.[3] Their toxicity may be associated with their prominence on rocks at low tide and their avoidance by beach foraging mammals and birds.[5] Females grow faster than males, attaining a length of about 45 centimeters after 3 years compared with 34 centimeters for males, and 57 centimeters at 7 years compared to 52 centimeters. At 13 years females reach 72 centimeters.[4] Food of young under one-half inch in length (11 mm) was copepods, their nauplii, amphipods, and barnacle larvae. From 14 to 22 millimeters food consisted of copepods and fish larvae.[1] Food of juveniles and adults consists, in order of importance, of crustaceans, fishes and molluscs.

Distribution   Baja California (Turtle Bay) to the Queen Charlotte Islands in British Columbia and Samsing Cove near Sitka in southeastern Alaska.[6] Abundant at moderate depths. Adults sometimes found in very shallow water (1 m).

Utilization   In spite of its acceptable size the cabezon is not generally used commercially or highly regarded in the sports fishery.

References   1 Barraclough 1967a; 2 Clothier 1950; 3 Hubbs and Wick 1951; 4 O'Connell 1953; 5 Pillsbury 1957; 6 Quast 1968; 7 Roedel 1948b.

541

MANACLED SCULPIN

Synchirus gilli Bean 1889

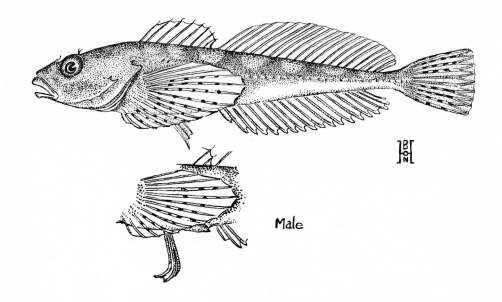

Male

Scientific names from the Greek *syn* (together) and *cheir* (hand — fused pectoral fins); and Theodore Gill, U.S. ichthyologist.

Description   Body very elongate, its depth about 7 into standard length, moderately compressed. Head rather slender, its length about 3.4 into standard length. Mouth terminal, rather small, directed forward, lower jaw included in the upper, and extending about as far as the anterior end of orbit. Upper lip thick. Teeth fine and pointed in rows in both jaws. Interorbital space flat with raised rims on orbits, its width about 6 into length of head. Opercular membranes joined and free of isthmus. Caudal peduncle slender and compressed, its least depth about 20 into standard length. Anus far forward, about one-quarter of distance from pelvic fin base to anal origin. A midventral concavity in both sexes. Anal

papilla robust, cylindrical, with a slender tip, recessed in the concavity between the anus and the anal fin.

Spines   Nasal stout and sharp. One preopercular spine, sharp, and widely bifid.

Fins   Dorsal (2), IX or X — 20 or 21, the first spine barely separated from the second. Caudal rounded. Anal 20 or 21. Pectorals 21 to 23, large, completely united anteriorly and ventrally with the rays curving inward. Pelvics I, 3, thoracic; in males the rays are expanded moderately and turned forward so that they are effective in clasping the female between their tips and the tip of the widely opened jaw,[3] in the female the fins are curved outward.[4]

Scales   Ctenoid, may be in a row on either side near base of dorsal fin, on lateral line canal well spaced, 38 to 40, otherwise absent. Cirri, postocular, 1, small. Three small cirri on edge of preoperculum. About 7 filamentous cirri along lateral line canal ending about the tip of the pectoral fin. One cirrus at the tip of each dorsal spine.

Colour   Green to yellowish brown on dorsal surface, paler below. About 7 light blotches across back. Vague pale blotches along lower side. Colour varies with habitat. Membranes of fins clear, some black pigment on rays of dorsal, pectoral, and caudal fins.

Size   Length to 2.5 inches (6.4 cm).

Recognition   Readily identified by the united pectoral fins.

Life History   Found in broad leafed algae growing on floats in strong currents at Friday Harbor. Mature at 2 inches (5.1 cm)

and ripe in early May. Eggs pink and adherent. Adheres to aquarium walls in captivity. Temperature tolerance is low and mortalities occur at about 13 C. Food includes small crustaceans.

Distribution   From San Miguel Island, southern California and Monterey Bay,[1] central California, to Sitka, southeastern Alaska,[4,6] Washington.[2,5] In British Columbia on both sides of Vancouver Island. Clings to barnacles on pilings and rocks with its paired fins.

References   1 Bolin 1950; 2 De-Lacy, Dryfoos, and Miller 1963; 3 Krejsa 1964; 4 Miller and Erdman 1948; 5 Walker 1953; 6 Wilimovsky 1954.

ROUGHSPINE SCULPIN

Triglops macellus (Bean 1883)

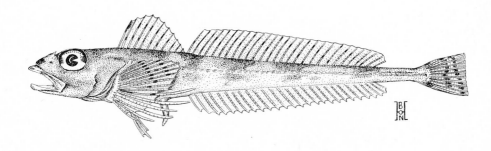

Scientific names from *Trigla* (a genus of fish with lateral plates) and the Greek *ops* (like); and the Latin *macer* (thin) and *ella* (diminutive).

In Clemens and Wilby 1946 this species was called *Prionistius macellus,* the rough-spined sculpin.

Description   Body very elongate, depth about 8.2 into standard length, almost cylindrical in cross section. Head length about 4.1 into standard length. Mouth terminal, rather large, directed forward. Snout pointed. Upper jaw extending to anterior part of pupil. Fine teeth, in bands on jaws and vomer. Interorbital space slightly concave, narrow, its width about 17 into length of head. Eye oval, its length about 4.4 into length of head, its lower third light in colour. Opercular membranes fused and free of isthmus. Caudal peduncle slender and subcylindrical in cross section, its least depth about 3.5 into standard length. Anal papilla large, conical, curved forward, constricted at tip. Anus about midway between pelvic insertion and anal origin.

Spines   Nasal short, sharp, directed backward. Preoperculars 3, all small and sharp, directed backward, decreasing in size from above down.

Fins   Dorsal (2), XI — 28 or 29. Caudal small and truncate. Anal 28 or 29, origin below origin of rayed dorsal. Pectorals 15 to 17, lower 5 to 7 rays greatly exserted and expanded. Pelvics I, 3, thoracic.

Scales   Skin below lateral line canal in a series of folds running down and back. Scales ctenoid, very small, covering upper head and body above lateral line canal, on rays of dorsal, caudal, and pectoral fins and on edges of skin folds. Lateral line canal sloping slightly downward from anterior end and then straight along midside. Moderate-sized scales along lateral line canal, 50 to 53.

Colour   Olive green to light brown on dorsal surface, cream on ventral surface, silvery on throat. Five dark saddles across back. Fins translucent with faint brown bars on rayed dorsal, caudal, and pectoral. Black spot at edge of membrane of spinous dorsal between first 2 spines. Males with a dark spot on the side of the snout.

Size   Length to 8 inches (20 cm).

Recognition   Noteworthy for the slender body, the oblique folds of skin on each side of the body edged with minute scales, the absence of a row of large scales on the upper side, and the single row of fine prickles across the upper side of the eyeball.

Distribution   Washington,[1] near the Alaskan peninsula,[3] and the Bering Sea.[2] Records are available for southern, central, and northern parts of British Columbia. From 10 to 50 fathoms (18–92 m).

References   1 DeLacy, Dryfoos, and Miller 1963; 2, 3 Wilimovsky 1954, 1964.

RIBBED SCULPIN

Triglops pingeli Reinhardt 1832

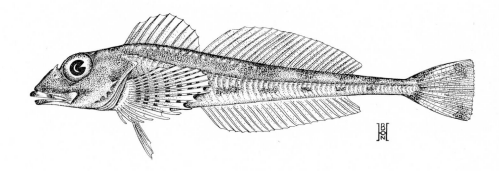

Scientific names from *Trigla* (a genus of fish with lateral plates) and the Greek *ops* (like); and from the name of an unidentified individual.

This species was recorded as *Triglops beani* in Clemens and Wilby 1946 and 1961.

The French name is *faux-trigle barde*.

Description   Body elongate, terete, its depth about 7.8 into standard length, moderately stout anteriorly, tapering evenly to a slender caudal peduncle. Head pointed, gently arched, its length about 4 into standard length. Mouth terminal, rather large, directed forward. Upper jaw reaching midpoint of pupil. Teeth fine, in bands, on jaws and vomer. Interorbital space narrow, somewhat concave, its width about 13 into length of head. Eye large, oval, its length about 3.5 into length of head. Opercular membranes fused to each other and free of isthmus. Caudal peduncle slightly compressed, its least depth about 21 into standard length. Anal papilla elongate, conical, curved forward. Anus midway between insertion of pelvic fins and origin of anal fin.

Spines   Nasals short, sharp, conical, directed backward. Frontals and parietals blunt, small, and prostrate. Preoperculars 4, all blunt, the lower 2 much so, directed partly downward.

Fins   Dorsal (2), X or XI — 23 to 26. Caudal truncate, small. Anal 23 to 26, origin below that of the rayed dorsal. Pectorals 17 or 18, the lower 7 or 8 rays moderately exserted but not especially thickened. Pelvics I, 3, thoracic.

Scales   Skin below lateral line canal in a series of folds running down and back. Scales ctenoid, small, covering upper part of head and back above lateral line canal, on rays of dorsal, caudal and pectoral fins and along edges of the skin folds. A row of enlarged raised scales for the first two-thirds of the length, about one-third of the distance from the dorsal insertion to the lateral line canal. Enlarged scales along lateral line canal 49 or 50. Lateral line canal slopes down from anterior end, then runs straight to base of caudal fin. Three diffuse rows of scales across upper part of the eyeball.

Colour   Light olive brown on dorsal surface, white below. Five dark saddles across back, In males, narrow black stripe along body below lateral line canal, separated from it by a narrow silvery streak; in females the stripe represented by a series of irregular dark areas.

Size   Length to 8 inches (20 cm).

Recognition   Noteworthy for the tapering body, the oblique folds of skin on each side of the body below the lateral line canal edged with minute scales, the row of raised, rough scales at the anterior end along the upper part of each side, and the rows of prickles along the upper side of each eyeball.

Distribution   From Washington to the Bering Sea[3] and Aleutian Islands.[4] Rare in the Chukchi Sea. Common at 10 to 50 fathoms (18–92 m) in the Bering Sea.[1] Off Hokkaido.[2] In the North Atlantic north of Cape Cod. In British Columbia reported from the general vicinity of Victoria.

References   1 Andriashev 1937; 2 Watanabe 1960; 3, 4 Wilimovsky 1954, 1964.

FAMILY AGONIDAE   POACHERS

The Agonidae is a family of small, bottom fishes set apart by having the body completely covered with rows of bony plates which meet but do not overlap. The centre of abundance for the family is the North Pacific. There is a rayed dorsal fin and usually a spinous dorsal. The anal fin is without spines; the pectoral is expanded and fanlike; and the pelvic is reduced to one spine and two rays. The cheek is completely filled in with the suborbital bones. Agonidae are most frequently found at moderate depths but are sometimes taken at great depths (to 1200 m), and some species are occasionally found in tide pools. Poachers and alligatorfishes.

KEY TO THE AGONIDAE

1 Mouth ventral, directed downward, surrounded by large cirri ....
  .... *Agonus acipenserinus,* Sturgeon poacher, p. 550

or 1 Mouth terminal or subterminal, directed mostly forward, cirri not clustered
  close to mouth 2

2 Dorsal fins 1 .... *Anoplagonus inermis,* Smooth alligatorfish, p. 552

or 2 Dorsal fins 2 3

3 Gill membranes united, free of isthmus 4

or 3 Gill membranes joined to isthmus 7

4 Plates on body smooth or only slightly keeled ....
  .... *Pallasina barbata aix,* Tubenose poacher, p. 565

or 4 Plates on body armed with rough spines 5

5 Body robust and deep, rising steeply behind head to dorsal origin; caudal
  fin asymmetrical ....
  .... *Hypsagonus quadricornis,* Fourhorn poacher, p. 560

or 5 Body slender without steep rise behind head .... Genus *Occella* 6
  (An 83-millimeter specimen of the pricklebreasted poacher, *Stellerina xyosterna*
  taken off Sherringham Point in Juan de Fuca Strait at 90 meters on February 2,
  1965, is being recorded by W. E. Barraclough and A. E. Peden. The specimen is
  in the British Columbia Provincial Museum. It is notable for having a first dorsal
  fin originating behind the nape, a body slightly depressed anteriorly, gill membranes
  free of the isthmus, no tubular snout or barbel at the symphysis, and no large plates
  on the breast, or teeth on the vomer or palatines.)

6 Nasal spine represented (if at all) by a blunt protuberance; anus nearer
  pelvic base than anal origin; anal rays about 9; no spinous plates on breast
  .... *Occella verrucosa,* Warty poacher, p. 562

or 6 Nasal spine present, hooked backward; anus nearer anal origin than pelvic
  base; anal rays 10 to 12, spinous plates on breast ....
  .... *Occella impi,* Pixie poacher, p. 561

7 Plates on body smooth; body stout ....
  .... *Bothragonus swani,* Rockhead, p. 558

or 7 Plates on body with rough spines; body moderately slender 8

NORTHERN SPEARNOSE POACHER

Agonopsis emmelane (Jordan and Starks 1895)

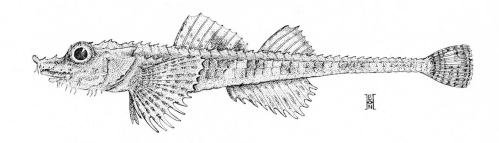

Scientific names from *Agonus* (generic name of one of the poachers) and the Greek *opsis* (like); and *en* (in) and *melane* (ink — dark colour).

This species was recorded by Clemens and Wilby 1946 as *Averruncus emmelane* Jordan and Starks, the window-tailed seapoacher. Clemens and Wilby 1961 used the common name windowtail poacher.

Description   Body elongate, depth about 7.5 into standard length, greatest immediately behind head, slightly depressed throughout. Head slightly depressed, about 3.9 into standard length, moderate occipital pit dorsally at back of head divided by longitudinal ridge. Mouth small, inferior but directed mostly forward. Upper jaw longer. Snout with longitudinal pit. Lips thickened, covered with fine papillae in front of jaws bearing small teeth. Interorbital space strongly concave between high orbital ridges, with 3 raised longitudinal ridges. Eyes about 3.9 into length of head, 2 or several rows of spiny processes on upper side of eyeball. Gill membrane joined to isthmus. Caudal peduncle long.

Spines   On snout, 2 pair, the anterior ones large, stout, blunt, directed forward, and covered with skin; the posterior ones small, sharp, naked,

and directed backward and laterally. Nasals behind pit on snout, sharp, naked, fine, directed up. At anterior end of orbit a large, flattened, multifid protuberance. Frontal arising from serrate orbital ridge, stout, sharp, directed backward. Stout spines overlapping backward in row from frontal and from back of eye. Small rough spines in groups under and before eyes, and in a larger row forming an incomplete shelf under and behind eye.

Fins   Dorsals (2), VII to IX — 7 or 8, closely placed. Caudal rounded. Anal 10 or 11, originating under fourth quarter of first dorsal, rays fleshy and extending well beyond membrane. Pectorals about 14, broad, rays fleshy, the lower 8 or so extending well beyond fin membrane. Pelvics I, 2, thoracic.

Scales   Replaced by hard plates which usually have spines or keels, arranged in 4 rows on either side at anterior end of body and 6 rows in posterior part of caudal peduncle, 2 lateral on each side, one dorsal, and an unkeeled ventral row. Lateral line canal slightly waving, progressing down from anterior end, and then straight, 38 to 42 pores. Cirri: on snout 1 or 2 pairs, on side of upper jaw, 1 pair; 3 pairs above end of maxillary, several under lower jaw, several close to edge of operculum, 1 on each of most of branchiostegals.

Colour   Light brown on dorsal surface, white to brownish beneath. Dark saddlelike markings across back and on sides, 6 or more, continued as dark bars on dorsal, anal, and pelvic

549

fins. Dark on tip of snout and on pelvic fins. Caudal generally dark with a conspicuous semi-transparent light spot not reaching margin.

Size   Length to 8 inches (20 cm).

Recognition   Recognizable by the pointed snout with its two blunt, skin-covered spines, the slightly inferior mouth, and the semitransparent light spot not reaching the margin on the caudal fin.

Distribution   Recorded from California through Washington[2] to southeast Alaska.

In British Columbia from surface to 70 fathoms (0–128 m) off the southern west coast of Vancouver Island. A 15-millimeter individual from the Strait of Georgia had been eating crab larvae.[1]

References   1 Barraclough and Fulton 1968; 2 DeLacy, Dryfoos, and Miller 1963.

STURGEON POACHER

Agonus acipenserinus Tilesius 1811

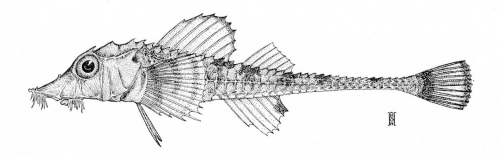

Scientific names from the Greek *a* (without) and *gonia* (joints); and the Latin *acipenserinus* (like a sturgeon).

In 1946 Clemens and Wilby used the common name sturgeon-like sea-poacher.

Description   Body elongate, depth about 6 into standard length, tapered posteriorly to a long, fine caudal peduncle, about as wide as deep throughout. Head about 3.3 into standard length, rather flattened above

and below. Mouth moderate in size, ventral, directed downward, not completely closing, weakly protrusible. Snout flattened, broadly pointed. Lips loose and fleshy. Teeth minute. Interorbital space flat between moderately raised edges of the orbit. Eye moderate in size, about 4.3 into length of head. Gill membrane joined to isthmus. Anus immediately behind pelvic fins.

Spines   On nasals, 2 pair; 1 anterior pair directed forward, cylindrical; 1 bluntly pointed pair directed up. An unpaired, small, single, blunt, median spine at the tip of the snout. Another single or branched spine median on the snout. Frontal spines sharp, curved, directed back from raised rim of orbits. Parietal spines blunt, prominent, arising from strong ridges. A second well-formed ridge extends back from the posterior edge of the orbit.

Fins   Dorsal (2), VIII to X — 7 to 9, both well forward, moderately separated. Caudal rounded. Anal 6 to 9. Pectorals 16 to 18, expanded, bottom 4 rays emarginate. Pelvics I, 2, thoracic, in males length about equal to snout, in females half as long.

Scales   Replaced by rows of plates bearing spines, 4 rows on each side anteriorly, reduced to 2 lateral, and dorsal and ventral series toward tail fin. Lateral line canal starts near top of operculum forward, about midside for posterior three-quarters of body, 30 to 40 pores. Cirri large on lower side of end of snout, and at ends of maxillary in dense multifid clusters. A few single cirri on lower jaw.

Colour   Light grayish brown on dorsal surface, light yellow to orange on ventral surface, orange spot under each eye. Dark saddlelike markings across back and sides, bright yellow on cirri, dusky on fins, dark blotch on posterior tip of anal fin in older individuals.

Size   Length to 12 inches (30.5 cm).

Recognition   Recognizable by the shiny plates along the sides, the inferior mouth with striking clusters of cirri at its corners and on the lower part of the snout.

Life History   Swimming has been observed to be mainly through undulating movements of the pectoral fin. Crustaceans and marine worms are included in the food.

Distribution   Known from Oregon, Tillamook County, and off Waldport[2,4] through British Columbia, Alaska, and both sides of the Bering Sea to Anadyr Gulf.[1,3] Common along the whole coast of British Columbia where it is taken abundantly between 10 and 30 fathoms (18–55 m).

References   1 Andriashev 1937; 2 Bond 1959; 3 Schmidt 1936; 4 Starks 1911.

SMOOTH ALLIGATORFISH

Anoplagonus inermis (Günther 1860)

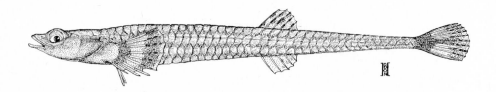

Scientific names from the Greek roots *an* (without), *plac* (scales or spines), and *Agonus* (a genus of poachers); and the Latin *inermis* (unarmed).

In 1946 and 1961 Clemens and Wilby used the common names smooth sea-poacher and smooth poacher.

Description　Body elongate, depth about 9 or 10 into standard length. Anterior part of the body slightly depressed, dorsal and ventral surfaces concave, the dorsal markedly so, greatest girth about tips of pectoral fins, tapering evenly to caudal peduncle. Head about 5.1 into standard length, strongly depressed. Spineless. Mouth terminal, rather small, directed slightly upward with the lower jaw projecting. Interorbital space slightly concave, not quite as wide as diameter of eye. Eye about 5 into length of head. Gill membrane joined over isthmus.

Fins　Dorsal (1), 5 or 6, small. Caudal well rounded. Anal 4 or 5, small, under dorsal. Pectorals 9, rays fleshy, last 3 with ends free from membrane. Pelvics I, 2, thoracic.

Scales　Reduced to smooth plates, a few quite thin in thoracic region. Plates in 4 rows on each side anteriorly. Sharp bends in rows 1 and 4 produce dorsal and ventral concavities

referred to above. In caudal peduncle region there are 6 rows of plates, 2 on each side, one dorsal and one ventral. Ventral row only slightly curved. Sharpened bends in rows on dorsal surface and upper side. Lateral line canal curved down from anterior end, straight for posterior two-thirds of body. Pores 41 to 44.

Colour　Brown dorsally, brownish gray below. Darker band from snout to base of pectoral. Vertical dark bars on pectoral and oblique bars on dorsal fin formed by mottling, minute spots on anal, faint dark bars across body. Caudal fin dark with light patches dorsal and ventral.

Size　Length to 6 inches (15 cm).

Recognition　Noteworthy for its smooth plates; soft, single, rayed dorsal fin; two light patches on its caudal fin, and the broadly concave dorsal surface.

Distribution　Known from the State of Washington[1] to the Gulf of Alaska and Korea.[2,3] In British Columbia most records are from the southern Strait of Georgia. Taken also near Sooke, in Hecate Strait, and in Burke Channel.

References　1 DeLacy, Dryfoos, and Miller 1963; 2, 3 Wilimovsky 1954, 1964.

GRAY STARSNOUT

Asterotheca alascana (Gilbert 1895)

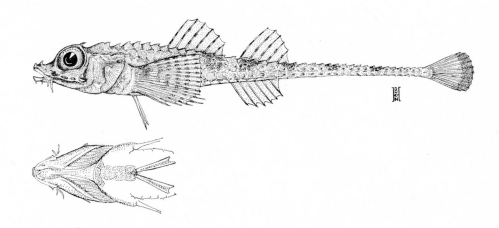

Scientific names from the Greek *astero* (star) and *theca* (case); and Alaska.

Description   Body elongate, depth about 8 into standard length, depth greatest a short distance behind head, tapered, slightly depressed, more so in caudal peduncle. Head about 4.4 into standard length, somewhat depressed. Mouth terminal, small, directed forward. Upper jaw slightly projecting. Interorbital space narrow and deeply concave. Eye large, its diameter about 3 into length of head, 5 to 8 spinous projections in a single line on the upper side of the eyeball. Gill membrane united and joined to the isthmus with a small free fold. Caudal peduncle long and slender.

Spines   At end of snout 5 or more small spines allegedly in the form of a star. Nasals moderate and short. Frontals sharp, directed backward. A ridge under each eye. Shallow transverse occipital pit on top of head preceded by 2 pairs of blunt spines.

Fins   Dorsal (2), V to VIII — 5 to 7, moderately developed and placed fairly close together (about one-third to one-half the fin base). Caudal rounded. Anal 6 to 8, originating about halfway below interspace between dorsals. Pectorals about 15 with lower 5 or 6 rays extending well beyond membrane. Pelvics I, 2, thoracic.

Scales   Replaced by plates with spines, anteriorly, 4 rows on each side; on caudal peduncle 2 rows on each side, an unpaired dorsal row, an unpaired row without spines ventrally. Lateral line canal curved downward from anterior end and then straight. A pair of cirri, often 1 large and 1 small, at the end of the maxillary, and 1 or more small cirri on each lower jaw.

Colour   Greenish gray to light brown on dorsal surface, very light brown on ventral surface. Five or 6 dark brown saddlelike markings across back and on sides. Dark brown bars on dorsal and caudal fins. Paired fins light.

Size   Length to 5 inches (13 cm).

Recognition   Distinguished by the "star shaped" arrangement of spines on the rostral plate of the snout, the origin of the anal fin at a point between the two dorsals, the single pair of plates in front of the pelvic

553

fins, and the absence of spines on the sub-orbital bones.

Distribution   From northern California (41.19 N) through Washington,[1] British Columbia, Alaska, to the Bering Sea.[3]

The species is common in British Columbia from Race Rocks off southern Vancouver Island to Rennell Sound, Queen Charlotte Islands, including the Strait of Georgia. Depths are recorded from 10 fathoms (18 m) in British Columbia to 138 fathoms (252 m) in Alaska.[2]

References   1 DeLacy, Dryfoos, and Miller 1963; 2 Grinols 1965a; 3 Wilimovsky 1954.

SPINYCHEEK STARSNOUT

Asterotheca infraspinata (Gilbert 1904)

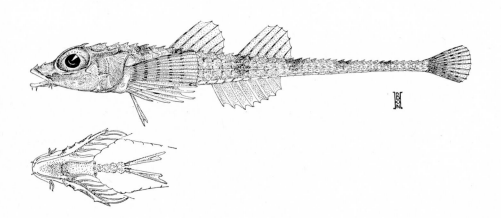

Scientific names from the Greek *astero* (star) and *theca* (case); and the Latin *infra* (below) and *spinata* (spined).

Description   Body very elongate, depth about 8.5 or 9 into standard length, somewhat depressed, tapered toward caudal peduncle from behind head. Head about 4.2 into standard length, slightly compressed. Mouth terminal, small, directed slightly upward. Jaws about equal. Interorbital space strongly concave, its width less than half length of eye. Eye large, its diameter about 3 into length of head, 5 to 7 spiny projections on upper side of eyeball in a single line. Gill membrane united by a free fold which in turn is united to the isthmus. Caudal peduncle compressed.

554

Spines   A cluster of small spines on rostrum reputed to look like a star. Nasal spine small, short, and curved, projecting backward. Frontals obtuse, directed backward. Two pairs of spines on top of head point backward, immediately in front of shallow transverse occipital pit. A low ridge underneath each eye.

Fins   Dorsal (2), V to VIII — 5 to 7, rather small and well separated. Caudal rounded. Anal 6 to 8, originating below posterior part of first dorsal. Pectorals about 15, the lower longer and incompletely joined by membrane. Pelvics I, 2, thoracic.

Scales   Replaced by spine-bearing bony plates in 4 rows on each side anteriorly, giving way in caudal peduncle to 2 lateral rows, 1 dorsal and 1 spineless ventral row. Lateral line canal curving down slightly from anterior end, then straight, 37 to 39 pores. Cirri, 2 large on end of each maxillary, small cirri beneath side of lower jaw just anterior to middle, and a fine cirrus beneath the point of the lower jaw.

Colour   Dorsal surface light olive green to light brown, paler beneath. Five or 6 dark saddle markings across back and sides. Dark bars on dorsal, caudal, and pectoral fins. Pelvics and anals light.

Size   Length to 4.75 inches (12.1 cm).

Recognition   Recognizable by having the cluster of small spines on a movable plate on the snout, the anal fin originating below the first dorsal fin, and the single pair of plates in front of the pelvic fins.

Distribution   Known from northern California (41.19 N),[2] Washington,[1] British Columbia, to the Bering Sea.[3] It has been recorded from southern British Columbia in waters of and off the southern part of the Strait of Georgia and off the west coast of Vancouver Island.

References   1 DeLacy, Dryfoos, and Miller 1963; 2 Fitch 1966a; 3 Wilimovsky 1954.

BIGEYE POACHER

Asterotheca pentacanthus   (Gilbert 1890)

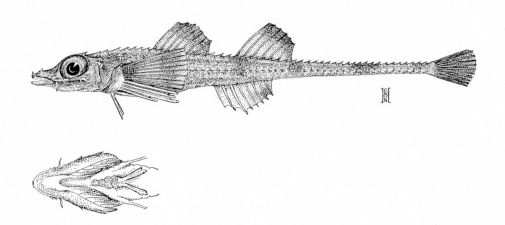

Scientific names from the Greek *astero* (star) and *theca* (case); and *penta* (five) and *acantha* (spine).

Clemens and Wilby 1961 recorded this species as bigeye starsnout, *Asterotheca pentacantha*.

Description   Body elongate, its depth about 9 into standard length, greatest depth a short distance behind head, tapered, slightly depressed, more so in caudal peduncle. Head about 4.7 into standard length, somewhat depressed. Mouth terminal, small, directed forward. Jaws about even. Interorbital space narrow and deeply concave. Eye large, about 2.8 into length of head, 4 to 6 blunt, spinous projections in a single line on upper part of eyeball. Gill membrane united and joined to the isthmus with a free fold. Caudal peduncle long and slender. Anal papilla of male directed backward.

Spines   At end of snout, 5, or more, small spines, allegedly in the form of a star, on a movable rostral plate. Nasals moderate and sharp. Frontals sharp, directed backward. A ridge under each eye. A shallow transverse occipital pit on top of head, preceded by 2 pairs of blunt spines.

Fins   Dorsal (2), V to VIII — 6 or 7, moderately developed and placed fairly close together (separated by about one-half a fin base). Caudal rounded. Anal 6 to 8, originating below interspace between dorsal fins, closer to first. Pectorals about 15, with lower 4 or 5 rays greatly exserted and thickened. Pelvics I, 2, thoracic.

Scales   Replaced by plates with spines, anteriorly 4 rows on each side, on caudal peduncle 2 rows on each side, an unpaired row dorsally, and an unpaired spineless row ventrally. Lateral line canal curves down at anterior end and then straight. Pores in lateral line canal 39 to 42. Cirri at posterior end of maxillary, 2; 1 or more small cirri on each side of lower jaw.

Colour   Olive brown on dorsal surface, paler below. Five or 6 dark brown saddlelike markings on back and sides. Dark brown to dusky on dorsal, caudal, and pectoral fins. Pelvic and anal fins pale.

Size   Length to 7.75 inches (19.7 cm).

Recognition   Distinguished by the star-shaped arrangement of spines on the rostral plate on the end of the snout, the origin of the anal fin below the space between the two dorsal fins, the two pairs of plates immediately in front of the pelvic fins, and the absence of spines in front of the suborbital bone.

Distribution   Southern California at 75 to 497 fathoms (137–910 m),[2] through Oregon at 100 to 150 fathoms (183–275 m),[2,4] Washington at 178 fathoms (326 m),[2,4] British Columbia, Gulf of Alaska (Chirikof Island), and the Bering Sea.[5] Two British Columbia records are from the Strait of Georgia off Galiano Island at 72 fathoms (132 m),[1] and off the west coast of Vancouver Island.[3]

References   1 Clemens and Wilby 1961; 2 Grinols 1965a; 3 McAllister personal communication; 4 Schultz and DeLacy 1936; 5 Wilimovsky 1954.

BLACKFIN POACHER

Bathyagonus nigripinnis Gilbert 1890

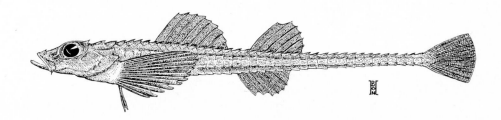

Scientific names from the Greek *bathos* (deep) and *Agonus* (a poacher); and the Latin *niger* (black) and *pinna* (fin).

Description   Body very elongate, depth about 10 into standard length. Evenly tapered from end of pectoral fin to rather slender caudal peduncle. Body generally about as wide as deep but slightly compressed in caudal peduncle. Head somewhat depressed, its length about 4.7 into standard length. Mouth terminal, small, directed very little upward, lower jaw slightly longer. Interorbital very narrow and strongly concave with a strong longitudinal ridge in the centre. Eye very large, its diameter about 3.0 into length of head. Gill membrane attached to isthmus.

Spines   On plate at end of snout 5 minute spines. Nasal spine small, sharp, directed backward. Frontal small, sharp, directed backward. A ridge of confluent poorly developed spines under the eyes.

557

Fins   Dorsal (2), VI to VIII — 6 or 7, separated by a little less than half the base of either. Caudal rounded. Anal 7 to 9. Pectorals 15, lower 4 or 5 rays thicker but membrane reaching nearly to ends. Pelvics I, 2, thoracic.

Scales   Replaced by spine-bearing plates in 4 rows on each side of forward part of the body but reduced to 2 rows plus dorsal and ventral rows behind the second dorsal fin. Lateral line canal slightly curving down from anterior part of body but nearly straight, pores 40 to 44. A large and a small cirrus on the maxillary near its posterior end.

Colour   Light brown on dorsal surface, dusky light brown on ventral surfaces. Dark blue on ventral surface of head. All the fins very dark.

Size   Length to 8 inches (20 cm).

Recognition   Noteworthy for the dark colour on the fins, the protruding lower jaw, and the large eye.

Distribution   Oregon through Washington, British Columbia and Alaska to the Bering Sea,[2] at depths from 50 to 500 fathoms (92–920 m) and off Kamchatka[1] to 682 fathoms (1250 m). In British Columbia known from the southern Strait of Georgia. Common in shrimp nets operating below 50 fathoms (92 m).

References   1 Andriashev 1937; 2 Grinols 1965a.

ROCKHEAD

Bothragonus swani (Steindachner 1877)

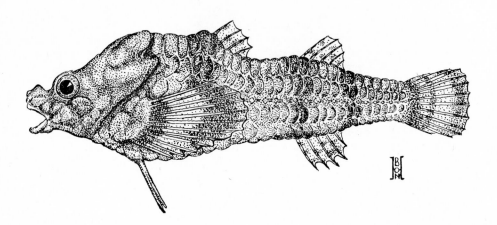

Scientific names from the Greek *bothros* (pit) and *Agonus* (a poacher); and James G. Swan of Port Townsend, Washington.

Clemens and Wilby 1946 assigned the name deep-pitted sea-poacher *Bothragonus swanii* to this species and in 1961 used deep-pitted poacher.

Description   Body depth about 3.5 into standard length, body depth and width almost equal immediately behind head, compressed farther back. Head about 2.7 into standard length, slightly depressed, shaped like a wedge, blunted at the snout. A very noticeable occipital pit on top of the head, several processes extending into pit from posterior edge. Mouth small, terminal, directed somewhat upward. Interorbital space concave, about 8.2 to 8.9 into standard length.[3] Eye small, about 5 or 6 into length of head, margin of eyeball with a series of spinelike projections. Gill membrane joined to broad isthmus.

Spines   No sharp spines, rounded protuberances on frontal bones over eyes, on sides of occipital pit, and numerous elsewhere.

Fins   Dorsal (2), II to V — 4 or 5, small. Caudal rounded. Anal 4 or 5. Pectorals about 10, large, supported well out from sides of body. Pelvics I, 2, very narrow and rays appear fused, thoracic.

Scales   Replaced by rounded, raised bony plates placed edge to edge in 8 rows on most of body, 7 on caudal peduncle. Lateral line canal curving sharply downward in its anterior third, straight to centre of caudal peduncle, about 32 pores. Cirri on lips, dentary and isthmus, too small for ready observation.

Colour   Very variable, depending on background.[5] Brown with dark bars, orange with bluish bars, or scarlet with brown bars.[3]

Size   Length to 3.5 inches (8.9 cm).

Recognition   Distinguished by the rounded plates and a broad head having a deep cavity with processes inside.

Distribution   Recorded from Sonoma County, California, through Oregon and Washington to British Columbia, Kodiak Island southeast Alaska, and Alaska. British Columbia records are from Williams Head to the Queen Charlotte Islands.[1,2,3,4,6,7]

References   1 Bean and Weed 1920; 2 Haig 1951; 3 Houck 1958; 4 Hubbard and Reeder 1965; 5 Quast 1968; 6 Schultz 1930; 7 Snow 1959.

FOURHORN POACHER

Hypsagonus quadricornis (Cuvier 1829)

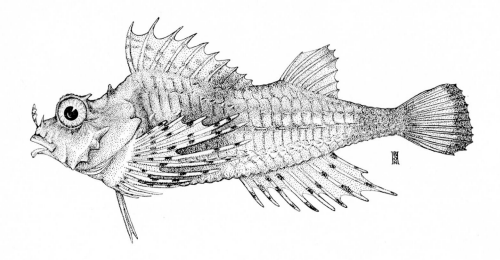

Scientific names from the Greek *hypsi* (high) and *Agonus* (a poacher); and the Latin *quattuor* (four) and *cornu* (horn).

Clemens and Wilby 1946 used the common name four-horned sea-poacher for this species.

Description   Body depth about 3.5 into standard length, somewhat compressed dorsally, sturdy ventrally. Head about as long as body depth, a slight depression at the occiput. Strong cranial ridges. Mouth terminal, small, directed slightly upward, below a blunt snout. Jaws about equal, lips rather thick. Interorbital space deeply concave between raised edges of orbits. Eye moderate in size, about 4.5 into length of head, in very prominent raised orbit. Gill membrane united, free from isthmus. Caudal peduncle compressed and sturdy.

Spines   Nasals slender, sharp, curved backward. Frontals directed back and out, sturdy and blunt, arising from orbit. Occipitals directed up

and out, sturdy and blunt. Preopercular, 5, all stout and blunt, 4 of them in a roughly stellate cluster and 1 below and forward. A large blunt protuberance behind angle of jaw.

Fins   Dorsals (2), IX to XI — 6 or 7, spinous dorsal originating from prominent ridge on back, rayed dorsals from a smaller ridge. Caudal rounded, lower part slightly larger. Anal 9 or 10, rays long, exserted. Pectorals about 13, distal ends of lower 7 or 8 free from membrane. Pelvics I, 2, thoracic.

Scales   Scales replaced by rows of plates bearing spines: below lateral line canal, in 2 rows, one complete with about 29 strong spines on side, and another with rounded spines toward midventral line and extending to about middle of anal fin; above lateral line canal, 2 broken rows, (1) from near occiput to the origin of rayed dorsal, and (2) 3 or 4 large spaced-out spines starting above pelvic fin and passing into a close row of smaller spines, extending above midside from below the posterior part of the first dorsal to the end of the caudal peduncle. Lateral line canal nearly straight. An unpaired nasal cirrus, moderately slender, about diameter of eye in length, cross-striped, sometimes branched.

Colour   Brown with various markings of yellow and brown on dorsal surfaces. Paler on ventral surface. Several dark bars across body and fins. Dark margin on tail fin. The fish is frequently covered by a hydroid animal giving it a plumose appearance.

Size   Length to 3.5 inches (8.9 cm).

Recognition   Notable for stout body with spinous plates, abrupt elevation before well-developed dorsal fins, high-set eyes, and prominent spines on top of head, and cirrus on top of snout.

Distribution   From Puget Sound along the west coast of North America to Bering Sea, the west coasts of Kamchatka, Shantar Islands, elsewhere in the Okhotsk Sea.[1,2,3] At moderate depths through British Columbia.

References   1 Matsubara 1955; 2 Popov 1933; 3 Shmidt 1950.

PIXIE POACHER

Occella impi Gruchy 1970

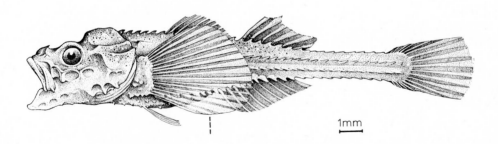

1mm

Scientific names from the Latin *occa* (harrow) and *ella* (diminutive); and *impi* (an arbitrary combination of letters).

Description   Body elongate, about 5 into standard length, robust anteriorly, tapering to a moderate caudal peduncle, slightly compressed. Head length about 3.5 into standard length, rather deep. Mouth terminal, small, directed upward. Lower jaw somewhat protruding. Upper jaw barely extending to anterior part of eye. Small teeth on jaws, vomer, and palatines. Inter-orbital space broad and slightly concave. Eye small, the orbit length about 5 into length of head. Gill membranes joined and free of isthmus. Caudal peduncle long and moderately stout with little change in depth throughout its length, its least depth about 14 into standard length. Anus closer to anal origin than pelvic base.

Spines   Nasal spines present but low. Supraorbital and occipital crests present, without spines. Ridges on opercular and supraopercular regions. Broad pits along lower jaw and subocular ridge.

Fins   Dorsal (2), IX — 6. Caudal rounded. Anal 9, originating and terminating ahead of rayed dorsal. Pectorals 18, long, reaching beyond origin of rayed dorsal, lower 6 rays exserted. Pelvics I, 2, thoracic, short.

Scales   Replaced by plates with ridges or spines in 4 rows on each side of the anterior part of the body, 8 rows replaced by 6 on the anterior end of caudal peduncle, 2 laterally on each side, one dorsally, and a ridged row ventrally. Various pricklelike plates on thoracic and throat regions. Lateral line canal high anteriorly, along midside posteriorly, pores 36. A flaplike barbel at end of upper jaw.

Colour   The preserved specimen is generally brownish with the ventral surface only slightly lighter, posterior end of caudal peduncle darker. Distal tips of both dorsal fins lightly dotted with brown, the rest colourless. Central portion of base of caudal fin brownish, distally the pigment fanning out to cover entire fin. A brownish stripe on the upper third of base of

pectoral fin expands to cover entire distal third of fin.

Size   Length 0.8 inch (2 cm).

Recognition   Noteworthy for the deep head, the pits along the lower jaw and suborbital ridge, posterior position of anus, pricklelike plates on breast, few dorsolateral plates.

Distribution   Known only from the type specimen taken at the mouth of the Skonun River, Graham Island, 54 N, 132 W.

If the type specimen indicates usual sizes in the population, the species may be fairly common and widely distributed.

References   Bailey and Gruchy 1970; Chesnon 1835; Gruchy 1970.

WARTY POACHER

Occella verrucosa (Lockington 1880)

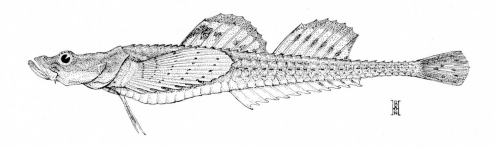

Scientific name from the Latin *occa* (harrow) and *ella* (diminutive); and *verrucosus* (warty).

Clemens and Wilby 1946, 1961 called this species *Occa verrucosa* (Lockington 1880) but it has been pointed out that the generic name was used earlier for a bird,[5,6] and a new name has been proposed.[2] Clemens and Wilby 1946 used the common name warty sea-poacher.

562

Description   Body depth extremely variable, about 7.0 into standard length, robust in anterior quarter of length, tapering to slender caudal peduncle. Most of body slightly compressed. Caudal peduncle slightly compressed. Head about 4 into standard length, much compressed. Mouth terminal, small, directed upward, lower jaw protruding and heavy. Interorbital space broad, about equal to diameter of eyeball, slightly concave. Eye small, about 4.5 to 5 into length of head. Gill membranes joined and free from isthmus.

Spines   Spines on head much reduced or absent except for preopercular spine which is sometimes doubled. Cranial ridges all much reduced.

Fins   Dorsal (2), VIII or IX — (6)7 to 8(9), touching or nearly so. Caudal rounded. Anal (10)11 or 12, long based and rather low. Pectorals about 14 or 15, broad, lower 4 to 6 rays thickened and not joined by membrane as far as their ends. Pelvics I, 2, thoracic. In males long pelvics reaching as far as the origin of the anal fin.

Vertebrae   35 to 37.

Scales   Replaced by plates with ridges or spines in 4 rows on each side of anterior part of the body, 8 rows replaced by 6 for a short distance at the posterior end of caudal peduncle, 2 laterally on each side, 1 dorsally and an unridged row ventrally. Various plates on thoracic and throat regions. Lateral line canal originating very high, sweeping down to midside about end of pectoral fin. Pores on lateral line canal 37 to 40. Cirrus at the end of each maxillary.

Colour   Dark gray or brown on upper surface, paler beneath. Line of demarcation very clear on head. Some specimens may show 6 or more dark saddle-shaped markings over back and extending on sides. On dorsal fins, dark bands following free margins of fins. Longitudinal dark colouring follows rays of caudal fin, especially at distal ends. Rows of dark spots on rays of pectoral fin, and a bright orange spot in its centre. Dark spots on eyeballs more abundant on upper part.

Size   Length to 8 inches (20 cm).

Recognition   Noteworthy for its long, compressed head, free of spines; robust, tapered body; and long anal fin.

Distribution   Known from California, Washington, British Columbia, and Bristol and Shelikof bays in Alaska.[2,3] Records are from depths of 10 to 36 fathoms (18–66 m). British Columbia records are from the west coast of Vancouver Island,[1] off Amphitrite Point,[4] north of the Queen Charlotte Islands at Naden Harbour and McIntyre Bay.[3,4]

References   1 Barraclough 1947; 2 Bailey and Gruchy 1970; 3 Dryfoos 1961; 4, 5 Gruchy 1969, 1970; 6 Iredale and Whitley 1969.

PYGMY POACHER

Odontopyxis trispinosa Lockington 1879

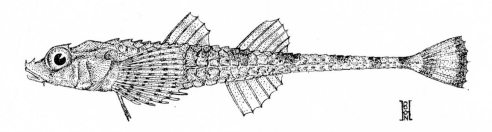

Scientific names from the Greek *odons* (tooth) and *pyxis* (box); and the Latin *tres* (three) and *spinus* (spine).

Description   Body very elongate, depth about 8.5 into standard length, slightly depressed throughout length. Head somewhat depressed, about 4.7 into standard length. Well-developed occipital pit with small, median, longitudinal ridge. Mouth inferior, very little behind snout, small, directed forward. Teeth on both jaws, minute. Interorbital space a rather narrow trough. Eye moderate, its diameter about 4.2 into length of head. Gill membrane broadly fused to isthmus. Caudal peduncle long, slender, tapered, slightly compressed.

Spines   On rostral plate, 1 median, upright, sharp spine. A pair on nasals, sharp, directed backward. A pair on frontals over rear of orbit, sharp, directed strongly backward. Three to five spine-like structures on the upper side of the eyeball in a single row.

Fins   Dorsals (2), III to VI — 5 to 7, spaced by about two-thirds of the length of the first fin. Caudal small and rounded. Anal 5 to 7, slightly in advance of second dorsal. Pectorals broad, about 13, lower 5 to 7 rays free of membrane at ends. Pelvics I, 2, thoracic.

Scales   Replaced by spiny plates disposed so as to make 4 serrate ridges on each side in the anterior part of the body, and 5 altogether on the caudal peduncle, where a ventral unpaired row of plates is smooth. Variations in scale patterns occur.[3] Lateral line canal almost straight. A reduced cirrus at the end of the maxillary.

Colour   Gray to olive green on the dorsal surface, lighter ventrally. Six or more dark saddle-like markings on back and sides. Dusky cross bars on dorsal, caudal, and pectoral fins. Anal and pelvic fins pale.

Size   Length to 3.2 inches (8.1 cm).

Recognition   This poacher has spines on the body plates only moderately developed, a small vertical spine at the end of the snout, and a moderately developed occipital pit divided by a noticeable longitudinal ridge.

Life History   Young individuals, 0.5 to 0.75 inch (14–19 mm) long, were found to be eating copepods, euphausiids, decapod larvae, and *Oikopleura*.[1,4] Swimming is with the pectoral fins.

Distribution   From Cedros Island, Baja California through southern California, Washington,[5] and British Columbia to southeast Alaska,[6] at depths between 10 fathoms (18 m) (British Columbia), and 204 fathoms (373 m) (California).[2]

References   1 Barraclough, Robinson, and Fulton 1968; 2 Grinols 1965a; 3 Hubbs 1942; 4 Robinson, Barraclough, and Fulton 1968a; 5 Starks 1911; 6 Wilimovsky 1954.

TUBENOSE POACHER

Pallasina barbata aix (Starks 1896)

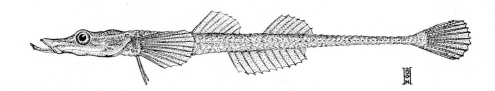

Scientific names from Petrus Simon Pallas, well-known naturalist and author; and the Latin *barbatus* (with a beard); and the Greek *aix* (slender).

The subspecies is recorded here to recognize the existence of a very similar but recognizable form. It is *Pallasina barbata barbata* (Steindachner 1876) which occurs from the Bering Sea along the Asian Coast through the Okhotsk Sea to Japan.[1,6,8]

Clemens and Wilby 1961 assigned the name tubesnout poacher to this species.

Description   Body very elongate, depth about 15 into standard length. Head very slender, about 4.2 into standard length. Mouth terminal, small, directed slightly upward, lower jaw projecting. Snout bluntly pointed. Interorbital space flat. Cranial ridges low. Eye rather small, its diameter about 5 into length of head, distinctly entering dorsal profile. Gill membranes joined together and free from isthmus. Caudal peduncle very long and slender.

Spines   Nasal and frontal spines very much reduced or absent.

Fins   Dorsal (2), VI or VII — 7 or 8, Caudal rounded. Anal 11 or 12, base long, extending through the last quarter of first dorsal to last fifth of second dorsal. Pectorals about 12, rounded. Pelvics I, 2, thoracic.

Scales   Replaced by bony plates, only slightly keeled and without spines, in 8 rows on anterior part of body and 6 posteriorly. Lateral line canal nearly straight, 45 or 46 pores. A barbel on the lower jaw directed straight forward, appearing as part of jaw.

Colour   Dorsal surface and posterior part of ventral surface gray or brown with black dots. Rest of ventral surface and fins light.

Size   Length to 5 inches (13 cm).

Recognition   Recognizable by very elongate, smooth, general form and head,

565

and the prominent forward-directed barbel on the lower jaw.

Distribution   From Mendocino County, California, through Oregon, Washington, Puget Sound, and British Columbia to the Gulf of Alaska,[3,4,6,7,9] Kamchatka and Japan.

British Columbia records[2] are from shallow water on the west coast of Vancouver Island, and from Burrard Inlet[5] at about 40 feet (12 m).

References   1 Andriashev 1937; 2 Barraclough 1952; 3 Bond 1959; 4 Hemphill and Follett 1958; 5 Lamb personal communication; 6 Popov 1933; 7 Radovich 1961; 8 Shmidt 1950; 9 Vernick 1963.

BLACKTIP POACHER

Xeneretmus latifrons (Gilbert 1890)

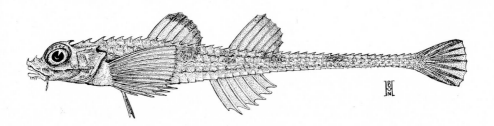

Scientific names from the Greek roots *xen* (strange) and *eretmus* (oar); and the Latin *latis* (wide) and *frons* (forehead).

Description   Body elongate, depth immediately behind head about 8.5 into standard length, tapered, width about same, slightly depressed in caudal peduncle. Head about 5 into standard length, somewhat depressed. Mouth terminal, small, directed forward, jaws about equal. Interorbital space concave, moderate, about half length of eye. Eye large, diameter about 3 into length of head, in dorsal profile, 3 to 5 spinous projections in row on upper side of eyeball. Gill membranes united, joined to isthmus through a free fold. Caudal peduncle long and slender.

Spines   A single backward-curved spine over snout on rostral plate. A pair of similar diverging spines on nasal. A sharp backward-directed spine on frontal above posterior part of eye. Two pairs of spines on top of head immediately in front of low occipital depression. A series of 4 to 6 depressed spines form a ridge under each eye.

Fins   Dorsal (2), VI or VII — 7 or 8, similar in size, separated by about half the base. Caudal rounded. Anal 7 to 9, placed ahead of second dorsal, rays extending well beyond membrane. Pectorals broad, 4 or 5 lower rays moderately projecting beyond membrane. Pelvics I, 2, thoracic.

566

Scales   Replaced by plates bearing spines in 4 well-organized rows on each side anteriorly, and, on caudal peduncle 2 on each side, one dorsally, and another without spines ventrally. Lateral line canal gently decurved anteriorly and then straight, 39 to 41 pores. A large cirrus near end of posterior end of maxillary. Shorter, finer cirri under lower jaw, near tip.

Colour   Light brown on dorsal surface, lighter brown to cream below. Darker brown saddlelike markings on back and sides, 7 or 8. Fins pale with darker edges on both dorsals and on caudal.

Size   Length to 7.5 inches (19 cm).

Recognition   Noteworthy for its single, rigid, rostral spine on the end of the snout and the black margin on the first dorsal fin.

Life History   In California apparently spawns in spring. Larvae are pelagic.

Lives to at least an age of 6 years.[2] Food mainly mysids. Eaten in turn by flatfishes, hake, and lancetfish.

Distribution   Cape Colnett, Baja California,[2] southern California to southern British Columbia through Washington[1,4] and Oregon at depths from 218 fathoms (400 m) (California) to 10 fathoms (18 m) in British Columbia.[3]

In British Columbia it has been recorded from Ucluelet and in various waters contiguous to the southern Strait of Georgia, to northern British Columbia.[2] A specimen collected at Narrows Arm in Sechelt Inlet suggests tolerance to water with low oxygen content.

References   1 DeLacy, Dryfoos, and Miller 1963; 2 Fitch and Lavenberg 1968; 3 Grinols 1965a; 4 Starks 1911.

BLUESPOTTED POACHER

Xeneretmus triacanthus (Gilbert 1890)

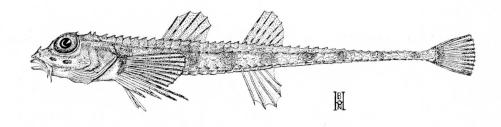

Scientific names derived from the Greek roots *xen* (strange) and *eretmus* (oar); and *tri* (three) and *acanthos* (spine).

Description   Body elongate, greatest depth immediately behind head, about 10 into standard length, moderately wide

567

anteriorly, tapering evenly to a slender caudal peduncle, which is slightly depressed. Head rather slender, its length about 4.6 into standard length, somewhat depressed. Mouth terminal, small, and directed forward and up. Jaws about equal. Snout pointed. Rostral plate free of nasals. Fine teeth on both jaws, vomer, and palatines. Interorbital space narrow and concave, its width about 15 into length of head or 5 into length of eye. Eye rather large and oval, its length about 3.3 into length of head, eyeball with 3 to 5 spinous projections on its upper surface. Gill membrane joined to isthmus. Caudal peduncle long and slender, its least depth 60 or more into standard length.

Spines On rostral plate a single small upright median spine and a pair of smaller ventrolateral spines; prominent backward-directed nasal, postocular, parietal, and occipital spines; low suborbital, preopercular, opercular, and suprascapular spines present.

Fins Dorsal (2), V or VI, 6 or 7, similar in size, separated by about two-thirds length of base. Caudal small and truncate. Anal 6, originating below origin of rayed dorsal. Pectorals 13, lower 4 rays separated from upper rays by a notch and exserted, the ray immediately below notch notably long. Pelvics I, 2, thoracic, short.[1]

Scales Replaced by plates bearing spined ridges in 4 well-organized rows on each side anteriorly, and, on caudal peduncle 2 rows on each side plus 1 dorsal, and another, without spines, ventral. Lateral line canal high anteriorly, along midside posteriorly, pores about 40. A pair of round fleshy barbels at tip of each maxillary, the posterior one about twice the length of the anterior one; 3 or 4 small barbels along each lower jaw, at mandibular pores.

Colour Preserved specimen brownish with ventral surface lighter; 6 dark blotches on sides, the most anterior at the bases of the pectorals; rays and spines of fins dark or dusky, but only distal parts of anal and caudal membranes dusky.

Size Length to about 7 inches (17.8 cm).

Recognition Noteworthy for the two fleshy barbels at the tips of the maxillae and the origin of the anal fin being below the origin of the second dorsal.

Distribution The bluespotted poacher is known from near San Diego[5] through southern and northern California, Oregon, and Washington at depths of 40 to 204 fathoms (73–373 m).[2] In southern British Columbia at Brentwood Bay and near Round Island[3] and at Kwatna Inlet (52.03 N, 127.34.5 W).[4]

References 1 Gilbert 1890; 2 Grinols 1965a; 3 Peden 1972 personal communication; 4 Peden and Gruchy 1971; 5 Schultz and DeLacy 1936.

FAMILY CYCLOPTERIDAE   LUMPFISHES AND SNAILFISHES

The Cyclopteridae is a group of small and medium-sized fishes mostly of northern waters, modified in a variety of ways. Most have pelvic fins modified to form an adhering disc by which the fish clings to bottom rocks. Fishes may be elongate and scaleless, or globular. One of the globular forms has a protective armour of horny cones and two dorsal fins, the other is naked and has only one short dorsal fin. The elongate forms have single long anal and dorsal fins. Pectoral fins in all forms are wide based and large, sometimes two-lobed, and the gill openings are small. Some tadpole-shaped species lack both pelvic fins and adhering discs and may be pelagic. Larger species have been used as food and as sources of a good red "caviar."

568

KEY TO THE CYCLOPTERIDAE

	1	Pelvic fins modified to form a flattened adhesive disc with thickened edge 3
or	1	Pelvic fins absent; no flattened adhesive disc 2
	2	Anus below vertical from gill opening, opening downward; gill opening extending downward to behind tenth to fourteenth pectoral ray .... *Paraliparis deani,* Prickly snailfish, p. 593
or	2	Anus below vertical from eye, opening forward into a trough which extends as far as lower jaw; gill opening small, limited to area in front of pectoral fin base .... *Nectoliparis pelagicus,* Tadpole snailfish, p. 591
	3	Body moderately elongate, its depth more than 3 into standard length; dorsal and anal fins reaching or overlapping caudal base 5
or	3	Body stout and short, its depth about half standard length; there is a recognizable caudal peduncle (Cyclopteridae of some classifications) 4
	4	Body scattered with large horny protuberances .... *Eumicrotremus orbis,* Pacific spiny lumpsucker, p. 577
or	4	Body smooth .... *Aptocyclus ventricosus,* Smooth lumpsucker, p. 571
	5	Ventral adhering disc with its posterior margin behind vertical from gill opening .... Genus *Liparis* 9
or	5	Ventral adhering disc with its posterior margin ahead of vertical from gill opening 6
	6	Nostril double; anal fin barely reaching caudal; pyloric caeca more than 300; dorsal fin definitely notched; anus about halfway between posterior margin of disc and origin of anal fin .... *Polypera greeni,* Lobefin snailfish, p. 594
or	6	Nostril single; anal fin extends on caudal for at least a third of caudal length, or confluent; pyloric caeca fewer than 30; dorsal fin not notched; anus much closer to posterior margin of disc than to origin of anal fin .... Genus *Careproctus* 7
	7	Dorsal and anal fins meeting caudal at about half caudal length; snout bulbous; disc large, its length about 3 into length of head; eye small, its diameter about 6 into length of head .... *Careproctus ovigerum,* Abyssal snailfish, p. 575
or	7	Dorsal and anal fins completely confluent with caudal; snout pointed or bluntly pointed; disc small, its length more than 6 into length of head; eye large, its diameter 3 or 4 into length of head 8

SMOOTH LUMPSUCKER

Aptocyclus ventricosus (Pallas 1770)

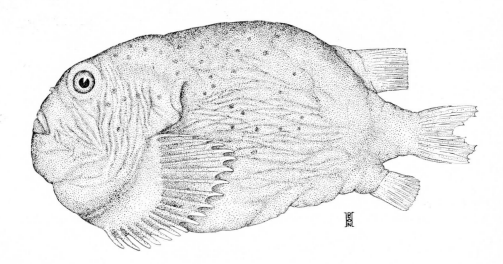

Scientific names from the Greek *(h)apto* (touching) and *cyclos* (circles); and the Latin *ventricosus* (large bellied).

Description Body short, depth about 2.0 into standard length, almost globular anteriorly. Head about 2.7 into standard length, deep. Mouth terminal, small, directed slightly upward. Upper jaw about 2.8 into length of head. Profile in continuous curve from mouth to middle of back. Nostrils paired. Lower jaw thick and prominent. Interorbital space and snout broad and convex. Eye small. Opercular opening very small above base of the pectoral fin. Generally an amorphous-appearing fish. Caudal peduncle compressed.

Fins Dorsal (1), 8 or 9, far back on body. Caudal rounded. Anal 7 to 9, only slightly behind dorsal. Pectorals about 19 or 20, large, and broadly based. All these fins with broadened rays entering the fin profile, especially those on the ventral part of the pectoral. (The caudal fin in the specimen drawn was damaged.) Pelvics, thoracic, modified to form a clinging disc with a thickened margin on the ventral surface of the body.

Scales No scales or lateral line canal.

Colour Brownish gray with dark spots on the dorsal surface. Muddy gray on the ventral surface.

Size Length to 10.7 inches (27 cm).

Recognition Distinguished by the short stout body, the smooth skin, the adhesive pelvic disc, and the single dorsal fin.

Life History The males are reported to guard the eggs. Small lumpsuckers are eaten by fur seals in the Bering Sea.

Distribution From British Columbia to the Okhotsk Sea through Alaska, the Bering Sea, including Korf Gulf, Kam-

571

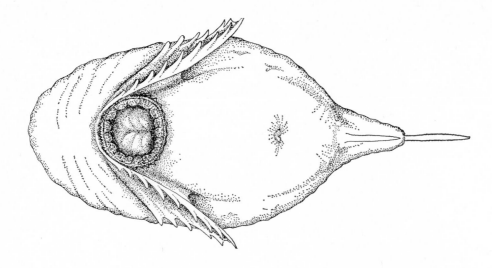

chatka and the Commander Islands.[1,3] Recorded from Honshu Island at Wakaso Bay on the Sea of Japan and Misaki.[2] A littoral form to 123 fathoms (225 m). Canadian records are restricted to the northern part of the province: Dean Channel; Moresby Island (Queen Charlotte Islands), Mathieson Channel; and Portland Canal.

References 1 Grinols 1965a; 2 Matsubara 1955; 3 Popov 1933. See also Clemens and Wilby 1952.

SMALLDISK SNAILFISH

Careproctus gilberti Burke 1912

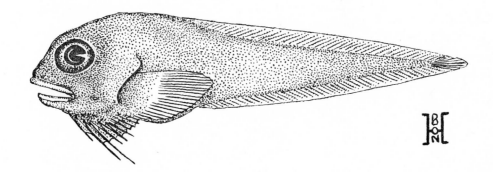

Scientific names from the Greek *kara* (head) and *proktos* (anus); and C. H. Gilbert, U.S. ichthyologist.

Small-disked liparid was used as the common name for this species by Clemens and Wilby 1946.

Description   Body depth about 3.7 into standard length, stout and broad anteriorly, more compressed and tapered to a fine tail posteriorly, generally tadpolelike. Head length about 3.4 into standard length, broad and very deep. Mouth terminal, large, directed mostly forward. Upper jaw extending to posterior part of eye, includes lower jaw. Snout bluntly rounded. Teeth fine, some with lateral lobes, in rows diagonally across upper jaw, in 2 or 3 rows following lower jaw. Interorbital space broad, nearly flat, its width about 2.2 into length of head. Eye large, its diameter about 3 into length of head. Gill opening moderate, extending about to fourteenth ray of pectoral fin. Anus near posterior margin of pelvic disc. Pyloric caeca 10 to 12.

Fins   Dorsal (1), about 55, extending to about halfway along caudal. Caudal narrow, truncate. Anal about 46 to 48, extending to about halfway along caudal. Pectorals about 31, long based, middle rays short, lower rays much exserted. Pelvics modified to form an adhesive disc with thickened margin, small, slightly wider than long, its length about 8 into length of head, below eye.

Scales   No scales or lateral line canal. Skin very loose and delicate.

Colour   Creamy white to pale pink, sometimes pale brown dorsally. Dusky on fins. Silvery on lower half of blue eyes. Viscera show as a dark mass.

Size   Length to 3.5 inches (8.9 cm).

Recognition   Noteworthy for its tadpolelike appearance, very small adhesive disc placed far forward below large eye, gill opening extending down to fourteenth ray of pectoral fin, and the interrupted pectoral fin.

Distribution   Oregon[1] to southeast Alaska[2] and the Aleutian Islands at Unalaska Island.[3] From 102 to 482 fathoms (187–886 m). In Canada off Fort Rupert, Hecate Strait, and Seymour Inlet. Rare.

References   1 Grinols 1965a; 2, 3 Wilimovsky 1954, 1964.

BLACKTAIL SNAILFISH

Careproctus melanurus Gilbert 1891

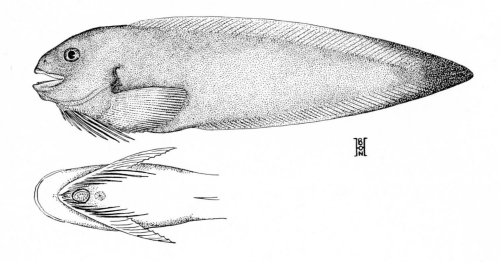

Scientific names from the Greek *kara* (head) and *proktos* (anus); and *melas* (black), and *ura* (tail).

Black-tailed liparid was the common name used for this species by Clemens and Wilby 1946.

Description   Body rather elongate, its depth about 3.6 into standard length, compressed, tapered to a fine tail. Head blunt, compressed, its length about 4.9 into standard length. Mouth terminal, large, directed forward. Upper jaw barely reaching anterior edge of eye. Jaws about even. Snout and lower jaw blunt. Teeth in close-set bands in both jaws, slender and very small, without cusps but a little widened and flattened below tip. Interorbital space broad but difficult to define, its width about 2.8 into length of head. Eye large, partly covered, its diameter about 4 into length of head. Gill opening entirely above pectoral fin,

rather large. Anus near posterior margin of pelvic disc. Pyloric caeca 20 to 27.

Fins   Dorsal (1), 54 to 58, profile smooth, long, low, extending about halfway along length of caudal fin. Caudal narrow, slightly rounded. Anal 37 to 50, extending about halfway along caudal. Pectorals about 30 or 31, lower 6 rays slightly thickened and completely exserted, the next 5 greatly to moderately exserted and longer than the rays immediately above them, no real notch in fin, its insertion nearly horizontal. Pelvics modified to form a small adhesive disc with a thickened margin, placed far forward, below eye, width about 1.2 into length, its length about 6.5 into length of head.

Scales   No scales or lateral line canal.

Colour   Off-white to pale rose on body. Ends of pectoral and edges of posterior parts of dorsal and anal, and most of caudal fins, black. Lining of mouth and gill cavity, and tongue, black.

574

Size   Length to 10.4 inches (26.4 cm).

Recognition   Noted for the very small adhesive disc placed below eye, gill opening entirely above pectoral fin, black on posterior edges of dorsal and anal fins and on caudal fin.

Distribution   From southern California off Santa Catalina Island between 240 and 310 fathoms[2] (440–568 m) and off California to 451 fathoms (825 m), and Oregon to 750 fathoms (1370 m) to British Columbia.[4] British Columbia records off south end of Moresby Island at 51.23 N, 130.34 W at 876 fathoms (1600 m), Swanson Channel at 49 fathoms (90 m) in January 1953, off the mouth of the Fraser River,[1] and off Esteban Point in 133 to 160 fathoms (243–293 m) at 49.10 N, 127 W.[3] Benthic, uncommon.

References   1 Barraclough and Waldichuk 1954; 2 Fitch 1966b; 3 Forrester and Wilson 1963; 4 Grinols 1965a.

ABYSSAL SNAILFISH

Careproctus ovigerum (Gilbert 1895)

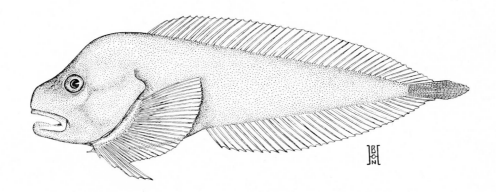

Scientific names from the Greek *kara* (head) and *proktos* (anus); and the Latin *ovum* (egg) and *gero* (bear).

Clemens and Wilby 1946 used abyssal liparid as the common name for this species.

Description   Body rather elongate, its depth about 3.6 into standard length, greatest depth at posterior part of head, compressed, body tapering to narrow caudal base. Head length about 3.6 into standard length, upper profile of head concave, occiput raised. Mouth terminal, moderate in size, directed forward. Snout blunt and rounded. Upper jaw extending about to anterior margin of orbit. Teeth slender, without lateral cusps, in wide bands at tips of both jaws, bands narrow laterally, all teeth directed

575

backward. Interorbital space raised and rounded, its width about 2.7 into length of head. Eye moderate in size, diameter about 6.2 into length of head. Cheeks inflated. Gill slit relatively long, extending to about the eighth pectoral ray. Anus far forward, near posterior margin of adhesive disc. Pyloric caeca 19.

Fins   Dorsal (1), 43, confluent with caudal, starting above gill opening. Caudal long, slender, pointed. Anal 34, confluent with caudal. Pectorals 34, upper part rounded with rays decreasing in length evenly to about the sixth from the bottom which, like those immediately below, is much increased in length and exserted. Pelvics modified to form a large, nearly circular. adhering disc, its length about 2.9 into head length, its posterior margin anterior to gill opening.

Scales   Scales absent. Lateral line canal absent. Skin moderately loose, thin, transparent.

Colour   Light, inconspicuously mottled with light brown.

Size   Length to 12.5 inches (32 cm).

Recognition   Notable for the high dorsal fin with an unbroken profile, the relatively large gill opening, extending about as far as the eighth pectoral ray, and the large anteriorly placed adhering disc.

Life History   The only specimen of this species known is a male taken at a depth of 1588 fathoms (2910 m) off Moresby Island, Queen Charlotte Islands, at 52.39 N, 132.38 W. The testes were enlarged and the fish carried in its mouth a spherical mass of large developing eggs apparently of the same species. It is assumed that this is an example of parental care.[2]

Distribution   Off northern British Columbia at great depths.

References   1 Gilbert 1895 *(Bathyphasma);* 2 Jordan and Evermann 1898.

576

PACIFIC SPINY LUMPSUCKER

Eumicrotremus orbis (Günther 1861)

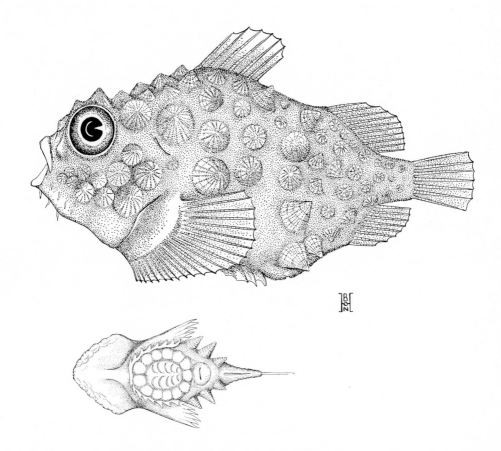

Scientific names from the Greek *eu* (truly), *micros* (small), and *trema* (aperture); and the Latin *orbs* (sphere).

Description   Body very short, stout, almost globular, its depth about 1.8 into standard length, and its width 2.3 into standard length. Head deep and wide, its length about 2.8 into standard length. Mouth terminal, small, directed forward. Upper jaw not reaching anterior edge of orbit. Jaws about equal. Lips thickened. Snout vertical, with lower jaw forming a flat area. Teeth small, conical, in patches at front of jaws and on sides in rows. Interorbital space broad, flat (and rough), its width about 1.6 into length of head. Eye large, its diameter about 3 into length of head. Opercular opening very small, less than eye diameter, and centred behind bottom of orbit. Caudal peduncle (and body anterior to it) compressed, its least depth about 9 into standard length.

Fins   Dorsal (2), VI or VII — 9 to 11, well separated. Caudal rather narrow, rounded. Anal 8 to 10. Pectorals about 25, with a long base extended to ventral surface, all rays slightly exserted, ventral ones more so. Pelvics with rays ossified and modified to support all of a large adhesive disc with thickened fringed margin,[2] thoracic.

Scales   Body and head generously arrayed with prominent firm cones having fine lines radiating from summits, probably representing modified ctenoid scales. Cones in turn, intervening spaces, and spines of dorsal fin covered with smaller spiny scales of various sizes. Body scattered with small folds and flattened papillae, a short series of columnar papillae in a row under and behind lower jaw. Lateral line canal absent.

Colour   Light to dark green, sometimes light brown on dorsal surface; light brown or plum on ventral surface. Lavender on lips. Tubercles in males are dull orange or reddish brown, in females pale green. Tubercles in females are larger and more numerous than in males.[3]

Size   Length to 5 inches (12.7 cm).

Recognition   Recognized by stocky body and head covered with spiny conical protuberances, and ventral adhesive disc with a fringed, thickened margin.

Life History   Spiny lumpsuckers are abundant off the beach at Lumberman's Arch in Vancouver, Burrard Inlet, in winter, becoming common in October. They are small individuals, apparently all females about 1 inch (25 mm) long, preparing to spawn, as they contain large eggs.[4,8] Probably spawn in February.[3] Common elsewhere in Burrard Inlet and taken in shrimp trawls. Observed at low tide attached to rocks in fast tidal currents. Recorded from as deep as 80 fathoms (146 m). Three individuals were found in the stomach of a lancetfish in Alaska.

Distribution   From   Washington through British Columbia, Alaska,[7] and Aleutian Islands[10] to the Bering Sea[9] as far as Saint Lawrence Island[1] and down the Asian Coast through Kamchatka,[6,7] Kuril Islands, and Okhotsk Sea to Sakhalin.[5]

References   1 Andriashev 1937; 2, 3 Arita 1967, 1969; 4 Lamb personal communication; 5 Matsubara 1955; 6 Popov 1933; 7 Shmidt 1950; 8 Vancouver Public Aquarium Staff 1969; 9, 10 Wilimovsky 1954, 1964.

SPOTTED SNAILFISH

Liparis callyodon (Pallas 1811)

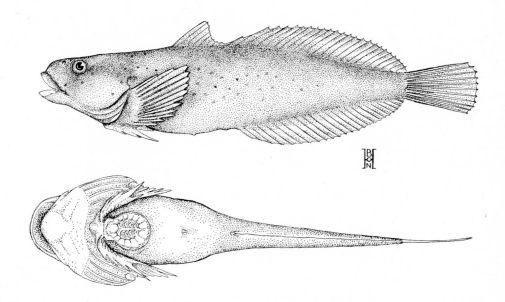

Scientific names from the Greek *liparos* (sleek skinned); and *callos* (beautiful) and *odons* (tooth — tricuspid teeth).

Clemens and Wilby 1946 used the common name Pallas's liparid for this species.

Description Body elongate, nearly cylindrical anteriorly, compressed farther back, depth greatest behind midlength, about 4.2 into standard length. Head depressed, its length about 3.7 into standard length. Mouth terminal, small, directed forward, overhung by upper lip and snout. Upper jaw extends about three-quarters of distance to anterior edge of orbit. Snout bluntly rounded. Teeth in bands on jaws, trilobed. Interorbital space moderately convex, smooth, its width about 3 into length of head. Eye round, its diameter about 7 or 8 into length of head. Opercular membranes with branchiostegals fused to isthmus. Gill openings small, not extending beyond first ray of pectoral fin. Caudal peduncle much reduced and compressed. Vent about halfway between posterior edge of adhering disc and insertion of anal fin.

Fins Dorsal (1), 33 to 35, strongly lobed anteriorly, extending to base of caudal fin. Caudal fin small, truncate. Anal 25 to 27, barely extending below base of caudal fin. Pectorals 28 to 31, well developed, broadly based, notched between third and fourth rays from ventral edge, lower 7 rays exserted and folded back on the rest of the fin. Pelvics modified to form an adhering disc, its diameter about 2.5 into length of head.

Scales Scales absent. Lateral line canal absent. Skin notably loose and translucent. Rows of pores on head.

Colour Olive brown on fins and body, paler below and modified parts of paired fins almost white. Sparse rows of small dark spots on back and sides. Edges of vertical fins dark.

579

Size   Length to 5 inches (12.7 cm).

Recognition   Noteworthy for the lobe at the anterior end of the dorsal fin and the sparse dark dots on the upper sides and back of the body.

Distribution   A shore species, frequently encountered in tide pools from Washington[1] to the Bering Sea[2] and western Aleutian Islands.[3] In British Columbia recorded from the Strait of Georgia, Discovery Passage, and Queen Charlotte Islands.

References   1 DeLacy, Dryfoos, and Miller 1963; 2, 3 Wilimovsky 1954, 1964.

RIBBON SNAILFISH

Liparis cyclopus Günther 1861

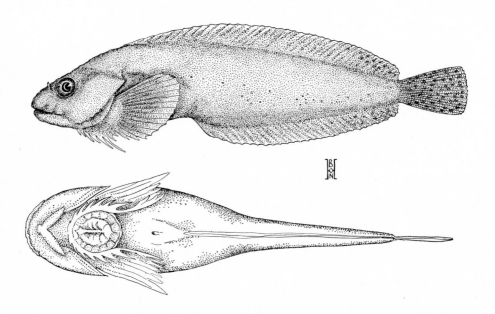

Scientific names from the Greek *liparos* (sleek skinned); and *cyclos* (round) and *poys* (foot).

The common name proposed in Clemens and Wilby 1946 was Günther's liparid. The illustration there and in 1961 may be of another species (*L. dennyi?*).

Description   Body elongate, depth about 4.2 into standard length, deepest at about midway point, compressed. Head moderate, its length about 3.8 into body length, depressed. Mouth terminal, small, directed forward, upper lip overhanging lower. Upper jaw extending about halfway to anterior edge of orbit. Snout bluntly rounded. Posterior nostril oval. Teeth trilobed, in bands on both jaws. Interorbital space broad, about 3 into length of head, gently rounded. Eye small, its diameter about 6 into length of head. Gill opening extending down only to point between fifth and tenth rays of pectoral fin. Caudal peduncle not identifiable.

Fins   Dorsal (1), 35 to 37, not lobed, extending to caudal base. Caudal small, narrow, with dorsal and ventral portions subparallel, end bluntly rounded. Anal 29 to 31, not reaching caudal fin. Pectorals 29 to 32, with 2 lobes, the upper rounded, and a lower lobe with exserted rays lying outside the upper one. Pelvics modified into an adhesive, nearly circular disc, with a thickened margin, its diameter 2 to 2.5 into length of head.

Scales   Scales and lateral line canal obscure but a row of pores along midside. Pores on chin, evenly spaced.

Colour   Olive brown quite uniformly throughout with general fine black stippling. Rather larger dark spots arranged in meandering lines on middle and lower sides, in bars on unpaired fins, diagonal on dorsal and anal, vertical on caudal.

Size   Length to 4.5 inches (11.4 cm).

Recognition   Distinguished by dorsal fin barely reaching caudal, anus not quite halfway from posterior edge of pelvic disc to origin of anal fin, the gill opening extending downward only to between fifth and tenth rays of pectoral fin, and the subcircular adhesive disc.

Distribution   Found from Washington[1] to Alaska, in the Bering Sea[2,3] and off the Aleutian Islands.[4] In British Columbia from Juan de Fuca Strait at 100 fathoms (183 m), Esquimalt Harbour, Vancouver Island, and Masset and Skidegate inlets of the Queen Charlotte Islands.

References   1 DeLacy, Dryfoos, and Miller 1963; 2 Grinols 1965a; 3, 4 Wilimovsky 1954, 1964.

MARBLED SNAILFISH

Liparis dennyi Jordan and Starks 1895

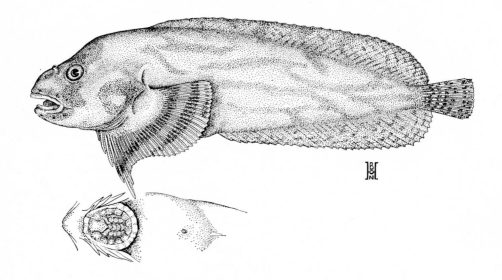

Scientific names from the Greek *liparos* (sleek skinned); and C. L. Denny of Seattle, Washington.

Recorded by Clemens and Wilby 1946 as Denny's liparid.

Description   Body elongate, its depth about 3.5 into standard length, greatest depth under pectoral fin, compressed. Head length about 3.3 into standard length, dorsal profile slightly concave. Mouth terminal, rather small, directed forward and slightly up. Upper jaw not quite reaching anterior margin of eye. Lower jaw included. Snout bluntly rounded. Lips fleshy. Teeth small, trilobed, in bands on both jaws. Interorbital space broad, raised at eyes but flat in middle, its width about 2.8 into length of head. Eye small, diameter about 7 into length of head. Gill opening moderate, extends down to between tenth and fifteenth

pectoral fin rays. Anus closer to anal fin origin than to posterior margin of adhering disc.

Fins   Dorsal (1), 37 to 40, may be slightly lobed anteriorly in smaller individuals, extending on caudal fin for about one-fifth caudal length. Caudal narrow, rounded. Anal 30 to 34, extending on caudal for about one-third caudal length. Pectorals 36 to 39, upper part rounded, lower 4 rays thickened and exserted, fourth to seventh lowest rays lengthened so that the fin is notched. Pelvics modified to form an adhering disc with thickened edges, thoracic, almost circular, its length about 2.2 to 2.4 into length of head, posterior margin behind vertical from gill opening.

Scales   Scales absent. Lateral line canal absent. Skin smooth and loose.

Colour   Olive to dark brown or black with darker mottlings or wavy lines, or with white dots.

Size   Length to 12 inches (30.5 cm).

Recognition   Noteworthy for the small eye with a diameter 7 to 7.5 into length of head, the anal fin extending on caudal fin for about one-third of caudal length, and the gill opening extending down to a point between the tenth and fifteenth pectoral rays.

Life History   Ripe females running faintly pink eggs were taken in Active Pass on January 17, 1934. Food includes crustaceans.

Distribution   Washington,[2] Puget Sound[1] to the Gulf of Alaska.[3] Common in British Columbia at depths between 40 and 123 fathoms (73–225 m).

References   1 DeLacy, Dryfoos, and Miller 1963; 2 Schultz and DeLacy 1936; 3 Wilimovsky 1954.

TIDEPOOL SNAILFISH

Liparis florae (Jordan and Starks 1895)

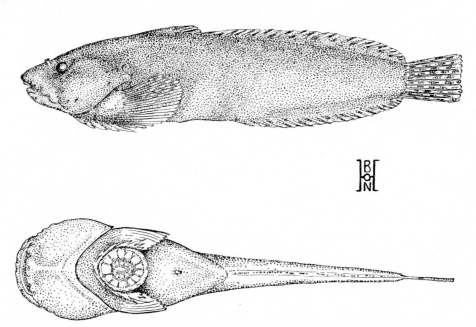

Scientific names from the Greek *liparos* (sleek skinned); and Mrs Flora Hartley Green, Stanford University.

Clemens and Wilby 1946 recorded this species as the shore liparid.

583

Description   Body rather elongate, its depth about 3.5 into standard length, rather depressed anteriorly and compressed through most of the posterior two-thirds. Head compressed, its length about 3.5 into standard length. Mouth almost terminal, rather small, directed forward. The angle of the upper jaw is only about one-third of the distance to the anterior edge of orbit. Lower jaw included. Snout bluntly rounded. Second nostril present but much reduced. Teeth small, trilobed. Interorbital space wide, moderate, nearly 3 into length of head, broadly arched. Eye small, its diameter about 6 or 7 into length of head. Gill opening extends ventrally to point between third and fifth rays of the pectoral fin. Caudal peduncle very short.

Fins   Dorsal (1), 31 to 33, divided after about the fourth ray into 2 sections, a small lobe anteriorly and a larger well-developed fin extending posteriorly. Caudal with almost parallel sides and truncate. Anal 25 to 27, rather narrow, not quite reaching the caudal. Pectorals 29 to 33 with 2 lobes, the upper rounded and lying along the side, the ventral lobe partly folded underneath with prominent exserted rays overlapping the adhesive disc. Pelvics modified to form an adhesive disc, thoracic, slightly longer than wide, length 2.0 to 2.4 into length of head.

Scales   Scales and lateral line canal absent. Prominent pores in rows on both jaws and extending back from lower jaw on gill cover.

Colour   Colour rather uniform from brown to olive green to dusky purple. Dark speckling in rows on side and more prominently on caudal, dorsal, and anal fins. In fresh specimens red spots on side of body.

Size   Length to 5 inches (12.7 cm).

Recognition   Recognized by its loose skin, gill openings extending to between the third and fifth rays, and a dorsal fin that is apparently divided into two lobes. The margin of the first lobe folds back on itself when the fin is depressed.

Distribution   Recorded from southern California to the Bering Sea.[1] In British Columbia records are from False Narrows, near Nanaimo, Burrard Inlet, and the west coast of Vancouver Island.

References   1 Wilimovsky 1964.

584

SLIPSKIN SNAILFISH

Liparis fucensis Gilbert 1895

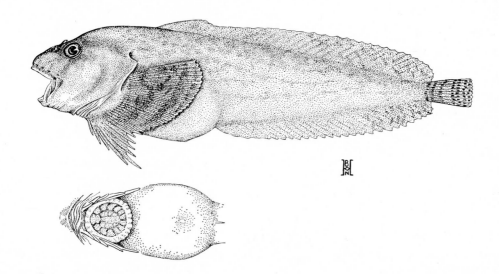

Scientific names from the Greek *liparos* (sleek skinned); and (of) Juan de Fuca Strait.

Recorded by Clemens and Wilby 1946 as Juan de Fuca liparid.

Description   Body rather elongate, its depth about 3.3 into standard length, compressed. Head length about 3.1 into standard length, dorsal profile generally convex, dipping over eyes. Mouth terminal, rather small, directed forward and slightly up. Upper jaw reaching posterior part of eye. Lower jaw included. Snout bluntly pointed. Lips fleshy. Teeth small, trilobed, arranged in diagonal rows in bands in upper and lower jaws. Interorbital space moderate, slightly and irregularly convex, its width about 3 into length of head. Eye small, diameter 6 to 7 into length of head. Gill opening extending down to point between twelfth and sixteenth rays of pectoral fin. Anus much closer to anal fin origin than to firm posterior margin of adhesive disc.

Fins   Dorsal (1), 33 to 35, small lobe anteriorly, barely reaching caudal fin. Caudal narrow, rounded. Anal 27 to 29, extending on caudal fin only slightly more than does dorsal. Pectorals 34 to 43, upper part rounded, rays seventh to third from ventral edge thickened, longer, exserted to give fin a notched outline, tip usually reaching anus. Pelvics modified to form an adhering disc with thickened edges, thoracic, almost circular in outline, length 2 to 3 into length of head, position well behind vertical from gill opening.

Scales   Scales absent. Lateral line canal absent. Skin smooth and loose.

Colour   Olive to dark brown, frequently tinged with pink. Irregular dark bands or blotching on dorsal, anal, caudal, and pectoral fins. May take form of a diagonal light band on caudal fin.

Size   Length to 7 inches (18 cm).

Recognition   Notable for having the anal fin extending on caudal fin for less than one-fifth of latter's length, and the

585

gill opening extending ventrally to between twelfth and sixteenth pectoral rays.

Life History   Females with ripening eggs were taken in Burrard Inlet in February. Shrimps and other crustaceans are included in the food.

Distribution   Northern California through Oregon and Washington to southeast Alaska.[1,2] In British Columbia down to 212 fathoms (388 m). Fairly common.

References   1 Schultz and DeLacy 1936; 2 Wilimovsky 1954.

SLIMY SNAILFISH

Liparis mucosus Ayres 1855

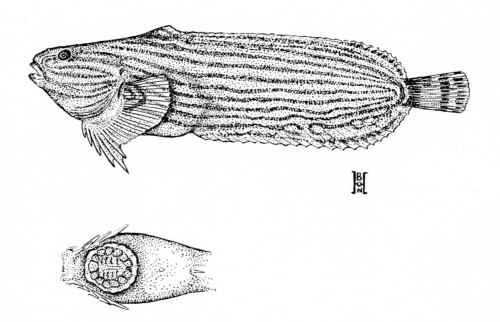

Scientific names from the Greek *liparos* (sleek skinned); and the Latin *mucosus* (slimy).

Description   Body elongate, depth about 4 into standard length, slightly compressed anteriorly, compressed through

posterior part of body. Head depressed, its length about 3.8 into standard length. Snout blunt. Mouth subterminal, moderate in size, directed forward. Lower jaw included. Upper jaw extends to a point about halfway between snout and anterior margin of eye. Teeth small, strongly trilobed. Inter-

586

orbital space moderate, about 3.2 into length of head. slightly convex. Eye small, its diameter about 6 into length of head. Opercles smooth. Gill opening extends down to point opposite base of first 3 to 6 pectoral rays. Caudal peduncle not discernible.

Fins Dorsal (2), 28 to 30 in 2 parts, the first short, low and rounded, the second almost reaching the caudal, rays longer posteriorly. Caudal narrow with rounded end. Anal 22 to 24, low, reaching base of caudal fin, posterior rays longer. Pectorals 27 to 32, inserted at opercular opening, well developed, broadly based, with lower lobe of fin with thickened exserted longer rays extending forward but not quite reaching midventral line. Pelvics modified to form a circular, adhering disc, its diameter about half length of head, thoracic, inserted below gill opening.

Scales Scales and lateral line canal absent. Skin loose, smooth and transparent, sometimes with minute thin prickles. A row of 6 large pores along lower side of lower jaw.

Colour Extremely variable. Sometimes without pattern, a uniform colour somewhat paler below — bright red, brown, pink, olive, brownish, greenish yellow. Some have nearly parallel, horizontal, darker stripes of various widths covering body but not much on fins. Others have reticulate patterns. Generally with a darker bar at base of caudal fin. Dorsal and anal fins tend to have more pigment.

Size Length at least to 2.75 inches (7 cm).

Recognition Noteworthy for the relatively fewer rays in dorsal, anal, and pectoral fins than *L. florae* or *L. callyodon*, the gill slit extending down to a point between the third and sixth pectoral rays, and the low, rounded first dorsal fin. The fin membrane of the first dorsal does not fold back on itself when the fin is depressed as in *L. florae*.

Distribution Baja California to Washington[2] and British Columbia. In British Columbia found at Sooke and Ucluelet[1] at depths of less than 12 feet (4 m) below low tide. Uncommon. Possibly favours ocean conditions.

References 1 Peden 1966a; 2 Schultz and DeLacy 1936.

SHOWY SNAILFISH

Liparis pulchellus Ayres 1855

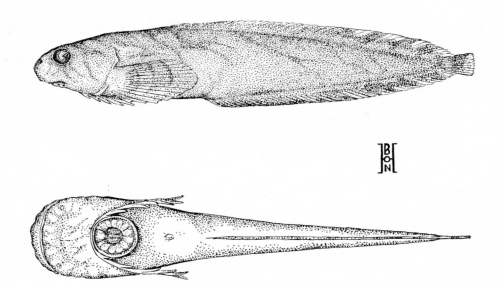

Scientific names from the Greek *liparos* (sleek skinned); and the Latin *pulchellus* (pretty).

Clemens and Wilby in 1961 used the common name shorttail snailfish for this species, and in 1946, continuous-finned liparid.

Description Body elongate, depth about 5 into standard length, slightly depressed anteriorly and moderately compressed through its posterior two-thirds. Head depressed, about 4 into standard length, blunt anteriorly. Nostril double. Mouth subterminal, moderate in size, directed downward. Lower jaw included. Upper jaw not extending as far as anterior margin of eye. Teeth small, trilobed. Interorbital space wide, about 7 into length of head, almost flat, slightly raised above level of orbit rim. Eye about 5 into length of head. Opercles smooth, the gill opening small and not ex-tending below fourth ray of pectoral fin. Caudal peduncle not discernible.

Fins Dorsal (1), 47 to 53, low and with smooth profile. Caudal reduced but distinct. Anteriorly above and below attached to dorsal and anal. Anal 39 to 41. Pectorals 36 or 37, well developed and broadly based with a lower forward extension with thickened rays exserted extending forward but not quite to the midventral line. Pelvics modified to form a circular adhering disc, its diameter about 2.3 into length of head, thoracic.

Scales Scales and lateral line canal absent. Skin very loose, smooth and transparent. Three prominent pores under each side of lower jaw.

Colour Light to dark brown, lighter on ventral surface. Dots or wavy dark longitudinal lines sometimes present. Edges of median fins darker posteriorly. Light edges on pectoral fins. Oblique dark bars on young.

588

Size   To 10 inches (25 cm).

Recognition   Recognizable by the loose skin, broad head with widely spaced eyes, the caudal fin joined to dorsal and anal fins, and the smooth profile of the dorsal fin.

Life History   It is taken in shrimp trawls operating down to 50 fathoms (92 m) as well as in shore seines. In British Columbia the young have been found to eat copepods.[2] In California dominant food is found to be mainly crustaceans and polychaete worms with the crustaceans, cumaceans and amphipods, most important at early stages, and worms and decapod crustaceans most important in sizes over 80 millimeters. Isopods, mysids, and flatfishes were also among the food organisms.[1] Female showy snailfish contain about 940 maturing eggs at 94 millimeters length and about 4650 at 160 to 170 millimeters.[1]

Distribution   From California to Unalaska[4] and the Bering Sea.[1,3] It is common along the whole coast of British Columbia and abundant in the southern Strait of Georgia.

References   1 Johnson 1969; 2 Robinson, Barraclough, and Fulton 1968a; 3, 4 Wilimovsky 1954, 1964.

RINGTAIL SNAILFISH

Liparis rutteri (Gilbert and Snyder 1898)

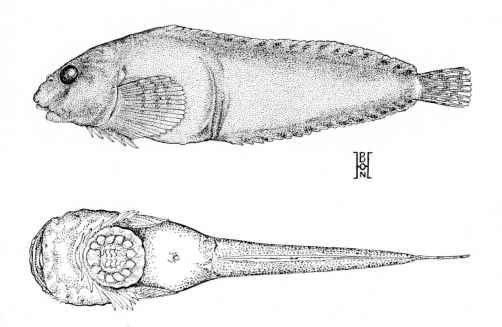

Scientific names from the Greek *liparos* (sleek skinned); and C. Rutter, of the U.S. Fish Commission.

Clemens and Wilby 1946 used the common name ring-tailed liparid for this species.

Description   Body depth about 3.3 into standard length, subcylindrical anteriorly and compressed through its posterior two-thirds. Head conical anteriorly, its length about 4.5 into standard length. Mouth inferior, barely terminal, moderate in size, directed forward and down. Upper jaw not extending halfway to anterior margin of eye. Teeth trilobed and small. Nostrils double. Interorbital space moderate, about 2.3 into length of head, nearly flat. Eye small, its diameter 6 or 7 into length of head. Gill opening extending above base of pectoral fin. Caudal peduncle reduced to a token.

Fins   Dorsal (1), 30 to 32, low with undulating outline somewhat wider near anterior end and notably broadened through posterior half. Caudal small, almost truncate, barely free of dorsal and contiguous with anal fin. Anal 23 to 27, narrow. Pectorals 30 to 33 in 2 sections, a moderately expanded dorsal part and partly folded under it a lower section with thickened exserted rays, the fins from the 2 sides not quite meeting at the midventral line. Pelvics modified to form an adhesive, nearly circular disc, thoracic, the length of the disc 1.4 to 1.8 into length of head.

Scales   Scales and lateral line canal absent. Skin very loose, smooth, and transparent. Pores around mouth.

590

Colour Black to bluish slate or brown. Sparse rows of longitudinal black spots on sides. A prominent white band at the base of the tail, and paler markings sometimes on fins. Caudal speckled.

Size Length to 4.5 inches (11.4 cm).

Recognition Recognizable by the loose skin, the undulating profile of the dorsal fin, the small gill openings above the base of the pectoral fin, and the white band at the base of the caudal fin.

Life History A 22-millimeter (1-inch) specimen was found to have eaten copepods.[1] The species appears to be one of moderate depths.

Distribution Records from California to the Bering Sea.[2] In British Columbia recorded from the west coast of Vancouver Island and the southern Strait of Georgia.

References 1 Barraclough, Robinson, and Fulton 1968; 2 Wilimovsky 1954.

TADPOLE SNAILFISH

Nectoliparis pelagicus Gilbert and Burke 1912

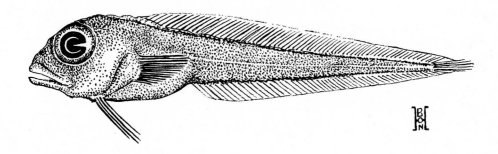

Scientific names from the Greek *nektos* (swimming) and *Liparis* (a genus of related fishes); and *pelagos* (sea).

Clemens and Wilby 1946 used tadpole liparid as the common name for this species.

Description Body elongate, depth about 4.8 into standard length, compressed, greatly so posteriorly, greatest depth at occiput, tapered evenly to narrow caudal base. Head length about 4.3 into standard length. Mouth terminal, rather small, directed forward. Upper jaw reaching as far as anterior edge of eye. Snout very short, blunt. Teeth minute, in a single row in lower jaw only. Lower jaw included. Interorbital space broad, slightly and evenly convex, its width about 2.6 into length of head. Eye large, about twice as long as snout, its diameter about 2 into length of

591

head. Opercular opening long, gill membranes not joined to each other or to isthmus. Anus below vertical from eyes, opening into a trough extending as far as lower jaw and arising from a forward extension of an abdominal paunch, genital pore ventral to anus, pointing forward, and papilla ventral to genital pore and pointing downward. Pyloric caeca about 8.

Fins   Dorsal (1), about 53, with straight outline, confluent with caudal, extending to about half its length. Caudal very narrow, appears truncate but may be pointed in undamaged specimens. Anal about 48, extending on caudal fin like dorsal. Pectorals about 18 to 21, divided into 2 separate lobes with or without inconspicuous intervening rays, 3 or 4 lower rays thickened and lengthened to about length of head, giving appearance of another fin. Pelvics absent, no ventral adhering disc.

Scales   Scales and lateral line canal absent.

Colour   Silvery beneath loose transparent skin, prominent black pigment spots on head and body, and sparsely on posterior parts of upright fins. Dark on operculum and lining of mouth. Peritoneum black. Body sometimes enclosed in a mass of jelly.

Size   Length to 2.5 inches (6.4 cm).

Recognition   Recognized by the tadpolelike appearance, the pectoral fin in two separated lobes, the anus opening under vertical from eyes into a forward-running trough, and absence of a ventral adhering disc.

Life History   Evidently tolerates a wide range of depths. In British Columbia taken on two occasions by shrimp trawlers operating in English Bay at 30 to 40 fathoms (55–73 m). Other British Columbia records are from the Strait of Georgia at 120 fathoms (220 m), and Sechelt Inlet at 130 fathoms (238 m) on stagnant bottom. Taken at surface in Saanich Inlet.[1]

Distribution   Southern California,[3] Oregon,[3] Alaska,[3] Bering Sea,[2,6] Okhotsk Sea,[4,5] Hokkaido,[4,5] at depths from 300 to 633 fathoms (550–1160 m) (or 1217 fathoms (2230 m), to be confirmed). British Columbia records are from the southern part of the province where collecting has been more active.

References   1 Barraclough, Robinson, and Fulton 1968; 2 Gilbert and Burke 1912; 3 Grinols 1965a; 4 Matsubara 1955; 5 Shmidt 1950; 6 Wilimovsky 1954.

PRICKLY SNAILFISH

Paraliparis deani Burke 1912

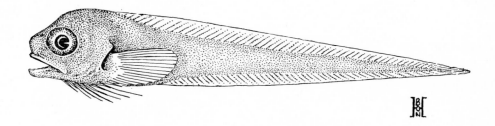

Scientific names from the Greek *para* (near) and *Liparis* (a genus of related fishes); and Dr B. Dean, U.S. ichthyologist and bibliographer.

Clemens and Wilby 1946 called this fish prickly liparid.

Description   Body elongate, its depth (at anterior end of dorsal fin) 6 to 7 into standard length, compressed, becoming shallower sharply anteriorly, then tapering gradually to a pointed tail. Head expanded, compressed, its length about 5.3 into standard length. Mouth terminal, moderate in size, directed forward. Upper jaw extends to posterior part of pupil, includes lower jaw. Snout high and blunt, slightly overhanging upper jaw. Teeth small, conical, some with small shoulders near point, in irregular bands, bands wider in upper jaw. Interorbital slightly concave, bones transparent, its width about 5 into length of head. Eye large, oval, its length about 3 into length of head. Opercles smooth, gill opening extends down to between tenth and thirteenth rays of pectoral fin. Anus vertically below gill opening. Genital pore immediately behind anus.

Fins   Dorsal (1), 56 to 59, no raised lobe at anterior end, extending to about half length of caudal fin. Caudal reduced but recognizable, attached to dorsal and anal, pointed. Anal 44 to 49, extends about to half length of caudal fin. Pectorals 18 to 21, lower rays greatly exserted. Pelvics (and adhering disc) absent.

Scales   Scales absent except as minute prickles on lower surface of pectoral fin.[1] Lateral line canal absent. Skin loose and transparent.

Colour   Translucent pale brown in preservative. Silvery ventrally, with black specks. Pinkish on lips and fins. Dark peritoneum.

Size   Length to 4 inches (10 cm).

Recognition   Noteworthy for the very slender posterior part of the body, the absence of pelvic disc, greatly exserted lower rays of pelvic fin which is notched without being really divided into two, gill openings starting above insertion of pelvic fin, and anus opening downward.

Life History   Apparently mature, 2-millimeter eggs were found in females taken in February.

Distribution   Northern California at 389 to 551 fathoms (712–1001 m), British Columbia and southeastern Alaska at 30 to

274 fathoms (55–501 m).[2] Apparently not rare but not recorded from off Oregon or Washington. In British Columbia off Nanaimo, at 111 fathoms (203 m). Off Fort Rupert in 36 fathoms (66 m), English Bay at 35 to 70 fathoms (64–128 m). Chatham Sound.

References 1 Burke 1930; 2 Grinols 1965a.

LOBEFIN SNAILFISH

Polypera greeni (Jordan and Starks 1895)

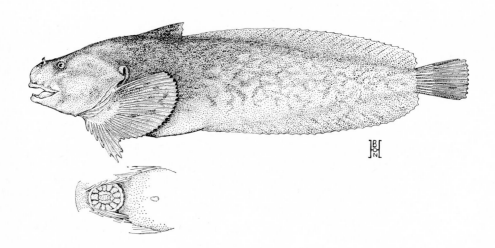

Scientific names from the Greek *poly* (many) and *pera* (pouches — pyloric caeca); and Ashdown Green, Canadian naturalist and collector.

Clemens and Wilby 1946 used the common name Green's liparid for this species.

Description Body elongate, depth about 3.7 into standard length, compressed. Head depressed, profile concave, large, its length about 3.4 into standard length. Mouth terminal, moderate in size, directed forward. Snout blunt. Upper jaw not extending as far as anterior edge of orbit. Jaws about even. Lips thickened and lobed. Teeth in patches on both jaws in diagonal rows, sharply conical, each tooth with small shoulders near the tip. Interorbital space depressed in profile, broad and almost flat between eyes, width about 2.7 into length of head. Eye small, diameter about 15 into length of head in large specimens, sunken. Opercular opening extending about to third pectoral fin ray, not beyond fourth.

Fins Dorsal (1), 37 to 40, well marked-off curved anterior lobe, membrane extending on caudal fin for less than one-fifth of caudal length. Caudal narrow, rounded. Anal 31 or 32, its membrane definitely extending on caudal fin. Pectorals 33 to 37, large, upper part rounded, all rays slightly exserted, more so at bottom of fin where last 6 rays are much exserted and thickened with enough lengthening of some to produce a second lobe to the fin. Pelvics fused to form a ventral adhering disc, nearly circular, its length 2.3 to 2.8 into length of head.

Scales Scales and lateral line canal absent. Skin extremely loose, covered with fine wrinkles, broken or continuous and with many papillae, especially on exposed edges of fins. Pyloric caeca over 300.

Colour Light brown to bluish black on dorsal surface, ventral surface blotched cream to light brown.

Size Length to 12.2 inches (31 cm).

Recognition Recognized by the distinct anterior lobe of the dorsal fin, the short gill opening not extending beyond the fourth ray of the pectoral fin, the small eyes, the large number of pyloric caeca.

Distribution Washington to Bering Sea.[1,2] In British Columbia better known from the southern part, but probably generally distributed.

References 1 Schultz and DeLacy 1936; 2 Wilimovsky 1954.

ORDER PLEURONECTIFORMES
(Heterosomata)

Among the Pleuronectiformes the skull is asymmetrical and both eyes are on the same side of the head. Colour of the body on the blind side is usually much paler than on the eyed side. The upright fins are long and ordinarily the fins are without spines. There is no gasbladder. Pelvic fins usually have fewer than seven rays. The base of the pelvic fin is attached directly to the cleithrum. Newly hatched young are symmetrical and free swimming as plankton but during development one eye makes a remarkable migration and the transformed young settle to the bottom, blind side down. Ordinarily they are bottom fishes, sometimes in very deep water, although some make forays to the surface. Several are valuable commercial species. Two of the six families are found in British Columbia. Halibut, soles, flounders, and sanddabs.

FAMILY BOTHIDAE   LEFTEYE FLOUNDERS

In the Bothidae eyes and colour are on the left side of the fish. The pelvic fin of the eyed side is on the edge of the abdominal ridge. Generally small fishes of no great commercial importance, usually found in rather shallow water close to the bottom. There are two species found in British Columbia. Sanddabs.

KEY TO THE BOTHIDAE

1   Bony ridge above lower eye; interorbital space concave; scales along lateral line canal more than 60; diameter of lower eye longer than snout ....
.... *Citharichthys sordidus,* Pacific sanddab, p. 596

or   1   No bony ridge above lower eye; interorbital space flat to convex; scales along lateral line canal fewer than 60; diameter of lower eye about equal to length of snout ....
.... *Citharichthys stigmaeus,* Speckled sanddab, p. 598

PACIFIC SANDDAB

Citharichthys sordidus (Girard 1854)

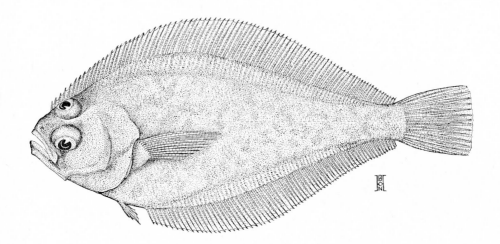

Scientific names from *Citharus,* the name of an allied genus derived in turn from the Greek *citharos* (rib — fish lies on side), and *ichthys* (fish); and the Latin *sordidus* (sordid — dull in colour).

Clemens and Wilby 1946, 1961 used the common names mottled sand dab and mottled sanddab for this species.

Description   Body compressed, highly asymmetrical with dark colour restricted to left side. Head asymmetrical with both eyes on the left side, deep and blunt. Mouth terminal, moderate in size and gape. Jaws about symmetrical, the top of the lower jaw heavy with a median knob. Maxillary extending to forward part of lower eye. Eyes

596

large, lower somewhat forward of the upper, and longer than the snout. Interorbital space moderate and concave. A high sharp bony naked ridge above the lower eye.

Fins   Dorsal (1), 86 to 102, originating just ahead of the upper eye. Caudal rounded. Anal 67 to 81. Pectorals rather large and pointed. Pelvics 6, thoracic, that on the eyed side on the edge of the abdominal ridge.

Gill Rakers   Usually 15 or 16 on lower arch.

Vertebrae   38 to 39 (mean of 22 counts, 38.5)[4].

Scales   Imbricated, thin and deciduous. Ctenoid on eyed side of body, cycloid on blind side.[3] Lateral line canal with 61 to 70 scales, nearly straight, running downward slightly in anterior part of body. No accessory branch.

Colour   On the eyed side shades of dull brown or tan irregularly mottled with dark. Black on dorsal, caudal, and anal fins. On freshly caught males dull orange spots and blotches. Off-white to pale brown on blind side.
In young the eyed side is light olive green, finely and sparsely speckled with brown, black, and orange, especially on fins.

Size   Length to 16 inches (41 cm).

Recognition   A flatfish with the strong colour and eyes on the left side of the body, the length of the lower eye greater than that of the snout, and a high bony ridge above the lower eye. No striking light and dark bands on the unpaired fins.

Life History   Spawning takes place around February in Puget Sound.[7] Eggs are clear, with a single oil globule about 0.1 millimeter in diameter. There are indications that females may spawn a second time during the spawning season.
In California lengths at age I, average 95 millimeters; II, 148 millimeters; III, 192 millimeters; and at age VII, males 246 millimeters and females 274. Fifty percent of the females are mature at 191 millimeters.[2]

Distribution   From Baja California to the Bering Sea[1,5,6,8] at depths down to 167 fathoms (306 m) but more common in shallow water. Generally distributed and fairly common in shallow waters of British Columbia.

Utilization   A small but steady demand occurs for this species in British Columbia but records of quantities handled are not dependable. It is relatively more important in California where it is regarded as a delicacy.

References   1 Alverson, Pruter, and Ronholt 1964; 2 Arora 1951; 3 Batts 1964; 4 Clothier 1950; 5 Grinols 1965a; 6 Roedel 1948b; 7 Smith 1936; 8 Wilimovsky 1954.

SPECKLED SANDDAB

Citharichthys stigmaeus Jordan and Gilbert 1882

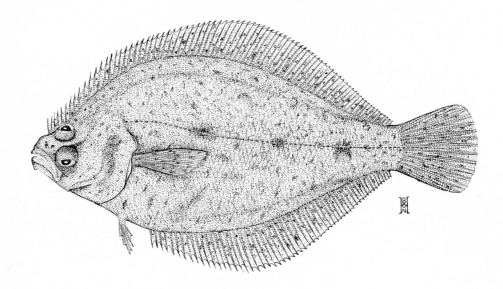

Scientific names from *Citharus,* the name of an allied genus derived in turn from the Greek *citharos* (rib — fish lies on side) and *ichthys* (fish); and *stigmaios* (speckled).

Description   Body compressed, highly asymmetrical with strong colour restricted to left side. Head asymmetrical with both eyes on the left side, deep and bluntly pointed. Mouth terminal, moderate in size and gape. Jaws about symmetrical, tip of the lower jaw with a median knob. Maxillary extends to forward part of the lower eye. Eyes large, lower barely forward of the upper, shorter or the same length as the snout. Interorbital space narrow, flat or convex, no ridge above lower eye. Caudal peduncle rather slender.

Fins   Dorsal (1), 79 to 92, first 2 or 3 rays ahead of upper eye. Caudal rounded. Anal 59 to 72. Pectorals rather large and rounded to an angle. Pelvics 6, thoracic, that on the eyed side on the edge of the abdominal ridge.

Gill Rakers   Usually 8 or 9 on lower arch.

Vertebrae   Mean 35.7.[2,4]

Scales   Imbricated, deciduous, rather large, mostly ctenoid on both sides of body.[1] Lateral line canal with 52 to 58 scales (higher counts to 68 are recorded), gradually sloping downward and then straight without an accessory branch.

Colour   Olive brown on eyed side, finely and sharply speckled with black. Soiled white to cream on the blind side.
Young nearly uniform gray on eyed side, finely speckled with black, resembling sandy beach in coloration. Translucent.

Size   Length to 6 inches (15 cm).

598

Recognition　　This is a small speckled "left-handed" flatfish with a snout shorter than the length of the lower eye and without a ridge above the lower eye.

Distribution　　From Baja California to southeast Alaska.[3,5] In British Columbia recorded from the west coasts of Vancouver and Moresby islands, and captured frequently in trawls operating in shallow water and on sandy beaches in the Strait of Georgia. Because of its small size it is probably frequently overlooked and is of no commercial importance.

References　　1 Batts 1964; 2 Clothier 1950; 3, 4 Townsend 1935, 1936; 5 Wilimovsky 1954.

FAMILY PLEURONECTIDAE　　　　　　　　　　　　RIGHTEYE FLOUNDERS

In these flatfishes the eyes and colour are usually on the right hand side of the fish and the pelvic fins are placed symmetrically. The family includes small to large fishes and some of them are of substantial commercial importance. Nineteen species have been recorded from off the coast of British Columbia. Most of them are designated as halibut, soles, or flounders.

KEY TO THE PLEURONECTIDAE

599

ARROWTOOTH FLOUNDER

Atheresthes stomias (Jordan and Gilbert 1880)

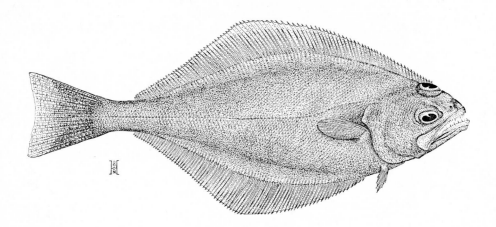

Scientific names from the Greek *athor* (spike — on corn) and *esthio* (eat — arrow-shaped teeth); and *stoma* (mouth — large).

Clemens and Wilby 1946 referred to this species as the long-jaw flounder. Commonly referred to as turbot by British Columbia fishermen.

Description   Body compressed, highly asymmetrical with colour restricted to right side. Head asymmetrical with both eyes on right side, long. Mouth very large, terminal, with wide gape and nearly symmetrical. Point of jaw heavy. Teeth well developed on both sides of jaws and arrow shaped. Maxillary extending beyond posterior margin of the lower eye. Snout pointed. Eyes large, the lower somewhat in advance of the upper which is close to the median line of the head and enters profile. Interorbital space low. Caudal peduncle long.

Fins   Dorsal (1), 92 to 109 in British Columbia,[12] originating over middle of upper eye. Caudal shallowly lunate. Anal 72 to 90 in British

Columbia,[12] no spine at origin. Pectorals small. Pelvics 6, thoracic.

Gill Rakers   14 to 16 in British Columbia.[12]

Vertebrae   47 to 49.[12]

Scales   Unevenly imbricated, rather large, irregular in size, thin, deciduous, ctenoid on eyed side and cycloid on blind side.[4] Lateral line canal about 135, slightly decurved and then straight without an accessory branch.

Colour   Brown to olive brown on eyed side. Darker on margins of scales. White on blind side, finely dotted with black.

Size   Length to 2 feet 9 inches (84 cm).

Recognition   Distinguished by the very large mouth with the maxillary extending behind the eyes, the arrow-shaped teeth, and the left eye on the upper margin of the head.

Life History   Larvae were taken between 200 meters and the surface off northern British Columbia in June.[11] Larvae under an inch (10–19 mm) in Saanich Inlet in July were eating copepods, and eggs, and juvenile stages of copepods.[3] Shrimps and herring are eaten. In California important foods are ocean shrimp, krill, other shrimps, sanddabs, and miscellaneous fishes.[7]

Distribution   Central California[10] to the eastern Bering Sea. In the Bering Sea it meets about on a line with Saint Matthew Island (172 W),[2] overlaps with, and is replaced by the closely related *Atheresthes evermanni*.[12] A single small specimen of *Atheresthes* from the Chukchi Sea is recorded.[1] It is taken in depths down to the 400- to 499-fathom (730–900-m) range.[1,8,9]

Young *Atheresthes* were found at depths greater than 700 meters. The species is plentiful through British Columbia and is abundant further north.

Utilization   Although this is a large, thick, plentiful fish, no market as human food has been established. Significant quantities up to 7 million pounds (3180 metric tons) annually have been used for mink feed.[5,6]

References   1 Alverson, Pruter, and Ronholt 1964; 2 Andriashev 1937; 3 Barraclough and Fulton 1968; 4 Batts 1964; 5, 6 Forrester 1958, 1968; 7 Gotshall 1969; 8 Grinols 1965a; 9 Nikol'skii 1961; 10 Roedel 1948b; 11 Taylor 1967a; 12 Wilimovsky, Peden, and Peppar 1967.

ROUGHSCALE SOLE

Clidoderma asperrimum (Temminck and Schlegel 1846)

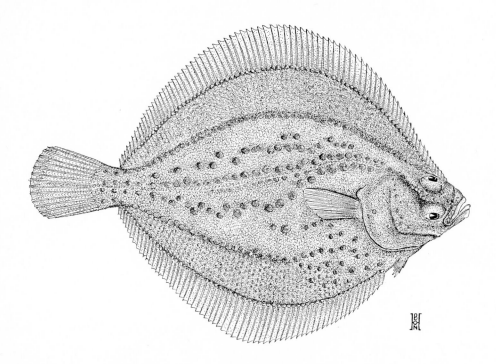

Scientific names from the Greek *cleido* (key or clavicle) and *derma* (skin); and the Latin *asperrimum* (very rough).

Description   Body depth about 1.5 to 2.0 into standard length, compressed, highly asymmetrical with colour restricted to right side. Head 3 to 4 into standard length, asymmetrical with both eyes on right side, rather deep, rounded. Mouth small, terminal, with narrow gape, asymmetrical. Maxillary extending to point below forward part of lower eye; on blind side, it is longer by a fifth to a half. Teeth in 2 rows on both jaws much better developed on blind side. Snout roundly pointed. Eyes large, 4.2 to 5 into length of head, the lower slightly in advance of the upper. Interorbital ridge low and narrow. Caudal peduncle slender.

Fins   Dorsal (1), 75 to 89, originating above or ahead of the upper eye. Caudal broadly rounded. Anal 61 to 72, no spine in front, about 2.5 into length of head on eyed side and a quarter shorter on blind side. Pectorals 12 to 14, bluntly rounded. Pelvics 6, thoracic.

Scales   Ordinary scales absent. On eyed side rough bony tubercles with larger tubercles arranged in 6 more or less definite longitudinal rows. Smaller tubercles on snout, around eyes, in poorly organized radiating rows around dorsal and ventral edges of body and on inner parts of dorsal and anal fin rays. All tubercles have hairlike spines. Blind side smooth. Lateral line canal with a low arch over pectoral fin and straight on posterior part of the body. A short accessory branch over the eye.[4]

Colour   Brownish on eyed side. The blind side gray.

Size   Length to 21.5 inches (55 cm).

Recognition   Recognizable by the rough tubercles on the eyed side and the absence of scales from the blind side.

Distribution   From southern British Columbia to Nagasaki, Japan. Recorded from Korea, Sakhalin, Hokkaido, and the Kuril Islands.[1,2,3] The only two records from the eastern Pacific are from Esteban Deep at 185 to 190 fathoms (339–348 m) (49.04 N, 127.53 W).[5]

References   1 Andriashev 1937; 2 Grinols 1965a; 3 Matsubara 1955; 4 Norman 1934; 5 Welander, Alverson, and Bergman 1957.

DEEPSEA SOLE

Embassichthys bathybius (Gilbert 1891)

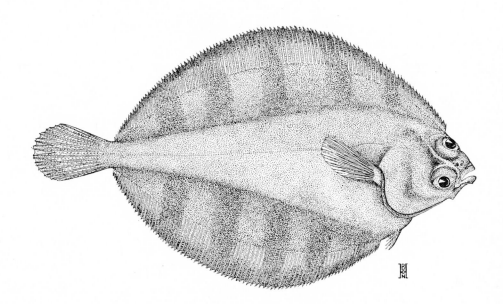

Scientific names from the Greek *en* (in) and *bassos* for *battos* — *bathos* (deep), and *ichthys* (fish); and *bathos* (deep) and *bios* (life).

Description   Body compressed short, depth about 2.2 into standard length with dorsal and ventral thirds very compressed, highly asymmetrical, with colour different on 2 sides. Head about 4.6 into standard length, asymmetrical with both eyes on right side. Mouth small, terminal, with narrow gape, asymmetrical. Maxillary extending to forward part of lower eye. Teeth moderately developed on both sides of both jaws, better in the lower jaw and on the blind side, at least 7 in jaws on eyed side. Snout narrowly rounded. Eyes large, about 3.2 into length of head, lower considerably in advance of upper (almost above in only Canadian specimen). Interorbital ridge high and narrow. Gill opening extending slightly above uppermost pectoral fin ray.

Fins   Dorsal (1), 109 to 117, rays unbranched, origin over posterior edge of pupil (behind eye in Canadian specimen). Caudal imperfectly rounded. Anal 95 to 98, rays unbranched. Pectorals 11, short. Pelvics 5 or 6, thoracic. (In Canadian specimen pelvics joined by a membrane.)

Gill Rakers   10 or 11 on lower first arch (6 + 16 on Canadian specimen).

Scales   Small, cycloid. Lateral line canal with about 165 along its length (222 in Canadian specimen), slightly arched over pectoral and then straight, no accessory dorsal branch.

Colour   Brown becoming darker toward margins of body, black toward tips of dorsal and anal fin rays. In fresh specimens pale blue blotches on body arranged on upper and lower thirds to form 5 broad bluish areas. Black on tips of branchiostegal membranes and both jaws. Heavy dusky brown on blind side.

Size   Length to 18.5 inches (47 cm).

Recognition   Notable for the high degree of compression on the upper and lower thirds of the body. The gill opening is short. There is a high ridge between the eyes, a short slender caudal peduncle, and no remarkable lengthening of the pectoral fin on the eyed side.

Distribution   Known from off southern California[3] to southeastern Alaska.[6] It is recorded from depths of 175 to 750 fathoms (320–1370 m), mostly from deeper than 400 fathoms (730 m) where it does not appear to be uncommon. A record from 48.14.1 N, 125.02.2 W at 530 fathoms (970 m) is here considered as being off British Columbia.[1,2,4,5]

References   1 Alverson, Pruter, and Ronholt 1964; 2 Grinols 1965a; 3 Hagerman 1950; 4 Hubbs 1959; 5 Welander and Alverson 1954; 6 Wilimovsky 1954.

PETRALE SOLE

Eopsetta jordani (Lockington 1879)

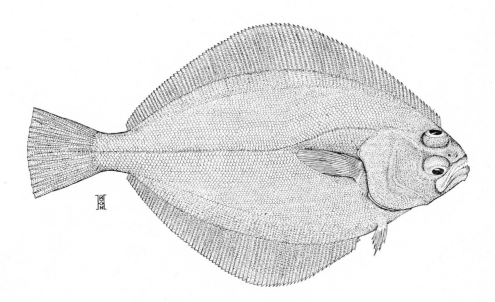

Scientific names from the Greek *eos* (morning) and *psetta* (flounder); and President (Stanford University) David Starr Jordan, great inciter of ichthyology in the United States.

Clemens and Wilby 1946, 1961 used the well-established Canadian name brill for this species.

Description   Body compressed, highly asymmetrical, with colour restricted to right side. Head asymmetrical with both eyes on right side, deep, compressed, blunt, gives the impression of being flat. Mouth terminal, large, with wide gape, almost symmetrical. Maxillary extending to point below posterior part of eye. Teeth are developed in both jaws, in a double row in the upper jaw, and single row in the lower. Snout rounded. Eyes moderate in size separated by a broad interorbital space. Caudal peduncle compressed, slender.

Fins   Dorsal (1), 87 to 101, originating over the middle part of eye. Caudal longest in the middle ending in a very broad 'V'. Anal 67 to 79. Well-developed spine at the origin of the anal fin. Pectorals rather large and bluntly pointed. Pelvics 6, thoracic.

Vertebrae   41 to 44 (mean of 55 counts, 42.2).[20]

Scales   Imbricated, small, not readily deciduous, ctenoid on eyed side, cycloid on blind side,[5] about 30 diagonal rows between dorsal fin and lateral line canal at widest part of body. Lateral line canal with 88 to 100 scales, decurved gently from a wave at the anterior end and straight posteriorly, no accessory branch.

Colour   Uniform olive brown on eyed side. Blind side white, with pink sometimes showing through faintly. Faint dusky blotches on dorsal and anal fins. Very rarely ambicoloured; in one such case, there were minor distortions of the upper eye and dorsal fin.[12]

607

Size   Length to 27.5 inches (70 cm).[8]

Recognition   This large deep flatfish can be recognized by a combination of the following characters: mouth large with maxillary extending well under eye, teeth in two rows in the upper jaw. Scales small, 88 to 100 in lateral line canal. No elongated free spines at origin of dorsal fin.

Life History   The main spawning ground for petrale sole from northern British Columbia is Esteban Deep around 200 fathoms (366 m) off the central part of Vancouver Island where spawning is in late winter and early spring. The spawners, congregated there, disperse along shore through Queen Charlotte Sound and Hecate Strait, and return to the spawning grounds in subsequent years. The eggs are about 1.3 millimeters in diameter and float close to the surface where prevailing southerly winds drive them toward the northeast, where they sink on encountering less dense water before reaching shallow shore water. In the laboratory eggs at 7 C hatch in 8 or 9 days to produce 3.0 millimeter larvae which absorb the yolk sac in about 10 days.[11] Early young have never been found off Canada. Off California near Eureka two specimens were taken with eye-migration complete and colour lacking on the blind side. They were 21 and 22 millimeters in total length.[17] Juveniles aged 1 and 2 years have been found on bottom at 10 to 39 fathoms (18–71 m) but this is not necessarily the regular habitat. As success of spawning depends upon meteorological and oceanographic conditions, it is variable from year to year with resulting changes in abundance and sizes of fish in the stock. Fish found on Forty-Mile Bank in fall and summer spawn at Willapa Deep off southern Washington. There is evidence of a series of more or less separate stocks of petrale sole from Alaska to California.[4,6,7,10,15]

Petrale sole from catches of the southern population in British Columbia of selected ages show the following ages for males and females:

Age	Males (mm)	Females (mm)
III	304	315
IV	337	342
VII	393	428
XII	448	507
XVII	489	566
XXII	–	599

Different year classes show different rates of growth.[15] Fifty percent of the males are mature at 380 millimeters (age VII) and females at 440 millimeters (age VIII).[10] Hecate Strait populations generally mature at a larger size, and populations off the Columbia River rather smaller.[7,14,15] Some individuals are still immature at age X. A 420-millimeter female contains about 400,000 eggs, and a 570-millimeter fish at least 1,200,000. The oldest petrale soles encountered were 25 years for females and 19 for males.[10]

Food varies with availability, locality, and season. Euphausiids, sand lance, herring, and shrimps are the most important foods off British Columbia. However, petrale sole have an effective predatory mouth and a wide variety of bottom fishes and invertebrates are taken.[14]

Distribution   From northern Baja California[6] to the Gulf of Alaska and the Bering Sea.[9,13,21] At depths from the surface to 300 fathoms (550 m). Individuals generally distributed through coastal British Columbia with fishable concentrations along the west coast of Vancouver Island, off Cape Scott, through Queen Charlotte Sound and Hecate Strait, and in Dixon Entrance. Commercial abundance in 170 to 250 fathoms (310–460 m) in winter, 40 to 70 fathoms (73–128 m) during the rest of the year.[1,2,3,10]

Utilization   Because of its large size and excellent quality either as fresh or frozen fillets, the petrale sole is highly regarded throughout the Pacific coast. The Canadian fishery reached a peak of 6.7

million pounds (3040 metric tons) in 1948. For various reasons production has sustained substantial fluctuations not shown in the 5-year averages in millions of pounds (454 metric tons).[16]

Years	Average catch
1936–40	0.1
1941–45	0.4
1946–50	3.2
1951–55	1.2
1956–60	0.9
1961–65	1.1
1966	1.1
1967	1.3
1968	1.0
1969	0.4
1970	0.5

Livers of large petrale sole are a rich source of vitamin A.[18,19]

References   1 Alverson 1960; 2 Alverson and Chatwin 1957; 3 Alverson, Pruter, and Ronholt 1964; 4 Barraclough 1954b; 5 Batts 1964; 6 Best 1963c; 7 Cleaver 1949; 8 Clemens and Wilby 1961; 9 Evermann and Goldsborough 1907; 10 Forrester 1969b; 11 Forrester and Alderdice 1967; 12 Forrester and Smith 1971; 13 Grinols 1965a; 14 Harry 1959; 15 Ketchen and Forrester 1966; 16 Larkin and Ricker 1964; 17 Porter 1964; 18, 19 Swain and Barraclough 1946a, b; 20 Townsend 1936; 21 Wilimovsky 1954.

REX SOLE

Glyptocephalus zachirus Lockington 1879

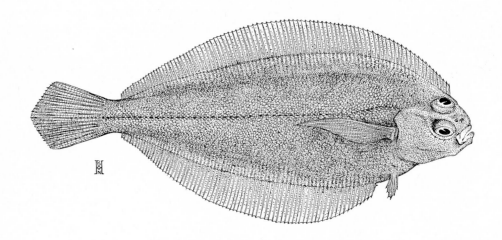

Scientific names from the Greek *glyptos* (sculptured) and *cephalos* (head); and *za* (superlative — long) and *cheir* (hand — long pectoral fin).

Description   Body much compressed, highly asymmetrical with strong colour restricted to right side. Head asymmetrical with both eyes on right side, short, compressed, rounded. Mouth small, terminal, with narrow gape, asymmetrical. Maxillary extending to point below anterior part of lower eye. Teeth mainly on lower side of jaw. Snout rounded. Eyes large, lower slightly in advance of upper, separated by an interorbital ridge. Gill opening extending above base of pectoral fin. Caudal peduncle short.

Fins   Dorsal (1), 87 to 110, originating above middle of upper eye. Caudal longest in centre with posterior margin like a broad 'V'. Anal 78 to 93, sharp spine exposed at origin. Pectoral on eyed side greatly elongate, especially in large individuals, not extended on blind side. Pelvics 6, thoracic.

Vertebrae   62 to 65.[7]

Scales   Imbricated, small, cycloid, uniform over body. Lateral line canal 132 to 138, nearly straight and without an accessory branch.

Colour   Uniform light brown on eyed side, white to dusky on blind side, fins dusky especially toward tips. Young are quite translucent.

Size   Length to 23.2 inches (59 cm).

Recognition   Long pectoral fin on eyed side, almost straight lateral line canal without an accessory branch.

Life History   Little is known about the life history of this species and deductions must be made in doubt. Spawning in Hecate Strait apparently occurs in March and early April.[4] Young are not found inshore but occasionally juveniles about 10

610

centimeters long, presumably 1-year-old, occur in shallow water and down to 60 fathoms (110 m). Larger juveniles to 30 centimeters are found to 80 fathoms (146 m). Rex sole more than 38 centimeters are too infrequent in data to support generalizations but may be best represented at intermediate depths. Females are more abundant in catches. The rex sole grows slowly and lives long — up to at least 24 years.[6] The species is delicate and does not survive handling well. Individuals with eyes and stronger colour on the left side are very rarely encountered.[3]

Distribution   Southern California to the Bering Sea. Recorded from the surface down to 400 fathoms.[4,5] Not recorded from the western Bering Sea or Commander Islands.[2] In northern waters off the Alaska peninsula. Apparently most abundant in water deeper than 200 fathoms (366 m).[1] The rex sole is rather generally distributed through coastal British Columbia.

Utilization   Although of prime quality and reasonably abundant the rex sole has not been much used in Canada. The generally small size of the fish encountered and their thinness make for inefficient handling in an industry geared to filleting. Landings are of the order of 100,000 pounds annually, mostly taken in the autumn in Hecate Strait.[6]

References   1 Alverson, Pruter, and Ronholt 1964; 2 Andriashev 1937; 3 Follett, McCormick, and Best 1960; 4 Forrester personal communication; 5 Grinols 1965a; 6 Needler 1954; 7 Townsend 1936.

FLATHEAD SOLE

Hippoglossoides elassodon Jordan and Gilbert 1880

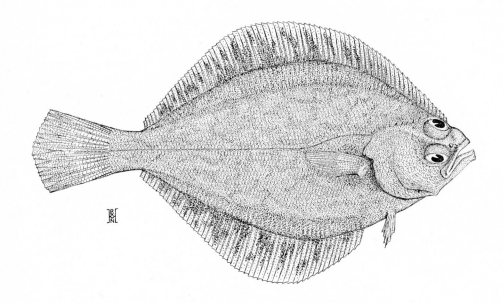

Scientific names from *Hippoglossus* (generic name for halibut) and the Greek *oides* (like); and *ellas* (diminutive) and *odons* (tooth).

Description   Body much compressed, leading to the fishermen's name "cigarette paper" for small specimens, highly asymmetrical with colour restricted to right side. Head asymmetrical with both eyes on right side, moderately deep and compressed. Mouth large, terminal, with wide gape, and nearly symmetrical. Lower jaw protruding. Teeth well developed in both sides of jaws in single row on each jaw. Maxillary extending to a point below pupil of eye. Snout pointed. Eyes large, almost in line, separated by a narrow raised interorbital space. Caudal peduncle slender.

Fins   Dorsal (1), 75 to 85 in British Columbia[14] originating over anterior part of upper eye. Caudal almost truncate with small elongation in centre. Anal 55 to 68 in British Columbia.[14] Well-developed spine at origin of fin. Pectorals rather large with rounded tips. Pelvics 6, thoracic.

Gill Rakers   On lower arch 16 to 24 (in British Columbia).[14]

Vertebrae   42 to 46.[13]

Scales   Imbricated, small, deciduous, mostly ctenoid on eyed side, mostly cycloid on blind side except on caudal peduncle, and in a band across the lateral line canal,[3] in diagonal row between dorsal fin and lateral line canal at widest part of body, 40 to 50. Lateral line canal 86 to 91 (in British Columbia),[11] in flattened arch over pectoral fin and then straight, no accessary branch.

Colour   Uniform gray to olive brown on eyed side, sometimes blotched with dusky brown. White on blind side. Dusky blotches on dorsal and anal fins.

Size   Length to 18 inches (46 cm).

Recognition   The following combination of characters serve to identify this flatfish: mouth nearly symmetrical, extending as far as the pupil of the eye but not beyond, caudal fin nearly straight or slightly rounded, an exposed spine at the base of the anal fin, no dorsal branch to the lateral line canal, teeth on the upper jaw in one row, body notably thin.

Life History   In Puget Sound generally males mature at age II and females at age III. In some parts of the Sound fish of age I may be found in spawning condition.[9] Spawning is from March to late April. Eggs are large (2.75–3.75 mm) with a large perivitelline space.[4] Females have egg counts ranging from about 72,000 (a 20-cm fish, age I) to almost 600,000 (38 cm — age V). Eggs hatch in 9 to 20 days depending on incubation temperatures within the range 9.8 to 2.4 C.[5,9] At the time of hatching larval lengths are between 3.3 millimeters and about 6.0 millimeters with incubation temperatures of 3.0 C and 6.0 to 9.8 C but by the time the yolk sac is absorbed larvae are similar in size. The yolk sac is absorbed in 6 to 17 days at 9.6 C and 4.5 C.[5] Food

items in Puget Sound are clams and worms.[12] Crustaceans are also eaten.

Distribution   From northern California, off Point Reyes,[10] through Oregon, Washington, British Columbia, southeast Alaska, Gulf of Alaska, Bering Sea, the Kuril Islands, possibly the Okhotsk Sea to Japan,[2,6,8,11,14] but not extending into the northern part of the Bering Sea or the Chukchi Sea where the related *Hippoglossoides robustus* appears to take over. Considerable doubt exists about the validity of various species; *H. elassodon* is found at depths ranging from the surface to 300 fathoms (550 m).[7] In the British Columbia and southeast Alaska area the flathead sole occurs mainly at depths between 150 to 200 fathoms (275–366 m),[1] but young are commonly taken at shallow depths in the Strait of Georgia and elsewhere.

References   1 Alverson, Pruter, and Ronholt 1964; 2 Andriashev 1937; 3 Batts 1964; 4 English 1966; 5 Forrester and Alderdice 1968; 6 Gilbert and Burke 1912; 7 Grinols 1965a; 8 Matsubara 1955; 9 Miller 1969; 10 Nitsos personal communication; 11 Shmidt 1950; 12 Smith 1936; 13 Townsend 1936; 14 Wilimovsky, Peden, and Peppar 1967.

PACIFIC HALIBUT

Hippoglossus stenolepis Schmidt 1904

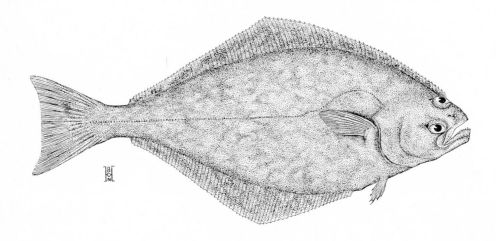

Scientific names from the Greek *hippos* (horse) and *glossa* (tongue); and *steno* (narrow) and *lepis* (scale).

Clemens and Wilby 1946 listed this species as halibut and it is probable that name will remain current.

Description   Body compressed, highly asymmetrical, with colour restricted to right side, its depth about 2.7 into standard length. Head asymmetrical with both eyes on right side, compressed and moderately deep, its length about 3.7 into standard length. Mouth terminal, large, with a wide gape, nearly symmetrical, directed forward and up. Upper jaw extends to midorbit of lower eye. Lower jaw protrudes. Teeth conical, sharp, well developed in both jaws, a double row in upper jaw, single in lower. Interorbital space narrow and a little concave, its width about 20 into length of head in small specimens, wider in large fish. Eyes oval, length about 5.2 into length of head in small specimens, the upper eye in advance of the lower. Opercular membranes joined but free of isthmus. Caudal peduncle compressed, its least depth about 13 into standard length.

Fins   Dorsal (1), 90 to 106 in British Columbia,[20] originating above anterior part of pupil in upper eye, generally low, higher in middle. Caudal spread and slightly forked. Anal 69 to 80 in British Columbia,[20] higher anteriorly but all low. Not preceded by a prominent spine. Pectorals about 19, small. Pelvics 6, thoracic, almost symmetrical.

Vertebrae   49 to 51, mean 50.2.

Scales   Cycloid on both sides of fish, very small, overlapping. Lateral line canal arching over pectoral fin and then nearly straight down midside, about 150 scales along lateral line canal.

Colour   Dark brown or gray marbled with paler shades on eyed side. Normally white on blind side.

Size   Length to 8 feet 9 inches (267 cm), a female. The longest male record is

614

4 feet 7 inches (140 cm). Maximum eviscerated heads-off weights are 475 and 123 pounds (216 and 56 kg).[2] The average landed size is about 35 pounds (16 kg).[5]

Recognition   Recognized by the slightly forked tail, the sturdy body, the moderately large, almost symmetrical mouth with conical teeth, the arched lateral line canal, and the numerous smooth scales. (Note colour illustration Plate I.)

Life History   Halibut spawn in the wintertime mostly from November to January and from 150 to 225 fathoms (275–412 m) deep. On the average females mature at 12 years of age (between 8 and 16); males mature considerably younger. A large female produces 2 to 3 million eggs annually. Egg diameters range from 3.0 to 3.5 millimeters; the yolk is large, there is no pigment on the developing embryo, the shell has an extremely finely punctate surface, and there are no markings around the micropyle beyond faint irregularly radiating lines.[4,19] Eggs and larvae are pelagic for 4 to 5 months after spawning. Eggs may be encountered any place between 22 and 511 fathoms (40 and 935 m) depth but are mainly concentrated between 55 and 109 fathoms (100 and 200 m). Newly hatched larvae are usually found below 109 fathoms (200 m). They average 11.2 millimeters long (between 8 and 15 mm), they are symmetrical, with huge yolk sacs, the core of tail is only a rod, and they are without pigment except for the eyes. At a length of about 18 millimeters the yolk sac is no longer evident, the eye on the left side of the head is showing signs of migrating so that its top can be seen from the right side, the rays for the growing caudal fin are well developed, but the clusters of pigment spots, which are characteristic of late larval stages, are not yet evident. By about 30 millimeters the young fish are recognizable by their resemblance to adults, and general pigmentation hides the juvenile clusters of pigment cells. However, the tail is still rounded

and the eyes are notably large. With growth young fish rise in the water and are found predominately at about 55 fathoms (100 m) by 3 to 5 months. They are carried inshore by surface currents and become established on bottom at about 6 to 7 months. Later, with increasing age and size, they move out into deeper water. They first become available to the offshore commercial fishery at about 5 to 7 years of age. The species occurs from near surface to 600 fathoms (1100 m) but is most common between 30 and 225 fathoms (55–422 m).[19]

Immature halibut which predominate off the British Columbia coast usually make only restricted migrations on and off the feeding and fishing grounds. Mature fish make extensive migrations related to spawning and movement of as much as 1000 miles (1600 km) is recorded.[18]

In Hecate Strait and Queen Charlotte Sound halibut are about 9 centimeters long at 1 year of age, 23 at 2, 38 at 3, 48 at 4, 57 at 5, and 91 at 10. At 15 years they are about 112 centimeters on Goose Island Banks and 125 centimeters in northern Hecate Strait, which is the fastest growing area studied. Females grow considerably faster than males. Growth rate is subject to much annual variation, some of which appears to be density dependent and inversely related to the abundance of young fish, and some of which is related to fluctuating conditions in the sea.[16]

Food consists of fishes, crabs,[5] clams, squids, and other invertebrates. There are few reports of halibut being caught by other animals but there must be a considerable toll by predation or disease even among large halibut, as instantaneous natural mortality rates have been estimated at 0.30[18] and 0.31.[10]

Distribution   Southern California at Santa Rosa Island (33.58 N, 120.06 W)[2] and Point Piedras Blanca (35.40 N, 121.17 W),[11] northern California, Oregon, Washington, British Columbia, Alaska,[6] to the Bering Sea as far as Norton Sound[2] and about halfway between Saint Matthew Island and Saint Lawrence Island[14], off Anadyr, Kuril Islands,[15] and Kamchatka[12,15] northeast of Sakhalin Island, and Okhotsk Sea but not in its northern part,[15] off Hokkaido and north of northeastern Japan.[9] Benthic to 600 fathoms (1100 m).

Utilization　　Before the first Europeans visited the Pacific coast of North America an extensive Indian fishery used a special and effective hook for the halibut which played a role in the original economy of the area. With the completion of the railways across Canada and the northern United States, transcontinental shipments of halibut, caught by European methods, became possible and were made regularly by the end of the century. At that time the combined Canadian and United States catches were about 10 million pounds. Fish were originally caught through shore-based operations and later by sailing (U.S.) and steam (Canada) vessels carrying dories for handline fishing. By 1910 removal of accumulated stocks from inshore banks, and the availability of vessels capable of working in exposed areas, led to the development of a truly deep-sea fishery. About 10 years later the availability of the dependable and cheaper diesel engine opened the way for the more effective longlining method of fishing from the main vessel and in 1944 the old dory method of fishing became illegal. About 1931 the fishery had reached a point where accumulated stocks had all been caught off and increasing fishing effort no longer led to greater production. In 1932 the fishery came under regulation through the International Fisheries Commission. Stocks have gradually rebuilt, partly as a result of reduction in fishing, and, apparently, partly because of improving ocean conditions for halibut production.[1,2,3,7,13,17]

Basing decisions on evident differences in make up of halibut stocks, the International Fisheries Commission divided the coast into 4 major Areas for research and management: 1 South of Willapa Harbor, Washington; 2 Willapa Harbor to Cape Spencer, Alaska; 3 West of Cape Spencer; and 4 the Bering Sea. Canadian and United States fishermen both fish in Areas 2, 3, and 4. The available data on their average annual catches are summed in millions of pounds (454 metric tons) in the following adapted[8] tabulation, supplemented by information obtained directly from the International Pacific Halibut Commission:

Years	Area 2	Area 3	Area 4
1902,1904,1905	24.1		
1907,1910	50.9		
1911–15	52.8		
1915		23.7	
1916–20	29.3	14.5	
1921–25	28.8	20.5	
1926–30	23.8	28.8	
1931–35	22.3	22.6	
1936–40	26.2	24.2	
1941–45	25.3	27.4	
1946–50	28.1	28.8	
1951–55	31.9	29.4	
1956–60	31.8	32.9	2.5
1961	28.8	36.4	4.0
1962	28.7	38.8	7.3
1963	26.2	36.9	8.1
1964	19.6	37.9	2.3
1965	24.4	37.6	1.3
1966	23.4	37.6	1.2
1967	20.0	33.1	2.4
1968	16.6	30.9	1.3
1969	22.7	34.7	1.2
1970	19.9	33.9	1.1

In general, Canadian landings in recent years have been rather more than half of the totals. Production from Area 1 has never been substantial.

References　　1 Alverson, Pruter, and Ronholt 1964; 2 Bell 1969, personal communication; 3 Bell and Pruter 1958; 4 English 1966; 5 Gray 1964; 6 Grinols 1965a; 7 Ketchen 1956a; 8 Larkin and Ricker 1964; 9 Matsubara 1955; 10 Myre 1967; 11 Phillips 1958b; 12 Popov 1933; 13 Ricker 1963; 14 Schmidt 1934; 15 Shmidt 1950; 16 Southward 1967; 17 Thompson and Freeman 1930; 18 Thompson and Herrington 1930; 19 Thompson and Van Cleve 1936; 20 Townsend 1936.

(HYBRID) SOLE

Inopsetta ischyra (Jordan and Gilbert 1881)

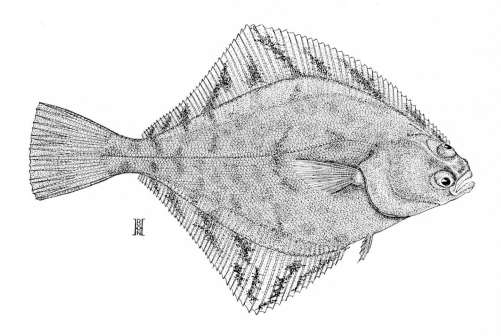

Scientific names from the Greek *inos* (strength) and *psetta* (flounder); and *ischyros* (robust).

Clemens and Wilby 1961 list this form as a species with **forkline sole** as the common name.

This fish is reputedly a hybrid between the English sole, *Parophrys vetulus* and the starry flounder, *Platichthys stellatus* [1,2,6,8,10] and occurs frequently enough to have been given the binomial scientific name. Electropherograms show close likeness to the English sole, less to the starry flounder, and none to the rock sole *Lepidopsetta bilineata,* which has been considered as a possible parent.[12] The form is quite variable and the possibility of back crosses cannot be ignored.[5,7]

Description   Body compressed, highly asymmetrical with colour restricted to right side. Head asymmetrical with both eyes on right side, slender, bluntly rounded. Mouth small, terminal, with narrow gape, asymmetrical. Upper jaw extending to forward edge of lower eye. Teeth on both sides of jaws but only near symphysis on jaw of eyed side. Eyes moderate in size, the upper slightly behind the lower. Interorbital space moderate with a moderate ridge between the eyes. Caudal peduncle moderate.

Fins   Dorsal (1), 68 to 76, originating above middle of upper eye. Caudal rounded. Anal 49 to 57, small sharp spine exposed at origin. Pectorals about 12, moderate size, and with rounded tips. Pelvics 6, thoracic.

Scales   Imperfectly imbricated, ctenoid on eyed side of body, both ctenoid and cycloid on blind side and on dorsal and anal fins.[2] Lateral line canal 76 to 91, main line almost straight, extending on caudal fin, accessory branch short, forked posteriorly with each branch ending over the operculum.

Colour   Olive brown on the eyed side, variously mottled with lighter or darker, pale on blind side. Dorsal and anal fins with faint dark bars.

Size   Length to 18 inches (46 cm).

Recognition   Noteworthy for a main lateral line canal with only slight undulations, a short forked accessory branch of the lateral line canal which does not extend beyond the operculum, and rough scales on both sides of the body and on dorsal and anal fins.

Distribution   Northern California[5] and Oregon[8] through Washington[3] and British Columbia to Alaska and the Bering Sea at depths down to 360 fathoms (660 m).[4,9] The centre of abundance appears to be Puget Sound.[11] Canadian records are from Clo-oose, Sydney Inlet, and Union and Fanny bays of the Strait of Georgia.

References   1 Aron 1958b; 2 Batts 1964; 3 DeLacy, Dryfoos, and Miller 1963; 4 Grinols 1965a; 5 Herald 1941a; 6 Hubbs and Kuronuma 1942; 7 Norman 1934; 8 Reed 1964; 9 Schultz and DeLacy 1936; 10 Schultz and Smith 1936; 11 Smith 1936; 12 Tsuyuki personal communication.

BUTTER SOLE

Isopsetta isolepis (Lockington 1880)

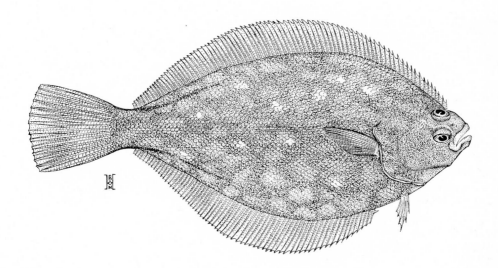

Scientific names from the Greek *isos* (equal) and *psetta* (flounder); and *isos* (equal) and *lepis* (scale).

Description   Body much compressed, highly asymmetrical with colour restricted to right side. Head asymmetrical with both eyes on right side, rather slender. Mouth terminal, small, with narrow gape, asymmetrical. Maxillary extends to a point below forward part of lower eye. Jaws and teeth strongest on blind side. Snout roundly pointed. Eyes small. Interorbital space narrow, flat. Caudal peduncle moderate.

Fins   Dorsal (1), 78 to 92 (82 to 86 in 6 British Columbia specimens),[12] originating above eye. Caudal rounded. Anal 58 to 69 (61 to 68 in British Columbia), small, sharp, exposed spine before anal fin. Pectorals rather small, bluntly pointed. Pelvics 6, thoracic.

Vertebrae   39 to 42 (mean of 97 counts, 40.2).[12]

Scales   Imbricated, rather large, strongly ctenoid on eyed side, partly cycloid on blind side, ctenoid on head and fin rays. Lateral line canal 78 to 84, slightly curved downward over the pectoral fin without a strong arch, then straight, accessory dorsal branch close to dorsal fin, passing backward to a point above the pectoral fin between midpoint and tip.

Colour   On eyed side, gray, irregularly blotched. In fresh specimens sometimes with clear yellow or green spots. On blind side, white. Bright yellow on tips of dorsal and anal fin rays.

Size   Length to 18 inches (46 cm), a female. The largest male recorded from landings is 15.3 inches (39 cm).[2]

Recognition   Rough scales on eyed side of body, head, and fins. Lateral line canal with moderate dorsal accessory branch, curved but not strongly arched over pectoral fin. Yellow on edges of dorsal and anal fins.

619

Life History   Spawning takes place from February (Bellingham Bay)[4,8,9] or March (Skidegate Inlet)[11] to late April. Eggs are non-adhesive, transparent, spherical, with a diameter of 1.031 millimeters (0.937–1.10 mm). The perivitelline space is small. No oil globule or micropyle is apparent.[8] The specific gravity is about 1.021, with the result that the eggs are demersal in Skidegate Inlet where they were found. In Hecate Strait there is general depth stratification with the young inshore along Graham Island. In summer there is migration to shallow water and in winter to deeper water. North–south migrations are mostly restricted to spawners. The Hecate Strait population is distinct from those of Washington and Oregon. Butter sole spawning in Skidegate Inlet is mainly confined to Hecate Strait[5,6] or to northern Hecate Strait.[9] Growth rates calculated from commercial catches show differences associated with sex, region, season, and year class. Ordinarily females reach 30-centimeter length at age V or VI and males at VI or VII.[5,6] Beyond age VII mortality rates increase for both sexes and they are higher for males than for females. The oldest recorded female was 11 years (35 cm) and males 10 years (34–39 cm).[2] The food includes chaetopod marine worms, young herring, and shrimps,[11] and sand dollars.

Distribution   Southern California to southeast Alaska. Usually in shallow water but recorded from the 150- to 200-fathom (274–366-m) zone in western Alaska.[1,3,10] Occurring rarely off the southern part of Vancouver Island and in the Strait of Georgia. Abundant in summer in shallow silty depressions in northwest Hecate Strait, and as a spawning concentration in late winter in Skidegate Inlet.

Utilization   Because of its rather small size, thinness, and rough scales that necessitate skinning fillets with the high labour and waste costs involved, the butter sole is not favourably regarded by processors in spite of the good flavour of the flesh. Only a small part of the catch is filleted and the rest is used for mink feed. Annual catches in millions of pounds (454 metric tons)[7] are given below.

1931–1940	0
1941–1945	0.7
1946–1950	0.3
1951–1955	1.2
1956–1960	0.6
1961–1965	0.1
1966	0.2
1967	0.7
1968	0.4
1969	0.3
1970	1.3

Annual catches probably average 10 to 5 percent of the stock.[7]

References   1 Alverson, Pruter, and Ronholt 1964; 2 Forrester 1969b; 3 Grinols 1965a; 4, 5, Hart 1944, 1948; 6 Kutty 1963; 7 Larkin and Ricker 1964; 8 Levings 1968; 9 Manzer 1949; 10 Roedel 1948b; 11 Smith 1936; 12 Townsend 1936.

ROCK SOLE

Lepidopsetta bilineata (Ayres 1855)

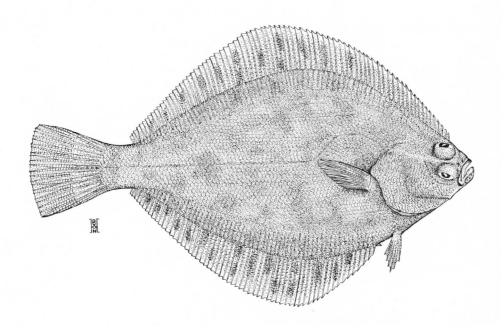

Scientific names from the Greek *lepis* (scale) and *psetta* (flounder); and the Latin *bilineata* (two lined).

Description Body compressed, highly asymmetrical with colour restricted to right side. Head asymmetrical with both eyes on right side, rather deep and blunt. Mouth terminal, small, with narrow gape, asymmetrical, directed upward. Teeth and jaws better developed on blind side. Maxillary extends to forward part of lower eye. Eyes small, lower slightly in advance. Interorbital space quite flat. Caudal peduncle moderate.

Fins Dorsal (1), 65 to 82, originating over forward part of eye. Caudal tending to be longest in the centre with posterior margin a broad 'V'. Anal 50 to 65, sharp spine exposed at origin. Pectorals 10 to 13, rather small, asymmetrical in 41 percent of British Columbia specimens, with eyed side having more rays in 81 percent of these.[13] Pelvics 6, thoracic.

Gill Rakers On first arch 6 to 12.

Vertebrae 39 to 42.

Scales Imbricated, ctenoid on eyed side, especially toward caudal peduncle, some tuberculate, mostly cycloid on blind side, extending on dorsal, anal, and caudal fin rays.[3] Lateral line canal with 75 to 92 pores, prominent arch over pectoral fin, then straight, accessory dorsal branch close to dorsal fin, short, not extending beyond point above posterior margin of the operculum.

Colour Variable. Dark browns or grays mottled with lighter or darker. Dorsal, anal, and caudal fins irregularly mottled with dark. Blind side whitish, to yellow toward tail.

621

Size   Reaches a length of 23.5 inches 60 cm), a female 15 years old. Largest male 21 inches (53 cm).[6]

Recognition   Noteworthy for its lateral line canal with a prominent abrupt arch and short accessory branch. Rough tuberculate scales on eyed side of body.

Life History   Spawning takes place in Puget Sound between February and about April 10.[12] Spawning grounds of the largest Canadian stocks north of Vancouver Island and in Hecate Strait have not been located. Smallest mature females were 31 centimeters and males 28 centimeters corresponding probably to age IV. The largest immature female was 43 centimeters and male 36 centimeters. Females 35 centimeters in length produce about 400,000 eggs and 46-centimeter fish about 1,300,000.[6] Eggs are yellowish orange, demersal, and adhesive, with a diameter about 0.92 millimeter and a specific gravity around 1.047. Depending on temperature, between 6.5 and 8 C, they hatch in 9 to 18 days.[4,5,6] Off Kamchatka eggs hatch in 25 days at 3 C.[6] Ocean conditions influence survival rates of year broods and thus the sizes and abundance of fishes in subsequent catches.[8] Larvae are about 5 millimeters long at hatching. Yolk sac is absorbed in 10 to 14 days. Young in Kamchatka are swimming on their sides at about 0.8 inch (20 mm). They occur in shallow water on beaches in some localities. On some fishing grounds the stock is characterized by marked changes in recruitment from year to year.[7] At Cox Island, females averaged 38.6 centimeters at age VII and 47.6 at age XI. At the same ages males averaged 34.2 and 37.7 centimeters. In males growth slowed sharply beyond age VIII.[10] Growth is much slower toward the northwest.[7] The oldest recorded female was 22 years (52 cm) taken off Mexicana Point. The oldest male was 15 years (41 cm).[6] Natural mortality rate appears to increase with age.[7] Mollusc siphons (sometimes exclusively), clams, polychaete worms, shrimps, small crabs, brittle stars, and sand lance have been recorded in the food.[7,11]

Distribution   The *Lepidopsetta bilineata* complex of forms extends from southern California, where it is scarce, around the North Pacific basin through the Bering and Okhotsk seas to Korea and the Sea of Japan. Wilimovsky et al.[13] recognize three subspecies, *Lepidopsetta bilineata bilineata* (Ayres) on the Canadian coast and southward which intergrades around the Queen Charlotte Islands with an essentially northern form *Lepidopsetta bilineata perarcuatus* (Cope 1873), which in turn intergrades with *Lepidopsetta bilineata mochigarei* (Snyder 1912) about the southern Okhotsk Sea and southern Kuril Islands.

Throughout British Columbia the species is generally distributed and it is particularly abundant toward the north, from Cape Scott to Dixon Entrance. It is mostly caught in Canada at shallow depths between 20 and 30 fathoms (37 and 55 m)[1] (40 fathoms (73 m)[6]). It occurs from the surface to 200 fathoms (366 m)[6] but is scarce below 100 fathoms (183 m).[2,6] There is a summer movement into shallower water.

Utilization   The rock sole is highly regarded as a food fish and is the most used of the smaller flatfish species in Canada. The growth of the fishery is shown in the following tabulation giving average annual production in millions of pounds (454 metric tons).[9]

1931–35	0.1
1936–40	0.1
1941–45	0.6
1946–50	1.9
1951–55	3.5
1956–60	3.8
1961–65	3.0
1966	7.1
1967	5.5
1968	6.7
1969	6.7
1970	4.5

Relations between stock density, and growth and mortality rates suggest that fuller use could be advantageously made of newly recruited fish on the Butterworth–Warrior Rocks fishing grounds.[7]

References 1 Alverson 1960; 2 Alverson, Pruter, and Ronholt 1964; 3 Batts 1964; 4, 5, 6 Forrester 1964b, c, 1969b; 7 Forrester and Thomson 1969; 8 Ketchen, Peterson, and Forrester 1951; 9 Larkin and Ricker 1964; 10 Levings 1965; 11 Roedel 1948b; 12 Smith 1936; 13 Wilimovsky, Peden, and Peppar 1967.

YELLOWFIN SOLE

Limanda aspera (Pallas 1811)

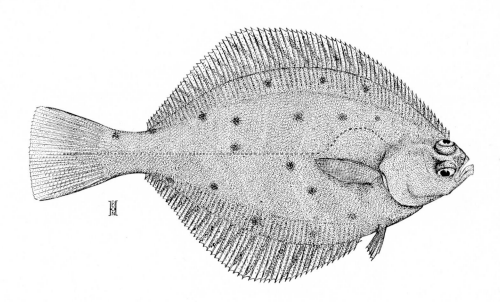

Scientific names from the Latin *limanda* (old man — for a European flatfish); and *asper* (rough).

Description Body compressed, highly asymmetrical with colour restricted to right side. Head asymmetrical with both

623

eyes on right side, pointed. Mouth terminal, small, with narrow gape, asymmetrical, directed upward. Maxillary barely extending to forward part of the eye. Teeth mainly on lower side of jaw. Snout bluntly rounded, shorter than diameter of eye. Eyes moderately large, almost side by side. Interorbital space narrow. Caudal peduncle rather deep.

Fins   Dorsal (1), 61 to 69, starting above posterior part of eye. Caudal rounded at edges. Anal 48 to 58 with fine sharp spine exposed at the origin. Pectorals bluntly pointed. Pelvics 6, thoracic.

Vertebrae   39 to 40 (mean of 23 counts, 39.4).[8]

Scales   Slightly imbricated, ctenoid on both sides of body, on rays of dorsal, caudal, and anal fins. Lateral line canal with 73 to 89 scales, sharply arched over pectoral fins, no accessory branch.

Colour   On eyed side light brown mottled with darker. Yellow cast to unpaired fins. Narrow black line at bases of paired fins fading in preservative. Faint dark bars on dorsal and anal fins. On blind side white with fins yellow.

Size   Length to 17.6 inches (45 cm) (in Bering Sea).

Recognition   Arched lateral line canal over pectoral fin and no accessory branch. Fins scaly with yellow colour. Ctenoid scales on both sides of body.

Life History   Little is fully known about the life history. In Asian waters males reach maturity at 20 centimeters between 4 and 5 years, females at 23 or 24 centimeters at 6 or 7 years.[5] The growth rate in early years in the Hecate Strait area (Skidegate Inlet) is about the same as in Peter the Great Bay.[4] More than a million eggs may be produced.[5] Recorded food is hydroids, worms, molluscs, and brittle stars.

Distribution   From southern British Columbia to the Bering Sea but not common (not recorded) from Hecate Strait to Kodiak Island. Down the Asian coast to Okhotsk Sea, Hokkaido, Fusan, and Peter the Great Bay. Not found by early investigators in Chukchi Sea[2,6,7] but discovered later.[1] It is the dominant flatfish in the Bering Sea.[1] The most southerly record for North America is in Barkley Sound. Another record is for Port Simpson, and individuals are occasionally taken in Skidegate Inlet, Queen Charlotte Islands.[3] It is a shallow-water species; on North American fishing grounds it is most abundant at less than 50 fathoms (92 m) and it has not been recorded at more than 100 fathoms (183 m).[1] Although it is of excellent quality and is suitably thick for filleting, the yellowfin sole is nowhere in Canadian waters common enough to support a fishery or to earn commercial recognition.

References   1 Alverson, Pruter, and Ronholt 1964; 2 Andriashev 1937; 3 Hart 1944; 4 Kitano 1969; 5 Nikol'skii 1961; 6 Popov 1933; 7 Shmidt 1950; 8 Townsend 1936.

SLENDER SOLE

Lyopsetta exilis (Jordan and Gilbert 1880)

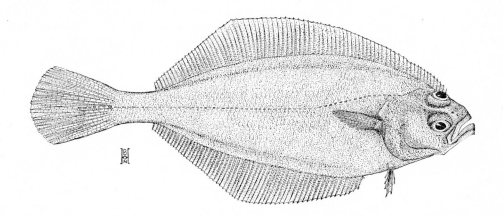

Scientific names from the Greek *lyo* (loosen) and *psetta* (flounder); and the Latin *exilis* (slender).

Description   Body depth about 3 into standard length, compressed, highly asymmetrical with colour restricted to right side. Head asymmetrical with both eyes on right side, slender, bluntly pointed. Mouth large, terminal, wide gape, almost symmetrical. Maxillary extending to anterior edge of pupil of lower eye. Teeth moderately well developed on both sides of both jaws, in upper jaw in 2 rows. Lower jaw prominent and blunt. Snout bluntly pointed. Eyes large, lower only slightly in advance of upper. Interorbital space with a high ridge running into anterior end of lateral line canal. Caudal peduncle moderate.

Fins   Dorsal (1), 72 to 78, originating over anterior part of upper eye with usual-sized rays. Caudal rounded. Anal 57 to 65, preceded by a sharp spine. Pectorals small and narrow. Pelvics 6, thoracic.

Vertebrae   In California 43 to 46.[4] 42 to 45.[9]

Scales   Imbricated, large, thin, deciduous, all ctenoid on eyed side, mostly ctenoid on blind side except on central part under dorsal fin,[2] small scales on dorsal, caudal, and anal fins. Scales from lateral line canal to dorsal fin at widest place 20 to 24. Lateral line canal sloping down gently from head to point just behind pectoral fin, then straight and flat. Scales along lateral line canal 65 to 73. No accessory lateral line canal.

Colour   Pale brown on eyed side, minute dark points outlining margins of each scale. Pale orange-yellow to white on blind side. Fins dusky.[7] Median fins pale at edges.

Size   Length up to 13.7 inches (35 cm).[1]

Recognition   Slender form, moderately large mouth extends about to middle of lower eye, large thin deciduous scales, pale brown coloration.

Life History   The slender sole spawns in Puget Sound in April,[8] and ripe females have been found in the Strait of Georgia in late February. Fifty percent of males are mature at about 14 centimeters total length, and females at about 16 centimeters.[5]

Distribution   Known from Baja California to southeast Alaska[7,9,10] at shallow to moderate depths (280 fathoms (513 m) in California).[6] It is taken throughout coastal British Columbia on the west coast of Vancouver Island, the Strait of Georgia,[8] and Hecate Strait.

Utilization   Although the flesh is of good quality, the slender sole is too small and too slender to be attractive for commercial use.

References   1 Alverson, Pruter, and Ronholt 1964; 2 Barraclough 1967a; 3 Batts 1964; 4 Clothier 1950; 5 Forrester personal communication; 6 Grinols 1965a; 7 Roedel 1948b; 8 Smith 1936; 9 Townsend 1936; 10 Wilimovsky 1954.

DOVER SOLE

Microstomus pacificus (Lockington 1879)

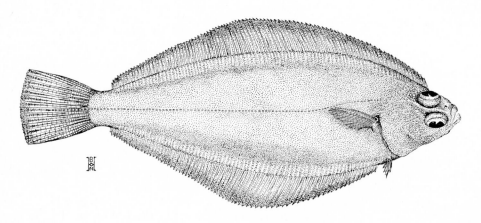

Scientific names from the Greek *micro* (small) and *stoma* (mouth); and *Pacific* (Ocean).

Description   Body compressed, highly asymmetrical with strong colour restricted to right side, depth 2.8 to 3.2 into standard length. Head asymmetrical with both eyes on right side, short, its length 4.5 to 4.7 into standard length, slender. Mouth terminal, small, with narrow gape,

somewhat asymmetrical. Maxillary extending to below anterior part of lower eye. Teeth almost limited to blind side, never more than 3 in either jaw of eyed side. Snout finely rounded. Eye moderate, protruding, entering profile, upper substantially posterior to lower. Interorbital ridge prominent. Gill opening barely extending above base of pectoral fin. Caudal peduncle short and rather shallow. The species is noteworthy in having a loop of the intestine in a long extension of the body cavity

626

extending posteriorly beside the haemal arches.

Fins   Dorsal (1), 90 to 116, originating above the middle of the upper eye. Caudal imperfectly rounded. Anal 80 to 96. There is no sharp exposed spine at its origin. The first caudal haemal arches in this species are not excessively developed as in most of our flatfishes[4] and this lack contributes to the notable flaccid character of the whole body. It has been described, "It drapes." Pectorals shorter than head. Pelvics 6, thoracic.

Vertebrae   50 to 54 (mean of 11 counts, 50.9).[4]

Scales   Very small, imbricated, cycloid, deciduous, uniform over the body. Lateral line canal 137 to 146, rather indistinct, practically straight with a barely perceptible curve over the pectoral fin. A short supratemporal branch is not connected with the main lateral line canal. Freshly caught specimens produce a great deal of slime. This repugnant characteristic led to delay in use of the species by industry, and to a vernacular name, "slime sole."

Colour   On eyed side rich uniform shades of brown or mottled. Young sometimes with yellowish spots on sides. Blind side light to fairly dark gray, sometimes blotched with dull red. Dusky on fins, especially toward tips.

Size   Length to 28 inches (71 cm).[3,7]

Recognition   Nearly straight lateral line canal with an unconnected lateral branch. Gill openings barely extending above base of pectoral fin. Excessive production of slime. Flaccid body.

Life History   Egg diameters average 2.33 millimeters and are between 2.05 and 2.57 millimeters. They are covered with vermiculate wrinkles. Early larvae have a spine on either side of the head. The pelagic life is prolonged over several months. All flatfish are almost bilaterally symmetrical on hatching. In most the blind-side eye moves quite early in larval life to the eyed side, the young settle down to living with the blind side on the bottom, and metamorphosis is complete. However, in the dover

sole the pelagic life is prolonged through several months and metamorphosis is so delayed that postlarvae 48 millimeters long are encountered and young may be still pelagic at 100 millimeters. The delay in metamorphosis affects the distribution of the species. Lengths (off California) reach around 28.5 centimeters by age III. After that females grow faster so that by age X they are about an inch (25 mm) longer than males. Males are mature at lengths of about 39 centimeters, females at 45 centimeters.[8] Off Oregon 50 percent of females are mature at 38 to 40 centimeters. At 42.5 centimeters fecundity was 52,000, and at 57.5 centimeters 266,000.[9] Females seem to live longer. In California a female 36.2 centimeters had 37,000 eggs, and fecundities go as high as 230,000 at 50.4 centimeters. Spawning in California occurs from November to February.[8] Migrations up and down the coast do not ordinarily appear to be extensive but from fishing grounds off Washington movements have been observed northward for 110 miles (204 km) and southward for 366 miles (680 km).[13] The usual habitat is on soft bottom and at all metamorphosed stages feeding is on the bottom, concentrated on burrowing forms. One of the most hardy of the flatfishes.

Distribution   Northern Baja California to the Bering Sea. Recorded from the surface to depths of 600 fathoms (1100 m).[5,6] Generally distributed on suitable bottom throughout coastal British Columbia including the Strait of Georgia.

Utilization   In the early days of flatfish exploitation dover sole was neglected throughout its area of distribution,[3,10,11,12] because of its unappealing softness and sliminess. More recently the excellent quality of the flesh and its good keeping qualities in frozen storage have made it one of the more important of the small flatfishes on the Pacific coast.[1,2,10] Canadian landings over the history of the groundfish fishery in millions of pounds (454 metric tons) are:[10]

1931–1945	0
1946–1950	0.4
1951–1955	0.7
1956–1960	0.3
1961–1965	0.4
1966	0.5
1967	0.2
1968	0.2
1969	0.8
1970	3.0

References   1 Alverson 1960; 2 Alverson, Pruter, and Ronholt 1964; 3 Clemens and Wilby 1946; 4 Clothier 1950; 5 Follett, McCormick, and Best 1960; 6 Grinols 1965a; 7, 8 Hagerman 1949, 1952; 9 Harry 1959; 10 Larkin and Ricker 1964; 11 Roedel 1948b; 12 Smith 1936; 13 Westrheim and Morgan 1963. See also Best 1963d.

ENGLISH SOLE

Parophrys vetulus Girard 1854

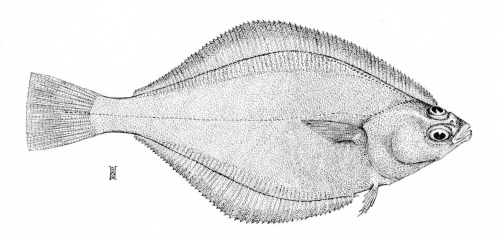

Scientific names from the Greek *para* (near) and *ophrys* (eyebrow — narrow interorbital space); and *vetulus* (old man — fancied resemblance).

The common name lemon sole is well established in British Columbia.

Description   Body compressed, highly asymmetrical with colour restricted to right side. Head asymmetrical with both eyes on right side, slender, pointed. Mouth terminal, small, with narrow gape, asymmetrical. Maxillary extends to forward part of lower eye. Jaws and teeth strongest on blind side. Snout broadly pointed. Eyes large, upper somewhat posterior to lower, entering the profile. Interorbital space narrow with a high ridge. Caudal peduncle moderate.

Fins Dorsal (1), 72 to 92, originating above middle of upper eye. Caudal imperfectly truncate. Anal 54 to 70, exposed spine before anal fin. Pectorals inclined to be pointed. Pelvics 6, thoracic.

Vertebrae 41 to 44 (mean of 18 counts, in California, 42.5).[5]

Scales Imbricated, cycloid anteriorly on both sides of body, ctenoid posteriorly on eyed side, ctenoid on cheeks, absent on fins.[3] Lateral line canal 89 to 105, slightly decurved, then straight, accessory dorsal branch long, close to dorsal fin, extending back to a point over the pectoral fin.

Colour Shades of uniform brown on the eyed side. On blind side pale yellow to white, tinged with reddish brown, particularly on head. Tips of fins darker. Young variously coloured, from gray to brown, minutely spotted, often of sandy appearance on eyed surface. In young less than 2 inches (51 mm) in length there are often bright yellow lines on the blind side at the bases of dorsal and anal fins.

Size Length to 22.5 inches (57 cm), a female. The largest male encountered was 19.3 inches (49 cm).[7]

Recognition Lateral line canal without a high arch over pectoral fin and with a long accessory branch. Pointed head and jaws. Scales on body smooth anteriorly and rough posteriorly.

Life History Spawning in British Columbia (Baynes Sound) is mainly from January to March.[23] Females produce around 150,000 eggs at 30 centimeters, and 1,900,000 at 44 centimeters.[9,12] Fifty percent of females are mature at 29.5 centimeters and of males at 26.0 centimeters. Eggs are pelagic but sink several hours before hatching. Newly fertilized eggs have a diameter of 0.9 millimeter (0.89–0.93 mm). The egg shell is covered with minute wrinkles making a delicate reticulate pattern, and small regularly spaced pores. Inside the yolk many small clear oil droplets are linked in a chain above a few larger scattered drops.[21] In California the eggs hatch in about 90 hours to produce larvae about 2.8 millimeters long that float upside down suspended by a buoyant yolk sac.[4] Time to hatching varies with temperature.[1,4,21] In Washington hatching starts after about 98 hours at about 10.6 C and continues for about 10 hours[21] (6 days[7]). Larvae reach about 4.6 millimeters in 9 to 12 days and the yolk sac disappears in 9 to 10 days at 10.6 C or 5 to 6 days at 13.0 C.[4,7,21] Young are pelagic for 6 to 10 weeks.[7] By the end of August in the Strait of Georgia young are about 4 inches (10 cm) long, by the end of the second year about 8 inches (20 cm). In early life English sole are found in the intertidal zone and quite shallow water. With growth they move into deeper water. There is, through life, a recognizable shift of concentration into shallow water in the spring and deeper water in winter.[14] Growth patterns differ among localities.[19,20] English sole are first accepted by the fishery at lengths of about 12 inches (30.5 cm) corresponding to 3 completed years for females and 4 for males.[11] Success in reproduction varies from year to year and affects the sizes of the fish caught.[16] In the important Hecate Strait population survival of young was found to be related to development time and possibly to accurate transport by water movements from spawning grounds to nursery grounds.[14] Laboratory experiments led to the conclusion that reproductive success at the extremes of the range may be limited by water temperature.[1] English sole make extensive migrations such as from Butterworth–Warrior Rocks to Two Peaks grounds in Hecate Strait at 4 miles (7.4 km) per day,[13] south from the west coast of Vancouver Island,[18] from Goose Island grounds 700 miles (1100 km) to California, or the Strait of Georgia 600 miles (960 km) to Eureka, Oregon. However, growth and tagging studies provide good evidence of segregated major stocks and some isolated populations.[8,10,14,15] Under conditions of high population density, and possibly otherwise, English sole are subject to a myxosporidian disease which destroys the market acceptability of the "milky" fish without making them toxic.[6,24] Food of this small-mouthed flounder consists mainly of clams and clam siphons, other small molluscs, marine worms, small crabs and shrimps, and brittle stars.

Distribution   From San Cristobal Bay in Baja California to Unimak Island in western Alaska[7] between the surface and 300 fathoms (550 m). Commercial quantities at less than 70 fathoms (128 m).[2] Generally distributed in coastal British Columbia with small isolated populations at the heads of many inlets.

Utilization   The English sole has long been a popular fish in British Columbia and local consumers have learned to relish the "iodine" flavour that can be detected in some inshore catches. The following tabulation of annual production in millions of pounds (454 metric tons) shows the importance and long acceptance of the species.[17]

1931–35	0.4
1936–40	0.5
1941–45	1.2
1946–50	2.5
1951–55	2.0
1956–60	1.7
1961–65	1.5
1966	1.2
1967	1.5
1968	1.9
1969	2.1
1970	2.5

Present utilization of the stock by Canadian and U.S. exploitation is around 25 or 30 percent annually, and for some populations close to market it may be higher.[22]

References   1 Alderdice and Forrester 1968; 2 Alverson 1960; 3 Batts 1964; 4 Budd 1940; 5 Clothier 1950; 6, 7, 8 Forrester 1956, 1969b, c; 9 Harry 1959; 10, 11, 12, 13, 14 Ketchen 1945, 1947a, b, 1950b, 1956b; 15 Ketchen and Forrester 1955; 16 Ketchen, Peterson, and Forrester 1951; 17 Larkin and Ricker 1964; 18, 19 Manzer 1946b, 1951; 20 Manzer and Taylor 1946; 21 Orsi 1968; 22 Pruter and Van Cleve 1954; 23 Taylor 1946; 24 Wellings, Ashley, and McArn 1969

STARRY FLOUNDER

Platichthys stellatus (Pallas 1811)

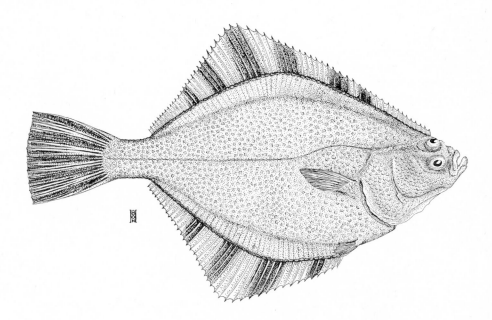

Scientific names from the Greek *platy* (flat) and *ichthys* (fish); and the Latin *stellatus* (starry).

Commonly referred to as "flounder" in the British Columbia fishing industry. Also called grindstone because of the roughness of the skin.

Description Body depth about 2.4 to 2.8 into standard length, compressed, highly asymmetrical with colour generally restricted to one side. Head about 3.6 to 3.8 into standard length, asymmetrical with both eyes on the coloured side, rather slender and pointed. Mouth small, terminal, with narrow gape, asymmetrical. Maxillary reaching to point below forward part of lower eye. Teeth mainly on blind side of jaw. Snout bluntly pointed. Eyes small, the lower considerably in advance of the upper. Interorbital space moderately wide, and nearly flat.

Fins Dorsal (1), 52 to 66, originating over middle of upper eye. Caudal broadly arched. Anal 38 to 47, with an exposed spine near origin and strongly supported by a very heavy first haemal spine. Pectorals bluntly pointed. Pelvics 6, thoracic.

Vertebrae 34 to 37.[6,21]

Scales Stellate, with well-separated spinous plates, without circuli, irregularly placed and more numerous on eyed side. On the blind side in bands along bases of dorsal and anal fins, separated by cycloid scales.[5] Lateral line canal with 63 to 78 pores, somewhat decurved and then straight. No accessory branch.

631

Colour On eyed side dark brown to nearly black with vague blotchings. On blind side, white to creamy white occasionally blotched. Prominent black radiating bands on dorsal and anal (4–7), and caudal fins (4–6) separated by white to orange stripes.

Size Length to 36 inches (91 cm); weight to 20 pounds (9.1 kg).

Recognition Distinguished by the prominent dark bands on the unpaired fins and the rough, stellate, plates on the body.

Life History Starry flounders spawn in shallow water in February and April in Puget Sound[20] and about the same period in British Columbia. In California spawning is in December and January. Males are mature at age II (California) (300 mm)[15] and most females at age III (350 mm).[15,20] The eggs are pale orange, and their membranes have very fine vermiculate wrinkles but no sculptured pattern. They have diameters between 0.89 and 0.94 millimeter (but 0.97–1.01 off Hokkaido[23]), are slightly lighter than sea water, and are non-adhesive. Larvae are between 1.93 and 2.08 millimeters long on hatching, and, like the young of other flatfishes, are symmetrical. Young 5 to 12 millimeters long eat mainly copepods and their nauplii, as well as barnacle larvae and Cladocera.[4,17,18] They are transformed (to asymmetry) at about 10.5 millimeters. Lengths corresponding to years of growth are: 1, 105 millimeters; 2, 310; and 4, 340. Females are somewhat longer than males at higher ages and live longer.[15] In Canada larger individuals grow about 25 millimeters per year.[10] Ordinarily starry flounders do not migrate very much[10] but one tagged at the outlet of the Columbia River was recaptured 125 miles (200 km) to the north.[22] The starry flounder is noteworthy among flatfishes in the region for its tolerance of low salinities. Young are commonly taken in the Fraser River, and in California were found abundantly at salinities of 10 to 6 parts per thousand.[8]

In the USSR the species enters the Amur River.[13] Food reported includes crabs, shrimps, worms, clams and clam siphons, other small molluscs, and small fishes (Clemens and Wilby 1961), nemertean worms, and brittle stars. Feeding stops at low water temperatures. Little digestion takes place in the stomach which seems to be mainly involved in holding food.[12] The starry flounder is one of the few species which may ordinarily have the eyes and colour on either side. There is a definite regional trend in the degree of right-handedness. From California to southeast Alaska left-handed flounders are from 50 to 60 percent of the samples. Around Kodiak Island and the Alaskan Peninsula 68 percent are left handed, and in Japan, all are left handed.[9,11] The south to north trend toward left-handedness is continued through British Columbia on both sides of Vancouver Island and gives evidence of local populations within the region.[7]

Distribution Southern California[19] to Alaska, Bering Sea, Chukchi Sea, and Okhotsk Sea, and south to central Honshu (Japan) and Korea. [3,11,13,14,16] The species is mainly found in shallow water but catches in excess of 150 fathoms (275 m) are reported.[1,2] The species is encountered commonly along the whole British Columbia coast, mainly in shallow water.

Utilization The starry flounder is not highly regarded as a commercial species in British Columbia but moderate quantities, under half a million pounds (a metric ton) annually are marketed.

References 1 Alverson 1960; 2 Alverson, Pruter, and Ronholt 1964; 3 Andriashev 1937; 4 Barraclough 1967c; 5 Batts 1964; 6 Clothier 1950; 7 Forrester 1969a; 8 C. Hubbs 1947; 9 Hubbs and Hubbs 1945; 10 Manzer 1952; 11 Matsubara 1955; 12 Miller 1967; 13 Nikol'skii

1961; 14 Okada 1955; 15 Orcutt 1950; 16 Popov 1933; 17, 18 Robinson, Barraclough, and Fulton 1968a, b; 19 Roedel 1948b; 20 Smith 1936; 21 Townsend 1936; 22 Westrheim 1955; 23 Yusa 1957. **See** also Miller 1965.

C-O SOLE

Pleuronichthys coenosus Girard 1854

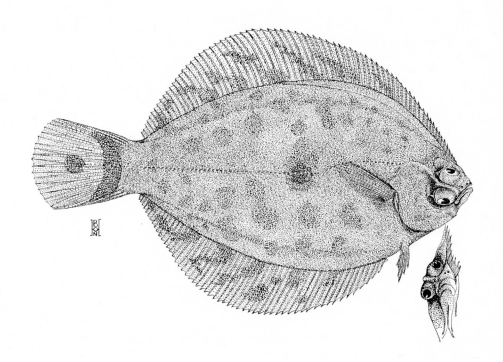

Scientific names from the Greek *pleuron* (side) and *ichthys* (fish); and the Latin *coenosus* (muddy).

Description   Body short, compressed, and highly asymmetrical with colour restricted to right side. Head asymmetrical with both eyes on right side, deep. Mouth small, terminal, with narrow gape, asymmetrical. Maxillary extending to below fore part of lower eye. Lips thick. Teeth mainly on blind side of jaws. Eyes large, protruding, closely set, obscuring interorbital space. Interorbital ridge prominent with a relatively inconspicuous downward-projecting ridge posteriorly. Caudal peduncle deep.

633

Fins   Dorsal (1), 65 to 78, high, origin with first 5 or 6 rays on the blind side. Caudal deep and rounded. Anal 46 to 56, high. Small spine hidden before anal fin. Pectorals moderately long and bluntly pointed. Pelvics 6, thoracic.[3]

Vertebrae   36 to 38 (mean of 10 counts, 36.9).[4]

Scales   Cycloid, on both sides of body. Well separated, deeply embedded in tough skin, on fins.[1] Lateral line canal 61 to 70, slightly decurved then straight; accessory dorsal branch long, close to dorsal fin, extending to point about midlength of body.

Colour   Dark brown to black on eyed side, conspicuous black spot about size of eye on middle of body, sometimes similar spot on middle of caudal fin. Dark bar sometimes curved across base of caudal fin, particularly conspicuous in young fish. Creamy white on blind side, very dark on all fins.

Size   Length to 14 inches (36 cm).

Recognition   Deep, ovate, body with high dorsal and anal fins, the embedded scales, the origin of the dorsal fin with the first 5 or 6 rays on the blind side of the body, the spot in the middle of the side of the body.

Life History   Eggs are pelagic with near neutral buoyancy, appear cloudy. They have about a 1.88-millimeter diameter and are covered by hexagonal or pentagonal figures about 0.042 millimeter across. At 13.8 C they hatch in about 12 days to produce larvae about 5.5 millimeters long.[2] In summer young are common in shallow water but adults frequently inhabit deeper water. They are captured in small quantities by trawls and marketed, but the tough skin makes filleting difficult.

Distribution   San Quentin, Baja California to southeastern Alaska, at depths of 10 to 191 fathoms (18–350 m). The species is abundant in the Strait of Georgia and has been recorded off the west coast of Vancouver Island.

References   1 Batts 1964; 2 Budd 1940; 3 Clemens and Wilby 1961; 4 Clothier 1950.

CURLFIN SOLE

Pleuronichthys decurrens Jordan and Gilbert 1880

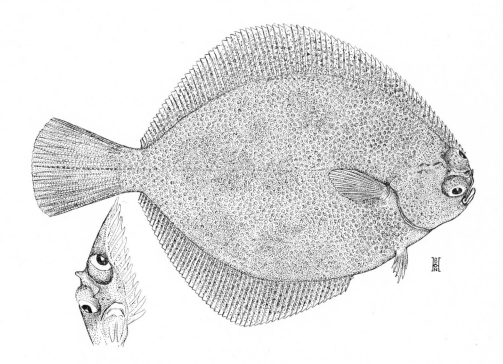

Scientific names from the Greek *pleuron* (side) and *ichthys* (fish); and the Latin *decurrens* (running down).

Description Body short, compressed, and highly asymmetrical with colour restricted to right-hand side. Head asymmetrical with both eyes on right side, deep. Mouth small, terminal, with narrow gape, asymmetrical. Maxillary extending to below fore part of lower eye. Lips thick. Teeth mainly on blind side of jaws. Eyes large, protruding, closely set, obscuring interorbital space. Interorbital ridge narrow with prominent tubercle at each end. A prominence in front of each eye and 2 or 3 other tubercles behind upper eye. Caudal peduncle deep.

Fins Dorsal (1), 67 to 79, high, origin very far forward at angle of mouth, first 9 to 12 rays on the blind side. Caudal deep and rounded. Anal 46 to 52, high, sharp spine before fin. Pectorals moderately large and rounded. Pelvics 6, thoracic.

Vertebrae (37)38 to 39.[2]

Scales Cycloid on both sides of body. Well separated, deeply embedded in tough skin, on fins. Lateral line canal 80 to 91, slightly decurved, then straight, an accessory branch long, close to dorsal fin, passing backward to point about midlength of body.

Colour Brown to black on the eyed side, mottled, finely spotted, no black spot on middle of body, creamy white on blind side, very dark on all the fins.

Size   Length to 12 inches (30 cm).

Recognition   Deep, ovate, body with high dorsal and anal fins, the embedded scales, the origin of the dorsal fin at the angle of the mouth with the first 9 to 12 rays on the blind side, prominent protuberances at both ends of interorbital ridge.

Life History   Eggs are pelagic with almost neutral buoyancy. They are 1.44-millimeter spheres (range 1.31–1.50), covered with a fine hexagonal pattern. After about 7 days at 13.8 C they hatch to produce larvae about 3.9 millimeters in length.[1]

Distribution   Baja California to southeastern Alaska.[4] Abundant on Hecate Strait Flats where young predominate. In California taken at depths from 21 to 291 fathoms (38–533 m). Little used commercially in Canada but moderately important in California.[3]

References   1 Budd 1940; 2 Clothier 1950; 3 Roedel 1948b; 4 Wilimovsky 1954.

SAND SOLE

Psettichthys melanostictus Girard 1854

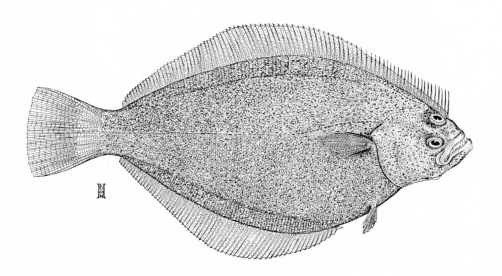

Scientific names from the Greek *psetta* (flounder) and *ichthys* (fish); and *melas* (black) and *stictos* (specks).

Description   Body compressed, highly asymmetrical with colour restricted to right side. Head asymmetrical with both

636

eyes on right side, deep. Mouth large, terminal, with wide gape, and almost symmetrical. Maxillary extending to point below pupil of eye. Snout bluntly pointed. Eyes rather small. Interorbital space wide and low. Caudal peduncle deep and flattened.

Fins   Dorsal (1), 72 to 88, beginning above point in front of eye, first 8 or more rays elongated and free from attachment of fin membrane for about half their lengths, the proportion of rays free lessening posteriorly. Caudal rounded. Anal 53 to 66. Well-developed, sharp spine directed forward at the origin of the anal fin. Pectorals small. Pelvics 6, thoracic.

Vertebrae   37 to 39 (mean of 19 counts is 38.3).[11]

Scales   Imbricated, ctenoid on eyed side, cycloid on blind side except toward ventral edge where some ctenoid scales occur,[2] on bases of dorsal, caudal, and anal fin rays. Lateral line canal with 98 to 112 scales along length, sloping downward gently to point beyond tip of pectoral fin, then straight, accessory dorsal branch extending only briefly beyond bases of pelvics.

Colour   Variable. On eyed side light green to brown, everywhere well speckled with fine black points. Dull yellow on tips of dorsal and anal rays in some specimens.

Size   Length to 24.8 inches (63 cm).

Recognition   This is a large-mouthed, large flatfish, covered with fine dark points all over its eyed side and with the first eight or more dorsal rays elongated and free from the fin membrane.

Life History   The spawning period extends from January in Puget Sound and the end of March in Bellingham Bay[10] to April in northern British Columbia[5] and July in Sydney Inlet.[7] The pelagic eggs are about 1.0 millimeter in diameter, clear, and transparent with no oil globule.[4] They are slightly less dense than sea water. They hatch in about 5 days at 7 to 9 C to produce larvae averaging 2.8 millimeters long. Early larvae are distinguished by orange pigment outlining the body cavity. Metamorphosis is well under way at 23 millimeters and is complete by 27 millimeters.[6] Sizes at age for male and female sand sole are: III, 25 and 28 centimeters; V, 31 and 35 centimeters; VII, females, 37 centimeters.

Food has been found to consist of fishes including speckled sanddabs, herring[8] and anchovies as well as crustaceans, worms, and molluscs. In Washington feeding takes place with little interruption throughout the year.[8]

Distribution   Southern California to the Alaskan Peninsula,[1,9] Bering Sea.[3] Essentially a shallow-water form not recorded from deeper than 100 fathoms (183 m). The species is generally distributed inshore in shallow water on sandy bottom in coastal British Columbia but does not appear to form large aggregations.

References   1 Alverson, Pruter, and Ronholt 1964; 2 Batts 1964; 3 Clemens and Wilby 1961; 4 English 1966; 5 Hart 1944; 6 Hickman 1959; 7 Manzer 1947; 8 Miller 1967; 9 Roedel 1948b; 10 Smith 1936; 11 Townsend 1936. See also Miller 1965.

GREENLAND HALIBUT OR GREENLAND TURBOT

Reinhardtius hippoglossoides (Walbaum 1792)

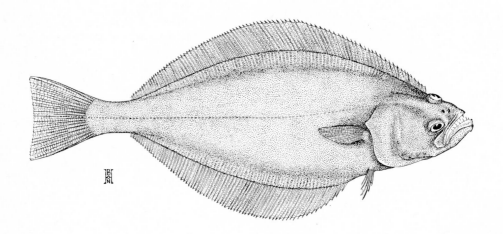

Scientific names from Professor J. Reinhardt, University of Copenhagen, student of Greenland fishes; and *Hippoglossus* (halibut), and the Greek *eidos* (resemblance).

The French name for this species is *flétan du Groenland*.

The common name for this species was attacked (in 1969) by Pacific coast fishing interests in both Canada and the United States as it lends support to commercial misrepresentation in marketing, in competition with Pacific halibut, of significant landings from the Atlantic coast.[2] The name Greenland turbot is now assigned as the least objectionable alternative name for use in North America.

Description Body much compressed, asymmetrical with colour on right side notably darker. Head highly asymmetrical with both eyes on right side, elongate and rather slender. Mouth terminal, large, with wide gape, nearly symmetrical. Maxillary extending to point behind lower eye. Teeth well developed on both sides of both jaws in a single series. Lower jaw projects. Eye

small, lower eye somewhat in advance, the upper on the margin of the head. Interorbital space broad and convex. Preopercular bone with a sharp angle at its posterior lower margin and a series of pores on flat surface following around the angle.[9] Caudal peduncle rather slender.

Fins Dorsal (1), 83 to 108, originating behind posterior edge of the upper eye.[3] Caudal slightly forked to truncate. Anal 62 to 79. No spine at origin of anal fin.[3] Pectorals 11 to 15, mean 13.6, small. Pelvics 6, thoracic.

Gill Rakers Short and stout, about 14 to 20.

Vertebrae 60 to 64.

Scales Ctenoid and small on both sides. Lateral line canal running downward slightly at anterior end, then straight. No accessory branch.

Colour On eyed side black. On blind side dark with lighter blotches. (Atlantic specimens may be lighter).[4]

638

Size   In Atlantic to 40 inches (102 cm) and 25 pounds (11.3 kg). The British Columbia specimen is 25 inches (64 cm).

Recognition   A flatfish with a large, projecting jaw, prominent teeth in a single series, dark coloration on the blind side, and a preopercular bone with a right-angled posterior margin with a series of pores. The species resembles the arrowtooth flounder with which it has no doubt been confused.

Life History   Little information is available on the life history. In Asian waters it is reported to eat such fishes as pollock and zoarcids, and crabs.

Distribution   Present in deep waters of the northern Pacific and Atlantic oceans by what appear to be two races of a single species. In the Pacific from northern Baja California to Honshu Island, Japan, through the Bering and Okhotsk seas, Sakhalin and Kamchatka.[5,6,8] Of very rare occurrence in the southern part of the range and individuals captured are regarded as strays from prolific northern breeding stocks.[3,7] The only British Columbia specimen was taken on La Pérouse Bank, 48.19 N, 126.06 W, in about 300 fathoms (550 m).[9] In the Atlantic to the Bay of Fundy.[1]

References   1 Barrett 1968; 2 Bell 1967; 3 Hubbs and Wilimovsky 1964; 4 Leim and Scott 1966; 5 Nikol'skii 1961; 6 Schmidt 1934; 7 Schott 1966; 8 Shmidt 1950; 9 Westrheim and Pletcher 1966. See also Best 1963a.

ORDER TETRAODONTIFORMES
(Plectognathi)

Fishes in this order are medium to large in size. The mouth is small and the teeth are fused into a beaklike plate. Maxillary and premaxillary are fused. Gill openings are small. Pelvic fins are absent. The spinous dorsal is absent or, if present, has only very few spines. Anal and rayed dorsal are opposite each other and well back on the body. The order displays a wide range in integument. These are usually fishes of the warmer seas and they occur in a great variety of shapes. There is only one representative of the group in British Columbia waters.

FAMILY MOLIDAE   MOLAS

Individuals in this family may reach great size. The skin is leathery and rough. Dorsal and anal fins are entirely of stiff rays, they are about equal and opposite, short based, and very long. Caudal peduncle and tail fin are absent. The only representative of the family in British Columbia waters is the ocean sunfish, which is a fairly common stray into the west coast inlets and inshore areas.

OCEAN SUNFISH

Mola mola (Linnaeus 1758)

Scientific names for this species are from the Latin *mola* (a millstone).

The French name for the species is *môle commun*.

Description   Body truncate, its depth about 1.3 into standard length to flexing point at base of clavus (a specialized tail), outline variable, in some individuals depth about the same from the pectoral fins to the posterior end of dorsal fin, much compressed. Head deep, compressed, length (snout to anterior edge of gill "pore") about 2.7 into standard length. Swollen ridge on side of head above eye very prominent in large specimens. Mouth terminal, small, directed forward, almost rectangular when open. Snout long, upper jaw overhung by a bony pad. Lower jaw not reaching one-fifth of distance to orbit. Teeth fused and beaklike. Interorbital space deeply vaulted and wide, its width about 1.9 into length of head. Eye small, round, its diameter about 6 into length of head. Gill opening small, resembling an enlarged pore on side of head, closed by a flaplike valve marked by a crescentic cavity which may be part of a sucking apparatus.

Fins   Dorsal (1), 15 to 18, high and rigid, its length about one-half body depth, and its base about half height. Caudal very short and thick, a band along the whole deep posterior margin of the body, the "clavus," with 5 to 13 lobes increasing in size and decreasing in number with fish size, separated by ossicles related to the rays. Anal 15 to 18, mirroring dorsal. Pectorals about 11, small, rounded immediately behind gill opening, directed upward. Pelvics absent.

Scales   No scales or lateral line canal. Body covered by a thick, leathery skin, swollen with collagenlike material,[4] carrying numerous rough, bony tubercles.

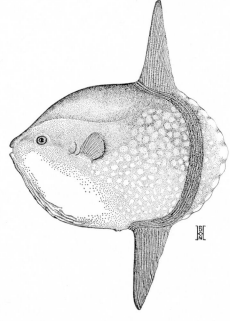

Colour   Dark gray above, sides gray brown with silver reflections. Belly dirty white. Sides with lighter spots, about the size of the eye. Light band along base of caudal, and, less marked, at bases of dorsal and anal fins.

Size   Length to 10 feet 10 inches (3.30 m) and an estimated weight of 1800 pounds (820 kg).[10] Another, 8 feet 6 inches (2.6 m) long, weighed 3102 pounds (1410 kg).[2]

Recognition   Immediately recognized by the compressed truncate form, the high matching dorsal and anal fins, the rough leathery skin, the porelike gill opening, and the absence of pelvic fins.

Life History   A moderate-sized female 4 feet 6 inches (1.37 m) long contained 300 million eggs. Hatching and early development are not known for *Mola mola* but eggs and larvae of closely related species are free floating, quite ordinary in general appearance aside from numerous spines and protuberances. After metamorphosis young *Mola mola* are deeper than long, still with a variety of protuberances, but no tail, and no lobes in the clavus. After a length of 2 feet (61 cm) is reached, the bony tubercle on the snout of male starts to protrude forward, and on the female, upward. With growth of the fish the clavus grows between the ossicles supporting it to produce lobes, 9 to 12 in both sexes at first, but in large males five become very large, and the others become reduced.[2,8] In Monterey Bay ocean sunfish 2 to 3 feet long (61–91 cm) were directly observed to swim upright quite actively by sculling movement of the dorsal and anal fins,[7] as deduced from the massive musculature.[4] Sometimes they jumped clear of the water. The ocean sunfish is sometimes observed at the surface floating on its side, raising the question as to the cause of the morbidity or mortality,[2,3] if such it is. *Mola mola* occurrence seems to be related with occurrence of the jellyfish *Aurelia*. Food includes jellyfish, both medusa and comb jellies, and in addition Crustacea, brittle stars, molluscs, algae, larval eels, and other fishes of considerable size.[2]

Distribution   In the temperate and tropical seas of the world, both inshore and at sea,[5,6,8,9] possibly less abundant in the southern hemisphere where a closely related species occurs also.[2] In northern British Columbia, and reported from southeast Alaska.[10] Quite frequently observed along the coast and in the outside inlets of British Columbia floating on its side, or in seine hauls. Two specimens recorded from inside waters at Butedale and Quathiaski Cove, and in Puget Sound.

References   1 Evermann 1915; 2 Fraser-Brunner 1951; 3 Gotshall 1961; 4 Gregory and Raven 1934; 5 Jordan 1921; 6 Leim and Scott 1966; 7 Myers and Wales 1930; 8 Roedel 1948b; 9 Schmidt 1921; 10 Wilimovsky 1954.

GAZETTEER

GAZETTEER

General locations, latitudes and longitudes of most of the places mentioned in the text. Minutes of latitude or longitude where given are separated by a decimal point from the degrees. In a few cases tenths of a minute are shown following a second decimal point.

Active Pass	Southern Strait of Georgia	48.52 N	123.18 W
Adak	Aleutian Island	51.52 N	176.39 W
Admiralty Island	Southeast Alaska	57.50 N	134.30 W
Afognak Island	Gulf of Alaska	58.15 N	152.30 W
Agattu Island	Aleutian Chain	52.25 N	173.35 E
Ain River	Masset Inlet, Q.C.I.	53.44 N	132.24 W
Aklavik	Mackenzie River, Canadian Arctic	68.12 N	135.00 W
Akutan Island	Aleutian Chain	54.10 N	165.55 W
Alberni (Inlet)	Head in central Vancouver Island	49.14 N	124.49 W
Alert Bay	Cormorant Island, Queen Charlotte Sound	50.35 N	126.55 W
Aleutian Islands	Eastern Alaska	55.00 N	163.00 W
Amchitka Island	Aleutian Chain	51.30 N	179.00 E
Amphitrite Point	West Vancouver Island	48.55 N	125.32 W
Amur Bay Liman	East coast USSR	64.30 N	177.45 E
Amur River	East coast USSR	52.56 N	141.10 E
Anadyr Gulf Zaliv	Eastern Siberia	64.00 N	179.00 W
Anadyr River	Eastern Siberia	64.55 N	176.05 E
Aniva Bay	South end Sakhalin Island	46.16 N	142.48 E
Anthony Island	West of southern Queen Charlotte Islands	52.05 N	131.13 W
Arctic Red River	Tributary of Mackenzie River	67.27 N	133.46 W
Argentina	Central South America	34.00 S	64.00 W
Ashcroft	Central British Columbia	50.43 N	121.17 W
Atka Island	Aleutian Chain	52.15 N	174.30 W
Attu Island	Aleutian Chain	52.55 N	173.00 E
Avacha Bay	Kamchatka Peninsula	53.07 N	158.33 E
Babine Lake	Northern British Columbia	54.15 N	126.00 W
Baja California		30.00 N	115.00 W
Bajo Point	Nootka Island	49.35 N	126.40 W
Baker Pass(age)	Northern Strait of Georgia	50.01 N	124.47 W
Banderas Bay	Mexico	20.40 N	105.25 W
Banks Island, B.C.	Hecate Strait	130.00 N	53.20 W
Barkley Sound	West Vancouver Island	48.50 N	125.20 W
Bathurst Inlet	Arctic Canada	70.35 N	128.00 W
Bella Bella	Central British Columbia	52.09 N	128.07 W
Bella Coola	At head North Bentinck Arm, central British Columbia	52.21 N	126.53 W
Bentinck Island	Southeast of Vancouver Island	47.17 N	123.32 W
Bering Island	Western Bering Sea	55.00 N	165.15 E
Bering Sea		60.00 N	175.00 W
Black Sea	Eastern Europe	43.00 N	35.00 E

Blying Sound	Gulf of Alaska	59.50 N	149.15 W
Bonavista	Newfoundland, Canada	48.39 N	53.07 W
Bonilla Island	Hecate Strait in northern British Columbia	43.30 N	130.40 W
Bowen Island	Howe Sound, Strait of Georgia	49.10 N	123.22 W
Brazil	Atlantic side of South America	9.00 S	53.00 W
Brentwood Bay	South Vancouver Island	48.35.6 N	125.28.5 W
Bristol Bay	Alaska	58.00 N	159.00 W
Brooks Peninsula	Vancouver Island	50.10 N	126.49 W
Burke Channel	Central British Columbia	52.15 N	127.20 W
Burrard Inlet	Southern British Columbia	49.18 N	123.00 W
Butedale	Northern British Columbia	53.09.5 N	128.41.5 W
Bute Inlet	Off northern Strait of Georgia	50.35 N	124.53 W
Calvert Island	Central British Columbia	51.35 N	128.00 W
Cape Bathurst	Beaufort Sea, Arctic Canada	70.35 N	128.00 W
Cape Buchon	Central California	35.15 N	120.54 W
Cape Chaplina	Eastern Siberia	65.25 N	172.28 W
Cape Colnett	Baja California	31.00 N	116.20 W
Cape Flattery	Northwest point of Washington State	48.22 N	124.42 W
Cape of Good Hope	South point of Africa	34.24 S	18.30 E
Cape James	Hope Island	50.57 N	127.50 W
Cape Knox	Northwest Queen Charlotte Islands	54.11 N	133.04 W
Cape Navarin	East Asia	62.16 N	179.10 E
Cape Olytorsky	Eastern Siberia	60.00 N	170.40 E
Cape Saint Elias	Southeast Alaska	59.52 N	144.30 W
Cape Saint James	South Queen Charlotte Islands		
Cape San Lucas	Baja California	22.50 N	109.55 W
Cape Scott	Northwest end Vancouver Island	50.46 N	128.25 W
Cape Spencer	Southeast Alaska	58.14 N	136.40 W
Carmel	Coast central California	36.33 N	121.55 W
Carmichael Passage	Between Moresby and Louise Islands, Queen Charlotte Islands	52.57 N	131.55 W
Cascade Inlet	Central British Columbia coast	52.24 N	127.25 W
Cedros Island	Off central Baja California	28.10 N	115.15 W
Chatham Sound	Off north Canadian Pacific mainland	54.30 N	130.30 W
Cherry Point	Vancouver Island south of Cowichan Bay	48.41 N	123.30 W
Chesapeake Bay	Atlantic coast of United States	38.40 N	76.25 W
Chile	West coast of South America	30.00 S	71.00 W
Chirikof Island	North Gulf of Alaska	55.50 N	155.35 W
Chukchi Sea	Arctic between North America and Asia	68.00 N	170.00 W
Chukol Peninsula	Extreme east of Asia	66.00 N	172.00 W
Clallum County	Washington State	48.10 N	123.49 W
Clayoquot Sound	Vancouver Island	49.15 N	126.00 W
Clearwater River	Hudson Bay, Quebec		
Clinton	Central British Columbia	51.05 N	121.35 W

646

Clio Channel	Alternate to western Johnstone Strait	50.35 N	126.27 W
Clo-oose	West coast of Vancouver Island	48.39 N	124.49 W
Columbia River	Boundary between states of Oregon and Washington. Outlet	46.13 N	124.00 W
Commander (Komandorskije) Islands	Bering Sea	55.00 N	167.00 E
Comox	East Vancouver Island	49.40 N	124.55 W
Connecticut River	Northwestern United States	41.17 N	72.21 W
Cook Inlet	Off the Gulf of Alaska	60.30 N	152.00 W
Coos Bay	South central coast of Oregon	43.23 N	124.16 W
Copper River	Alaska	60.16 N	145.32 W
Coronado	Southern California	32.41 N	117.11 W
Courtenay Bay	East Vancouver Island	49.40 N	124.53 W
Cowichan Lake	Southern Vancouver Island	48.54 N	124.20 W
Cowichan River	Southern east coast of Vancouver Island	48.46 N	123.38 W
Cox Island	North tip Vancouver Island	50.48 N	128.37 W
Craig	Alaska	55.29 N	133.06 W
Cuba	Western north tropical Atlantic	21.30 N	80.00 W
Cultus Lake	Southern British Columbia, south of Chilliwack	49.00 N	121.00 W
Day Harbor	Gulf of Alaska	60.00 N	149.06 W
Dean Channel	Central British Columbia	52.22 N	127.26 W
Deep Bay	Vancouver Island, central Strait of Georgia	49.27 N	124.43 W
Deep Cove	Off Burrard Inlet	49.19 N	122.52 W
Departure Bay	Strait of Georgia, Vancouver Island	49.12 N	123.57 W
Descanso Bay	California	35.51 N	116.35 W
Dez(h)neu(a) Cape (Village)	Bering Strait	66 06 N	169.45 E
Discovery Island	South of Vancouver Island	48.20 N	123.15 W
Discovery Passage	North of Strait of Georgia	50.10 N	125.25 W
Dixon Entrance	Between Queen Charlotte Islands and Alaskan Islands	54.30 N	132.00 W
Drew Harbour	Off channel north of Strait of Georgia	50.06 N	125.12 W
Drury Inlet	Central British Columbia	50.54 N	127.04 W
Ecuador	West coast of South America	2.00 S	77.30 W
Eel River	Humboldt Co , California	40.40 N	124 20 W
Eliza Island	Washington State, off Bellingham Bay	48 38 N	122.35 W
Elkhorn Slough	Central California	37.48 N	121.53 W
Elsie Lake	Central Vancouver Island	49.26 N	125.07 W
English Bay	Near Vancouver, B.C.	49.17 N	123.14 W
Ensenada	Baja California	31.52 N	116.37 W
Esperanza Inlet	West coast of Vancouver Island	49.50 N	127.00 W
Esquimalt (Harbour)	South end Vancouver Island	48.26 N	123.24 W

Estevan Point (Esteban)	Middle west coast of Vancouver Island	49.22 N	136.32 W
Etorofu (Itorup) Island	Kuril Islands	44.54 N	147.30 E
Falkland Islands	Southwest Atlantic	51.45 S	59.00 W
False Narrows	Southern Strait of Georgia	49.08 N	123.46 W
Fanny Bay	Off Baynes Sound of Strait of Georgia	49.30 N	124.49 W
Fife Point	East coast north end of Graham Island, Q.C.I.	54.04 N	131.40 W
Fitz Hugh Sound	Off central British Columbia	51.37 N	127.56 W
Flores Island	Off central west coast Vancouver Island	49.20 N	120.10 W
Florida	Southeastern United States	28.00 N	82.00 W
Formosa	East Pacific	24.00 N	121.00 E
Fort Rupert	North Vancouver Island	50.42 N	127.24 W
Fraser River outlet		49.05 N	123.20 W
Friday Harbor	San Juan Island, Washington State	48.32 N	123.01 W
Fusan (Pusan)	Korea	35.06 N	129.03 E
Gabriola Bluff	Southern Strait of Georgia	49.09 N	123.50 W
Galiano Island	Southern Strait of Georgia	48.55 N	123.25 W
Galapagos Islands	Equatorial east Pacific	0.30 S	90.30 W
Gensan	China Yellow Sea	39.00 N	127.30 E
Georgia Strait		49.20 N	124.00 W
Goletas Channel	Immediately north of Vancouver Island	50.52 N	127.52 W
Goose Bay	Central British Columbia	51.22 N	127.50 W
Goose Islands	Queen Charlotte Sound	51.53 N	128.28 W
Goto(retto) Island(s)	Off Kyusho, Japan	32.50 N	129.00 E
Graham Island	Queen Charlotte Islands	53.30 N	132.30 W
Greenland (South)	Northwest Atlantic	60.00 N	44.00 W
Guadaloupe Island	Off Baja California	29.00 N	118.16 W
Gulf of California	Mexico	26.00 N	110.00 W
Gulf Islands	Southern Strait of Georgia		
Gulf of Panama	Central America	8.00 N	79.10 W
Gulf of St. Lawrence	East coast of Canada	48.00 N	62.00 W
Hakai Pass(age)	Opening into Queen Charlotte Sound	51.40 N	128.10 W
Hammond Bay	Strait of Georgia, Vancouver Island	49.15 N	123.58 W
Hardy Bay	Northeast of Vancouver Island	50.45 N	127.28 W
Haro Strait	Southern Strait of Georgia	48.30 N	123.11 W
Harrison Lake	Off lower Fraser River	49.31 N	121.59 W
Hawaii (and Islands)	Central Pacific	20.00 N	157.45 W
Hay River	Tributary to Great Slave Lake	60.51 N	115.44 W
Haystack Island	Outlet Portland Canal	54.43 N	130.37 W
Hecate Strait	Between Queen Charlotte Islands and coast islands	53.00 N	131.00 W

Herschel Island	North of Yukon Territories	69.35 N	139.05 W
Hesquiat Harbour	Central west coast of Vancouver Island	49.27 N	126.23 W
Hokkaido Province (Island)	Japan	43.00 N	143.00 E
Holman Island	West of Victoria Island in Arctic	70.32 N	117.43 W
Hondo Island	Part of southern Japan	32.07 N	130.12 E
Honshu Island	Japan	35.00 N	129.00 E
Hope Island	Queen Charlotte Sound	50.55 N	127.58 W
Hornby Island	Central Strait of Georgia	49.32 N	124.40 W
Howe Sound	Off southern Strait of Georgia	49.25 N	123.20 W
Humboldt Bay	Southern Oregon	40.45 N	124.30 W
Huntington Beach	Southern California	33.39 N	117.60 W
Ibaraki	Honshu Island, Japan	36.30 N	140.30 E
Iceland	North Atlantic	65.00 N	18.00 W
Icy Bay	Alaska	60.00 N	141.20 W
Indian Arm	Off Burrard Inlet in southern British Columbia	49.20 N	122.50 W
Indigirka River	East Siberia	70.48 N	148.54 E
Japan	Northwest Pacific	36.00 N	138.00 E
Jervis Inlet	Off Strait of Georgia	49.48 N	124.00 W
Joassa Channel	Horsfall and Dufferin islands, central British Columbia coast		
Johnstone Strait	Northeast of Vancouver Island	50.25 N	126.00 W
Juan de Fuca Strait	Between Olympic Peninsula and Vancouver Island	48.15 N	124.00 W
Kaisun Bay	West side Moresby Island, Q.C.I.	32.02 N	132.28 W
Kamchatka	East USSR	57.00 N	160.00 E
Kidluit Bay	Canadian Arctic		
Kingcome Inlet	Mainland off Queen Charlotte Strait	50.46 N	126.23 W
Knight Inlet	Central British Columbia	50.40 N	126.00 W
Kodiak Island	South of Alaska Peninsula	57.30 N	153.30 W
Kolyma River	East Siberia	69.30 N	161.00 E
Komandorskije (Commander) Islands	Boundary southwest Bering Sea	55.00 N	167.00 E
Korea	East Asia	37.00 N	128.00 E
Korf Gulf	East coast north Kamchatka	60.00 N	166.00 E
Kotzebue Sound	Northwest Alaska	66.20 N	163.00 W
Krenitzen Islands	Aleutian Chain	54.08 N	166.00 W
Kruzof Island	Off southeast Alaska	57.14 N	136.13 W
Kuril(e) Islands	North of Japan	46.00 N	150.00 E
Kuril–Kamchatka Trench	Northwest Pacific off Kuril Islands	45.00 N	150-154 E
Kwantung (Guangdong)	South Chinese Province	23.00 N	113.00 E
Kyuquot Sound	Vancouver Island	50.03 N	127.10 W

Ladysmith (Harbour)	East coast of Vancouver Island	48.59	N	123.49	W
Lagoon Bay	Central British Columbia	52.05	N	127.50	W
La Jolla	Southern California	32.50	N	117.16	W
Lake Michigan	Northcentral United States	44.00	N	87.00	W
Lake Ontario	Canada–U.S. boundary	43.40	N	78.00	W
Lake Washington	Washington State (at Seattle)	47.37	N	121.15	W
Langara Island	North Queen Charlotte Islands	54.14	N	130.00	W
La Pérouse Bank	Off southern Vancouver Island	48.35	N	125.48	W
La Push	Washington	47.50	N	124.38	W
Lena River	Siberia	72.25	N	126.40	E
Little Qualicum River	East coast of central Vancouver Island	49.22	N	124.29	W
Loch Aire	British Isles				
Lofoten Islands	Off northwestern Norway	68.30	N	15.00	E
Long Beach	Southern California	33.46	N	118.11	W
Los Angeles (Harbor)	Southern California	33.35	N	118.16	W
Los Coronados Islands	Baja California	32.25	N	117.22	W
Loughborough Inlet	Central British Columbia	50 30	N	125.35	W
Luck Point	Alaska	55.59	N	132.42	W
Lynn Canal	Alaska	58.50	N	135.15	W
Madeira	Eastern Atlantic Ocean	32.44	N	17.00	W
Magdalena Bay	Baja California, Mexico	24.40	N	112.00	W
Magellan Strait	South end of South America	53.00	S	71.00	W
Malaspina Inlet	Off north Strait of Georgia	50.00	N	124.43	W
Malcolm Island	Queen Charlotte Strait	50.39	N	127.02	W
Malibu Beach	California	34.02	N	118.42	W
Mandarte Island	Miners Channel near Victoria	48.38	N	124.29	W
Maquinna Point	Nootka Island (off west coast of Vancouver Island)	49.37	N	126.50	W
Maritime Territories	East USSR	45.00	N	135.00	E
Masset Inlet	North Queen Charlotte Islands	53.43	N	132.18	W
Mathieson Channel	Central British Columbia	52.19	N	128.23	W
Mayne Bay	Barkley Sound	48.58	N	128.24	W
Mazatlan	Mexico	23.13	N	106.25	W
McIntyre Bay	North of Queen Charlotte Islands	54.00	N	132.00	W
Mediterranean Sea	Between Europe and Africa	35.00	N	20.00	E
Medniji Island	Bering Sea	54.45	N	167.35	E
Mexicana Point	Hope Island	50.55	N	128.00	W
Milbanke Sound	Central British Columbia	52.21	N	128.00	W
Misaki	Japan	35.10	N	139.37	E
Mistaken Island	Strait of Georgia	49.19	N	124.13	W
Moneron Island	East of south end of Sakhalin Island	46.17	N	141.15	E
Monterey Bay	Central California	36.45	N	121 50	W
Moresby Island	Queen Charlotte Islands	53.00	N	132.00	W
Moss Landing	Central California	36.48	N	121.47	W
Murman Coast	Western Arctic USSR	65.00	N	37.00	E
Mussel Point	Central California	34.56	N	120.40	W

650

Naden Harbour	North end of Graham Island	54.00 N	132.30 W
Nanaimo Harbour	Vancouver Island	49.10 N	123.56 W
Nanoose Bay	East coast of Vancouver Island	49.17 N	124.10 W
Narrows Arm	Sechelt Inlet of Strait of Georgia	49.43 N	123.47 W
Nass River	Northern boundary of British Columbia	55.05 N	130.12 W
Neah Bay	West coast of Washington State	48.22 N	124.37 W
Newfoundland	Eastern Canada	52.00 N	56.00 W
Newport Beach	Southern California	33.37 N	117.56 W
New Zealand	South Pacific Ocean	41.00 S	174.00 E
Nootka Island	Middle of southwest coast of Vancouver Island	49.42 N	126.50 W
North Arm	Off Burrard Inlet in southern British Columbia	49.20 N	122.50 W
North Carolina	Atlantic United States	35.30 N	80.10 W
Norton Sound	Alaska	64.00 N	164.00 W
Norway	Northwest Europe	62.00 N	10.00 E
Nova Scotia	Atlantic coast of Canada	45.00 N	63.00 W
Novaya Zemlya	North of Siberia in Arctic Ocean	74.00 N	57.00 E
Nushagak River	Bristol Bay, Alaska	59.00 N	158.00 W
Ob River	Western Siberia	66.45 N	69.30 E
Observatory Inlet	Northern British Columbia coast	55.15 N	129.53 W
Okhotsk Sea	East of USSR	55.00 N	150.00 E
Oregon	Central west coast of United States	44.00 N	121.00 W
Oslo	Norway	59.55 N	10.45 E
Ououkinsh Inlet	Northern west coast of Vancouver Island	50.07 N	127.32 W
Paita	Peru	5.05 S	81.10 W
Panama	Central America	9.00 N	80.00 W
Peel River	Tributary of Mackenzie River	67.42 N	134.32 W
Pender Harbour	North shore Strait of Georgia	47.37 N	124.04 W
Pender Island	Southern Strait of Georgia	48.48 N	123.17 W
Pendrell Sound	Redondo Island north of Strait of Georgia	50.15 N	124.44 W
Penobscot River	Maine, USA	44.30 N	68.50 W
Peru	West coast of South America	10.00 S	76.00 W
Peter the Great Bay	Pacific USSR	42.40 N	132.00 E
Petropavlosk	Kamchatka	53.01 N	158.39 E
Point Arguello	California	34.35 N	120.39 W
Point Bande(a)	Northern Baja California	31.43 N	116.43 W
Point Barrow	North Alaska	71.32 N	156.30 W
Point Buchon	Central California	35.15 N	120.45 W
Point Cabras	Northern Baja California	31.20 N	116.30 W
Point Chamalu (Bay)	Baja California	30.50 N	116.11 W
Point Conception	California	34.27 N	120.27 W
Point Dume	Southern California	34.00 N	118.48 W
Point Grey	Strait of Georgia	49.17 N	123.15 W

Point Loma	Southern California	)2.41 N	117.14 W
Point Piedras Blanca	Southern California	)5.40 N	121.17 W
Point Reyes	California	38.00 N	123.01 W
Point Sal	California	34.54 N	120.40 W
Point Sur	Central California	36.18 N	121.54 W
Porlier Pass	Strait of Georgia	49.00 N	123.35 W
Port Arthur (Lüshun, Zhg.)	Manchuria	38.47 N	121.13 E
Port Clarence	Alaska	65.15 N	166.30 W
Port Dick	Gulf of Alaska	59.02 N	151.01 W
Port Hardy	Northeast coast of Vancouver Island	50.43 N	127.25 W
Port Harrison	Hudson Bay, Quebec	58.30 N	78.15 W
Port John Lake	King Island, central British Columbia coast	52.09 N	127.48 W
Portland Canal	Northern British Columbia	)5.00 N	130.00 W
Port Orchard	Puget Sound, Washington	47.35 N	122.35 W
Port San Juan	Vancouver Island	48.32 N	124.27 W
Port Simpson	Northern British Columbia	54.34 N	130.23 W
(Port) Wrangel	Southeast Alaska	56.28 N	132.23 W
Pribilof Islands	Bering Sea	57.00 N	170.00 W
Prince Rupert (Harbour)	Northern British Columbia	54.20 N	130.20 W
Prince of Wales Island	Southeastern Alaska	55.30 N	133.00 W
Prince William Sound	North Gulf of Alaska	60.30 N	147.00 W
Providence Bay	Near northeast point of Asia	64.30 N	173.20 W
Puffin Island	Alaska	56.15 N	135.00 W
Puget Sound	Northwest Washington	47.50 N	122.30 W
Pyramid Lake	Nevada	40.00 N	119.35 W
Quathiaski Cove	Quadra Island at north end of Strait of Georgia	50.02 N	125.13 W
Quatsino Sound	Northern west coast of Vancouver Island	50.32 N	127.36 W
Queen Charlotte Islands	Off northwest British Columbia	52.54 N	131.133 W
Queen Charlotte Sound		51.20 N	129.00 W
Queen Charlotte Strait	North of Vancouver Island	50.40 N	127.00 W
Redondo Islands	North Strait of Georgia	50.13 N	124.48 W
Reef Island	Hecate Strait	52.52 N	131.31 W
Rennell Sound	Queen Charlotte Islands	53.25 N	132.45 W
Revillagigedo Islands	Pacific off Mexico	19.00 N	111.30 W
Richards Island (Richardson Island)		69.20 N	134.30 W
Rivers Inlet	Central coast of British Columbia	51.39 N	127.30 W
Robben Island (Ostrov Tulenij)	Western Okhotsk Sea	48.30 N	144.12 E
Rose Harbour	South Queen Charlotte Islands	52.10 N	131.05 W
Rose Spit	North Queen Charlotte Islands	54.14 N	131.38 W
Round Island	Southern Strait of Georgia	49.07 N	123.47 W

Sacramento Reef	Baja California		
Sacramento River	California, San Francisco Bay	38.03 N	121.56 W
Sagami Bay	Japan	35.00 N	139.30 E
Saint Lawrence Island	North Bering Sea	63.00 N	172.00 W
Saint Matthew Island	Bering Sea	60.25 N	171.00 W
Saint Michael(s) Island	Alaska	63.29 N	162.02 W
Saint Paul Island	Alaska	57.10 N	170.15 W
Sakhalin Island (Ostrov Sachalin) (Saghalein)	East Asia	51.00 N	143.00 E
Sanak Islands	Aleutian Islands	54.25 N	162.35 W
San Benito Island	Off Baja California	28.25 N	115.35 W
San Cristobal Bay	Baja California	27.16 N	114.35 W
San Diego	Southern California	32.43 N	117.09 W
San Juan	Southwest Vancouver Island	48.33 N	124.29 W
San Juan Islands	Gulf of Georgia	48.30 N	123.00 W
San Martin Island	Baja California	30.30 N	116.10 W
San Miguel Island	Southern California	34.02 N	120.22 W
San Quentin	Baja California	30.18 N	115.53 W
Santa Barbara Island	Off California	33.23 N	119.01 W
Santa Cruz	California	36.58 N	122.01 W
Santa Monica	Southern California	33.56 N	118.33 W
Santa Rosa Island	Southern California	34.00 N	120.05 W
Santa Rosalia Bay	Baja California	28.38 N	114.10 W
Santo Tomas Bay	Baja California	31.33 N	116.24 W
Saturna Island	Southern Strait of Georgia	48.47 N	123.08 W
Schooner Cove	West coast of Vancouver Island	49.02 N	125.49 W
Scotch Fir Point	Mainland shore of Strait of Georgia	49.45 N	124.15 W
Seattle	On Puget Sound, Washington State	47.36 N	122.20 W
Sebastian Viscaino Bay	Baja California	28.00 N	114.30 W
Sechelt Inlet	Off Strait of Georgia	49.41 N	123.52 W
Selwyn Inlet	Queen Charlotte Islands	52.52 N	131.45 W
Semisopochnoi Island	Aleutian Chain	52.00 N	179.35 E
Senegal	West coast of Africa	14.00 N	14.00 W
Seymour Inlet	Central British Columbia	51.04 N	127.24 W
Shantar Islands	Western Okhotsk Sea	54.50 N	137.40 E
Shelikof Strait	Alaska	58.00 N	154.00 W
Sherringham Point	Vancouver Island in Juan de Fuca Strait	48.23 N	123.55 W
Shetland Islands	Northeast Atlantic	60.30 N	1.30 W
Shikoku Island	Japan	30.30 N	133.30 E
Shimushira	Kuril Islands	46.40 N	152.00 E
Shubenacadie Lake	Nova Scotia	44.55 N	63.36 W
Shumagin Islands	South of Alaska Peninsula	55.07 N	149.45 W
Sitka	Alaska	57.03 N	135.14 W
Skeena River	Northern British Columbia. Outlet	54.08 N	130 07 W
Skidegate Inlet	Betweeen main Queen Charlotte Islands	53.15 N	132.00 W
Skidegate Lake	Moresby Island	53.06 N	132.00 W
Slave River	Tributary to Great Slave Lake	61.18 N	113.39 W
Smith Sound (Inlet)	Central British Columbia	51.16 N	127.45 W

Sooke	South Vancouver Island	48.22 N	123.45 W
South Carolina	Atlantic United States	34.00 N	81.00 W
Spain	West Europe	40.00 N	4.00 W
Spitzbergen Island	Arctic, north of Norway	78.00 N	19.00 E
Squamish River	Howe Sound, Strait of Georgia	49.24 N	123.11 W
Strait of Georgia		49.20 N	124.00 W
Stuart Lake	Mainland, northern British Columbia	54.30 N	124.40 W
Swanson Channel	Southern Strait of Georgia	48.47 N	120.23 W
Sydney Inlet	West coast Vancouver Island	49.20 N	126.15 W
Tahsis Inlet	Nootka Sound	49.52 N	126.40 W
Taiwan	Off East Asia	23.30 N	121.00 E
Taku River	Southeast Alaska	58.26 N	133.59 W
Tasu Sound	West coast of Queen Charlotte Islands	52.51 N	132.08 W
Tatar Strait	Off East Asia	50.00 N	141.00 E
Terpenija Bay	South of Sakhalin Island	48.30 N	143.30 E
Teslin Lake	Yukon–Southeast Alaska boundary	60.15 N	132.57 W
Tillamook County	Western Oregon	45.25 N	123.39 W
Toba Inlet	Off northern Strait of Georgia	50.22 N	124.42 W
Todos Santos Bay	Baja California	23.28 N	110.14 W
Tofino	West coast of Vancouver Island	49.09 N	125.54 W
Tokahu	Japan	35.30 N	133.40 E
Tomales Bay	Central California	38.10 N	122.55 W
Tone River	Japan	35.44 N	140.51 E
Toyama Bay	West coast of Japan	36.50 N	137.10 E
Triangle Island	Entrance to Queen Charlotte Sound	50.51 N	129.04 W
Trinity Bay	Newfoundland	48.00 N	53.30 W
Tsuruga Bay	West coast Japan	35.39 N	136.04 E
Tumin River	East coast USSR	49.18 N	140.22 E
Turtle Bay	Baja California	27.39 N	114.51 W
Ucluelet	Vancouver Island	48.56 N	125.34 W
Umnak Island	Aleutian Islands	53.25 N	168.10 W
Unalakleet	Norton Sound, Bering Sea	63.53 N	160.47 W
Unalaska Island	Gulf of Alaska	53.45 N	166.45 W
Ungava Bay	Northern Quebec	59.30 N	67.30 W
Unimak Island	Aleutian Islands	54.50 N	164.00 W
Union Bay	Northern Strait of Georgia	49.35 N	124.53 W
Union Lake	Washington State	47.38 N	122.20 W
Uruguay	Central Atlantic, South America	33.00 S	56.00 W
Valparaiso	Chile, South America	33.02 S	71.38 W
Vancouver	Washington	45.39 N	122.40 W
Vancouver Island	Off southern British Columbia	50.00 N	126.00 W
Vargas Island	Off west coast of Vancouver Island	49.11 N	126.00 W
Victoria	Southeast end Vancouver Island	48.25 N	122.20 W
Wakaso Bay	Sea of Japan	35.21 N	134.22 E
Waldport	Coast of central Oregon	44.26 N	124.04 W

White Rock	Border Canada and U.S.	49.02 N	122.47 W
White Sea	Northwestern USSR	66.00 N	40.00 E
Wiah Point	North Graham Island	54.07 N	132.19 W
Wickaninnish Bay	West coast of Vancouver Island	49.02 N	125.43 W
Willapa Bay (Harbor)	Central coast of Washington State	46.40 N	124.00 W
Witless Bay	Avalon Peninsula, Newfoundland	47.17 N	52.50 W
Yaquima Bay	Oregon	44.37 N	124.04 W
Yellow Point	Vancouver Island, Strait of Georgia	49.02 N	123.49 W
Yellow Sea	Off East Asia	36.00 N	123.00 E
Yen(i)sei(y) River	Siberia	71.50 N	82.40 E
Yukon River (outlet)	Alaska	63.00 N	165.00 W

GLOSSARY

GLOSSARY

Abdomen — lower posterior part of body ahead of vent. Abdominal.

Aberrant — unusual in form or behaviour, appearing abnormal.

Abyssal — concerning deep water, more than 1500 fathoms (2750 m).

Acute — sharp.

-ad — a combining form meaning toward.

Adipose fin — a fleshy fin on the median line of the body, without rays and usually small. Not counted as a dorsal (or anal) fin.

Alevin — newly hatched salmon or related fish, (usually) with a yolk sac attached, before it emerges from the spawning gravel to begin swimming freely.

Ammocoete — larval form of lampreys.

Amphipod — small- or medium-sized compressed crustaceans with the body definitely segmented and the anterior appendages leglike.

Anadromous — going upstream to spawn, usually from salt to fresh water.

Anal — related to the anus or vent.

Anal fin — fin between the anus and the tail on the lower side of the body.

Anal papilla — appendage or protuberance in front of the genital pore and behind vent in sculpins and some of their relatives.

Anterior — related to the head end.

Anus — outlet opening of the digestive tract.

Asymmetrical — not symmetrical so that one side is not the mirror image of the other.

Axillary process — scalelike sheets of tissue arising from the base of a fin, usually the pelvic fin.

Barbel — fleshy, moderately slender protuberance, usually on head.

Bathypelagic — living away from the bottom in deep water.

Benthic — living in direct relation with the bottom.

Bifid — with the end divided and thus appearing double. Thus trifid — triple.

Biramous — once branched.

Branchial — concerning gills.

Branchiostegals — bony or cartilaginous supports of the ventral gill membranes below the gill cover.

Bryozoa(n) — very small mosslike animals that grow on rocks or on other animals and plants.

Buccal — related to the mouth.

Caddis — rather primitive insects whose aquatic larvae build protective cases for themselves out of sand or fine trash.

Caecum (plural *caeca*) — a blind sac opening from the alimentary canal.

Canine — large conical teeth (resembling the eye tooth in a dog).

Cardiform — (of teeth) — coarse and sharp.

Caudal — related to the tail.

Caudal peduncle — the posterior part of the body of a fish that supports the tail fin: usually the part of the body from the posterior base of the anal fin to the end of the vertebral column.

Centrum (plural *centra*) — the main, cylindrical usually, part of a vertebra or unit of the backbone.

Cephalopod(a)(s) — highly developed molluscs with specialized eyes and with the head and foot coalesced. Includes squid and octopus.

Chaetognath(a) — free-swimming arrow-shaped worms with hooklike horny jaws and expanded tails. Arrow worms.

Chiton — a marine mollusc with a row of bony plates along its back.

Cirrus (plural *cirri*) — fine or compound and thin flexible appendage or fringe.

Cladocera — small crustaceans with two-valve shells, that swim by means of very large biramous antennae. Young develop in large, evident brood pouches. A few saltwater forms; most occur in fresh water.

Claspers — modified median portions of pelvic fins in males of sharks, rays and chimaeras used for transferring sperm to the females.

Clavus — the bandlike tail of the ocean sunfish.

Cleithrum (*cleithral*) — a bone supporting the posterior edge of the gill opening.

Cloaca — a common opening for digestive, urinary, and reproductive tracts in many fishes.

Coalesce (*d*) — grown together.

Compressed — flattened from side to side.

Confluent — running into with little or no break (as adjoining fins).

Copepod — usually small depressed crustaceans with single median eyes, swimming by means of the antennae, etc. Very numerous free-swimming species. A common food for fishes. Many highly modified parasitic forms.

Coronal — (spine) between frontal and parietal bones of head.

Corselet — a band of modified scales on the anterior end of the body of tunas.

Cranial — concerning the brain case or cranium.

Crenulate — with edge finely notched.

Crustacea (*n*) — a very diverse group of animals with jointed external skeletons; including copepods, cladocerans, barnacles, amphipods, shrimps, crabs, and other forms.

Ctenoid — (of scales) having the posterior margin with fine teeth.

Ctenophore — comb-jellies or sea plums. Jellyfish with bands of fine hairlike cilia on the outer surface which provide feeble locomotion.

Cusp — point, as of a tooth.

Cycloid — (of scales) with smooth edges.

Decapod — so-called higher, and usually larger, Crustacea, such as, crabs, hermit crabs, shrimps, and lobster. The shell of the head and of the part of the body carrying the walking legs is fused into a single unit.

Deciduous — readily detached (of scales).

Decurved — curving downward from before backward.

Dentary — bone carrying teeth usually and forming anterior part of lower jaw.

Dentary elevation — a raised area at the symphysis of the lower jaw carrying teeth, sometimes fitting into a notch in the upper jaw.

Denticles — small teeth.

Dentition — arrangement of teeth.

Depensatory — tending to maintain or increase fluctuations in abundance.

Depressed — flattened from above downward.

Depressible — not rigidly fixed (of spines or teeth).

Depth — straight line distance vertically through a fish, usually the distance at the deepest point.

Desmid — microscopic unicellular freshwater green plants, each cell divided into identical halves, often with green pigment in complicated patterns.

Diatom — microscopic unicellular freshwater or saltwater green plants sometimes associated in strings. Cell walls are silica, usually showing very delicate complicated markings.

Dimorphism — condition in which different (sexes of) fishes differ notably in characters or in body proportions.

660

Dorsal — related to the back.

Dorsal fin — fin with rays, extending for a shorter or longer distance along the middle of the back of a fish.

Emarginate — (of fins) notched as a whole or between rays or spines.

Embedded — (of scales) completely enveloped in skin so that there is no free edge.

Entire — with a continuous margin.

Epiotic — bone at dorsal part of base of skull.

Erectile — capable of being moved to an erect position.

Esca — elaborate tassle on free end of the jointed appendage on the snout of some species of anglerfishes.

Euphausiid (acea) — Crustacea with all the thoracic segments fused with the head. These are free-swimming shrimplike forms — the most common kind of "red feed."

Evertible — capable of being turned outward.

Excised — with membranes cut away (of fins).

Exserted — (fin rays) much extended beyond margin of membrane.

Falcate — *falciform* — shaped like a sabre or sickle.

Fauna — the community of animals in an area.

Filament (ous) — thread (-like).

Finfold — a raised fold of tissue in the area where fins are customarily found but lacking the bony supports associated with true fins.

Finlet — small finlike structures following the main dorsal and anal fins in some species of fish, lacking rigid supports.

Flagellum — a fine long whiplike appendage, usually used in swimming or feeding.

Frenum — a median fold of skin joining the symphysis of the lower jaw to the lip.

Frontal — bone on top of head anterior to parietals and generally between the orbits of the eyes.

Furcate — forked.

Gasbladder (also called *swimbladder* or *air bladder)* — a sac filled with air or similar gases in the body cavity, either attached or not by a duct to the throat.

Gill arch — bony support of gills.

Gill cover — operculum. Flap protecting gills.

Gill membranes — thin flaps of tissue forming the bottom of the gill cavity, supported by branchiostegals.

Gill rakers — bony toothlike structures on the anterior edges of gill arches for protection or straining out food.

Gular — (concerning) bony plate or plates below chin and between sides of lower jaw.

Haemal spine (arch) — spine arising on ventral side of centrum (arch formed above fused distal ends of spines).

Halocline — part of the column of water in the ocean showing rapid change in salinity with depth.

Hermaphrodite — having both male and female organs in one body.

Heterocercal — the tail fin of a fish in which the upper lobe is much larger than the lower and in which the posterior vertebrae are turned upward to form a supporting axis.

Homocercal — the tail fin of a fish in which upper and lower lobes are more or less equal with the backbone ending at the middle of the base of the tail fin.

661

-id — a combining form meaning like.

-idae — technical combining form to represent a "family" of animals, the first part of the family name is the name of a typical genus.

Illicium — slender, forward-directed jointed appendage on snout of anglerfishes and their relatives, regarded as a modified fin ray.

Imbricated — overlapping, like shingles.

Incised — cut away (as between fin rays).

Included — of the closed lower jaw when it is overlapped by the upper.

Inferior — definitely on lower side (of head, re mouth, etc.).

Infra- — combining form meaning below.

Infraoral — below the mouth.

Insertion — base of a paired fin or the posterior end of the base of a median fin (dorsal or anal).

Inter- — combining form meaning between.

Interorbital space — narrowest distance across the head between the eye sockets or orbits.

Iridescent — displaying a wide range of changing colours.

Isohaline — a line joining points on a diagram or map which have water of the same salinity.

Isthmus — the narrow extension of the body below the head between the gill chambers.

Jugular — of or at the throat.

Keel — fleshy or bony ridge (as on scales, plates, caudal peduncle, etc.).

Lachrymal — bone immediately anterior to orbit, usually near midline.

Lamilla — a flattened, leaflike sheet of tissue.

Larva(l) — (concerning) young animals which are so imperfectly developed as to differ strongly from the adult (for example, by possessing a yolk sac).

Lateral — related to the side.

Lateral line — a series of modified scales with porelike openings to a sensory canal along the side of the fish.

Lenticular — shaped like two arcs of a circle joined along the flat sides.

Leptocephalo(u)s — highly compressed, small-headed larvae of eel-like fishes.

Lingual — related to the tongue.

Luminous (luminescent) organs — areas producing light on the body of a fish, usually without lenses, and may be diffuse.

Lunate — in the shape of a crescent moon (of tail fins).

Mandible — lower jaw.

Maxillary — bone of the upper jaw, in some fishes comprising the whole jaw, in others only the posterior part. Often with teeth.

Median — on or close to the plane dividing a fish into two mirror-image parts.

Meristic — (characters) involving numbers or counts.

Mesacoracoid — median bone in the series supporting pectoral fins in some kinds of fish.

Metamorphosis — the marked change in body form when fishes develop from their larval stages to conditions in which they resemble adults (or some intermediate stage).

Molar — (of teeth) rounded, for grinding.

Multi- — combining form meaning many.

Multifid — having several divisions or ends.

Mysid(acea) — Crustacea with a well-formed tail fin or telson, and the shell on the head fused with the first three or four segments of the thorax.

Nares — nostril(s).

Nasal — related to the nose. Bone on the upper anterior part of the head.

Notched — having an indentation, especially in a fin where the rays are shorter, as between spinous and soft-rayed parts, or where a fin is divided into two or more lobes.

Notochord — the cartilaginous support for the developing body before the formation of a vertebral column, persistent in lampreys and hagfishes and vestigial in higher forms.

Nuchal — related to the nape, immediately behind head.

Ocellus (plural *ocelli*) — eyelike pigment spot.

Ocular — related to the eye.

Oedema — accumulation of fluid in tissues of body.

Oesophagus — beginning of the digestive tract, between mouth and stomach.

-oid — combining form meaning like or similar to.

Oikopleura — minute tadpole-shaped free-swimming animals enclosed in a "house" and able rapidly to secrete a transparent envelope — regarded as very primitive and remote relatives of the vertebrate animals.

Operculum — bony flap covering gills in higher fishes, composed of opercular bones: opercle, preopercle, subopercle and interopercle.

Oral — pertaining to the mouth.

Orbit — bony cavity in skull where eyeball is housed.

Orbitosphenoid — small bone forming part of posterior of orbit.

Ossification — (cartilage usually) turning to bone.

Ostracod — small crustaceans with bivalve shells and the body only indistinctly apparent.

Oviparous — fishes which lay eggs that develop freely in the water.

Ovoviviparous — fishes which retain the fertilized egg in the body of the female where it undergoes all or most of its development to hatching, frequently receiving some nutrients and oxygen from the female but not developing a real placenta.

Palatines — paired bones usually extending backward and out, on the roof of a fish's mouth, frequently carrying teeth.

Palisade — (fence) of closely placed parallel stakes and thus, by analogy, a similar arrangement of teeth, etc.

Palp — feeler.

Papilla — fleshy projection (usually small).

Parietal — dorsal bone of skull enclosing brain case.

Pectoral — concerning anterior ventral (and lateral) parts of a fish.

Pectoral girdle — bony supporting system for the pectoral fin.

Pediculate — with a raised articulated base (of a fin).

Pelagic — living free from the bottom and near the surface.

Pelvic fins — paired fins on the lower part of the body, which may be near anus (abdominal), below or near pectoral fins (thoracic), or at throat (jugular). Sometimes called ventral fins.

Pelvic girdle — bony supports for the pelvic fins.

Peritoneum — lining of the abdominal cavity.

Pharyngeal — related to the pharynx. Pharyngeal bones, frequently armed with teeth.

Pharynx — respiratory part of the throat.

Photophore — specialized light-producing organ, well defined, usually with a lens and round reflector.

Pineal — a glandular part of the brain supposed to be related to a primitive eye.

Placoid — platelike (of scales).

Plankton — free-floating, small, living plants (phytoplankton) and animals (zooplankton).

Polychaete (worm) — an important group of elongate marine animals with spiny appendages, of which the common earthworm is a specialized streamlined member.

Pore — a blind (frequently) opening or pit, usually small and usually the site of a secretory or sensory function.

Postcleithral — bone posterior to the lower part of the gill opening and associated with the base of the pectoral fin.

Pre- — combining form meaning in front of.

Precaudal pit — cavity in front of the tail fin (in sharks).

Prefrontal — dorsal bone in skull between frontals and nasals.

Premaxillary — paired bone of the upper jaw, sometimes carrying teeth, sometimes comprising most of jaw, at others filling a short gap between maxillaries at the anterior end of the upper jaw.

Procumbent — lying down, depressed.

Protractile — capable of being extended forward and out.

Protuberance — outward bulge.

Pyloric caecum — one to very many blind glandular sacs opening from the digestive tract near the pyloris.

Pyloris — the often valvelike part of the digestive tract immediately beyond the stomach.

Quadrate — bone below orbit between angle of lower jaw and preoperculum.

Recessed — in or capable of being put into a cleft or groove.

Redd — the gravel spawning-nest of salmonlike fishes.

Reticulation — markings in the form of a network of lines.

Rhomboid(al) — four-sided figure with sides equal and parallel, but not usually equal.

Rostral — related to the snout or rostrum.

Rostrum — a bony extension or shelf on the snout of a fish.

Rotifer — microscopic animals of salt or fresh water with a disc of fine beating hairs surrounding the mouth to aid feeding and two prehensile "toes" at the end of a jointed telescopic tail.

Sagitta — an arrow worm or chaetognath.

Scute — a horny or bony plate.

Septum — (thin) dividing membrane.

Serrate — sawlike.

Shoulder girdle — pelvic girdle, the bones supporting the pectoral fin(s).

Sigmoid — the shape of a long drawn-out letter "s", a double curve.

Snout — the part of a fish's head in front of the eyes.

Sphenotic — bone above and behind eye.

Spine — sharp protuberance on the head or body of a fish.

   — fin support (ray) that is not branched or jointed; sometimes flexible, at other times sharp, rigid, and capable of causing injury.

Spinule — a small spine or a secondary spine.

Spiracle — opening in the head of such fishes as sharks, rays, hagfishes, and lampreys between the eye and the first gill opening, admitting water to the gill chamber(s).

Squamation — arrangement of scales.

Stellate — starlike in shape, arrangement, or in some other way.

Striae — striations, fine lines.

Sub- — combining form meaning below.

Subequal — nearly but not quite equal.

Subopercle — bone forming lower part of the gill cover.

Subterminal — near but not at end.

664

Supra- — combining form meaning above.

Supracleithral — bone supporting the posterior edge of the gill opening, dorsal to the cleithral.

Supraoccipital — bone usually forming nape at posterior dorsal part of head.

Supraoral — above the mouth.

Symphyseal — related to the symphysis.

Symphysis — point of junction of two bones, frequently the joining point of the two bones of the lower jaw.

Symplectic — small (usually) bone anterior to the preopercle, below and behind eye.

Terete — cylindrical and tapering.

Terminal — (of mouth) at or near anterior end of head.

Thoracic — related to the anterior part of the body, or the part of the body that would be the thorax in a mammal.

Tintinnids — minute primitive animals with cilia and bell-like shells.

Triton — a large marine snail.

Truncate — (as though) cut off.

Tubercle — a projection of the surface of an animal. Tuberculate, with tubercles.

Urinogenital — organs or functions common to both elimination and reproduction.

Velella — small colonial jellyfish with a vertical, sometimes purple sail.

Ventral — related to the undersurface or belly.

Vermiculation — coloured by irregular lines as though made by a worm.

Vesicle — small raised cavity filled with fluid.

Villiform — (of teeth) slender and crowded in bands.

Viviparity — the faculty of bringing forth living young (loosely applied to ovoviviparous species also).

Vomer(ine) — a median bone in the anterior part of the roof of the mouth in most fishes, sometimes carrying teeth.

Weberian apparatus — parts of anterior vertebrae modified to connect the gasbladder and the inner ear.

Zoea — a free living developmental stage of crustaceans marked by a great single dorsal spine and large eyes.

NOTES ON SPECIES ILLUSTRATIONS

NOTES ON SPECIES ILLUSTRATIONS

(Most of species illustrations throughout the text have been redrawn from actual specimens. Other sources are indicated where appropriate, partly in order to avoid confirming any errors in earlier illustrations. The *total length* of specimens is given with other details of interest to the user of this book. The page number on the left indicates the location of the illustration in the text).

17	Black hagfish. 48 cm. Not commonly seen. Specimen NMC
18	Pacific hagfish. 46 cm. Vancouver Island. BC 64-438
20	Pacific lamprey. 22 cm. Cultus Lake. BC 54-433
22	River lamprey. 17 cm. Moresby Island. BC 60-203
22	River lamprey. 11 cm. Off Fraser River
27	Sixgill shark. From photograph
28	Sevengill shark. 140 cm. UBC collection
30	Thresher shark. From Bigelow and Schroeder
32	White shark. From drawing. Only one British Columbia record
34	Basking shark. From Bigelow and Schroeder
36	Salmon shark. From Garman
38	Brown cat shark. 50 cm. Off Fraser River. UBC collection
39	Soupfin shark. From photograph
41	Blue shark. From photograph
43	Pacific sleeper shark. After Garman
44	Spiny dogfish. 53 cm. Moresby Island. BC 60-429
50	Pacific electric ray. 71 cm. Off Washington coast. UBC collection
54	Deepsea skate. From Gilbert. Probably uncommon
56	Big skate. 44 cm. Alaska. BC 62-987
58	Black skate. 41 cm. BC 57-53
59	Longnose skate. 22 cm. From photograph
61	Starry skate. 54 cm. Alaska. BC 65-728
63	Stingray. Pelagic, after Radovich (1961); Diamond, after Roedel and Ripley (1950). Uncommon
66	Ratfish. 48 cm. Alaska. BC 65-511
82	Green sturgeon. 107 cm. Alaska. BC 63-1064. Rare and sporadic in occurrence
83	White sturgeon. 70 cm. Mouth of Fraser River. BC 63-1095
86	Crossthroat sawpalate. After Garman (1899). Uncommon
88	Spaced snipe eel. 54 cm. Off British Columbia. BC 65-623

89	Closespine snipe eel. After Taylor. Uncommon
90	Slender snipe eel. 85 cm. Off California. BC 62-162
92	Longnose tapirfish. 47 cm. After Peden
95	American shad. 24 cm. Barkley Sound. BC 57-36. Introduced
96	Pacific herring. 18 cm. Queen Charlotte Islands. BC 60-438
100	Pacific sardine or pilchard. 30 cm. Goose Island. BC 53-228
104	Northern anchovy. 16 cm. Departure Bay. BC 66-127
108	Pink salmon. 46 cm. BC 56-498
112	Chum salmon. 70 cm. UBC collection
115	Coho salmon. 35 cm. BC 56-87
118	Sockeye salmon. 40 cm. Port John. BC 53-272
124	Chinook salmon. 50 cm. Hope. BC 54-97
127	Coastal cutthroat trout. 40 cm. Fraser River. BC 55-306
128	Rainbow trout or steelhead trout. 44 cm. Bulkley River, B.C. BC 56-453
131	Atlantic salmon. 21 cm. Douglas Channel. BC 62-14. Introduced. Only one British Columbia specimen recognized
133	Brown trout. 25 cm. Cowichan River. BC 60-156. Introduced. Locally well established
134	Dolly Varden trout. 33 cm. Vedder River. BC 59-610
138	Whitebait smelt. 11 cm. Off San Juan Harbour. Only one Canadian record
139	Surf smelt. 16 cm. Boundary Bay. ROM 9-6488-10
141	Capelin. 12 cm. Departure Bay. BC 61-408
143	Rainbow smelt. 18 cm. Alaska. Only one British Columbia record
145	Night smelt. 11 cm. Hecate Strait. BC 59-699. Uncommon in Canada
146	Longfin smelt. 14 cm. BC 53-49
148	Eulachon. 18 cm. Fraser River. BC 62-103
151	Bluethroat argentine. 18 cm. Off British Columbia. BC 65-623
153	Stout blacksmelt. Off Queen Charlotte Sound 7.8 cm. BC 65-615

154 Eared blacksmelt. 12 cm. Off Cape Saint James. Specimen NMC

155 Slender blacksmelt. 14 cm. Off Triangle Island. BC 64-444

156 Northern smoothtongue. 10 cm. Alaska. BC 62-930

158 Winged spookfish. From Gruchy drawing. Only one Canadian record

159 Barreleye. 9 cm. Off British Columbia. BC 65-624

161 Veiled anglemouth. 5.5 cm. Queen Charlotte Sound. BC 65-609. Uncommon

163 Silvery hatchetfish. 3.7 cm. Vancouver. BC 58-412. Uncommonly observed

165 Highfin dragonfish. 13 cm. Bowie Seamount. BC 65-632. One Canadian record

167 Longfin dragonfish. 17 cm. BC 64-213 and Bolin (1939) and Chapman (1939)

169 Shining loosejaw. 10 cm. North Pacific. BC 60-169. Uncommon

171 Pacific viperfish. 22 cm. Off British Columbia. BC 65-624

173 Shining tubeshoulder. After Parr. Uncommon

175 Longnose lancetfish. From Leim and Scott FRB Bulletin 155

177 Daggertooth. 32 cm. Off British Columbia. BC 58-403

179 Northern pearleye. 24 cm. Off British Columbia. BC 65-623

181 Slender barracudina. 22 cm. Off Tasu Sound. NMC 65-298

182 Ribbon barracudina. 23 cm. Off Cape Saint James. NMC 66-33

184 Scaly wearyfish. 19 cm. Off Tasu Sound. NMC 65-300. Uncommon

187 Dogtooth lampfish. 8.5 cm. Off British Columbia. BC 60-167. Not common off British Columbia

189 California headlightfish. 5.0 cm. Off Vancouver Island. BC 60-170

191 Pinpoint lampfish. 18 cm. Off Tasu Sound. ROM 26-415

193 Broadfin lampfish. 14 cm. Off Tasu Sound. ROM 26420

195 Patchwork lampfish. 13 cm. Off British Columbia. BC 65-621

196 Bigeye lanternfish. 6.4 cm. Off Queen Charlotte Islands. BC 65-610

198 Northern lampfish. 7.4 cm. Alaska. BC 65-392

200 Bigfin lanternfish. 10.5 cm. Off Alaska. BC 58-325

202 Blue lanternfish. 8 cm. Off British Columbia. ROM 26425

204 Carp. 4.0 cm. Strait of Georgia. Introduced in fresh water

207 Plainfin midshipman. 24 cm. Boat Harbour. BC 55-59

210 Northern clingfish. 8.6 cm. British Columbia–Alaska Boundary. BC 61-370

212 Kelp clingfish. 5.2 cm. Ucluelet. BC 65-127

214 Smooth dreamer. After Bertelsen

216 Spiny dreamer. After Gilbert. Only one specimen known from off British Columbia

218 Bulbous dreamer. After Chapman

220 Pacific flatnose. 39 cm. Off Kyuquot Sound. BC 60-553

222 Pacific cod. 28 cm. Alaska. BC 62-591

225 Pacific hake. 29 cm. Smith Sound. BC 65-53

226 Pacific tomcod. 20 cm. BC 53-301

228 Walleye pollock or Bigeye. 35 cm. Alaska. BC 65-389

230 Red brotula. 27 cm. Texada Island. BC 61-426

233 Bigfin eelpout. 24 cm. Smith Sound. BC 65-55

235 Twoline eelpout. 50 cm. Clayoquot Sound. BC 65-163

236 Soft eelpout. 13 cm. Alaska. BC 61-542

237 Longsnout eelpout. From Gilbert (1915)

238 Shortjaw eelpout. From Evermann and Goldsborough (1907)

239 Blackmouth eelpout. 14 cm. 45.51 N 124.55 W. U. Washington 19261. One British Columbia record

240 Bigtooth eelpout. Drawing by Iris Reynolds from Grinols. Only one British Columbia record

241 Pallid eelpout. From Gilbert (1915)

242 Shortfin eelpout. 18 cm. Alaska. BC 62-480

243 Black eelpout. 15 cm. Indian Arm. BC 59-530

244 Wattled eelpout. 30 cm. Alaska. BC 62-435

245 Blackbelly eelpout. 22 cm. Indian Arm. BC 59-530

247 Pacific softpout. From Gilbert (1895)

248 Cuskpout. From Clemens and Wilby (1961). Only one specimen known

251 Roughscale rattail. 25 cm. Off Vancouver Island. NMC 68-375

252 Smoothscale rattail. 23 cm. NMC 65-327

254 Filamented rattail. From Clemens and Wilby (1961). Only three specimens known

255 Bearded rattail. From drawing from D. McAllister. Only four specimens known — one from British Columbia

256 Pectoral rattail. 69 cm. Alaska. BC 62-464. Rare off British Columbia

258 Pacific saury. 24 cm. Alaska. BC 65-392

260 Topsmelt. 8.0 cm. Sooke. BC 62-861. Only one Canadian record

263 Highsnout melamphid. 9.2 cm. Off British Columbia. BC 65-623

264 Crested melamphid. 12 cm. Off British Columbia. BC 65-623

266 Oreo. 13 cm. Offshore. BC 64-11. Two immature specimens known from off British Columbia

269 Opah. From Leim and Scott FRB Bulletin 155

271 King-of-the-salmon. 186 cm. Sooke. BC 65-590

273 Tube-snout. 12 cm. Sooke. BC 62-867

276 Threespine stickleback. 7 cm. Alaska. BC 63-1450

278 Bay pipefish. Male 22 cm, female 25 cm. Joassa Channel. BC 53-233

280 Striped bass. After Leim and Scott. Only two records from Canadian Pacific coast. Introduced in California

283 Ocean whitefish. 20 cm. Baja California. BC 62-156

285 Whalesucker. 21 cm. Goose Island. BC 53-236

287 Jack mackerel. 20 cm. California. BC 54-533

289 (Pacific) pomfret. 30 cm. Off Washington coast. UBC collection

291 Manefish. 20 cm. Off British Columbia. BC 65-621

294 White croaker. 26 cm. California. BC 62-361. Only one Canadian record

295 White seabass. From Walford (1937). Uncommon

297 Pelagic armorhead. 29 cm. Off Vancouver Island. BC 58-381

300 Calico surfperch. 27 cm. Cape Flattery. BC 65-337. Only one specimen, taken at Cape Flattery

301 Redtail surfperch. 9.4 cm. Tofino. BC 64-463

303 Kelp perch. 13 cm. Burrard Inlet. BC 53-58

304 Shiner perch. 14 cm. Vancouver. BC 53-301

306 Striped seaperch. 12 cm. Tofino. BC 64-463

307 Walleye surfperch. 12 cm. California. BC 53-292

309 Silver surfperch. 10 cm. Tofino. BC 64-463

310 White seaperch. 11 cm. California. BC 53-295

312 Pile perch. 12 cm. Vancouver Island. BC 58-445

314 Pacific barracuda. 13 cm. Mexico. U. Washington 17493

316 (Pacific) sandfish. 20 cm. Long Beach near Tofino. BC 65-354

318 Searcher. 22 cm. Alaska. BC 62-446

319 Northern ronquil. 14 cm. Burrard Inlet. BC 54-95

322 Striped kelpfish. 16 cm. California. BC 53-296

323 Crevice kelpfish. 10 cm. California. BC 53-296. Uncommon in British Columbia

327 Y-prickleback. 7.5 cm. Bakers Pass. BC 65-295

328 Slender cockscomb. 10 cm. Howe Sound. BC 62-637

329 High cockscomb. 10 cm. Alaska. BC 63-85

331 Pearly prickleback. 24 cm. Alaska. NMC 66-268. From Alaska at the Canadian boundary

332 Decorated warbonnet. 27 cm. Off Fraser River. BC 55-150

333 Mosshead warbonnet. 11 cm. Howe Sound. BC 63-910

334 Longsnout prickleback. 27 cm. Smith Sound. BC 65-53

336 Daubed shanny. 11 cm. Queen Charlotte Strait. NMC 65-139. Rare in British Columbia. From North Pacific and North Atlantic Oceans

337 (Pacific) snake prickleback. 23 cm. Burrard Inlet. BC 61-484

338 Ribbon prickleback. 17 cm. UBC collection

339 Bluebarred prickleback. 13 cm. Puget Sound. U. Washington 2945

340 Whitebarred prickleback. 19 cm. Indian Arm. BC 59-530

341 Black prickleback. 17 cm. Vancouver Island. BC 63-806

343 Rock prickleback. 23 cm. BC 53-296

345 Penpoint gunnel. 10 cm. Vancouver. BC 54-444

346 Longfin gunnel. 11 cm. Pender Harbour. BC 63-934

347 Crescent gunnel. 12 cm. Point Atkinson. BC 56-622

348 Saddleback gunnel. 14 cm. Vancouver. BC 58-574

349 Red gunnel. 6.8 cm. Tofino. BC 65-129

350 Rockweed gunnel. 12 cm. California. BC 53-296

351 Wolf-eel. 113 cm. Alaska. BC 62-583

353 Quillfish. 13 cm. (body length). Haro Strait. NMC 69-113

355   Giant wrymouth. 65 cm. Puget Sound. BC 60-165

356   Dwarf wrymouth. 27 cm. Puget Sound. U. Washington 2333

357   Graveldiver. 11 cm. Sooke. BC 62-883

359   Prowfish. 49 cm. Alaska. BC 63-233

361   Pacific sand lance. 13 cm. Alaska. BC 62-991

363   Arrow goby. 3.1 cm. Boundary Bay. BC 58-311

365   Blackeye goby. 9 cm. Sooke. BC 62-495

366   Bay goby. 10 cm. Denman Island. BC 53-301

368   Frostfish. After Maul. Only one specimen ever recorded from British Columbia

371   Skipjack tuna. From Leim and Scott FRB Bulletin 155. Rare in British Columbia

373   Pacific bonito. From Walford (1937)

374   Chub mackerel. 36 cm. Barkley Sound. BC 62-249

376   Albacore. After Leim and Scott FRB Bulletin 155

379   Bluefin tuna. After Leim and Scott FRB Bulletin 155

381   Medusafish. 17 cm. Queen Charlotte Sound. BC 65-605

383   Pacific pompano. 24 cm. BC 65-356

384   Smalleye squaretail. 37 cm. Offshore. BC 62-801. Not common

386   Ragfish. 53 cm. Queen Charlotte Islands. BC 59-523

386   Ragfish. 28 cm. Alaska. BC 63-98

394   Rougheye rockfish. 27 cm. BC 62-998

396   Pacific ocean perch. 24 cm. BC 62-450

398   Brown rockfish. 16 cm. Hecate Strait. BC 59-669

400   Aurora rockfish. 31 cm. GBR 69-1-12

401   Redbanded rockfish. From photograph

403   Shortraker rockfish. 54 cm. Off Vancouver Island. Paratype UBC collection

405   Silvergray rockfish. 27 cm. BC 65-254

407   Copper rockfish. 24 cm. BC 57-209

409   Dusky rockfish. 29 cm. BC 65-707

410   Darkblotched rockfish. 40 cm. GBR 68-2-57

412   Splitnose rockfish. 17 cm. BC 61-613

414   Greenstriped rockfish. 27 cm. BC 59-584

415   Puget Sound rockfish. From drawing of type. Tentative record only

417   Widow rockfish. 44 cm. GBR 69-1-7

418   Yellowtail rockfish. 31 cm. BC 56-91

420   Chilipepper. 35 cm. Off Vancouver Island. BC 64-283. Only one Canadian record

421   Rosethorn rockfish. 28 cm. BC 53-204A

423   Shortbelly rockfish. 21 cm. Off Vancouver Island. BC 65-255. Not common

424   Quillback rockfish. 20 cm. BC 63-774

426   Black rockfish. 42 cm. BC 54-450A

428   Vermilion rockfish. 12 cm. San Juan Islands. U. Washington 11670

429   Blue rockfish. 27 cm. BC 65-553. Not common off British Columbia

431   China rockfish. 24 cm. BC 55-309

433   Tiger rockfish. 38 cm. BC 59-168

435   Bocaccio. 17 cm. BC 65-129

437   Canary rockfish. 27 cm. BC 64-339

439   Redstripe rockfish. 33 cm. Mexicana Point. BC 59-507

440   Yellowmouth rockfish. 42 cm. GBR 68-2-31

442   Yelloweye rockfish. 21 cm. BC 65-298

444   Stripetail rockfish. 31 cm. BC 56-91

446   Harlequin rockfish. 27 cm. Alaska. BC 70-22

448   Pygmy rockfish. 21 cm. BC 64-275

450   Sharpchin rockfish. 17 cm. BC 63-776

451   Shortspine thornyhead. 28 cm. BC 65-69

453   Longspine thornyhead. 20 cm. BC 67-11

455   Sablefish. 35 cm. Alaska. BC 65-94

458   Skilfish. 29 cm. Off British Columbia. BC 62-207

461   Kelp greenling. 14 cm. Washington. BC 60-238

463   Rock greenling. 24 cm. BC 63-1004

464   Masked greenling. 18 cm. Alaska. BC 93a. Known only in Canada from young in northern British Columbia

466   Whitespotted greenling. 20 cm. Alaska. BC 63-119

467   Lingcod. 23 cm. Queen Charlotte Islands. BC 60-416

470   Painted greenling. 16 cm. Howe Sound. BC 63-736

471   Longspine combfish. 21 cm. Fanny Bay. BC 62-209

478   Padded sculpin. 11 cm. Tofino. BC 64-463

479   Scalyhead sculpin. 7.0 cm. Bute Inlet. BC 61-301

481   Smoothhead sculpin. 12 cm. Long Beach, Tofino. BC 64-464

483   Puget Sound sculpin. 3.6 cm. Malaspina Strait. BC 63-934

484   Rosylip sculpin. 9 cm. Vancouver Island. BC 64-467

485   Spinynose sculpin. 6.8 cm. Keats Island. BC 63-732

487   Crested sculpin. 8 cm. Alaska. BC 62-595. Known only from northern British Columbia in Canada

672

489 Silverspotted sculpin. 14 cm. Alaska. BC 63-904

491 Roughback sculpin. 11 cm. Puget Sound. BC 55-377

493 Sharpnose sculpin. 5.3 cm. British Columbia. BC 63-409

494 Calico sculpin. 7 cm. Alaska. BC 65-29

496 Mosshead sculpin. 12 cm. Vargas Island. BC 61-465

497 Spinyhead sculpin. 20 cm. Alaska. BC 62-669

499 Buffalo sculpin. 18 cm. Vancouver. ROM collection

501 Soft sculpin. 7.0 cm. Alaska. BC 63-1422

502 Red Irish lord. 14 cm. Jervis Inlet. BC 63-936

504 Brown Irish lord. 15 cm. Ucluelet. BC 65-123

505 Bigmouth sculpin. 24 cm. Alaska. BC 62-420. Known in Canada only from northern British Columbia

507 Northern sculpin. 8.6 cm. Burrard Inlet. BC 53-55

508 Dusky sculpin. 7.6 cm. Howe Sound. BC 62-865

510 Threadfin sculpin. 12 cm. Malaspina Strait. BC 63-769

511 Frogmouth sculpin. 8.6 cm. Pendrell Sound. BC 65-393. Uncommon

513 Spotfin sculpin. 15 cm. Washington–British Columbia boundary. BC 64-442

515 Thorny sculpin. 17 cm. Alaska. BC 62-475. Only one British Columbia record

516 Longfin sculpin. 9 cm. Jervis Inlet. BC 63-936

518 Pacific staghorn sculpin. 18 cm. Burrard Inlet. BC 53-120

519 Blackfin sculpin. 14 cm. Alaska. BC 65-73

521 Great sculpin. 10 cm. Dean Channel. BC 61-228

522 Sailfin sculpin. 15 cm. Sooke. BC 62-495

523 Sailfin sculpin. 12 cm. Knight Inlet. UBC collection

525 Smallsail sculpin. 4.7 cm. BC 63-1004. In British Columbia known only from northern part

527 Tidepool sculpin. 9 cm. Departure Bay. BC 61-262

529 Saddleback sculpin. 4.6 cm. Sooke. BC 61-598

530 Fluffy sculpin. 9 cm. Long Beach, B.C. BC 64-461

532 Thornback sculpin. 14 cm. Banks Island. BC 62-541. Only one Canadian record

533 Tadpole sculpin. 4.6 cm. Rennell Sound. BC 61-734

535 Slim sculpin. 10 cm. Saturna Island. BC 63-1324

536 Darter sculpin. 7 cm. Hope Island. BC 63-784. Only one Canadian record

538 Grunt sculpin. 7 cm. Seymour Narrows. BC-62-22

540 Cabezon. 18 cm. Saturna Island. BC 59-114

542 Manacled sculpin. 6.2 cm. Sooke. BC 62-856

543 Roughspine sculpin. 16 cm. Hope Island. BC 63-784

545 Ribbed sculpin. 16 cm. Near Victoria. BC 60-202

549 Northern spearnose poacher. 15 cm. BC 53-66

550 Sturgeon poacher. 19 cm. BC 53-139

552 Smooth alligatorfish. 12 cm. BC 53-66

553 Gray starsnout. 10 cm. Burrard Inlet. BC 55-240

554 Spinycheek starsnout. 9.5 cm. Burrard Inlet. BC 54-95

556 Bigeye poacher. 24 cm. Alaska. BC 65-59. Only two British Columbia records

557 Blackfin poacher. 15 cm. English Bay. BC 53-103

558 Rockhead. 6 cm. Victoria. BC 61-199

560 Fourhorn poacher. 9 cm. Alaska. BC 62-459

561 Pixie poacher. 2.1 cm. Drawing supplied by C. G. Gruchy. Only one specimen known

562 Warty poacher. 16 cm. Alaska. BC 65-711

564 Pygmy poacher. 7.1 cm. British Columbia. BC 65-471

565 Tubenose poacher. 8 cm. Off Jordan River. BC 62-885

566 Blacktip poacher. 13 cm. Pendrell Sound. BC 65-469

567 Bluespotted poacher. 18 cm. Kwatna Inlet. NMC 65-258. Only one British Columbia record

571 Smooth lumpsucker. 14 cm. Dean Channel. BC 53-261

573 Smalldisk snailfish. 4.9 cm. Hecate Strait. BC 53-170. Rare in British Columbia.

574 Blacktail snailfish. 30 cm. Off Clayoquot Sound. NMC 65-423

575 Abyssal snailfish. From Jordan and Evermann. One specimen only known

577 Pacific spiny lumpsucker. 4.2 cm. Vancouver. UBC collection

579 Spotted snailfish. 10 cm. Alaska. BC 65-3

580 Ribbon snailfish. 8.2 cm. Alaska. BC 63-1308
582 Marbled snailfish. 23 cm. Denman Island. BC 62-553
583 Tidepool snailfish. 7 cm. Alaska. BC 65-512
585 Slipskin snailfish. 18 cm. Burrard Inlet. BC 55-243
586 Slimy snailfish. 5.1 cm. Ucluelet. BC 64-467. Rare in British Columbia
588 Showy snailfish. 7.3 cm. Burrard Inlet. BC 53-47
590 Ringtail snailfish. 7.4 cm. Alaska. BC 63-330
591 Tadpole snailfish. 4.8 cm. Sechelt Inlet. BC 62-27
593 Prickly snailfish. 7.3 cm. Stevens Passage. U. Washington 14761
594 Lobefin snailfish. 35 cm. Sooke. BC 62-890
596 Pacific sanddab. 15 cm. BC 61-700
598 Speckled sanddab. 15 cm. BC 57-308
602 Arrowtooth flounder. 28 cm. BC 55-14A

604 Roughscale sole. 19 cm. Japan. BC 56-347. Widely distributed but uncommon
605 Deepsea sole. 31 cm. BC 64-440
607 Petrale sole. 28 cm. BC 53-304
610 Rex sole. 35 cm. BC 63-1328
612 Flathead sole. 30 cm. BC 57-60
614 Pacific halibut. 65 cm. NMC collection
617 (Hybrid) sole. 36 cm. Union Bay. UBC collection
619 Butter sole. 34 cm. BC 62-424
621 Rock sole. 30 cm. BC 55-14A
623 Yellowfin sole. 17 cm. BC 60-448
625 Slender sole. 23 cm. BC 61-484
626 Dover sole. 32 cm. BC 59-530
628 English sole. 30 cm. BC 59-540
631 Starry flounder. 22 cm. Departure Bay. ROM 3462
633 C-O sole. 24 cm. BC 53-292
635 Curlfin sole. 34 cm. BC 56-579
636 Sand sole. 36 cm. BC 62-684
638 Greenland halibut or Greenland turbot. 30 cm. BC 63-1285
640 Ocean sunfish. 63 cm. UBC collection

Letters preceding specimen numbers indicate collections as follows :

BC — University of British Columbia

GBR — *G. B. Reed* vessel. Collection not finally catalogued at time of writing

NMC — National Museums of Canada

ROM — Royal Ontario Museum

U(niversity of) Washington

REFERENCES

REFERENCES

*Entries marked with an asterisk are not specifically referred to in the text
but are given here as sources of additional information.*

AHLSTROM, E. H. 1943. Studies on the Pacific pilchard or sardine (*Sardinops caerulea*) 4. Influence of temperature on the rate of development of pilchard eggs in nature. U.S. Fish Wildl. Serv. Spec. Sci. Rep. 23: 26 p.

1954. Distribution and abundance of egg and larval populations of the Pacific sardine. U.S. Fish Wildl. Serv. Fish. Bull. 93, Vol. 56: 83–140.

1966. Distribution and abundance of sardine and anchovy larvae in the California current region off California and Baja California, 1951–64: a summary. U.S. Fish Wildl. Serv. Spec. Sci. Rep. 534: 71 p.

AHLSTROM, E. H., AND O. P. BALL. 1954. Description of eggs and larvae of jack mackerel (*Trachurus symmetricus*) and distribution and abundance of larvae in 1950 and 1951. U.S. Fish Wildl. Serv. Fish. Bull. 97, Vol. 56: 209–245.

AHLSTROM, E. H., AND R. C. COUNTS. 1955. Eggs and larvae of the Pacific hake *Merluccius productus*. U.S. Fish Wildl. Serv. Fish. Bull. 99, Vol. 56: 295–329.

ALDERDICE, D. F., AND C. R. FORRESTER. 1968. Some effects of salinity and temperature on early development and survival of the English sole (*Parophrys vetulus*). J. Fish. Res. Bd. Canada 25(3): 495–521.

ALLEN, G. H. 1968. Fecundity of the brown ragfish *Icosteus aenigmaticus* Lockington, from northern California. Calif. Fish Game 54(3): 207–214.

ALLEN, G. W. 1966. Ocean migration and distribution of fin-marked coho salmon. J. Fish. Res. Bd. Canada 23(7): 1043–1061.

ALLIS, E. P. 1903. The skull and the cranial and first spinal muscles and nerves in *Scomber scomber*. J. Morphol. 18(2): 45–329.

ALVERSON, D. L. * 1951a. New records for marine fishes from southeastern Alaska. Copeia 1951(1): 86.

* 1951b. Deep-water trawling survey off the Washington Coast (August–October 18, 1951). U.S. Fish Wildl. Serv. Commer. Fish. Rev. 13(11): 1–16.

* 1953. Notes on the Pacific ocean perch. Wash. Dep. Fish. Fish. Res. Pap. 1(1): 22–24.

1960. A study of annual and seasonal bathymetric catch patterns for commercially important groundfishes of the Pacific northwest coast of North America. Pac. Mar. Fish. Comm. Bull. 4: 66 p.

1961. Ocean temperatures and their relation to albacore tuna (*Thunnus germo*) distribution in waters off the coast of Oregon, Washington, and British Columbia. J. Fish. Res. Bd. Canada 18(6): 1145–1152.

ALVERSON, D. L., AND B. M. CHATWIN. 1957. Results from tagging experiments on a spawning stock of petrale sole, *Eopsetta jordani* (Lockington). J. Fish. Res. Bd. Canada 14(6): 953–974.

ALVERSON, D. L., A. T. PRUTER, AND L. L. RONHOLT. 1964. A study of demersal fishes and fisheries of the northeastern Pacific Ocean. H. R. MacMillan Lecture Series in Fisheries, Inst. Fish. Univ. British Columbia. 190 p.

ALVERSON, D. L., AND M. E. STANSBY. 1963 The spiny dogfish (*Squalus acanthias*) in the northeastern Pacific. U.S. Fish Wildl. Serv. Spec. Sci. Rep. 447: 25 p.

ALVERSON, D. L., AND A. D. WELANDER. 1952. Notes on the scorpaenid fishes of Washington and adjacent areas, with a key for their identification. Copeia 1952(3): 138–143.

ALVERSON, D. L. AND S. J. WESTRHEIM. MS 1959. A review of the taxonomy and biology of the Pacific ocean perch and its fishery. ICNAF/ICES Redfish Symp. Pap. 3.

ANAS, R. E. 1959. Three-year-old pink salmon. J. Fish. Res. Bd. Canada 16(1): 91–94

ANDRIASHEV, A. P. 1937. A contribution to the knowledge of the fishes from the Bering and Chukchi seas. Explorat. des mers de l'URSS. fasc. 25, Inst. Hydro., Leningrad. p. 292–355, figs. 1–27. (Transl. by L. Lanz with N. J. Wilimovsky, U.S. Fish Wildl. Serv. Spec. Sci. Rep. 145: 81 p., 1945.)

1954. Fishes of the northern seas of the USSR. (Transl. from Russian by the Israel Program for Sci. Transl., Jerusalem, 1964, 617 p.)

ANON. 1934. News item. [*Trachurus symmetricus*]. Biol. Board Can. Pac. Progr. Rep. 21:7.

1935a. News item. [*Trachypterus rex-salmonorum*]. Biol. Board Can. Pac. Progr. Rep. 23: 24.

1935b. News item. [Lingcod fecundity]. Biol. Board Can. Pac. Progr. Rep. 23: 24

1935c. News item. [Pilchard size record]. Biol. Board Can. Pac. Progr. Rep. 23: 24.

1935d. News item. [Opah record]. Biol. Board Can. Pac. Progr. Rep. 25: 12.

1939. News item. [Pomfret in Skeena River], Fish. Res. Board Can. Pac. Progr. Rep. 41: 22.

1940. News item. [Small pilchards and anchovies in B.C. waters]. Fish. Res. Board Can. Pac. Progr. Rep. 45: 6.

1941a. News item. Young pilchards in British Columbia waters. Fish. Res. Board Can. Pac. Progr. Rep. 47: 11.

1941b. *Tetranarce californica*, the electric ray or torpedo. Fish. Res. Board Can. Pac. Progr. Rep. 47: 13.

1941c. The cat shark *Apristurus brunneus*. Fish. Res. Board Can. Pac. Progr. Rep. 49: 10.

1951. Record sized herring for British Columbia. Fish. Res. Board Can. Pac. Progr. Rep. 87: 33

1952. Contrast in dogfish migrations. Fish. Res. Board Can. Pac. Progr. Rep. 92: 20.

1954a. An unusual catch of green sturgeon. Fish. Res. Board Can. Pac. Progr. Rep. 100: 19.

1954b. A record tagged lingcod. Fish. Res. Board Can. Pac. Progr. Rep. 100: 19.

1956. North Pacific project. Fish. Res. Board Can. Pac. Progr. Rep. 107: 11.

APLIN, J. A. 1939. The occurrence of sauries in southern California. Calif. Fish Game 25(4): 243–244.

ARITA, G. S. MS 1967. A comparative study of the structure and function of the adhesive apparatus of the Cyclopteridae and Gobiesocidae. M.Sc. Thesis. Dep. Zool. Univ. British Columbia. 90 p.

1969. Sexual dimorphism in the cyclopterid fish *Eumicrotremus orbis*. J. Fish. Res. Bd. Canada 26(12): 3262–3265.

ARMSTRONG, R. H., AND P. C. WINSLOW. 1968. An incidence of walleye pollock feeding on salmon young. Trans. Amer. Fish. Soc. 97(2): 202–203.

ARO, K. V., AND G. C. BROADHEAD. 1950. Differences between egg counts of sockeye salmon at Lakelse and Babine lakes. Fish. Res. Board Can. Pac. Progr. Rep. 82: 17–19.

ARO, K. V., AND M. P. SHEPHARD. 1967. Salmon of the North Pacific Ocean. Pt. IV. Spawning populations of North Pacific Salmon. 5. Pacific salmon in Canada. Int. N. Pac. Fish. Comm. Bull. 23: 225–327.

ARON, W. 1958a. Preliminary report of midwater trawling studies in the North Pacific Ocean. Tech. Rep., Univ. Wash. Dep. Oceanogr. 58: 1–57.

1958b. Cytological and histological studies on the hybrid of *Platichthys stellatus* X *Parophrys vetulus*, with notes on its backcross to *P. vetulus*. Copeia 1958(2): 105–111.

1960. The distribution of animals in the eastern North Pacific and its relationship to physical and chemical conditions. Tech. Rep., Univ. Wash. Dep. Oceanogr. 63: 65 p.

1962. The distribution of animals in the eastern North Pacific and its relation to physical and chemical conditions. J. Fish. Res. Bd. Canada 19(2): 271–314.

ARON, W., AND P. MCCRERY. 1958. A description of a new species of stomiatid from the North Pacific Ocean. Copeia 1958(3): 180–183.

ARORA, H. L. 1948. Observations on the habits and early life history of the batrachoid fish, *Porichthys notatus* Girard. Copeia 1948(2): 89–93.

1951. An investigation of the California sand dab *Citharichthys sordidus* (Girard). Calif. Fish Game 37(1): 3–42.

ATKINSON, C. E. 1939. Notes on the life history of the tidepool johnny (*Oligocottus maculosus*). Copeia 1939(1): 23–30.

ATKINSON, C. E., J. H. ROSE, AND T. O. DUNCAN. 1967. Salmon of the North Pacific Ocean. Pt. IV. Spawning populations of North Pacific salmon. 4. Pacific salmon in the United States. Int. N. Pac. Fish. Comm. Bull. 23: 43–223.

AUGHTRY, R. H. 1953. A note on mass mortality of the myctophid fish *Tarletonbeania crenularis*. Copeia 1953(3): 190–192.

BAILEY, B. E., N. M. CARTER, AND L. A. SWAIN. 1952. Marine oils with particular reference to those of Canada. Fish. Res. Board Can. Bull. 89: 413 p.

BAILEY, R. M., J. E. FITCH, E. S. HERALD, E. A. LACHNER, C. C. LINDSEY, C. R. ROBINS, AND W. B. SCOTT. 1970. A list of common and scientific names of fishes from the United States and Canada. Amer. Fish. Soc. Spec. Publ. 6: 149 p.

BAILEY, R. M., AND C. G. GRUCHY. 1970. *Occella* to replace *Occa* for a genus of agonid fishes. J. Fish. Res. Bd. Canada 27(5): 981–983.

BALDWIN, W. J. 1961. First records of three northern fishes from the upper Gulf of California. Copeia 1961(4): 475–476.

BALI, J. B., AND C. E. BOND. 1959. The bigfin eelpout, *Aprodon cortezianus* Gilbert, common in waters off Oregon. Copeia 1959(1): 74–76.

678

BARNETT, M. A., AND R. H. GIBBS, JR. 1968a. Validity of the stomiatoid fish species *Bathophilus flemingi* and *B. indicus*. Copeia 1968(1): 197–198.

1968b. Four new stomiatoid fishes of the genus *Bathophilus* with a revised key to the species of *Bathophilus*. Copeia 1968(4): 826–832.

BARNHART, P. S. * 1936. Marine fishes of southern California. Univ. Calif. Press, Berkeley, 209 p.

BARRACLOUGH, W. E. 1947. A new record of a species of agonid fish, *Occa verrucosa* (Lockington) from the west coast of Vancouver Island, British Columbia. Can. Field-Natur. 61(2): 39.

1948a. The hag-fish (*Polistotrema stouti*) in British Columbia. Fish. Res. Board Can. Pac. Progr. Rep. 75: 57–58.

1948b. The decline of the soupfin shark fishery in British Columbia. Fish. Res. Board Can. Pac. Progr. Rep. 77: 91–94.

1948c. Measures of abundance in dogfish (*Squalus suckleyi*). Trans. Roy. Soc. Can. 3(42): 37–43.

1950. An inshore record of the bathypelagic fish, *Chauliodes macouni* Bean, from British Columbia. Copeia 1950(3): 241–242.

1952. The agonid fish, *Pallasina barbata aix* (Starks), from British Columbia. J. Fish. Res. Bd. Canada 9(3): 143–147.

1954a. A second inshore record of the bathypelagic viperfish *Chauliodus macouni* from British Columbia. Copeia 1954(1): 75.

1954b. Decline in availability of brill on the west coast of Vancouver Island as associated with a decline in recruitment. Fish. Res. Board Can. Pac. Progr. Rep. 98: 17–21.

1954c. Winter recaptures of tagged brill from deep water off the west coast of Vancouver Island. Fish. Res. Board Can. Pac. Progr. Rep. 100: 16–18.

1956. The occurrence of the two-pronged hatchet fish, *Argyropelecus sladeni,* in British Columbia. Copeia 1956(2): 109–110.

1959. The first record of a northern blennioid fish *Plectobranchus evides* Gilbert (family Stichaeidae) in British Columbia waters. J. Fish. Res. Bd. Canada 16(5): 759–760.

1964. Contribution to the marine life history of the eulachon *Thaleichthys pacificus*. J. Fish. Res. Bd. Canada 21(5): 1333–1337.

MS 1967a. Data record. Number, size and food of larval and juvenile fish caught with a two boat surface trawl in the Strait of Georgia, April 25–29, 1966. Fish. Res. Board Can. MS Rep. Ser. 922: 54 p.

MS 1967b. Number, size, and food of larval and juvenile fish caught with an Isaacs-Kidd trawl in the surface waters of the Strait of Georgia, April 25–29, 1966. Fish. Res. Board Can. MS Rep. Ser. 926: 79 p.

MS 1967c. Data record: Number, size composition, and food of larval and juvenile fish caught with a two-boat surface trawl in the Strait of Georgia, June 6–8, 1966. Fish. Res. Board Can. MS Rep. Ser. 928: 58 p.

1967d. Occurrence of larval herring (*Clupea pallasii*) in the Strait of Georgia during July, 1966. J. Fish. Res. Bd. Canada 24(11): 2455–2460.

1971. A sculpin (*Icelus spiniger*) new to coast waters of British Columbia. J. Fish. Res. Bd. Canada 28(12): 1922–1924.

BARRACLOUGH, W. E., AND T. H. BUTLER. 1961. Additional records of the argentinid fish, *Leuroglossus stilbius* Gilbert from British Columbia, with remarks on its taxonomy. J. Fish. Res. Bd. Canada 18(6): 1167–1169.

1965. First record of the dusky sculpin (*Icelinus burchami*) in British Columbia waters. J. Fish. Res. Bd. Canada 22(5): 1305–1307.

BARRACLOUGH, W. E., AND J. D. FULTON. MS 1967. Data record. Number, size composition, and food of larval and juvenile fish caught with a two-boat surface trawl in the Strait of Georgia, July 4–8, 1966. Fish. Res. Board Can. MS Rep. Ser. 940: 82 p.

MS 1968. Data record: Food of larval and juvenile fish caught with a surface trawl in Saanich Inlet during June and July 1966. Fish. Res. Board Can. MS Rep. Ser. 1003: 78 p.

BARRACLOUGH, W. E., AND K. S. KETCHEN. 1963. First record of the thornback sculpin, *Paricelinus hopliticus*, Eigenmann and Eigenmann, in British Columbia waters. J. Fish. Res. Bd. Canada 20(3): 851–852.

BARRACLOUGH, W. E., AND D. G. ROBINSON. 1971. Anomalous occurrence of carp (*Cyprinus carpio*) in the marine environment. J. Fish. Res. Bd. Canada 28(9): 1345–1347.

BARRACLOUGH, W. E., D. G. ROBINSON, AND J. D. FULTON. MS 1968. Data record. Number, size composition, weight, and food of larval and juvenile fish caught with a two-boat surface trawl in Saanich Inlet, April 23–July 21, 1968. Fish. Res. Board Can. MS Rep. Ser. 1004: 305 p.

BARRACLOUGH, W. E., AND M. WALDICHUK. 1954. Offshore characteristics in the deep waters of the Strait of Georgia as indicated by bathypelagic fish. J. Fish. Res. Bd. Canada 11(5): 501–506.

BARRACLOUGH, W. E., AND R. M. WILSON. 1971. The first record of whitebait smelt *Allosmerus elongatus* (Ayres) from Juan de Fuca Strait, British Columbia. J. Fish. Res. Bd. Canada 28(10): 1681.

BARRETT, B. E. 1968. First occurrence of Greenland halibut (*Reinhardtius hippoglossoides*) in the Bay of Fundy. J. Fish. Res. Bd. Canada 25(12): 2721–2722.

BARRETT, I., J. JOSEPH, AND G. MOSER. 1966. Electrophoretic analysis of hemoglobins of California rockfish, (genus *Sebastodes*). Copeia 1966(3): 489–494.

BARSUKOV, V. V. 1963. Intraspecific variability of morphological features in the Pacific Ocean perch *Sebastodes alutus* (Gilbert). Transl. VNIRO, 49, Rep. TINRO, 51: 231–252.

———— 1964. Taxonomy of the fishes of the family Scorpaenidae. Trans. VNIRO, 53, Trans. TINRO, 52(3): 233–266. Translated by Edith Rodero and R. H. Rosenblatt for U.S. Bur. Commer. Fish.

———— 1970. Vidovoi-sostav roda Sebastes v severnoi chasti Tikhogo Okeano. Opisanie novogo vida. Species composition of the genus *Sebastes* in the northern part of the Pacific Ocean. Description of a new species. Dokl. Akad. Nauk SSSR 195(4): 994–997.

BATTS, B. S. 1960. Further occurrence of the California pompano, *Palometa simillima* (Ayres) in Puget Sound, Washington. Copeia 1960(2): 146–147.

———— 1961. Intertidal fishes as food for the common garter snake. Copeia 1961(3): 350–351.

———— 1964. Lepidology of adult pleuronectiform fishes of Puget Sound, Washington. Copeia 1964(4): 666–673.

BAUCHOT, M-L. 1959. Étude des larves leptocephales du groupe *Leptocephalus lanceolatus* Strömman et identification à la famille des Serrivomeridae. Dana-Rep. 48: 1–148.

BAUCHOT-BOUTIN, M-L. 1953. Revision synoptique du genre *Serrivomer* (Anguilliformes). Bull. Mus. Nat. Hist. Natur., Paris 2, 25(4): 365–367.

———— 1954. Identification de *Serrivomer beani* Gill et Ryder (Téléostéem. Anguilliforme). Bull. Mus. Nat. Hist. Natur., Paris 2, 26(3): 301–306.

BAXTER, J. L. 1967. Summary of biological information on the northern anchovy *Engraulis mordax* Girard. Rep. Calif. Coop. Oceanic Fish. Invest. 1: 110–116.

BAYLIFF, W. H. MS 1954. A review of the Zoarcidae of the northeast Pacific Ocean. M.Sc. Thesis. Univ. of Wash., Dep. Fish. 189 p.

———— 1959. Notes on the taxonomy and distribution of certain zoarcid fishes in the northeastern Pacific 1959(1): 78–80.

BEAN, B. A., AND A. C. WEED. 1920. Notes on a collection of fishes from Vancouver Island, B.C. Trans. Roy. Soc. Can. Ser. 3, V(13): 69–83.

BEAN, T. H. * 1881a. A preliminary catalogue of the fishes of Alaskan and adjacent waters. Proc. U.S. Nat. Mus. 4: 239–272.

———— * 1881b. Notes on a collection of fishes made by Captain Henry E. Nichols, U.S.N., in British Columbia and Alaska, with descriptions of new species and a new genus (*Delolepis*). Proc. U.S. Nat. Mus. 4: 463–474.

———— * 1883a. Notes on a collection of fishes made in 1882 and 1883 by Captain H. E. Nichols, U.S.N., in Alaska and British Columbia, with a description of a new genus and species, *Prionistius macellus*. Proc. U.S. Nat. Mus. 6: 353–361.

———— * 1883b. Notes on some fishes collected by James G. Swan in Washington Territory, including a new species of *Macrurus*. Proc. U.S. Nat. Mus. 6: 362–364.

———— * 1889. Description of a new cottoid fish from British Columbia. Proc. U.S. Nat. Mus. 12: 641–642.

———— * 1890. New fishes, collected off the coast of Alaska and the adjacent region southward. Proc. U.S. Nat. Mus. 13: 37–45.

BELL, F. H. 1967. Memorandum Report: *Reinhardtius hippoglossoides* (Walbaum) and its common name. Int. Pac. Halibut Comm., Seattle, 38 + 10 p.

BELL, F. H., AND J. T. GHARRETT. 1945. The Pacific coast black cod, *Anoplopoma fimbria*. Copeia 1945(2): 94–103.

BELL, F. H., AND J. L. KASK. 1936. *Lampris regius* (Bonnaterre), the opah or moonfish from the North Pacific. Copeia 1936(1): 55–46.

BELL, F. H., AND A. T. PRUTER. 1958. Climatic temperature changes and commercial yields of some marine fisheries. J. Fish. Res. Bd. Canada 15(4): 625–683.

BELL, R. R. 1963. Preliminary age determination of bluefin tuna, *Thunnus thynnus*. Calif. Fish Game 49(4): 307.

BERG, L. S. * 1941. A classification of fishes, both recent and fossil. Tr. Zool. Inst. Akad. Nauk SSSR 5(2): 87–517. (Russian and English text.) Reprinted, 1947, by J. W. Edwards, Ann Arbor, Mich.

———— 1948. Freshwater fishes of the U.S.S.R. and adjacent countries. Acad. Sci. U.S.S.R. Zool. Inst.

Guide to fauna of U.S.S.R. 27 (1) 4th ed., 504 p. (Transl. from Russian by Israel Program for Sci. Transl., Jerusalem, 1962.)

BERTELSEN, E. 1951. The ceratioid fishes. Ontogeny, taxonomy, distribution, and biology. Dana-Rep. 39: 1–276.

BEST, E. A. 1957. Recent occurrences of the red brotula, *Brosmophycis marginata* (Ayres) in California waters. Calif. Fish Game 43(1): 97–98.

—— 1963a. Greenland halibut, *Reinhardtius hippoglossoides* (Walbaum) added to California fauna. Calif. Fish Game 49(3): 213–214.

—— 1963b. Contribution to the biology of the Pacific hake, *Merluccius productus* (Ayres). Rep. Calif. Coop. Oceanic Fish. Invest. 9: 51–56.

—— 1963c. Movements of petrale sole, *Eopsetta jordani* (Lockington), tagged off California. Pac. Mar. Fish. Comm. Bull. 6: 23–38.

—— 1963d. Catch localities for dover sole, *Microstomus pacificus* (Lockington), landed in California, 1950 through 1959. Calif. Dep. Fish. Game Fish. Bull. 121: 48–56.

—— 1964. Spawning of the longspine channel rockfish, *Sebastolobus altivelis* Gilbert. Calif. Fish Game 50(4): 265–267.

BEST, E. A., AND P. J. ELDRIDGE. 1969. Range extension of flag rockfish (*Sebastodes rubrivinctus*) to Aleutian Islands. J. Fish. Res. Bd. Canada 26(7): 1955–1956.

BETHUNE, W. 1948. Albacore log records. Fish. Res. Board Can. Gen. Ser. Circ. (Nanaimo) 12: 7–9.

—— 1949. Albacore log records. Fish. Res. Board Can. Gen. Ser. Circ. (Nanaimo) 17: 10–13.

BIGELOW, H. B., AND W. C. SCHROEDER. 1948. Lancelets, cyclostomes and sharks. Sharks. p. 59–576. *In* Fishes of the western North Atlantic. Mem. Sears Found. Mar. Res. 1(1): 1–588 p.

BILTON, H. T., AND S. A. M. LUDWIG. 1966. Times of annulus formation on scales of sockeye, pink, and chum salmon in the Gulf of Alaska. J. Fish. Res. Bd. Canada 23(9): 1403–1410.

BIRMAN, I. B. 1960. (New information on the marine period of life and the marine fishery of Pacific salmon.) Tr. Soveshch. Ikhtiol. Kom. Akad. Nauk SSSR 10: 151–164, Moscow. (Transl. from Russian by Fish. Res. Board Can. Transl. Ser. No. 357, 1962).

BÖHLKE, J. * 1953. A catalogue of the type specimens of recent fishes in the Natural History Museum of Stanford University. Stanford Ichthyol. Bull. 5: 1–168.

BOLIN, R. L. 1936a. Embryonic and early larval stages of the California anchovy, *Engraulis mordax* Girard. Calif. Fish Game 22(4): 314–321.

—— 1936b. A revision of the genus *Icelinus* Jordan. Copeia 1936(3): 151–159.

—— 1939a. A new stomiatoid fish from California. Copeia 1939(1): 39–41.

—— 1939b. A review of the myctophid fishes of the Pacific coast of the United States and of lower California. Stanford Ichthyol. Bull. 1(4): 89–156.

—— * 1944. A review of the marine cottid fishes of California. Stanford Ichthyol. Bull. 3(1): 1–135.

—— 1950. Remarks on cottid fishes occasioned by the capture of two species new to California. Copeia 1950(3): 195–202.

BOLTON, L. L. 1930. Sockeye tagging on the Fraser River, 1928. Bull. Biol. Board Can. 16: 8 p.

BOND, C. E. 1959. Records of agonid fishes from Oregon. Oreg. Fish. Comm. Res. Briefs 7(1): 79–80.

BONHAM, K. 1942. Records of three sharks on the Washington coast. Copeia 1942(4): 264–265.

—— 1954. Food of the dogfish *Squalus acanthias*. Wash. Dep. Fish. Fish. Res. Pap. 1(2): 25–36.

BONHAM, K., AND P. R. OLSON. 1955. The white sea bass *Cynoscion nobilis*, in Puget Sound. Copeia 1956(1): 64–65.

BONHAM, K., F. B. STANFORD, W. CLEGG, AND G. C. BUCHER. 1949. Biological and vitamine A studies of dogfish landed in the State of Washington. Wash. Dep. Fish. Biol. Rep. 49A: 83–114.

BORODULINA, O. D. 1968. Taxonomy and distribution of the genus *Leuroglossus* (Bathylagidae, Pisces). Amer. Fish. Soc. 8: 1. (Translated and produced by Scripta Technica, Inc.)

BOURNE, N., AND D. E. MCALLISTER. 1969. The black hagfish *Eptatretus deani* from British Columbia. J. Fish. Res. Bd. Canada 26(12): 3246–3248.

BOURNE, N. F., AND M. A. POPE. 1969. Deep-sea line fishing off British Columbia. J. Fish. Res. Bd. Canada 26(9): 2527–2531.

BRADBURY, M. G., AND D. M. COHEN. 1958. An illustration and a new record of the North Pacific bathypelagic fish *Macropinna microstoma*. Stanford Ichthyol. Bull. 7(3): 57–59.

BRAWN, V. M. MS 1964. Some functions of the swimbladder and its ducts in Atlantic and Pacific herring. Ph.D. Thesis. Dep. Zool., Univ. British Columbia.

—— 1969. Buoyancy of Atlantic and Pacific herring. J. Fish. Res. Bd. Canada 26(8): 2077–2091.

BREDER, C. M., JR. * 1929. Field book of marine fishes of the Atlantic coast. New York and London. 332 p.

BREDER, C. M. JR., AND D. E. ROSEN. 1966. Modes of reproduction in fishes. Natur. Hist. Press. Garden City, N.Y. 941 p.

BRELAND, O. P. 1943. Manual of comparative anatomy. McGraw-Hill Book Co., New York, N.Y.

681

BRETT, J. R., AND C. GROOT. 1963. Some aspects of olfaction and visual responses in Pacific salmon. J. Fish. Res. Bd. Canada 20(2): 287–303.

BRETT, J. R., AND D. MACKINNON. 1952. Some observations on olfactory perception in migrating adult coho and spring salmon. Fish. Res. Board Can. Pac. Progr. Rep. 90: 21–23.

1954. Some aspects of olfactory perception in migrating adult coho and spring salmon. J. Fish. Res. Bd. Canada 11(3): 310–318.

BREVOORT, C. B. 1856. Notes on some figures of Japanese fish. In M. C. Perry. Narrative of the expedition of an American squadron to the China Sea and Japan in the years 1852, 1853, and 1854, under the command of Commodore M. C. Perry, United States Navy. 33rd Congr. 2nd Ses. Ex. Doc. 96. Government of the United States 2: 255–288.

BRIGGS, J. C. 1951. A review of the clingfishes (Gobiesocidae) of the eastern Pacific with descriptions of new species. Proc. Calif. Zool. Club 1(10): 57–108.

1955. A monograph of the clingfishes (Order Xenopterygii). Stanford Ichthyol. Bull. 6: 1–224.

1960. Fishes of worldwide (circumtropical) distribution. Copeia 1960(3): 171–180.

BRIGHT, D. B. 1959. The occurrence and food of the sleeper shark Somniosus pacificus in a central Alaska bay. Copeia 1959(1): 76–77.

1960. A record of the porbeagle, Lamna nasus, from Cook Inlet, Alaska. Copeia 1960(2): 145–146.

BRITISH COLUMBIA FISHERIES DEPARTMENT. 1937. Report for 1936. Pilchard, p. 23.

1937–1957. Reports, 1936–1956.

BROCK, V. 1939. Occurrence of albacore (Germo alalunga) in mid-Pacific. Copeia 1939(1): 47.

BROCK, V. E. 1940. Note on the young of the sablefish Anoplopoma fimbria. Copeia 1940(4): 268–270.

1943. A northern record of Aprodon cortezianus Gilbert. Copeia 1943(3): 186.

1954. Some aspects of the biology of the aku, Katsuwonus pelamis, in the Hawaiian Islands. Pac. Sci. 8(1): 94–104.

BROCKLESBY, H. N. 1927. Determination of vitamin A content in liver oil of the dog-fish Squalus sucklii. Can. Chem. Metal. 11: 238–239.

BUCHANAN, D. A. MS 1935. The anatomy of the midshipman fish, Porichthys notatus. B.A. Thesis. Dep. Zool. Univ. British Columbia, 1935.

BUDD, P. L. 1940. Development of eggs and early larvae of six California fishes. Calif. Div. Fish Game Fish. Bull. 56: 50 p.

BUREAU OF MARINE FISHERIES. 1949. The commercial fish catch of California for the year 1947 with an historical review 1916–1947. Calif. Div. Fish Game Fish. Bull. 74: 267 p.

BURKE, C. V. * 1912. A new genus and six new species of fishes of the family Cyclogasteridae. Proc. U.S. Nat. Mus. 43: 567–574.

1930. Revision of the fishes of the family Liparidae. U.S. Nat. Mus. Bull. 150: 204 p.

BYERS, R. D. 1942. Salmon caught in Mexican waters. Calif. Fish Game 24(2): 217.

CALHOUN, A. J. 1953. Distribution of striped bass fry in relation to major water diversions. Calif. Fish Game 39(3): 279–299.

CALIFORNIA BUREAU OF MARINE FISHERIES. Production reports. Calif. Dep. Fish Game Fish. Bull. 89, 95, 102, 105, 108, 111, 117, 121, 125, 129, 132, 135.

CARL, G. C. * 1938. A spawning run of brown trout in the Cowichan River system. Fish. Res. Board Can. Pac. Progr. Rep. 36: 12–13.

CARL, G. C., W. A. CLEMENS, AND C. C. LINDSEY. 1959. The freshwater fishes of British Columbia. Brit. Columbia Prov. Mus. Handb. 5: 192 p.

CARL, G. C., AND G. V. WILBY. 1945. Some marine fish records for British Columbia. Can. Field-Natur. 59(1): 28–30.

CARTER, N. M. 1932. The oceanography of the fiords of southern British Columbia. Fish. Res. Board Can. Pac. Progr. Rep. 12: 7–11.

1968. Index and list of titles. Fisheries Research Board of Canada and associated publications 1900–1964. Fish. Res. Board Can. Bull. 164: 649 p.

CARTER, W. R. MS 1965. Racial variations of the arrow goby, Clevelandia ios (Jordan and Gilbert) 1882 in Puget Sound and on the coast of Washington State. M.Sc. Thesis. Univ. Wash. 91 p.

CHAPMAN, W. M. * 1938. The osteology of Zaprora silenus Jordan, with notes on its distribution and early life-history. Ann. Mag. Natur. Hist. 11(2): 89–117.

1939. Eleven new species and three new genera of oceanic fishes collected by the International Commission from the northeastern Pacific. Proc. U.S. Nat. Mus. 86(3062): 501–542.

1940. Oceanic fishes from the northeast Pacific Ocean. Occas. Pap. Brit. Columbia Prov. Mus. 2: 1–40.

1942. Basking shark on the Washington coast. Copeia 1942(1): 51.

1943. The osteology of the Pacific saury, *Cololabis saira*. Copeia 1943(3): 171–182.

1944. A new name for *Myctophum oculeum* Chapman. Copeia 1944(1): 54–55.

CHAPMAN, W. M., AND A. C. DeLACY. 1933. Notes on the fishes of the State of Washington. Copeia 1933(2): 102–103.

CHAPMAN, W. M., M. KATZ, AND D. W. ERICKSON. 1941. The races of herring in the State of Washington. Wash. Dep. Fish. Biol. Rep. 38A: 1–36.

CHAPMAN, W. M., AND L. D. TOWNSEND. 1938. The osteology of *Zaprora silenus* Jordan, with notes on its distribution and early life history. Ann. Mag. Natur. Hist. 11(2): 89–117.

CHATWIN, B. M. 1953. Tagging chum salmon in Johnstone Strait, 1949 and 1950. Fish. Res. Board Can. Bull. 96: 33 p.

1954. Growth of young lingcod. Fish. Res. Board Can. Pac. Progr. Rep. 99: 14–17.

1956a. Age and growth of lingcod (*Ophiodon elongatus*). Fish. Res. Board Can. Pac. Progr. Rep. 105: 22–26.

1956b. Further results from tagging experiments on lingcod. Fish. Res. Board Can. Pac. Progr. Rep. 107: 19–21.

1958. Mortality rates and estimates of theoretical yield in relation to minimum commercial size of lingcod (*Ophiodon elongatus*) from the Strait of Georgia, British Columbia. J. Fish. Res. Bd. Canada 15(5): 831–849.

CHATWIN, B. M., AND C. R. FORRESTER. 1953. Feeding habits of dogfish (*Squalus suckleyi* (Girard)). Fish. Res. Board Can. Pac. Progr. Rep. 95: 35–38.

CHESNON, C.-G. 1835. Essai sur l'histoire naturelle, Mm. Perisse. Lyon and Paris, 408 p.

CLARK, F. N. 1930. Size at first maturity of the white sea bass. Calif. Fish Game 10(4): 319–323.

1934. Maturity of the California sardine (*Sardina caerulea*) determined by ova diameter measurements. Calif. Div. Fish Game Fish. Bull. 42: 49 p.

1935. A summary of the life history of the California sardine and its influence on the fishery. Calif. Fish Game 21(1): 1–9.

1936. Variations in the number of vertebrae of the sardine *Sardinops caerulea* (Girard). Copeia 1936(3): 147–150.

1938. Small sardines taken off Oregon. Calif. Fish Game 24(1): 71.

1952. Review of the California sardine fishery. Calif. Fish Game 38(3): 367–380.

CLARK, F. N., AND J. F. JANSSEN, JR. 1945. Movements and abundance of the sardine as measured by tag returns. Calif. Div. Fish Game Fish. Bull. 61: 7–42.

CLARK, F. N., AND J. B. PHILLIPS. 1952. The northern anchovy (*Engraulis mordax mordax*) in the California fishery. Calif. Fish Game 38(2): 189–208.

CLARK, G. H. 1938. Weight and age determination of striped bass. Calif. Fish Game 24(2): 176–177.

CLARK, W. J. 1928. The recent invasion of Ray's bream (*Brama rayii*). Naturalist 855(629 c.s.): 107–109.

CLAUSSEN, L. G. 1959. A southern range extension of the American shad to Todos Santos Bay, Baja California, Mexico. Calif. Fish Game 45(3): 217.

CLEAVER, F. C. 1949. The Washington otter trawl fishery with reference to the petrale sole (*Eopsetta jordani*). Wash. Dep. Fish. Biol. Rep. 49A: 1–45.

1951. Fishery statistics of Oregon. Oreg. Fish. Comm. Contrib. 16: 176 p.

CLEMENS, H. B. 1961. The migration, age, and growth of Pacific albacore (*Thunnus germo*), 1951–1958. Calif. Dep. Fish Game Fish. Bull. 115: 128 p.

CLEMENS, H. B., AND G. A. FLITTNER. 1969. Bluefin tuna migrate across the Pacific Ocean. Calif. Fish Game 55(2): 132–135.

CLEMENS, W. A. 1930. Pacific salmon migration: the tagging of the coho salmon on the east coast of Vancouver Island in 1927 and 1928. Bull. Biol. Board Can. 15: 19 p.

1932. Pacific salmon migration. The tagging of the spring salmon on the east coast of Vancouver Island in 1927 and 1928 with notes on incidental tagging of other fish. Bull. Biol. Board Can. 27: 10 p.

* 1944. The Pacific salmon in British Columbia waters. Rep. Brit. Columbia Fish. Dep. 1943: 83–85.

CLEMENS, W. A., J. L. HART, AND G. V. WILBY. 1936. Analysis of stomach contents of fur seals taken off the west coast of Vancouver Island in April and May, 1935. Can. Dep. Fish. Ottawa. 20 p.

CLEMENS, W. A., AND G. V. WILBY. * 1933. Food of the fur seal off the coast of British Columbia. J. Mammalogy 14: 43–46.

1946. Fishes of the Pacific Coast of Canada. 1st ed. Fish. Res. Board Can. Bull. 68: 368 p.

1952. The first record of the smooth lumpsucker, *Cyclopterichthys ventricosus* (Pallas) in

British Columbia waters. J. Fish. Res. Bd. Canada 9(3): 141–142.

    1961. Fishes of the Pacific Coast of Canada. 2nd ed. Fish. Res. Board. Can. Bull. 68: 443 p.

CLOTHIER, C. R. 1950. A key to some southern California fishes based on vertebral characters. Calif. Div. Fish Game Fish. Bull. 79: 83 p.

COBB, J. N. 1927. Pacific cod fisheries. Rep. U.S. Commer. Fish. 1926,VII: 385–499.

COHEN, D. M. 1956. The synonymy and distribution of *Leuroglossus stilbius* Gilbert, a North Pacific bathypelagic fish. Stanford Ichthyol. Bull. 7(2): 19–24.

    1958. *Nansenia candida,* a new species of argentinid fish from the North Pacific, with notes on other species of *Nansenia.* Stanford Ichthyol. Bull. 7(3): 52–57.

    1964. Suborder Argentinoidea. p. 1–69. *In* Fishes of the Western North Atlantic. Mem. Sears Found. Mar. 1(4): 599 p.

    1966. The North Pacific deepsea fish name *Bathylagus milleri* Gilbert, a senior synonym of *Bathylagus alascanus* Chapman. Copeia 1966(4): 877–878.

COLLARD, S. N. 1970. Forage of some eastern Pacific midwater fishes. Copeia 1970(2): 348–354.

COLLIER, R. S. 1964. Report on a recent shark attack off San Francisco, California. Calif. Fish Game 50(4): 261–264.

COPE, E. D. * 1823. A contribution to the ichthyology of Alaska. Proc. Amer. Phil. Soc. 13: 24–32.

COWAN, I. M. 1938. Some fish records from the coast of British Columbia. Copeia 1938(2): 97.

COX, K. W. 1948. Sablefish run at Monterey Bay. Calif. Fish Game 34(1): 37.

    1963. Egg-cases of some elasmobranchs and a cyclostome from California waters. Calif. Fish Game 49(4): 271–289.

CRAMER, F. * 1895. On the cranial characters of the genus *Sebastodes.* Proc. Calif. Acad. Sci. 2(5): 573–610.

CRAWFORD, D. R. 1925. Another record of *Alepisaurus.* Copeia 1925(147): 73.

    1927a. Records of rare fishes from the North Pacific during 1925. Copeia 1927(160): 182–184.

    1927b. *Alepisaurus* caught on halibut hook. Copeia 1927(164): 66–67.

    1929. Further records of *Alepisaurus Ferox* from the Aleutian Islands. Copeia 1929(171): 39.

CROKER, R. S. 1942. Mackerel shark (*Lamna nasus*) taken in California. Calif. Fish Game 28(2): 124–125.

DANIEL, J. F. 1916. The anatomy of *Heptanchus maculatus.* The endoskeleton. Univ. Calif. Publ. Zool. 16(18): 349–370.

    1934. The elasmobranch fishes. 3rd ed. Univ. Calif. Press, Berkeley, Calif. 332 p.

DAUGHERTY, A. E., F. E. FELIN, AND J. MacGREGOR. 1955. Age and length composition of the northern anchovy catch off the coast of California in 1952–53 and 1953–54. Calif. Dep. Fish Game Fish. Bull. 101: 36–66.

DAVENPORT, D. 1966. Colour variant of bocaccio (*Sebastodes paucispinis*) in British Columbia waters. J. Fish. Res. Bd. Canada 23(12): 1981.

DEAN, B. 1906. Chimaeroid fishes and their development. Carnegie Inst. Wash. Publ. 32: 1–194.

DeLACY, A. C., AND R. L. DRYFOOS. 1962. Maturation and the young of rockfishes (*Sebastodes*). Res. Fish. 1962. Contrib. 139 Coll. Fish., Univ. Wash. p. 22–23.

DeLACY, A. C., R. L. DRYFOOS, AND B. S. MILLER. MS 1963. Preliminary checklist of the fishes of Puget Sound. Unpublished report, corrected to 1966.

DeLACY, A. C., C. R. HITZ, AND R. L. DRYFOOS. 1964. Maturation, gestation, and birth of rockfish (*Sebastodes*) from Washington and adjacent waters. Wash. Dep. Fish. Fish. Res. Pap. 2(3): 51–67.

DeLACY, A. C., AND W. M. MORTON. 1943. Taxonomy and habits of the chars *Salvelinus malma* and *S. alpinus* of the Karluk drainage system. Trans. Amer. Fish. Soc. 1942, 72: 78–91.

DeLACY, A. C., AND F. NEAVE. 1947. Migration of pink salmon in southern British Columbia and Washington in 1945. Fish. Res. Board Can. Bull. 74: 11 p.

DE MARTINI, E. E. 1969. A correlative study of the ecology and comparative feeding mechanism morphology of the Embiotocidae (surf-fishes) as evidence of the family's adaptive radiation into available ecological niches. Wasmann J. Biol., 27(2): 177–247.

DODIMEAD, A. J., F. FAVORITE, AND T. HIRANO. 1963. Review of oceanography of the subarctic Pacific region. Int. N. Pac. Fish. Comm. Bull. 13: 1–195.

DOE, L. A. E. 1955. Offshore waters of the Canadian Pacific coast. J. Fish. Res. Bd. Canada 12(1): 1–34.

DRYFOOS, R. L. 1961. Four range extensions of fishes from the northeastern Pacific. Copeia 1961 (4): 476–477.

    MS 1965. The life history and ecology of the longfin smelt in Lake Washington. Ph.D. Thesis. Univ. Wash. 159 p.

DUNG, D. I. Y., AND W. F. ROYCE. 1953. Morphometric measurements of Pacific scombrids. U.S. Fish Wildl. Serv. Spec. Sci. Rep. 95: 170 p.

684

DUNN, J. R., AND C. R. HITZ. 1969. Oceanic occurrence of black rockfish (*Sebastodes melanops*) in the central north Pacific. J. Fish. Res. Bd. Canada 26: 3094–3097.

DYMOND, J. R. 1928. Another prowfish (*Zaprora silenus*) record. Copeia 1969(169): 88–89.

1932a. Records of the alewife and steelhead (rainbow) trout from Lake Erie. Copeia 1932(1): 32–33.

1932b. The trout and other game fishes of British Columbia. Fish. Res. Board Can. Bull. 32: 51 p.

1940. Pacific salmon in the Arctic Ocean. Proc. 6th Pac. Sci. Congr. 3: 435.

1964. A history of ichthyology in Canada. Copeia 1964(1): 2–33.

DYMOND, J. R., J. L. HART, AND A. L. PRITCHARD. 1929. The fishes of the Canadian waters of Lake Ontario. Univ. of Toronto Studies. Biol. Ser. Publ. Ont. Fish. Res. Lab. 37: 1–35.

EASTMAN, D. S. MS 1962. Homing of the tidepool sculpin *Oligocottus maculosus* Girard. B.A. Thesis. Dep. Zool. Univ. British Columbia.

EBELING, A. W. 1962. Melamphaidae. I. Systematics and zoogeography of the species of bathypelagic fish genus *Melamphaeus* Günther. Dana-Rep. 58: 164 p.

EDSON, Q. A. 1954. Preliminary report on the Alaska sablefish fishery. Pac. Mar. Fish. Comm. Bull. 3: 73–85.

EIGENMANN, C. H. 1894. On the viviparous fishes of the Pacific coast of North America. Bull. U.S. Fish. Comm. 12: 381–478.

EIGENMANN, C. H., AND C. H. BEESON. * 1894a. *Pteropodus dallii* n.sp. Amer. Natur. 28: 66.

* 1894b. A revision of the fishes of the sub-family Sebastinae of the Pacific coast of America. Proc. U.S. Nat. Mus. 17: 375–407.

EIGENMANN, C. H., AND A. B. ULREY. 1894. A review of the Embiotocidae. p. 382–400. *In* C. H. Eigenmann. On the viviparous fishes of the Pacific coast of North America. Bull. U.S. Fish. Comm. 12: 381–478.

EISLER, R. MS 1957. Some effects of visible light on hatching, mortality, and early growth of salmonids. M.Sc. Thesis, Univ. Wash. 68 p.

ELLIS, D. V. 1966. Swimming speeds of sockeye and coho salmon on spawning migration. J. Fish. Res. Bd. Canada 23(2): 181–187.

ENG, H. MS 1949. The digestive, respiratory and urogenital systems of the Pacific coast lamprey, *Entosphenus tridentatus* with comparison to the eastern lamprey *Petromyzon marinus*. B.A. Thesis. Dep. Zool. Univ. British Columbia.

ENGLISH, T. S. 1966. English sole egg studies. Contract Rep. Northwest Pulp Pap. Assoc. 93 p.

EVERMANN, B. W. 1915. Note on an unusually large ocean sunfish. Copeia 1915(20): 1–2.

EVERMANN, B. W., AND E. L. GOLDSBOROUGH. 1907. The fishes of Alaska. Bull. U.S. Bur. Fish. 26: 219–360, 144 fig., 20 tables.

FANNIN, J. 1898. A preliminary catalogue of the collections of the natural history and ethnology in The Provincial Museum (Fishes: 59–63). Victoria, B.C. 196 p.

FARRIS, D. A. 1963. Reproductive periodicity in the sardine (*Sardinops caerulea*) and the jack mackerel (*Trachurus symmetricus*) on the Pacific coast of North America. Copeia 1963(1): 182–184.

FELIN, F. E. 1954. Population heterogeneity in the Pacific pilchard. U.S. Fish Wildl. Serv. Fish. Bull. 86, Vol. 54: 201–225.

FISHER, H. D. 1952. The status of the harbour seal in British Columbia, with particular reference to the Skeena River. Fish. Res. Board Can. Bull. 93: 58 p.

FISK, M. 1913. A review of the fishes of the genus *Osmerus* of the California coast. Proc. U.S. Nat. Mus. 46: 291–297.

FITCH, J. E. 1949. Some new and unusual fishes from southern California. Calif. Fish Game 34(3): 133–135.

1950. Notes on some Pacific fishes. Calif. Fish Game 36(2): 65–73.

1951a. Notes on the squaretail, *Tetragonurus cuvieri*. Calif. Fish Game 37(1): 55–59.

1951b. Studies and notes on some California marine fishes. Calif. Fish Game 37(2): 111–120.

1952a. Toxicity and taxonomic notes on the squaretail, *Tetragonurus cuvieri*. Calif. Fish Game 38(2): 251–252.

1952b. Distributional notes on some Pacific coast marine fishes. Calif. Fish Game 38(4): 557–564.

1953. Extensions of known geographical distributions of some marine fishes on the Pacific coast. Calif. Fish Game 39(4): 539–552.

1956. Jack mackerel. Calif. Coop. Oceanic. Fish. Invest., Progr. Rep. Apr. 1955–June 1956: 27–28.

1958. Age composition of the southern California catch of Pacific mackerel for the two seasons

1955–56 and 1956–57. Calif. Dep. Fish Game Fish. Bull. 106: 19–26.

1964. The ribbonfishes (family Trachipteridae) of the eastern Pacific Ocean, with a description of a new species. Calif. Fish Game 50(4): 228–240.

1966a. The poacher *Asterotheca infraspinata* (Gilbert) added to California's marine fauna, and a key to California Agonidae (Pisces). Calif. Fish Game: 52(2): 121–124.

1966b. Fishes and other marine organisms taken during deep trawling off Santa Catalina Island, March 3–4, 1962. Calif. Fish Game 52(3): 216–219.

1968. Otoliths and other fish remains from the Timms Point silt (early Pleistocene) at San Pedro, California. Los Angeles Cty. Mus. Contrib. Sci. 146 : 29 p.

FITCH, J. E., AND R. J. LAVENBERG. 1968. Deep-water fishes of California. Univ. Calif. Press, Berkeley and Los Angeles. 115 p.

FOERSTER, R. E. 1941. The mortality of young pilchards, 1941. Fish. Res. Board Can. Pac. Progr. Rep. 48: 3–8.

1943. News item. Pacific mackerel, *Pneumatophorus diego*. Fish. Res. Board Can. Pac. Progr. Rep. 56: 15.

1945. California soupfin shark captured in British Columbia. Fish. Res. Board Can. Pac. Progr. Rep. 64: 64.

1968. The sockeye salmon. Fish. Res. Board Can. Bull. 162: 422 p.

FOERSTER, R. E., AND A. L. PRITCHARD. * 1944. The identification of the young of five species of Pacific salmon, with notes on the fresh-water phase of their life-history. Rep. Brit. Columbia Fish. Dep. for 1943: 86–97.

FOLLETT, W. I. 1966. Man-eater of the California coast. Pac. Discovery 19(1): 18–22.

1970. Benthic fishes cast ashore by giant waves near Point Joe, Monterey County, California. Proc. Calif. Acad. Sci. IV, 37(15): 473–488.

FOLLETT, W. I., AND L. J. DEMPSTER. 1963. Relationships of the percoid fish *Pentaceros richardsoni* Smith, with description of a specimen from the coast of California. Proc. Calif. Acad. Sci. IV, 32(10): 315–338.

FOLLETT, W. I., R. B. McCORMICK, AND E. A. BEST. 1960. First records of sinistrality in *Microstomus pacificus* (Lockington) and *Glyptocephalus zachirus* Lockington, pleuronectid fishes of western North America with meristic data. Copeia 1960(2): 112–119.

FORD, E. 1921. A contribution to our knowledge of the life–histories of the dogfishes landed at Plymouth. J. Mar. Biol. Ass. U.K., N.S. 12(3): 468–505.

FORRESTER, C. R. 1956. The relation of stock density to "milkiness" of lemon sole in Union Bay, B.C. Fish. Res. Board Can. Pac. Progr. Rep. 105: 11.

1958. The recent rise in landings of whole fish for mink feed in British Columbia. Fish. Res. Board Can. Pac. Progr. Rep. 111: 20–21.

1964a. Laboratory observations on embryonic development and larvae of the Pacific cod (*Gadus macrocephalus* Tilesius). J. Fish. Res. Bd. Canada 21(1): 9–16.

1964b. Demersal quality of fertilized eggs of rock sole (*Lepidopsetta bilineata* Ayres). J. Fish. Res. Bd. Canada 21(6): 1531–1532.

1964c. Rate of development of eggs of rock sole (*Lepidopsetta bilineata* Ayres). J. Fish. Res. Bd. Canada 21(6): 1533–1534.

1968. Utilization of fish for animal food in B.C. Fish. Can. Apr. 1968: 17–21.

1969a. Sinistrality in *Platichthys stellatus* off British Columbia. J. Fish. Res. Bd. Canada 26(1): 191–196.

1969b. Life history information on some groundfish species. Fish. Res. Board Can. Tech. Rep. 105: 17 p.

1969c. Results of english sole tagging in British Columbia waters. Pac. Mar. Fish. Comm. Bull. 7: 10 p.

FORRESTER, C. R., AND D. F. ALDERDICE. 1967. Preliminary observations on embryonic development of the petrale sole (*Eopsetta jordani*). Fish. Res. Board Can. Tech. Rep. 41: 21 p.

1968. Preliminary observations on embryonic development of the flathead sole (*Hippoglossoides elassodon*). Fish. Res. Board Can. Tech. Rep. 100: 20 p.

FORRESTER, C. R., AND K. S. KETCHEN. 1955. Preliminary results of gray cod tagging in Georgia Strait in the winter of 1954–55. Fish. Res. Board Can. Pac. Progr. Rep. 103: 8–10.

FORRESTER, C. R., A. E. PEDEN, AND R. M. WILSON. 1972. First records of the striped bass, *Morone saxatilis* (Walbaum) in British Columbia waters. J. Fish. Res. Bd. Canada 29(3): 337–339.

FORRESTER, C. R., AND M. S. SMITH. 1971. Ambicoloration in a petrale sole (*Iopsetta jordani*). J. Fish. Res. Bd. Canada, 28(10): 1672–1674.

FORRESTER, C. R. AND J. A. THOMSON. 1969. Population studies on the rock sole *Lepidopsetta bilineata* of northern Hecate Strait, British Columbia. Fish. Res. Board Can. Tech. Rep. 108: 104 p.

686

FORRESTER, C. R., AND R. M. WILSON. 1963. A further record of the blacktail snailfish, *Careproctus melanurus* Gilbert, from British Columbia waters. J. Fish. Res. Bd. Canada 20(4): 1095–1096.

FOSKETT, D. R. 1951. Young salmon in the Nanaimo area. Fish. Res. Board Can. Pac. Progr. Rep. 86: 18–19.

FOWLER, H. W. * 1923. Records of west coast fishes. Proc. Acad. Natur. Sci. Philadelphia 75: 279–283.

———— 1941. The fishes of the groups Elasmobranchii, Holocephali, Isospondyli, and Ostarophysi obtained by the United States Bureau of Fisheries Steamer "Albatross" in 1907 to 1910, chiefly in the Philippine Islands and adjacent seas. Bull. U.S. Nat. Mus. 100(13): 879 p.

FRASER, C. M. *1916a. On *Clupea pallasii* Cuvier. Trans. Roy. Can. Inst. 11: 97–108.

———— 1916b. Ichthyological notes. Trans. Roy. Can. Inst. 11: 109–118.

———— 1923. Ichthyological notes. Contr. Can. Biol. N.S. 1(14): 285–296.

FRASER-BRUNNER, A. * 1949. A classification of the fishes of the family Myctophidae. Proc. Zool. Soc. London 118(4): 1019–1116.

———— * 1950. The fishes of the family Scombridae. Ann. Mag. Natur. Hist. (12)3: 131–163.

———— 1951. The ocean sunfishes (family Molidae). Bull. Brit. Mus. Natur. Hist. 1(6): 89–121.

FRY, D. H. JR. 1936a. A description of the eggs and larvae of the Pacific mackerel (*Pneumatophorus diego*). Calif. Fish Game 22(1): 28–29.

———— 1936b. A preliminary summary of the life history of the Pacific mackerel (*Pneumatophorus diego*). Calif. Fish Game 22(1): 30–36.

FRY, D. H. JR., AND P. M. ROEDEL. 1949. Tagging experiments on the Pacific mackerel. Calif. Div. Fish Game Fish. Bull. 73: 64 p.

GANSSLE, D., AND H. B. CLEMENS. 1953. California tagged albacore recovered off Japan. Calif. Fish Game 39(4): 443.

GARMAN, S. * 1892. The Discoboli, Cyclopteridae, Liparopsidae, and Liparidae. Mem. Mus. Comp. Zool. 14(2): 1–96.

———— 1899. Reports on an exploration off the West Coast of Mexico, Central and South America, and off the Galapagos Islands, in charge of Alexander Agassiz, by the U.S. Fish Commission steamer "Albatross" during 1891, Lieut. Commander Z. I. Tanner, U.S.N., commanding. XXVI. The fishes. Mem. Mus. Comp. Zool., Harvard Univ., 24, 2 vol., 431 p., 97 pl.

———— 1913. The Plagiostomia (sharks, skates, and rays). Mem. Mus. Comp. Zool. Harvard Univ., 36(2): 515 p., 77 pl.

GIBBS, R. H., AND N. J. WILIMOVSKY. 1966. Family Alepisauridae. p. 482–497. *In* Fishes of the western North Atlantic. Mem. Sears Found. Mar. Res. 1(5): 647 p.

GILBERT, C. H. * 1890. Preliminary report on the fishes collected by the steamer "Albatross" on the Pacific Coast of North America during the year 1889, with descriptions of twelve new genera and ninety-two new species. Proc. U.S. Nat. Mus. 13: 49–126.

———— 1895. The ichthyological collections of the steamer "Albatross" during the years 1890 and 1891. Rep. U.S. Comm. Fish. 19: 393–476.

———— 1912. A new genus and species of cottoid fish from Departure Bay, Vancouver Island. Contrib. Can. Biol. 1906–1910, 12: 215–216.

———— 1915. Fishes collected by the United States Fisheries steamer "Albatross" in Southern California in 1904. Proc. U.S. Nat. Mus. 48: 305–380.

———— 1917. On the occurrence of *Benthodesmus atlanticus* Goode and Bean on the coast of British Columbia. Smithson. Misc. Collect. 66(18): 1–2.

GILBERT, C. H., AND C. V. BURKE. 1912. Fishes from Bering Sea and Kamchatka. Bull. U.S. Bur. Fish. 30: 31–96.

GILBERT, C. H., AND C. L. HUBBS. 1916. Report on the Japanese macruroid fishes collected by the United States fisheries steamer "Albatross" in 1906, with a synopsis of the genera. Proc. U.S. Nat. Mus. 51: 135–214.

GILBERT, C. H., AND J. C. THOMPSON. * 1905. Notes on the fishes of Puget Sound. Proc. U.S. Nat. Mus. 28: 973–987.

GILCHRIST, J. D. F. * 1908. Description of fifteen new South African fishes, with notes on other species. Mar. Invest. S. Afr. 4: 143–171.

GILL, T. * 1882. Bibliography of fishes of the Pacific Coast of the United States to the end of 1879. Smithson. Misc. Collect. 23: 1–78.

GILMARTIN, M. 1962. Annual cyclic changes in the physical oceanography of a British Columbia fiord. J. Fish. Res. Bd. Canada 19(5): 921–974.

687

GINSBURG, I. 1953. The taxonomic status and nomenclature of some Atlantic and Pacific populations of yellowfin and bluefin tunas. Copeia 1953(1): 1–10.

    1954. Whitings on the coasts of the American continents. U.S. Fish. Wildl. Serv. Fish. Bull. 96, Vol. 56: 187–208.

GODFREY, H. 1958. A comparison of sockeye salmon catches at Rivers Inlet and Skeena River, B.C., with particular reference to age at maturity. J. Fish. Res. Bd. Canada 15(3): 331–354.

    1959a. Variations in annual average weights of British Columbia pink salmon, 1944–1958. J. Fish. Res. Bd. Canada 16(3): 329–337.

    1959b. Variation in the average weights of chum salmon caught in British Columbia waters, 1946 to 1958. J. Fish. Res. Bd. Canada 16(4): 553–554.

GODSIL, H. C. 1948. A preliminary population study of the yellowfin tuna and the albacore. Calif. Div. Fish Game Fish. Bull. 70: 90 p.

    1954. A descriptive study of certain tuna-like fishes. Calif. Dep. Fish Game Fish. Bull. 97: 185 p.

GODSIL, H. C., AND R. D. BYERS. 1944. A systematic study of the Pacific tunas. Calif. Div. Fish Game Fish. Bull. 60: 131 p.

GODSIL, H. C., AND E. K. HOLMBERG. 1950. A comparison of the bluefin tunas, genus *Thunnus* from New England, Australia, and California. Calif. Div. Fish Game Fish. Bull. 77: 55 p.

GOODE, G. B. * 1884. The food fishes of the United States, p. 163–682. *In* George Brown Goode [ed.] The fisheries and fishery industries of the United States. 1(3).

GOODE, G. B., AND T. H. BEAN. 1882. *Benthodesmus*, a new genus of deepsea fishes, allied to *Lepidopus*. Proc. U.S. Nat. Mus. 4: 379–383.

GORDON, C. D. MS 1965. Aspects of the age and growth of *Cymatogaster aggregata* Gibbons. M.Sc. Thesis. Dep. Zool., Univ. British Columbia. 90 p.

GOSLINE, W. A. 1966. The limits of the fish family Serranidae, with notes on other lower percoids. Proc. Calif. Acad. Sci. 4th Ser. 33(6): 91–111.

GOTSHALL, D. W. 1961. Observations on a die-off of molas (*Mola mola*) in Monterey Bay. Calif. Fish Game 47(4): 339–341.

    1969. Stomach contents of Pacific hake and arrowtooth flounder from northern California. Calif. Fish Game 55(1): 75–82.

GOTSHALL, D. W., AND T. JOW. 1965. Sleeper sharks (*Somniosus pacificus*) off Trinidad, California, with life history notes. Calif. Fish Game 51(4): 294–298.

GOTSHALL, D. W., J. G. SMITH, AND A. HOLBERT. 1965. Food of the blue rockfish, *Sebastodes mystinus*. Calif. Fish Game 51(3): 147–162.

GRAY, G. W. 1964. Halibut preying on large Crustacea. Copeia 1964(3): 590.

GREEN, A. H. * 1891a. The Salmonidae of British Columbia. Pap. Comm. Natur. Hist. Soc. Brit. Columbia 1: 6–17.

    * 1891b. The economic fishes of British Columbia. Pap. Comm. Natur. Hist. Soc. Brit. Columbia 1: 20–33.

    * 1891c. *Chirolophus polyactocephalus*. Pap. Comm. Natur. Hist. Soc. Brit. Columbia 1: 55–56.

    * 1893. Notes on the occurrence of new and rare fish in British Columbia. Bull. Natur. Hist. Soc. Brit. Columbia 1893: 9–10.

GREENE, C. W. 1924. Physiological reactions and structure of the vocal apparatus of the California singing fish, *Porichthys notatus*. Amer. J. Physiol. 70(3): 496–499.

GREENE, C. W., AND H. H. GREENE. 1924. Phosphorescence of *Porichthys notatus*, the California singing fish. Amer. J. Physiol. 70(3): 500–506.

GREENWOOD, P. H., D. E. ROSEN, S. H. WEITZMAN, AND G. S. MYERS. 1966. Phyletic studies of teleostean fishes, with a provisional classification of living forms. Bull. Amer. Mus. Natur. Hist. 131 (4): 341–455.

GREGORY, W. K. * 1933. Fish skulls: a study of the evolution of natural mechanisms. Trans. Amer. Phil. Soc., N.S. 23(2): 75–481.

GREGORY, W. K., AND H. C. RAVEN. 1934. Notes on the anatomy and relationships of the ocean sunfish (*Mola mola*). Copeia 1934(4): 145–151.

GREY, M. 1955. The fishes of the genus *Tetragonurus* Risso. Dana-Rep. 8(41): 1–75.

GRINOLS, R. B. MS 1965a. Check-list of the offshore marine fishes occurring in the northeastern Pacific Ocean, principally off the coasts of British Columbia, Washington, and Oregon. M.Sc. Thesis. Univ. Wash. 217 p.

    1965b. Addition of adult anglerfish, *Chaenophryne parviconus* Regan and Trewavas (Pisces: Oneirodidae), to the eastern subarctic Pacific Ocean. Calif. Fish Game 52(3): 161–165.

    1966. Northern records of the zoarcid, *Melanostigma pammelas*, in the eastern subarctic Pacific region. Copeia 1966(3): 601–602.

GRINOLS, R. B., AND C. D. GILL. 1968. Feeding behaviour of three oceanic fishes (*Oncorhynchus kisutch, Trachurus symmetricus,* and *Anoplopoma fimbria*) from the northeast Pacific. J. Fish. Res. Bd. Canada 25(4): 825–827.

GRUCHY, C. G. 1969. Canadian records of the warty poacher *Occa verrucosa* with notes on the standardization of plate terminology in the Agonidae. J. Fish. Res. Bd. Canada 26(6): 1467–1472.

1970. *Occella impi,* a new species of sea poacher from British Columbia with notes on related species (Agonidae, Pisces). J. Fish. Res. Bd. Canada 27(6): 1109–1114.

GRUCHY, C. G., AND V. D. VLADYKOV. 1968. Sexual dimorphism in anal fin of brown trout, *Salmo trutta,* and close relatives. J. Fish. Res. Bd. Canada 25(4): 813–815.

GUNTHER, A. * 1860. On the history of *Echeneis.* Ann. Mag. Natur. Hist. 3(5): 386–402.

* 1859–70. Catalogue of the fishes of the British Museum. 8 vol. London. 1. Acanthopterygii, 524 p., 1859; 2. Acanthopterygii, 548 p., 1860; 3. Acanthopterygii, 586 p., 1861; 4. Acanthopterygii, Pharyngognathi, and Anacanthini, 534 p., 1862; 5. Physostomi, 455 p., 1864; 6. Physostomi, 368 p., 1866; 7. Physostomi, 512 p., 1868; 8. Physostomi, Lophobranchii, Plectognathi, Dipnoi, Ganoidei, Chondropterygii, 549 p., 1870.

* 1874. Descriptions of new species of fishes in the British Museum. Ann. Mag. Natur. Hist. 4(14): 368-371.

1878. *Nemichthys infans.* Ann. Mag. Natur. Hist., Ser. 5, 2: 251.

1887. Report on the deep-sea fishes collected by H.M.S. "Challenger" during the years 1873–76. *In* Report of the scientific results of the Voyage of H.M.S. "Challenger" during the years 1873–76, 22(57): 268 p.

HAEDRICH, R. L. 1967. The stromateoid fishes: systematics and a classification. Bull. Mus. Comp. Zool. 135(2): 139 p.

HAGEN, D. W. 1967. Isolating mechanisms in threespine sticklebacks (*Gasterosteus*). J. Fish. Res. Bd. Canada 24(8): 1637–1692.

HAGERMAN, F. B. 1949. Large dover sole taken off Eureka. Calif. Fish Game 35(3): 202.

1950. The extension of the range of the deepsea flounder *Embassichthys bathybius* (Gilbert). Calif. Fish Game 36(2): 165–166.

1952. The biology of the dover sole, *Microstomus pacificus* (Lockington). Calif. Div. Fish Game Fish. Bull. 78: 64 p.

HAIG, J. 1951. Occurrence of the agonid fish *Bathragonus swani* in California. Copeia 1951(1): 102.

HALKETT, A. * 1913. Check list of the fishes of the Dominion of Canada and Newfoundland. King's Printer, Ottawa. 138 p.

HALLOCK, R. J., AND D. H. FRY, JR. 1967. Five species of salmon, *Oncorhynchus,* in the Sacramento River, California. Calif. Fish Game 53(1): 5–22.

HALSTEAD, B. W. 1950. The capture of the wattled eel-pout, *Lycodes palearis,* from Fidalgo Island, Washington, and the distributional record of this species. Copeia 1950(4): 317.

HALSTEAD, B. W., AND N. C. BUNKER. 1952. The venom apparatus of the ratfish *Hydrolagus colliei.* Copeia 1952(3): 128–138.

HANAMURA, N. 1967. Salmon of the North Pacific Ocean. Part IV. Spawning populations of North Pacific salmon. 1. Sockeye salmon in the Far East. Int. N. Pac. Fish. Comm. Bull. 23: 1–7.

HANAVAN, M. G., AND G. K. TANONAKA. 1959. Experimental fishing to determine distribution of salmon in the north Pacific Ocean and Bering Sea. U.S. Fish Wildl. Serv. Spec. Sci. Rep. Fish. 302: 22 p.

HARLING, W. R. 1966. Northern range extension record for the pygmy rockfish (*Sebastodes wilsoni*). J. Fish. Res. Bd. Canada 23(12): 1967–1968.

HARLING, W. R., D. DAVENPORT, M. S. SMITH, AND R. M. WOWCHUK. 1970. *G. B. Reed* Groundfish Cruise no. 70–3 off southwest Vancouver Island, September 9 to 25, 1970. Fish Res. Board Can. Tech. Rep. 221: 35 p.

HARRY, G. Y. 1959. Time of spawning, length at maturity, and fecundity of the English, petrale, and dover soles (*Parophrys vetulus, Eopsetta jordani,* and *Microstomus pacificus,* respectively). Fish. Comm. Oreg. Res. Briefs 7(1): 5–13.

HARRY, R. R. 1953a. Studies on the bathypelagic fishes of the family Paralepididae. A revision of the North Pacific species. Proc. Acad. Natur. Sci., Philadelphia 105: 169–230.

1953b. Studies on the bathypelagic fishes of the family Paralepididae. I. Survey of the genera. Pac. Sci. 7(2): 219–249.

HART, J. L. 1933a. The pilchard fishery of British Columbia. Bull. Biol. Board Can. 36: 27 p.

1933b. Statistical studies on British Columbia pilchards: vertebra counts. Trans. Roy. Soc. Can., Ser. 3, 27(5): 79–85.

1935. Horse mackerel off British Columbia. Copeia 1935(3): 140.

1937a. Tagging British Columbia pilchards (*Sardinops caerulea* Girard): methods and preliminary results. Rep. Brit. Columbia Fish. Dep. 1936: 49–54.

1937b. Sexual dimorphism in vertebral number in the capelin *Mallotus villosus* (Müller). J. Fish. Res. Bd. Canada 3(5): 417–420.

1937c. Year class variation in vertebra number among pilchards (*Sardinops caerulea*). Trans. Roy. Soc. Can., Ser. 3, 31(5): 71–77.

1938a. A brief account of the life-history of the pilchard. Rep. Brit. Columbia Fish. Dep. 1937: 50–56.

1938b. Tagging British Columbia pilchards (*Sardinops caerulea* (Girard)): insertions and recoveries for 1937–38. Rep. Brit. Columbia Fish. Dep. 1937: 57–63.

1942a. Reproduction in the dogfish. Fish. Res. Board Can. Pac. Progr. Rep. 51: 16–17.

1942b. Albacore food. Fish. Res. Board Can. Pac. Progr. Rep. 52: 9–10.

1942c. News item. Red snapper fecundity. Fish. Res. Board Can. Pac. Progr. Rep. 52: 18.

1943a. The pilchard *Sardinops caerulea* (Girard) on Canadian fishing grounds with special reference to an unusual abundance of young fish. Trans. Roy. Soc. Can., Ser. 3, 37(5): 55–73.

1943b. Rate of growth in lingcod. Fish. Res. Board Can. Pac. Progr. Rep. 56: 10–11.

1943c. Migration of lingcod. Fish. Res. Board Can. Pac. Progr. Rep. 57: 3–7.

1943d. News item. *Katsuwonus* and *Trachipterus* in British Columbia. Fish. Res. Board Can. Pac. Progr. Rep. 56: 16.

1943e. Tagging experiments on British Columbia pilchards. J. Fish. Res. Bd. Canada 6(2): 164–182.

1944. Flatfishes in Skidegate Inlet. Fish. Res. Board Can. Pac. Progr. Rep. 59: 10–11.

1948. Age and growth rate in the butter sole, *Isopsetta isolepsis*. Trans. Roy. Soc. Can., Ser. 3, 42(5): 65–72.

1949a. The lengths of albacore in the commercial catch. Fish. Res. Board Can. Gen. Ser. Circ. 17: 19–20.

1949b. Food of fish of the cod family. Fish. Res. Can. Pac. Progr. Rep. 79: 35–36.

1949c. Increased abundance of an unusual British Columbia fish, the California pompano. Can. Field-Natur. 63(3): 101–102.

1967. Fecundity and length–weight relationship in lingcod. J. Fish. Res. Bd. Canada 24(11): 2485–2489.

HART, J. L., AND W. E. BARRACLOUGH. 1948. Food of albacore. Fish. Res. Board Can. Nanaimo Biol. Sta. Circ. (Gen. Ser.) 12: 3–4.

HART, J. L., AND J. L. MCHUGH. 1939. Vertebral number in young British Columbia herring. Fish. Res. Board Can. Progr. Rep. 41: 20–21.

1944. The smelts (Osmeridae) of British Columbia. Fish. Res. Board Can. Bull. 64: 27 p.

HART, J. L., AND G. C. PIKE. 1948. Sizes of albacore landed in British Columbia. Fish. Res. Board Can. Nanaimo Biol. Sta. Circ. (Gen. Ser.) 12: 5–6.

HART, J. L., AND A. L. TESTER. 1934. Quantitative studies on herring spawning. Trans. Amer. Fish. Soc. 64: 307–312.

1937. The tagging of herring (*Clupea pallasii*) in British Columbia: methods, apparatus, insertions and recoveries during 1936–37. Rep. Brit. Columbia Commer. Fish. 1936: 55–67.

HART, J. L., A. L. TESTER, D. BEALL, AND J. P. TULLY. 1940. Proximate analysis of British Columbia herring in relation to season and condition factor. J. Fish. Res. Bd. Canada 4(5): 478–490.

HART, J. L., AND G. H. WAILES. 1932. The food of the pilchard *Sardinops caerulea* (Girard) off the coast of British Columbia. Contrib. Can. Biol. Fish., N.S. 7(19): 245–254.

HEATH, H. * 1910. The association of a fish with a hydroid. Biol. Bull. 19: 73–78.

HEMPHILL, D. V., AND W. I. FOLLETT. 1958. First record of the agonid fish *Pallasina barbata aix* Starks from California. Calif. Fish Game 44(3): 281–283.

HERALD, E. S. 1939. The opah (*Lampris regius*) and its occurrence off the California Coast. Calif. Fish Game 25(3): 228–232.

1941a. First record of the hybrid flounder, *Inopsetta ischyra*, from California. Calif. Fish Game 27(2): 44–46.

1941b. A systematic analysis of variation in the western American pipefish, *Syngnathus californiensis*. Stanford Ichthyol. Bull. 2(3): 49–73.

1953. The 1952 shark derbies at Elkhorn Slough, Monterey Bay, and at Coyote Point, San Francisco Bay. Calif. Fish Game 39(2): 237–243.

1968. Size and aggressiveness of the sevengill shark (*Notorynchus maculatus*). Copeia 1968(2): 412–414.

HERALD, E. S., AND W. E. RIPLEY. 1951. The relative abundance of sharks and bat stingrays in San Francisco Bay. Calif. Fish Game 37(3): 315–329.

HERLINVEAUX, R. H. 1961. Oceanography of Saanich Inlet in Vancouver Island, British Columbia. J. Fish. Res. Bd. Canada 19(1): 1–37.

690

HERLINVEAUX, R. H., AND J. P. TULLY. 1961. Some oceanographic features of Juan de Fuca Strait. J. Fish. Res. Bd. Canada 18(6): 1027–1071.

HEYAMOTO, H. 1962. Age of young sablefish, *Anoplopoma fimbria* (Pallas) 1811. J. Fish. Res. Bd. Canada 19(6): 1175–1177.

HEYAMOTO, H., AND C. R. HITZ. 1962. Northern range extensions of three species of rockfish (*Sebastodes rubrivinctus, S. aurora,* and *S. helvomaculatus*). Copeia 1962(4): 847–848.

HICKMAN, C. P. JR. 1959. The larval development of the sand sole (*Psettichthys melanostictus*). Wash. Dep. Fish. Fish. Res. Pap. 2(2): 38–47.

HIGH, W. L. 1966. Recent captures of the California pompano (*Palometa simillima*) and the sandfish (*Trichodon trichodon*) in Puget Sound. Wash. Dep. Fish. Fish. Res. Pap. 2(4): 53–54.

HITZ, C. R. 1961. Occurrence of two species of juvenile rockfish in Queen Charlotte Sound. J. Fish. Res. Bd. Canada 18(2): 279–281.

1962. Seasons of birth of rockfish (*Sebastodes* spp.) in Oregon coastal waters. Trans. Amer. Fish. Soc. 91(2): 231–233.

1964. Observations on egg cases of the big skate (*Raja binoculata* Girard) found in Oregon coastal waters. J. Fish. Res. Bd. Canada 21(4): 851–854.

1965. Field identification of northeastern Pacific rockfish (*Sebastodes*). U.S. Dep. Inter. Fish Wildl. Ser. Circ. 203: 59 p. + 3.

HITZ, C. R., AND A. C. DELACY. 1960. Reproduction and fecundity of rockfishes (*Sebastodes*). Res. Fish. 1960. Contrib. 77, Coll. Fish., Univ. Wash.

1961. Variation in the occurrence of coronal spines in *Sebastodes auriculatus*. Copeia 1961(3): 279–282.

1965. Clearing of the yolk in eggs of the rockfishes, *Sebastodes caurinus* and *S. auriculatus*. Trans. Amer. Fish. Soc. 94(2): 194–195.

HITZ, C. R., AND R. R. FRENCH. 1965. Occurrence of pomfret (*Brama japonica*) in the northeastern Pacific Ocean. U.S. Bur. Commer. Fish. Fish. Ind. Res. 3(1): 1–7.

HITZ, C. R., H. C. JOHNSON, AND A. T. PRUTER. 1961. Bottom trawling explorations off the Washington and British Columbia coasts, May–August 1960. Commer. Fish. Rev. 23(6): 1–11.

HOAR, W. S. 1951a. The chum and pink salmon fisheries of British Columbia, 1917–1947. Fish. Res. Board Can. Bull. 90: 46 p.

1951b. The behaviour of chum, pink, and coho salmon in relation to seaward migration. J. Fish. Res. Bd. Canada 8(4): 241–263.

1956. The behaviour of migrating pink and chum salmon fry. J. Fish. Res. Bd. Canada 13(3): 309–325.

HOBBS, K. L. 1929. A new species of *Centrolophis* from Monterey Bay, California. J. Wash. Acad. Sci. 19(20): 460–461.

HOLLAND, G. A. 1957. Migration and growth of the dogfish shark, *Squalus acanthias* (Linnaeus), of the eastern north Pacific. Wash. Dep. Fish. Res. Pap. 2(1): 43–59.

HOLMBERG, E. K., AND R. M. BUSH. 1969a. A guide to the salmon literature compilation 1960–1964. U.S. Dep. Comm. Clearing House for Federal Scientific and Technical Information.

1969b. Salmonid literature compilation 1960–64. U.S. Dep. Comm. Clearing House for Federal Scientific and Technical Information.

HOLMBERG, E. K., AND W. G. JONES. 1954. Results of sablefish tagging experiments in Washington, Oregon, and California. Pac. Mar. Fish Bull. 3: 103–119.

HOUCK, W. J. 1958. Another record of the agonid *Bothragonus swani* from California. Copeia 1958(1): 57.

HOURSTON, A. S. 1958. Population studies on juvenile herring in Barkley Sound, British Columbia. J. Fish. Res. Bd. Canada 15(5): 909–960.

1959a. Effects of some aspects of environment on the distribution of juvenile herring in Barkley Sound. J. Fish. Res. Bd. Canada 16(3): 283–308.

1959b. The relationship of the juvenile herring stocks in Barkley Sound to the major herring populations in British Columbia. J. Fish. Res. Bd. Canada 16(3): 309–320.

HUBBARD, J. D., AND W. G. REEDER. 1965. New locality records for Alaskan fishes. Copeia 1965(4): 506–508.

HUBBS, C. L. 1916a. Notes on the distribution of three California rays. Copeia 1916(37): 87–88.

1916b. Notes on the marine fishes of California. Univ. Calif. Publ. Zool. 16(13): 153–159.

1917. The breeding habits of the viviparous perch, *Cymatogaster*. Copeia 1917(47): 72–74.

* 1918a. A revision of the viviparous perches. Proc. Biol. Soc. Wash. 31: 9–14.

1918b. The fishes of the genus *Atherinops*, their variation, distribution, relationships and history. Bull. Amer. Mus. Natur. Hist. 38(13): 409–440.

1920. The bionomics of *Porichthys notatus* Girard. Amer. Natur. 54, 1920: 380–384.

1921. The ecology and life history of *Amphigonopterus aurora* and other viviparous perches of

California. Biol. Bull. 40(4): 181–209.

1925a. A revision of the osmerid fishes of the North Pacific. Proc. Biol. Soc. Wash. 38: 49–56.

1925b. Racial and seasonal variation in the Pacific herring, California sardine, and California anchovy. Calif. Div. Fish Game Fish. Bull. 8: 24 p.

1926a. The metamorphosis of the California ribbon fish *Trachypterus rex-salmonorum.* Pap. Mich. Acad. Sci. Arts Lett. 5: 469–476.

* 1926b. The supposed intergradation of the two species of *Sebastolobus* (a genus of scorpaenoid fishes) of Western America. Amer. Mus. Natur. Hist. Novitates 216: 1–4.

1927. Notes on the blennoid fishes of Western North America. Pap. Mich. Acad. Sci. Arts Lett. 7: 351–394.

1929. The generic relationships and nomenclature of the California sardine. Proc. Calif. Acad. Sci. 18(11): 261–265.

1933. *Crossochir koelzi* : a new Californian surf-fish of the family Embiotocidae. Proc. U.S. Nat. Mus. 82(21): 1–9.

1942. Peculiar variants of the agonid fish. *Odontopyxis trispinosus.* J. Fish. Res. Bd. Canada 6(1): 30–36.

1959. Initial discoveries of fish faunas on sea mounds and offshore banks in the eastern Pacific. Pac. Sci. 13(4): 311–316.

1964. History of ichthyology in the United States after 1950. Copeia 1964(1): 42–60.

1967. Occurrence of the Pacific lamprey, *Entosphenus tridentatus* off Baja California and in streams of southern California, with remarks on its nomenclature. San Diego Soc. Natur. Hist. Trans. 14(21): 301–312.

HUBBS, C. L., AND P. S. BARNHART. 1944. Extensions of range for blennioid fishes in southern California. Calif. Fish Game 30(1): 49–51.

HUBBS, C. L., AND W. I. FOLLETT. 1947. *Lamna ditropis,* new species, the salmon shark of the North Pacific. Copeia 1947(3): 194.

HUBBS, C. L., AND L. C. HUBBS. 1945. Bilateral asymmetry and bilateral variation in fishes. Pap. Mich. Acad. Sci. Arts Lett. 30: 229–310.

1954. Data on the life history, variation, ecology and relationships of the kelp perch, *Brachyistius frenatus,* an embiotocid fish of the Californias. Calif. Fish Game 40(2): 183–198.

HUBBS, C. L., AND K. KURONUMA. 1942. Hybridization in nature between two genera of flounders in Japan. Mich. Acad. Sci. Pap. (1941) 27: 267–306.

HUBBS, C. L., AND K. L. LAGLER. 1958. Fishes of the Great Lakes region. Bull. Cranbrook Inst. Sci. 26: 186 p.

HUBBS, C. L., G. W. MEAD, AND N. J. WILIMOVSKY. 1953. The widespread, probably anti-tropical distribution and relationship of the bathypelagic iniomous fish *Anotopterus pharao.* Bull. Scripps Inst. Oceanogr. Univ. Calif. 6(5): 173–198.

HUBBS, C. L., AND I. C. POTTER. 1971. Distribution, phylogeny, and taxonomy, p. 1–65. *In* M. W. Hardisty and I. C. Potter [ed.] The biology of lampreys. Vol. 1. Academic Press, Inc., London and New York.

HUBBS, C. L., AND L. P. SCHULTZ. 1932. A new blenny from British Columbia with records of two other fishes new to the region. Contrib. Can. Biol. Fish. 7(22): 319–324.

* 1933. Descriptions of two new American species referable to the rockfish genus *Sebastodes,* with notes on related species. Univ. Wash. Publ. Biol. 2(2): 15–44.

1939. A revision of the toadfishes referred to *Porichthys* and related genera. Proc. U.S. Nat. Mus. 86(3060): 473–496.

HUBBS, C. L., AND A. N. WICK. 1951. Toxicity of the roe of cabezon *Scorpaenichthys marmoratus.* Calif. Fish Game 37(2): 195–196.

HUBBS, C. L., AND N. J. WILIMOVSKY. 1964. Distribution and synonymy in the Pacific Ocean, and variation, of the Greenland halibut, *Reinhardtius hippoglossoides* (Walbaum). J. Fish. Res. Bd. Canada 21(5): 1129–1154.

HUBBS, CLARK. 1947. Mixture of marine and fresh-water fishes in the lower Salinas River, California. Copeia 1947(2): 147.

1952. A contribution to the classification of the blennioid fishes of the family Clinidae, with a partial revision of the eastern Pacific forms. Stanford Ichthyol. Bull. 4(2): 41–165.

HUNTER, J. R. 1968. Effects of light on schooling and feeding of jack mackerel, *Trachurus symmetricus.* J. Fish. Res. Bd. Canada 25(2): 393–407.

MS 1969. Pacific salmon in Arctic Canada. MS.

HUTCHINSON, A. H., C. C. LUCAS, AND M. MCPHAIL. 1929. Seasonal variations in the chemical and physical properties of the waters of the Strait of Georgia in relation to phytoplankton. Trans. Roy. Soc. Can. Ser. 3, 23(5): 177–184.

IDLER, D. R., AND W. A. CLEMENS. 1959. The energy expenditures of Fraser River sockeye salmon during spawning migration to Chilco and Stuart lakes. Int. Pac. Salmon Fish. Comm. Progr. Rep. 6: 80 p. New Westminster.

IREDALE, T., AND G. P. WHITLEY. 1969. Chesnon's "Essai sur l'histoire naturelle", 1835. Proc. Roy. Soc. New South Wales 1967–68: 43–45.

ISAACSON, P. A. 1964. Length-weight relationship of the white croaker. Trans. Amer. Fish. Soc. 93(3): 302–303.

1965. Southern range extension of the tomcod *Microgadus proximus*. Calif. Fish Game 51(1): 58.

IVERSEN, R. T. B. 1962. Food of albacore tuna, *Thunnus germo* (Lacépède), in the central and northeastern Pacific. U.S. Fish Wildl. Ser. Fish. Bull. 214, Vol. 62: 459–481.

JANSSEN, J. F. 1948. Summary of recovery of California sardine tags. On the Pacific Coast. Calif. Fish Game 34(1): 3–10.

JANSSEN, J. F., JR. 1938. Northern recovery of California sardine tags. Calif. Fish Game 24(1): 70.

JENSEN, P. T. 1957. An extension of the range of the long-finned smelt. Calif. Fish Game 43(1): 99.

JOHNSON, C. R. 1969. Contributions to the biology of the showy snailfish, *Liparis pulchellus* (Liparidae). Copeia 1969(4): 830–835.

JOHNSON, W. C., AND A. J. CALHOUN. 1952. Food habits of California striped bass. Calif. Fish Game 38(4): 531–534.

JORDAN, D. S. * 1893. Description of a new species of cyprinoid fish (*Couesius greeni*) from the headwaters of the Fraser River in British Columbia. Proc. U.S. Nat. Mus. 16: 313–314.

* 1896. Notes on fishes little known or new to science. Proc. Calif. Acad. Sci. 2(6): 201–244.

* 1905. A guide to the study of fishes. 2 vol.: 1, 624 p.; 2, 599 p. New York, N.Y.

1918. The "fat-priest fish" in California. Copeia 54: 1–2.

* 1919. On *Elephenor*, a new genus of fishes from Japan. Ann. Carnegie Mus. 12 : 329–392.

1921. Records of Pacific fishes. Copeia 93: 28.

* 1923. A classification of fishes including families and genera as far as known. Stanford Univ. Publ. Biol. Ser. 3(2): 77–243.

1931. History of zoological explorations of the Pacific Coast. Calif. Fish Game 17(2): 156–158.

JORDAN, D. S., AND B. W. EVERMANN. 1896–1900. The fishes of North and Middle America. Bull. U.S. Nat. Mus. 47:1–3313. Pt. 1, p. 1–1240, 1896; Pt. 2, p. 1241–2183, 1898; Pt. 3, p. 2183a–3136, 1899; Pt. 4, p. 3137–3313, 1900.

JORDAN, D. S., AND C. H. GILBERT. * 1880. Description of a new species of ray, *Raja rhina,* from the coast of California. Proc. U.S. Nat. Mus. 3: 251–253.

1881. Notes on the fishes of the Pacific coast of the United States. Proc. U.S. Nat. Mus. 4: 29–70.

1882. Description of a new species of goby (*Gobiosoma ios*) from Vancouver Island. Proc. U.S. Nat. Mus. 5: 437–438.

* 1883. A synopsis of the fishes of North America. Bull. U.S. Nat. Mus. 16: 1–1018.

* 1899. The fishes of Bering Sea, p. 433–492. *In* D. S. Jordan [ed.] Fur-seals and fur seal islands of the North Pacific Ocean, Pt. 3. Washington, D.C.

JORDAN, D. S., AND C. L. HUBBS. 1919. A monographic review of the family Atherinidae or silversides. Leland Stanford Jr. Univ. Stud. Ichthyol., Univ. Ser.: 1–88.

JORDAN, D. S., AND P. L. JOUY. * 1881. Checklist of duplicates of fishes from the Pacific coast of North America, distributed by the Smithsonian Institution in behalf of the United States National Museum. Proc. U.S. Nat. Mus. 4: 1–18.

JORDAN, D. S., AND E. C. STARKS. * 1895. The fishes of Puget Sound. Proc. Calif. Acad. Sci. 2(5): 785–855.

* 1903. A review of the fishes of Japan belonging to the family Hexagrammidae. Proc. U.S. Nat. Mus. 26: 1003–1013.

1904. A review of the Cottidae or sculpins found in the waters of Japan. Proc. U.S. Nat. Mus. 27(1358): 231–335.

* 1906. A review of the soles of Japan. Proc. U.S. Nat. Mus. 31: 161–246.

JOW, T. 1963. A record-size daggertooth taken off northern California. Calif. Fish Game 49(3): 215–216.

KAGANOVSKII, A. G. 1947. Some problems of the biology and population dynamics of pink salmon. Izvestiya tikhookeanskogo nauchno-isslledovat. El'skogo institua rybnogo khozyaistva i okeanografii 31: 3–57. Trans. Nat. Sci. Found. (Transl. from Russian by Israel Program for Sci. Transl., Jerusalem, 1961.)

KANAZAWA, R. H. 1952. Variations in the wolf eel, *Anarrhichthys ocellatus* Ayres, a fish inhabiting the eastern North Pacific Ocean. Calif. Fish Game 38(4): 567–574.

KATO, S., S. SPRINGER, AND M. H. WAGNER. 1967. Field guide to eastern Pacific and Hawaiian sharks. U.S. Dep. Inter. Fish Wildl. Circ. 471: 47 p.

KATZ, M. 1948. The fecundity of herring from various parts of the North Pacific. Trans. Amer. Fish. Soc. 1945: 72–76.

KATZ, M., AND D. W. ERICKSON. 1950. The fecundity of some herring from Seal Rock, Washington. Copeia 1950(3): 176–181.

KAUFFMAN, D. E. 1955. Noteworthy recoveries of tagged dogfish. Wash. Dep. Fish. Fish. Res. Pap. 1(3): 39–40.

KENDALL, W. C. 1924. A new record for the prowfish *Zaprora silenus* Jordan. Copeia 1924(12): 1–2.

KERMODE, F. * 1909. Visitor's guide to the natural history and ethnological collections in the Provincial Museum. Fishes: 75–92. Victoria, B.C. 92 p.

———— * 1913–1917. Rep. Brit. Columbia Prov. Mus. 1912, 1914, 1915, and 1916.

KETCHEN, K. S. 1945. Preliminary report on age and growth of lemon soles from British Columbia fishing grounds. Fish Res. Board Can. Pac. Progr. Rep. 63: 35–37.

———— MS 1947a. The age, growth, and mortality of the lemon sole *Parophrys vetulus* Girard on the British Columbia fishing grounds. M.A. Thesis. Dep. Zool. Univ. British Columbia.

———— 1947b. Studies on lemon sole development and egg production. Fish. Res. Board Can. Pac. Progr. Rep. 73: 68–70.

———— 1950a. A study of the winter trawl fisheries at Cape Lazo and Nanoose Bay in the Strait of Georgia with special reference to the capture of lingcod. Fish. Res. Board Can. Pac. Progr. Rep. 84: 64–67.

———— 1950b. The migration of lemon soles in northern Hecate Strait. Fish. Res. Board Can. Pac. Progr. Rep. 85: 75–79.

———— 1954. The rockfish *Sebastodes rubrivinctus* in British Columbia waters. J. Fish. Res. Bd. Canada 11(3): 335–338.

———— 1956a. Climatic trends and fluctuations in yield of marine fisheries of the northeast Pacific. J. Fish. Res. Bd. Canada 13(3): 357–374.

———— 1956b. Factors influencing the survival of the lemon sole (*Parophrys vetulus*) in Hecate Strait, British Columbia. J. Fish. Res. Bd. Canada 13(5): 647–694.

———— 1961. Observations on the ecology of the Pacific cod (*Gadus macrocephalus*) in Canadian waters. J. Fish. Res. Bd. Canada 18(4): 513–558.

———— 1964. Preliminary results of studies on growth and mortality of Pacific cod (*Gadus macrocephalus*) in Hecate Strait, British Columbia. J. Fish. Res. Bd. Canada 21(5): 1051–1067.

KETCHEN, K. S., AND C. R. FORRESTER. 1954. The sablefish fishery of British Columbia. Pac. Mar. Fish. Comm. Bull. 3: 57–72.

———— 1955. Migrations of lemon sole (*Parophrys vetulus*) in the Strait of Georgia. Fish. Res. Board Can. Pac. Progr. Rep. 104: 11–15.

———— 1966. Population dynamics of the petrale sole, *Eopsetta jordani*, in waters off western Canada. Fish. Res. Board Can. Bull. 153: 195 p.

KETCHEN, K. S., R. I. PETERSON, AND C. R. FORRESTER. 1951. Fluctuations in the length and age composition of lemon soles and rock soles in northern Hecate Strait. Fish. Res. Board Can. Pac. Progr. Rep. 87: 27–31.

KETCHEN, K. S., AND R. M. WILSON. 1961. A new record of the long-finned cod, *Antimora rostrata* Gunther, from British Columbia waters. J. Fish. Res. Bd. Canada 18(2): 291.

KILAMBI, V. R. MS 1965. Heterogeneity among three spawning populations of the surf smelt, *Hypomesus pretiosus* (Girard) in the State of Washington. Ph.D. Thesis. Univ. Wash. 154 p.

KINCAID, T. * 1919. An annotated list of Puget Sound fishes, 51 p. Olympia, Wash.

KITANO, Y. 1969. The age and growth of the yellowfin sole (*Limanda aspera*) in Hecate Strait, British Columbia. Fish. Res. Board Can. Tech. Rep. 109: 36 p.

KLAWE, W. L. 1961. Notes on larvae, juveniles, and spawning of bonito (*Sarda*) from the eastern Pacific Ocean. Pac. Sci. 15(4): 487–493.

KLIUKANOV, V. A. 1969. Morphological bases of classification of smelts of the genus *Osmerus*. Morfologicheskie osnovy sistematiki koriushek roda *Osmerus* (Osmeridae). Zoological Institute, USSR Academy of Science (Leningrad). Zool. J. 48(1): 99–109.

KNIGHT, W. 1968. Asymptotic growth: an example of nonsense disguised as mathematics. J. Fish. Res. Bd. Canada 25(6): 1303–1307.

KOBAYASHI, K., AND T. UENO. * 1956. Fishes from the northern Pacific and from Bristol Bay. Bull. Fac. Fish., Tokyo Univ. 6(4): 239–265.

694

KREJSA, R. J. 1964. Reproductive behaviour and sexual dimorphism in the manacled sculpin, *Synchirus gilli* Bean. Copeia 1964(2): 448–450.

KUTTY, M. K. MS 1963. An ecological study and theoretical consideration of butter sole (*Isopsetta isolepis*) population in Hecate Strait. Ph.D. Thesis. Dep. Zool. Univ. British Columbia.

LANE, R. K. 1962. A review of the temperature and salinity structures in the approaches to Vancouver Island, British Columbia. J. Fish. Res. Bd. Canada 19(1): 45–91.

　　1965. Wind, nearshore ocean temperature, and the albacore tuna catch off Oregon. Fish. Comm. Oreg. Res. Briefs 11(1): 25–28.

LARKIN, P. A., AND W. E. RICKER. 1964. Canada's Pacific marine fisheries. Past performance and future prospects. Inventory of the natural resources of British Columbia. p. 194–268.

LASKER, R. 1964. An experimental study of the effect of temperature on the incubation time, development, and growth of Pacific sardine embryos and larvae. Copeia 1964(2): 399–405.

LAVENBERG, R. J., AND J. E. FITCH. 1966. Annotated list of fishes collected by midwater trawl in the Gulf of California, March–April 1964. Calif. Fish Game 52(2): 92–110.

LEBRASSEUR, R. J. MS 1964a. Data record. Collections of fish taken in Isaacs-Kidd midwater trawl from northeastern Pacific Ocean 1958–59. Fish. Res. Board Can. MS Rep. Ser. Oceanogr. and Limnol. 175: 25 p.

　　1964b. Stomach contents of blue shark (*Prionace glauca* L.) taken in the Gulf of Alaska. J. Fish. Res. Bd. Canada 21(4): 861–862.

　　MS 1965. Stomach contents of salmonoids caught in the northeastern Pacific ocean — 1958. Fish. Res. Board Can. Nanaimo Biol. Sta. Circ. (Statist. Ser.) 15 (vol. 1).

　　1966. Stomach contents of salmon and steelhead trout in the northeastern Pacific Ocean. J. Fish. Res. Bd. Canada 23(1): 85–100.

LEBRASSEUR, R. J., AND D. A. DOIDGE. MS 1966. Stomach contents of salmonoids caught in the northeastern Pacific ocean. Fish. Res. Board Can. Nanaimo Biol. Sta. Circ. (Statist. Ser.) 20 (vol. 2); 21 (vol. 3); 22 (vol) 4; 23 (vol. 5).

LEBRASSEUR, R. J., AND P. R. PARKER. 1964. Growth rates of central British Columbia pink salmon (*Oncorhynchus gorbuscha*). J. Fish. Res. Bd. Canada 21(5): 1101–1128.

LEIM, A. H. 1924. The life history of the shad (*Alosa sapidissima* (Wilson)) with special reference to the factors limiting its abundance. Contrib. Can. Biol. 2(11): 161–284.

LEIM, A. H., AND W. B. SCOTT. 1966. Fishes of the Atlantic Coast of Canada. Fish. Res. Board Can. Bull. 155: 485 p.

LEMIER, E. H. 1951. Recent records of the great white shark *Carcharodon carcharias* on the Washington Coast. Copeia 1951(3): 249.

LEONG, C-C. MS 1967. Fecundity of surf smelt, *Hypomesus pretiosus* (Girard), in the State of Washington. M.Sc. Thesis. Univ. Wash. 99 p.

LEONG, R. J. H., AND C. P. O'CONNELL. 1969. A laboratory study of particulate and filter feeding of the northern anchovy (*Engraulis mordax*). J. Fish. Res. Bd. Canada 26(3): 557–582.

LEVINGS, C. D. MS 1965. A comparison of the growth rates of the rock sole, *Lepidopsetta bilineata* Ayres, in northern Pacific waters. B.Sc. Thesis. Dep. Zool. Univ. British Columbia.

　　1968. Fertilized eggs of the butter sole, *Isopsetta isolepis*, in Skidegate Inlet, British Columbia. J. Fish. Res. Bd. Canada 25(8): 1743–1744.

　　1969. The zoarcid *Lycodopsis pacificus* in outer Burrard Inlet, British Columbia. J. Fish. Res. Bd. Canada 26(9): 2403–2412.

LEWIS, R. C. 1929. The food habits of the California sardine in relation to the seasonal distribution of microplankton. Bull. Scripps Inst. Oceanogr. Univ. Calif. Tech. Ser. 2(3): 155–180.

LIMBAUGH, C. 1962. Life history and ecological notes on the *Aulorhynchus flavidus*, a hemibranch fish of western North America. Copeia 1962(2): 549–555.

LINDSEY, C. C. 1968. Temperatures of red and white muscle in recently caught marlin and other large tropical fish. J. Fish. Res. Bd. Canada 25(9): 1987–1992.

LORD, J. K. * 1866. The naturalist in Vancouver Island and British Columbia, 2 vol., 1, 358 p., 2, 375 p. Richard Bentley, London. 1866.

LUCAS, V. Z. MS 1930. Notes on the life-history of *Squalus sucklii* Girard. Fish. Res. Board Can. Biol. Ser. MS Rep. (Nanaimo). 6 p.

LYLES, C. H. 1969. Fishery statistics of the United States. Stat. Digest 61. U.S. Dep. Inter. 490 p.

MACGINITIE, G. E. 1930. The natural history of the mud shrimp *Upogebia pugettensis*. Ann. Mag. Natur. Hist. 10(6): 36–44.

　　1934. The natural history of *Callianassa californiensis* Dana. Amer. Mildl. Natur. 15: 166–177.

　　1935. Ecological aspects of a California marine estuary. Amer. Mildl. Natur. 16(5): 629.

695

1939. Some effects of fresh water on the fauna of a marine harbor. Amer. Mildl. Natur. 21(3): 681–686.

MACGREGOR, J. S. 1957. Fecundity of the Pacific sardine (*Sardinops caerulea*). U.S. Fish Wildl. Serv. Fish. Bull. 121, Vol. 57: 427–448.

1966a. Synopsis on the biology of the jack mackerel (*Trachurus symmetricus*). FAO Species Synopsis, 86. U.S. Fish Wildl. Serv. Spec. Sci. Rep. 526: 16 p.

1966b. Fecundity of the Pacific hake, *Merluccius productus* (Ayres). Calif. Fish Game 52(2): 111–116.

MAGNUSON, J. J. 1969. Digestion and food consumption by skipjack tuna (*Katsuwonus pelamis*). Trans. Amer. Fish. Soc. 98(3): 379–392.

MAHER, F. P., AND P. A. LARKIN. 1955. Life history of the steelhead trout of the Chilliwack River, British Columbia. Trans. Amer. Fish. Soc. 1954(84): 27–38.

MAKUSHOK, V. M. 1958. The morphology and classification of the northern blennioid fishes (Stichaeoidae, Blennioidei, Pisces). Proc. Zool. Inst. (Tr. Zool. Inst. Akad. Nauk SSSR 1958(25): 3–129 (83 text figs.)). Transl. Alice R. Gosline, U.S. Nat. Mus. Washington, D.C. 1959.

1963. The specific identity of *Nematonurus longifils* (Günther 1877) and *N. clarki* (Jordan and Gilbert 1898) and some remarks on age-dependent variations in Macruridae (Pisces). Tr. Inst. Okeanol. Muskva 73: 139–163.

MALINS, D. C., AND A. BARONE. 1970. Glyceryl ether metabolism : regulation of buoyancy in dogfish *Squalus acanthias*. Science 167(3914): 79–80.

MANZER, J. I. 1946a. Interesting movements as shown by the recoveries of certain species of tagged fish. Fish. Res. Board Can. Pac. Progr. Rep. 67: 31.

1946b. First year returns of lemon sole tags used off the west coast of Vancouver Island. Fish. Res. Board Can. Pac. Progr. Rep. 68: 51.

1947. A July spawning population of sand soles in Sydney Inlet. Fish. Res. Board Can. Pac. Progr. Rep. 73: 70–71.

MS 1949. The availability, exploitation, abundance and movement of the butter sole (*Isopsetta isolepis* Lockington) in Skidegate Inlet, Queen Charlotte Islands, during 1946. M.A. Thesis. Dep. Zool. Univ. British Columbia.

1951. Growth in lemon sole in northern Hecate Strait. Fish. Res. Board Can. Pac. Progr. Rep. 86: 13–15.

1952. Notes on dispersion and growth of some British Columbia bottom fishes. J. Fish. Res. Bd. Canada 8(5): 374–377.

1956. Distribution and movement of young Pacific salmon during early ocean residence. Fish. Res. Board Can. Pac. Progr. Rep. 106: 24–28.

1964. Preliminary observations on the vertical distribution of Pacific salmon (Genus *Oncorhynchus*) in the Gulf of Alaska. J. Fish. Res. Bd. Canada 21(5): 891–903.

1965. *Sarda lineolata* (Girard), a Pacific bonito, in the Strait of Georgia, British Columbia. J. Fish. Res. Bd. Canada 22(3): 853–855.

1969. Stomach contents of juvenile Pacific salmon in Chatham Sound and adjacent waters. J. Fish. Res. Bd. Canada 26(8): 2219–2223.

MANZER, J. I., AND F. H. C. TAYLOR. 1946. Rate of growth in lemon sole in the Strait of Georgia. Fish. Res. Board Can. Pac. Progr. Rep. 72: 24–27.

MARKLEY, M. H. 1940. Notes on the food habits and parasites of the stickleback, *Gasterosteus aculeatus* (Linnaeus), in the Sacramento River, California. Copeia 1940(4): 223–225.

MARR, J. C. 1948a. Observations on the spawning of oceanic skipjack (*Katsuwonus pelamis*) and yellowfin tuna (*Neothunnus macropterus*) in the northern Marshall Islands. U.S. Fish Wildl. Serv. Fish. Bull. 44, Vol. 51: 201–206.

1948b. Two additions to the known fish fauna of California. Copeia 1948(2): 140.

MARSHALL, N. B. * 1955. Studies of alepisauroid fishes. Discovery Rep. 27: 305–336.

1966. Family Scopelosauridae. p. 194–459. *In* Fishes of the western North Atlantic. Mem. Sears Found. Mar. Res. 1(5): 647 p.

MATSUBARA, K. 1943. Studies on the scorpaenoid fishes of Japan. Pt. 2 Anatomy, physiology, and taxonomy. Trans. Sigenkogaku Kenkyusyo 2: 171–486.

1955. Fish morphology and hierarchy. Parts I–II–III. Ishizaki-Shoten, Tokyo, Japan. 1605 p., 135 pl.

MATSUI, T. 1967. Review of the mackerel genera *Scomber* and *Rastrelliga* with description of a new species of *Rastrelliga*. Copeia 1967(1): 71–83.

MATSUMOTO, W. M., F. H. TALBOT, B. B. COLLETTE, AND R. S. SHOMURA. 1969. Pacific bonito (*Sarda chiliensis*) and skipjack tuna (*Katsuwonus pelamis*) without stripes. Copeia 1969(2): 397–398.

696

MAUL, G. E. 1953. Rediscovery of the trichiurid fish *Benthodesmus simonyi* (Steindachner) off Madeira. Proc. Zool. Soc. London 123(1): 167–170.

MAXFIELD, G. H. 1967a. Pacific salmon literature compilation – 1900–59. U.S. Dep. Commer. Clearinghouse for Federal Scientific and Technical Information Doc. P.B. 174, 101: 20 p. (processed).

    1967b. Pacific salmon literature compilation – 1900–59. U.S. Dep. Commer. Clearinghouse for Federal Scientific and Technical Information Doc. P.B. 174, 102, 645 microfiches (42, 341 p.). $185.

MCALLISTER, D. E. 1960. Keys to the marine fishes of Arctic Canada. Natur. Hist. Pap. Nat. Mus. Can., 5: 1–21.

    1961. A collection of oceanic fishes from off British Columbia with a discussion of the evolution of black peritoneum. Nat. Mus. Can. Bull. 171: 39–43.

    1963. A revision of the smelt family, Osmeridae. Nat. Mus. Can. Bull. 191: 43 p.

    1964. Fish collections from eastern Hudson Bay. Can. Field-Natur. 78(3): 131–206.

MCALLISTER, D. E., AND R. J. KREJSA. 1961. Placement of the prowfishes, Zaproridae, in the superfamily Stichaeoidae. Natur. Hist. Pap. Nat. Mus. Can. 11: 1–4.

MCALLISTER, D. E., AND E. I. S. REES. 1964. A revision of the eelpout genus *Melanostigma* with a new genus, and with comments on *Maynea*. Nat. Mus. Can. Bull. 199: 85–110.

MCALLISTER, D. E., AND S. J. WESTRHEIM. 1965. Widow rockfish, *Sebastodes entomelas*, new to British Columbia waters. J. Fish. Res. Bd. Canada 22(6): 1559–1564.

MCCRIMMON, H. R. 1968. Carp in Canada. Fish. Res. Board Can. Bull. 165: 92 p.

MCCRIMMON, H. R., AND T. L. MARSHALL. 1968. World distribution of brown trout, *Salmo trutta*. J. Fish. Res. Bd. Canada 25(12): 2527–2548.

MCDONALD, M. * 1890. Introduction and acclimation of new species. Rep. U.S. Fish Comm. 15: 51–53.

MCHUGH, J. L. 1939. The eulachon. Fish. Res. Board Can. Pac. Progr. Rep. 40: 17–22.

    1940a. Growth of young herring in Departure Bay in 1939. Fish. Res. Board Can. Pac. Progr. Rep. 42: 6–7.

    1940b. Where does the eulachon spawn? Fish. Res. Board Can. Pac. Progr. Rep. 44: 18–19.

    1942a. Variation of vertebral centra in young Pacific herring. J. Fish. Res. Bd. Canada 5(4): 347–360.

    1942b. Vertebral number of young herring in southern British Columbia. J. Fish. Res. Bd. Canada 5(5): 474–484.

    1952. The food of albacore (*Germo alalunga*) off California and Baja California. Bull. Scripps Inst. Oceanogr. Univ. Calif. 6(4): 161–172.

    1954. Geographical variation in the Pacific herring. Copeia 1954(2): 139–151.

MCHUGH, J. L., AND J. E. FITCH. 1951. An annotated list of the clupeoid fishes of the Pacific coast from Alaska to Cape San Lucas, Baja California. Calif. Fish Game 37(4): 491–495.

MCINERNEY, J. E. 1964. Salinity preference: an orientation mechanism in salmon migration. J. Fish. Res. Bd. Canada 21(5): 995–1018.

MCINERNEY, J. E., AND D. O. EVANS. 1970. Habitat characteristics of the Pacific hagfish, *Polistotrema stouti*. J. Fish. Res. Bd. Canada 27(5): 966–968.

MCKECHNIE, R. J., AND L. W. MILLER. 1971. The striped bass party boat fishery: 1960–1968. Calif. Fish Game 57(1): 4–16.

MCKENZIE, R. A. 1964. Smelt life history and fishery in the Miramichi River, New Brunswick. Fish. Res. Board Can. Bull. 144: 77 p.

MCMYNN, R. G. MS 1951. The effects of some constant and some changing conditions of salinity on the development and mortality of the eggs and larvae of the Pacific herring *Clupea pallasii* Cuvier. M.A. Thesis. Dep. Zool. Univ. British Columbia.

MCPHAIL, J. D. 1961. A systematic study of the *Salvelinus alpinus* complex in North America. J. Fish. Res. Bd. Canada 18(5): 793–816.

    1969. Two rare sculpins (Cottidae) new to the marine fauna of British Columbia. Can. Field-Natur. 83(4): 400–401.

    1970. A new species of prickleback, *Bryozoichthys marjorius* (Chirolophinae), from the eastern North Pacific. J. Fish. Res. Bd. Canada 27(12): 2362–2365.

MEAD, G. W. 1953. *Tarletonbeania taylori*, a new lanternfish from the western North Pacific. Zoologica 38(2): 105–108.

MEAD, G. W., AND R. L. HAEDRICH. 1965. The distribution of the oceanic fish, *Brama brama*. Bull. Mus. Comp. Zool. 134(2): 67 p.

MEAD, G. W., AND F. H. C. TAYLOR. 1953. A collection of oceanic fishes from off northeastern Japan. J. Fish. Res. Bd. Canada 10(8): 560–582.

MERRIMAN, D. 1941. Studies on the striped bass (*Roccus saxatilis*) of the Atlantic coast. U.S. Fish Wildl. Serv. Fish. Bull. 35, Vol. 50: 1–77.

MESSERSMITH, J. D. 1965. Southern range extension for chum and silver salmon. Calif. Fish Game 51(3): 220.

METTEN, H. 1939. Studies on the reproduction of the dogfish. Phil. Trans. Roy. Soc. London, Ser. B. 230(569): 217–238.

MILLER, B., AND D. W. GREENFIELD. 1965. A juvenile six-gill shark (*Hexanchus corinus*) from the San Juan Islands, Washington. J. Fish. Res. Bd. Canada 22(3): 857–859.

MILLER, B. C. 1967. Stomach content of adult starry flounder and sand sole in East Sound, Orcas Island, Washington. J. Fish. Res. Bd. Canada 24(12): 2515–2526.

MILLER, B. S. MS 1965. Food and feeding studies on adults of two species of pleuronectids (*Platichthys stellatus* and *Psettichthys melanostictus*) in East Sound, Orcas Island, Washington. M.Sc. Thesis. Univ. Wash. 131 p.

———— MS 1969. Life history observations on normal and tumor bearing flathead sole in East Sound, Orcas Island (Washington). Ph.D. Thesis. Univ. Wash. 131 p.

MILLER, D. J. 1956. Anchovy. Calif. Coop. Oceanic Fish. Invest. Progr. Rep., Apr. 1955 – June 1956: 20–26.

MILLER, D. J., AND J. SCHMIDTKE. 1956. Report on the distribution and abundance of Pacific herring (*Clupea pallasi*) along the coast of central and southern California. Calif. Fish Game 42(3): 163–187.

MILLER, R. R., AND D. S. ERDMAN. 1948. The range and characters of *Synchirus gilli*, a remarkable cottid fish of the northeastern Pacific. Copeia 1948(2): 85–89.

MILLER, R. R., AND C. L. HUBBS. 1969. Systematics of *Gasterosteus aculeatus*, with particular reference to intergradation and introgression along the Pacific coast of North America: a commentary on a recent contribution. Copeia 1969(1): 52–69.

MILLIKAN, A. E., AND B. H. PATTIE. 1970. Hermaphroditism in a Pacific hake, *Merluccius productus*, from Puget Sound, Washington. J. Fish. Res. Bd. Canada 27(2): 409–410.

MILNE, D. J. 1950. The difference in the growth of coho salmon on the east and west coasts of Vancouver Island in 1950. Fish. Res. Board Can. Pac. Progr. Rep. 85: 80–82.

———— 1952. The coho salmon run off the northern part of the west coast of Vancouver Island in 1951. Fish. Res. Board Can. Pac. Progr. Rep. 91: 28–30.

———— 1964. The chinook and coho salmon fisheries of British Columbia, with appendix by H. Godfrey. Fish. Res. Board Can. Bull. 142: 46 p.

MOFFETT, C. W. MS 1970. Random observations of some fish of the San Juan Island area, Bellingham, Washington. MS. 4 p.

MOISEEV, P. 1953. Cod and flounders of far eastern seas. Izv. Tikhookean. Nauch.-Issled. Inst. Ryb. Khoz. Okeanogr. 40: 1–287. (Transl. from Russian by Fish. Res. Board Can. Transl. Ser. No. 119, 1958).

MORGAN, A. R. 1961. Siletz Bay surf perch tagging. Fish. Comm. Oreg. Res. Briefs 8(1): 5–13.

MORRIS, R. W. 1956. Clasping mechanism of the cottid fish, *Oligocottus snyderi* Greeley. Pac. Sci. 10(3): 315–318.

MORROW, J. E., JR. 1964. Family Chauliodontidae, p. 274–289. *In* Fishes of the western North Atlantic. Mem. Sears Found. Mar. Res. 1(4): 599 p.

MORTON, W. M. 1970. On the validity of all subspecific descriptions of North American *Salvelinus malma* (Walbaum). Copeia 1970(3): 581–597.

MOSER, H. G. 1967. Reproduction and development of *Sebastodes paucispinis* and comparison with other rockfishes off southern California. Copeia 1967(4): 773–797.

MOSER, H. G., AND E. H. AHLSTROM. 1970. Development of lanternfishes (family Myctophidae) in the California current. Part 1. Species with narrow-eyed larvae. Bull. Los Angeles Cty. Mus. Natur. Hist. Sci. (7): 145 p.

MOTTLEY, C. M. 1929. Pacific salmon migration. Report on the study of the scales of the spring salmon, *Oncorhynchus tschawytscha*, tagged in 1926 and 1927 off the west coast of Vancouver Island, Contrib. Can. Biol. Fish., N.S. 3(30): 473–494, 3 pl.

MUNDIE, J. H. 1968. Ecological implications of the diet of juvenile coho in streams. (Abstract). Symposium salmon and trout in streams. Univ. British Columbia 1968.

MUNRO, J. A., AND W. A. CLEMENS. 1931. Water fowl in relation to the spawning of herring in British Columbia. Bull. Biol. Board Can. 17: 46 p.

MURPHY, G. L. 1966. Population biology of the Pacific sardine (*Sardinops caerulea*). Proc. Calif. Acad. Sci. 4(34)1: 1–84.

MYERS, G. S. 1950. Identity of the stromateid fish *Centrolophus californicus* with *Icichthys lockingtoni*. Stanford Ichthyol. Bull. 3(4): 181.

———— 1960. A new zeomorph fish of the family Oreosomatidae from the coast of California, with notes on the family. Stanford Ichthyol. Bull. 7(4): 89–98.

698

MYERS, G. S., AND J. H. WALES. 1930. On the occurrence and habits of ocean sunfish (*Mola mola*) in Monterey Bay, California. Copeia 1930(1): 11.
MYRE, R. J. 1967. Mortality estimates from tagging experiments on Pacific halibut. Int. Pac. Halibut Comm. Tech. Rep. 42: 1–41.

NAFPAKTITIS, B. G., AND M. NAFPAKTITIS. 1969. Lanternfishes (family Myctophidae) collected during cruises 3 and 6 of the R/V *Anton Bruun* in the Indian Ocean. Bull. Los Angeles Cty. Mus. Natur. Hist. Sci. (5): 79 p.
NAGASAKI, F. 1958. The fecundity of Pacific herring (*Clupea pallasi*) in British Columbia coastal waters. J. Fish. Res. Bd. Canada 15(3): 313–330.
NAKAMURA, N. 1948. On the relation between salinity content of the water and living conditions and productivity of carps in ponds near the sea. Tokyo Univ. Physiog. Sci. Res. Inst. Bull. 1(51). (Biol. Abstr.)
NARVER, D. W. 1969. Age and size of steelhead trout in Babine River, British Columbia. J. Fish. Res. Bd. Canada 26(10): 2754–2760.
NEAVE, F. 1943. Diurnal fluctuations in the upstream migrations of coho and spring salmon. J. Fish. Res. Bd. Canada 6(2): 158–163.
    1944. Racial characteristics and migrating habits in *Salmo gairdneri*. J. Fish. Res. Bd. Canada 6(3): 245–251.
    1949. Game fish populations of the Cowichan River. Fish. Res. Board Can. Bull. 84: 32 p.
    1952. Principles affecting the size of pink and chum salmon populations in British Columbia. J. Fish. Res. Bd. Canada 9(9): 450–491.
    1955. Notes on the seaward migration of pink and chum salmon fry. J. Fish. Res. Bd. Canada 12(3): 369–374.
    1959. Records of fishes from waters off the British Columbia coast. J. Fish. Res. Bd. Canada 16(3): 383–384.
    1964. Ocean migrations of Pacific salmon. J. Fish. Res. Bd. Canada 21(5): 1227–1244.
NEAVE, F., AND M. G. HANAVAN. 1960. Seasonal distribution of some epipelagic fishes in the Gulf of Alaska region. J. Fish. Res. Bd. Canada 17(2): 221–233.
NEEDLER, M. 1954. Confidential report. Fish. Res. Board Can. Pac. Biol. Sta., Nanaimo 1953: 128.
NIKOL'SKII, G. V. 1961. Special ichthyology. Transl. from Russian by Israel Program for Sci. Transl., Jerusalem.
NISHIMOTO, J. 1970. Western range extension of the rosethorn rockfish *Sebastes helvomaculatus* (Ayres). Calif. Fish Game 56(3): 204–205.
NORMAN, J. R. * 1930. Oceanic fishes and flatfishes collected in 1925–27. Discovery Rep. 2: 261–370.
    1934. A systematic monograph of the flatfishes (Heterosomata), Vol. 1. Psettodidae, Bothidae, Pleuronectidae. Brit. Mus. Natur. Hist.: VIII +459 p.

O'CONNELL, C. P. 1953. The life history of the cabezon, *Scorpaenichthys marmoratus* (Ayres). Calif. Dep. Fish Game Fish. 93: 76 p.
ODEMAR, M. W. 1964. Southern range extension of the eulachon, *Thaleichthys pacificus*. Calif. Fish Game 50(4): 305–307.
OKADA, Y. 1955. Fishes of Japan. Maruzen Co. Ltd., Tokyo. 434 p. + 28.
OKOMURA, O. 1970. Macrourina (Pisces). Fauna Japonica. Academic Press of Japan. 216 p.
ORANGE, C. J., AND B. D. FINK. 1963. Migration of a tagged bluefin tuna across the Pacific Ocean. Calif. Fish Game 49(4): 307-309.
ORCUTT, H. G. 1950. The life history of the starry flounder, *Platichthys stellatus* (Pallas). Calif. Div. Fish. Game Fish Bull. 78: 64 p.
ORSI, J. J. 1968. The embryology of the English sole, *Parophrys vetulus*. Calif. Fish Game 54(3): 133–155.
ORTON, G. L. 1964. Identification of *Leptocephala acuticeps* Regan as the larva of the eel genus *Avocettina*. Pac. Sci. 18(2): 186–201.
OSGOOD, W. H. * 1901. Natural history of the Queen Charlotte Islands, British Columbia. North American Fauna, 21, [Fishes p. 20]. U.S. Bur. Biol. Surv. Wash.
OTSU, T. 1960. Albacore migration and growth in the North Pacific Ocean as estimated from tag recoveries. Pac. Sci. 14(3): 257–266.
OUTRAM, D. N. 1958. The magnitude of herring spawn losses due to bird predation on the west coast of Vancouver Island. Fish. Res. Board Can. Pac. Progr. Rep. 111: 9–13.

699

PALMEN, A. T. 1954. Occurrence of the eel-pout, *Aprodon cortezianus* in Queen Charlotte Sound, B.C. Wash. Dep. Fish. Fish. Res. Pap. 1(2): 45.

    * 1956. A comparison of otoliths and interopercular bones as age indicators of English sole. Wash. Dep. Fish. Fish. Res. Pap. 1(4): 5–20.

PARKER, G. H. 1915. The directive influence of the sense of smell in the dogfish. Bull. U.S. Bur. Fish. 33: 61–68.

PARKER, R. R. 1960. Critical size and maximum yield for chinook salmon (*Oncorhynchus tshawytscha*). J. Fish. Res. Bd. Canada 17(2): 199–210.

    1963. On the problem of maximum yield from North Pacific sockeye salmon stocks. J. Fish. Res. Bd. Canada 20(6): 1371–1396.

    1964. Estimation of sea mortality rates for the 1960 brood-year pink salmon of Hook Nose Creek, British Columbia. J. Fish. Res. Bd. Canada 21(5): 1019–1034.

    1968. Marine mortality schedules of pink salmon of the Bella Coola River, central British Columbia. J. Fish. Res. Bd. Canada 25(4): 757–794.

PARR, A. E. *1927. The stomiatoid fishes of the order Gymnophotodermi. Bull. Bingham Oceanogr. Collect. Yale Univ. 3(2): 1–123.

    * 1928. Deepsea fishes of the order Iniomi from the waters around the Bahama and Bermuda Islands with annotated keys to the Sudidae, Myctophidae, Scopelarchidae, Evermannellidae, Omosudidae. Cetomimidae and Rondeletidae of the world. Bull. Bingham Oceanogr. Collect. Yale Univ. 3(3): 1–193.

    1929a. Notes on the species of myctophine fishes represented by type specimens in the United States National Museum. Proc. U.S. Nat. Mus. 76(10): 1–47.

    * 1929b. A contribution to the osteology and classification of the Orders Iniomi and Xenoberyces. Occ. Pap. Bingham Oceanogr. Collect. Yale Univ. 3(2): 1–45.

    * 1933. Deepsea Bercymorphi from the waters around the Bahama and Bermuda Islands. Bull. Bingham Oceanogr. Collect. Yale Univ. 3(6): 1–51.

    1953. A new genus of Searsidae from Japan. Amer. Mus. Novitates 1628: 7 p.

    1960. The fishes of the family Searsidae. Dana-Rep. 51: 109 p.

PARTLO, J. M. 1950. A report on the 1949 albacore fishery (*Thunnus alalunga*). Fish. Res. Board Can. Nanaimo Biol. Sta. Circ. (Gen. Ser.) 20: 1–37.

    1955a. Distribution, age, and growth of eastern Pacific albacore (*Thunnus alalunga* Gmelin). J. Fish. Res. Bd. Canada 12(1): 35–60.

    1955b. Histological studies on albacore (*Thunnus alalunga*) gonads from the eastern Pacific. J. Fish. Res. Bd. Canada 12(1): 61–67.

PASQUALE, N. 1964. Notable migrations of sablefish tagged in Puget Sound. Wash. Dep. Fish. Fish. Res. Pap. 2(3): 68.

PATTEN, B. G., D. T. RODMAN AND K. D. WALDRON. 1965. The Pacific bonito, *Sarda chiliensis* (Cuvier), in Puget Sound, Washington, Calif. Fish Game 51(4): 298–299.

PATTIE, B. H., AND C. S. BAKER. 1969. Extensions of the known northern range limits of ocean whitefish, *Caulolatilus princeps,* and California halibut, *Paralichthys californicus.* J. Fish. Res. Bd. Canada 26(5): 1371–1372.

PAULIK, G. J., AND A. C. DeLACY. 1958. Changes in the swimming ability of Columbia River sockeye salmon during upstream migration. Univ. Wash. Sch. Fish. Tech. Rep. 44: 40 p.

PAXTON, J. R. 1967. Biological notes on southern California lanternfishes (family Myctophidae). Calif. Fish Game 53(3): 214–217.

PEARCY, W. G. 1962. Egg masses and early development stages of the scorpaenid fish *Sebastolobus.* J. Fish. Res. Bd. Canada 19(6): 1169–1173.

PEARCY, W. G., AND C. L. OSTERBERG. 1968. Zinc-65 and manganese-54 in albacore *Thunnus alalunga* from the west coast of North America. Limnol. Oceanogr. 13(3): 490–498.

PEDEN, A. E. MS 1964. A systematic revision of the Hemilepidotinae, a subfamily of cottid fishes. M.Sc. Thesis. Dep. Zool. Univ. British Columbia. 162 p.

    1966a. Occurrences of the fishes *Pholis schultzi* and *Liparis mucosus* in British Columbia. J. Fish. Res. Bd. Canada 23(2): 313–316.

    1966b. Reexamination of two species of the stichaeid genus, *Anoplarchus. Copeia* 1966(2): 340–345.

    1966c. Rare marine fishes from British Columbia with first records of silver perch *Hyperprosopon ellipticum,* and shanny, *Leptoclinus maculatus.* J. Fish. Res. Bd. Canada 23(8): 1277–1280.

    1968. Two new specimens of the notocanthid fish, *Macdonaldia challengeri,* in the eastern North Pacific Ocean. J. Fish. Res. Bd. Canada 25(1): 181–188.

    1970. A new cottid fish, *Nautichthys robustus* from Alaska and British Columbia. Nat. Mus.

Can., Publ. Biol. Oceanogr. 2: 1–10.

1971. Extension of the known range of the masked greenling (*Hexagrammos octogrammus*) to British Columbia. J. Fish. Res. Bd. Canada 28(6): 927–928.

PEDEN, A. E. AND R. C. BEST. 1966. Northern record of a calico surfperch, *Amphistichus koelzi*. Calif. Fish Game 52(1): 56–57.

PEDEN, A. E., AND C. G. GRUCHY. 1971. First record of the bluespotted poacher, *Xeneretmus triacanthus*, in British Columbia. J. Fish. Res. Bd. Canada 28(9): 1347–1348.

PEDEN, A. E., AND K. W. STEWART. 1964. Extension of the known range of the atherinid fish, *Atherinops affinis*. Copeia 1964(1): 239–240.

PEPPAR, J. L. MS 1965. Some features of the life history of the cockscomb prickleback, *Anoplarchus purpurescens* Gill. M.Sc. Thesis. Dep. Zool. Univ. British Columbia. 159 p.

PEREYRA, W. T., W. G. PEARCY, AND F. E. CARVEY, JR. 1969. *Sebastodes flavidus*, a shelf rockfish feeding on mesopelagic fauna, with consideration of the ecological implications. J. Fish. Res. Bd. Canada 26(8): 2211–2215.

PETERS, W. C. H. * 1872. Über eine neue Gattung von Fischen aus der Familie der Cataphracti Cuv., *Scombrocottus salmoneus* von der Vancouvers-Insil. Monatsber. Deut. Akad. Wiss. Berlin. 1872: 568–570.

PHILLIPS, J. B. 1932. Unusually good fishing in and off Monterey Bay. Calif. Fish Game 18(1): 21–24.

1935. Experiment to determine the feasibility of the use of trammel nets in Monterey Bay. Calif. Fish Game 21(2):138–148.

1937. Record mackerel taken at Monterey. Calif. Fish Game 23(4): 337.

1942. Wall-eyed pollock caught in Monterey Bay. Calif. Fish Game 28(3): 155–156.

1943. Another wall-eyed pollock at Monterey. Calif. Fish Game 29(1): 83.

1948a Comparison of calculated fish lengths based on scales from different body areas of the sardine, *Sardinops caerulea*. Copeia 1948(2): 99–105.

1948b. Growth of the sardine, *Sardinops caerulea*, 1941–42 through 1946–47. Calif. Div. Fish Game Fish Bull. 71: 33 p.

1951. Pacific cod off central California. Calif. Fish Game 37(2): 351.

1952. Yellow sablefish (black cod) taken in Monterey Bay. Calif. Fish Game 38(3): 437–438.

1953a. Sleeper shark, *Somninosus pacificus*, caught off Fort Bragg, California. Calif. Fish Game 39(1): 147–149.

1953b. Additional Pacific cod taken off central California. Calif. Fish Game 39(4): 559.

1957. A review of the rockfishes of California. Calif. Dep. Fish Game Fish. Bull. 104: 157 p.

1958a. The fishery for sablefish, *Anoplopoma fimbria*. Calif. Fish Game 44(1): 79–84.

1958b. Southerly occurrences of three northern species of fish during 1957, a warmwater year on the California coast. Calif. Fish Game 44(4): 349–350.

* 1958c. Rockfish review. In the marine fish catch of California. Calif. Dep. Fish Game Fish Bull. 105: 7–25.

1964. Life history studies on ten species of rockfish (genus *Sebastodes*). Calif. Dep. Fish Game Fish Bull. 126: 70 p.

1966. Skilfish, *Erilepis zonifer* (Lockington), in California and Pacific northwest waters. Calif. Fish Game 52(3): 151–156.

1967. A longfin sanddab, *Citharichthys xanthostigma*, and a skilfish, *Erilepis zonifer*, taken in Monterey Bay. Calif. Fish Game 53(4): 297–298.

PHILLIPS, J. B., C.R. CLOTHIER, AND D. H. FRY. 1954. A racial study of Pacific coast sablefish, *Anoplopoma fimbria*, based on meristic counts. Pac. Mar. Fish. Comm. Bull. 3: 87–101.

PHINNEY, D. E., AND M. L. DAHLBERG. 1968. Western range extension of the surf smelt, *Hypomesus pretiosus pretiosus*. J. Fish. Res. Bd. Canada 25(1): 203–204.

PICARD, G. L. 1961. Oceanographic features of inlets in the British Columbia mainland coast. J. Fish. Res. Bd. Canada 18(6): 907–999.

PIKE, G. C. MS 1951. *Engraulis mordax* northern anchovy. M.A. Thesis. Dep. Zool., Univ. British Columbia.

1953. The Pacific sea lamprey. Fish. Res. Board Can. Pac. Progr. Rep. 97: 3–5.

1962. First record of the great white shark (*Carcharodon carcharias*) from British Columbia. J. Fish. Res. Bd. Canada 19(1): 363.

PILLSBURY, R. W. 1957. Avoidance of poisonous eggs of the marine fish *Scorpaenichthys marmoratus* by predators. Copeia 1957(3): 251–252.

PINCKARD, W. F. 1957. Pomfret off the British Columbia Coast. Fish. Res. Board Can. Pac. Progr. Rep. 109: 6–8.

701

PINKAS, L. 1966. A management study of the California barracuda *Sphyraena argentea* Girard. Calif. Dep. Fish Game Fish Bull. 134: 58 p.

——— 1967. First record of a Pacific cod in southern California waters. Calif. Fish Game 53(2): 127–128.

PITT, T. K. 1958a. Distribution, spawning and racial studies of the capelin, *Mallotus villosus* (Müller), in the offshore Newfoundland area. J. Fish. Res. Bd. Canada 15(3): 275–193.

——— 1958b. Age and growth of the capelin, *Mallotus villosus* (Müller), from Newfoundland and Grand Bank areas. J. Fish. Res. Bd. Canada 15(3): 295–311.

PLETCHER, F. T. MS 1963. The life history and distribution of lampreys in the Salmon and certain other rivers in British Columbia, Canada. M.Sc. Thesis. Dep. Zool. Univ. British Columbia. 195 p.

POPOV, A. M. 1933. Fishes of Avatcha Bay on the southern coast of Kamchatka. Copeia 1933(2): 59–67.

PORTER, P. MS 1964. Notes on fecundity, spawning, and early life history of petrale sole (*Eopsetta jordani*), with descriptions of flatfish larvae collected in the Pacific Ocean off Humboldt Bay, California. M.Sc. Thesis, Humboldt State Coll. 98 p.

PRAKASH, A. MS 1958. Food and feeding habits, maturity, and fecundity of spring salmon and coho salmon in southern British Columbia coastal waters. M.Sc. Thesis. Dep. Zool. Univ. British Columbia.

——— 1962. Seasonal changes in feeding of coho and chinook (spring) salmon in southern British Columbia waters. J. Fish. Res. Bd. Canada 19(5): 851–866.

PRAKASH, A., AND D. J. MILNE. 1958. Food as a factor affecting the growth of coho salmon off the east and west coasts of Vancouver Island, B.C. Fish. Res. Board Can. Pac. Progr. Rep. 112: 7–9.

PRASAD, R. R. 1958a. Reproduction in *Clevelandia ios* with an account of the embryonic and larval development. Proc. Nat. Inst. Sci. India, 25B.

——— 1958b. Notes on the habitat and habits of *Clevelandia ios*. Proc. Nat. Inst. Sci. India, 24B(6): 314–324.

PRINCE, E. E. 1897. The fisheries of Canada. II(3): 264–274. *In* Handbook of Canada. Brit. Ass. Adv. Sci. Toronto, 1897, 415 p.

PRITCHARD, A. L. 1929. A ragfish (*Icosteus aenigmaticus*) from Queen Charlotte Islands, B.C. Copeia 1929(171): 38.

——— 1930a. Pacific salmon migration: the tagging of the pink salmon and chum salmon in British Columbia in 1928. Bull. Biol. Board Can. 14: 17 p.

——— 1930b. A note on the occurrence of Ray's beam (*Brama raii* Bloch) on the west coast of the Queen Charlotte Islands, British Columbia. Copeia 1930(3): 88.

——— 1932. Pacific salmon migration. The tagging of the pink salmon and the chum salmon in British Columbia in 1929 and 1930. Bull. Biol. Board Can. 31: 16 p.

——— 1933. *Cololabis saira* from Queen Charlotte Islands, British Columbia. Copeia 1933 (2): 103–104.

——— 1934a. Do caddisfly larvae kill fish? Can. Field-Natur. 48(2): 39.

——— 1934b. Was the introduction of the muskrat to Graham Island, Queen Charlotte Islands, unwise? Can. Field-Natur. 48(6): 103.

——— 1934c. Note on the water ouzel *Cinclus mexicanus*. Can. Field-Natur. 48(3): 53.

——— 1934d. Pacific salmon migration: the tagging of the coho salmon in British Columbia in 1929 and 1930. Bull. Biol. Board Can. 40: 24 p.

——— 1934e. Pacific salmon migration: the tagging of the spring salmon in British Columbia in 1929 and 1930. Bull. Biol. Board Can. 51: 31 p.

——— 1936a. Factors influencing the upstream spawning migration of the pink salmon *Oncorhynchus gorbuscha* (Walbaum). J. Fish. Res. Bd. Canada 2(4): 383–389.

——— 1936b. Stomach content analyses of fishes preying upon the young of Pacific salmon during the fry migration at McClinton Creek, Masset Inlet, British Columbia. Can. Field-Natur. 50(6): 104–105.

——— 1937. Variation in time of run, sex proportions, size and egg content of adult pink salmon (*Oncorhynchus gorbuscha*) at McClinton Creek, Masset Inlet, B.C. J. Fish. Res. Bd. Canada 3(5): 403–416.

——— 1939a. A study of the natural propagation of the pink salmon, *Oncorhynchus gorbuscha*, in British Columbia. Trans. Amer. Fish. Soc. 69: 237–239.

——— 1939b. Homing tendency and age at maturity of pink salmon (*Oncorhynchus gorbuscha*) in British Columbia. J. Fish. Res. Bd. Canada 4(4): 233–251.

——— 1943. The age of chum salmon taken in the commercial catches of British Columbia. Fish. Res. Board Can. Pac. Progr. Rep. 54: 9–11.

——— 1944. Return of two marked pink salmon (*Oncorhynchus gorbuscha*) to the natal stream from distant places in the sea. Copeia 1944(2): 80–82.

    1945. Counts of gill rakers and pyloric caeca in pink salmon. J. Fish. Res. Bd. Canada 6(5): 392–398.

PRITCHARD, A. L., AND A. C. DeLACY. 1944. Migration of pink salmon (*Oncorhynchus gorbuscha*) in southern British Columbia and Washington in 1943. Fish. Res. Board Can. Bull. 66: 23 p.

PRITCHARD, A. L., AND A. L. TESTER. 1939. The food of spring salmon in British Columbia waters during 1939. Fish. Res. Board Can. Pac. Progr. Rep. 42: 3–7.

    1941. The food of spring salmon in British Columbia waters in 1940. Fish. Res. Board. Can. Pac. Progr. Rep. 47: 14–18.

    1942. The food of spring salmon in British Columbia waters in 1941. Fish. Res. Board Can. Pac. Progr. Rep. 53: 3–6.

    1943. Notes on the food of coho salmon in British Columbia. Fish. Res. Board Can. Pac. Progr. Rep. 55: 10–11.

    1944. Food of spring and coho salmon in British Columbia. Fish. Res. Board Can. Bull. 65: 23 p.

PRUTER, A. T. 1954. Age and growth of the Oregon sablefish, *Anoplopoma fimbria*. Pac. Mar. Fish. Comm. Bull. 3: 121–128.

    1959. Tagging experiments on sablefish at Holmes Harbor, Washington. Wash. Dep. Fish. Fish. Res. Pap. 2(2): 66–70.

PRUTER, A. T., AND R. VAN CLEVE. 1954. English sole in Holmes Harbor, Puget Sound. Wash. Dep. Fish. Fish. Res. Pap. 1(2): 1–16.

PYCHA, R. L. 1956. Progress report on white stugeon studies. Calif. Fish Game 42(1): 23–35.

QADRI, S. U. 1959. Some morphological differences between the subspecies of cutthroat trout, *Salmo clarkii clarkii* and *Salmo clarkii lewisi*, in British Columbia. J. Fish. Res. Bd. Canada 16(6): 903–922.

QUAST, J. C. 1964. Occurrence of the Pacific bonito in coastal Alaska waters. Copeia 1964(2): 448.

    1965. Osteological characteristics and affinities of the hexagrammid fishes, with a synopsis. Proc. Calif. Acad. Sci. Ser. 4, 31(21): 563–600.

    1968. New records of thirteen cottoid and blennioid fishes for Southeastern Alaska. Pac. Sci. 22(4): 482–487.

    1971. *Sebastes variegatus*, sp.n. from the northeastern Pacific Ocean (Pisces, Scorpaenidae). Fish. Bull. U.S. 69(2): 387–398.

RADOVICH, J. 1952. Food of the Pacific sardine, *Sardinops caerulea*, from central Baja California and southern California. Calif. Fish Game 38(4): 575–585.

    1961. Relationships of some marine organisms of the northeast Pacific to water temperatures particularly during 1957 through 1959. Calif. Dep. Fish Game Fish Bull. 112: 62 p.

    1963. Effects of ocean temperature on the seaward movements of striped bass, *Roccus saxatilis*, on the Pacific coast. Calif. Fish Game 49(3): 191–206.

RANDOLPH, P. B. 1898. The mating habits of viviparous fishes. Amer. Natur. 32: 305.

RASS, T. S. 1953. Biogeographical fishery complexes of the Atlantic and Pacific oceans and their comparison. J. Cons. Cons. Perma. Int. Expl. Mer 24(2): 243–254.

    1955. Glubokovodnye ryby Kurile-Kamshatskoy Vpadiny. Deep water fishes of the Kurile Kamchatka trench. Tr. Inst. Okeanol Akad. Nauk SSRS 12: 328–339.

RECHNITZER, A. B., AND C. LIMBAUGH. 1952. Breeding habits of *Hyperprosopon argenteum*, a viviparous fish of California. Copeia 1952(1): 41–42.

REED, P. H. 1964. Recent occurrences of intergeneric hybrid flounders, *Inopsetta ischyra* (Jordan and Gilbert), from California and Oregon. Calif. Fish Game 50(1): 118–121.

REEVES, J. E. 1966. An estimate of survival, mortality, and of the number of lingcod (*Ophiodon elongatus*) off the southwest coast of Vancouver Island, British Columbia. Wash. Dep. Fish. Fish. Res. Pap. 2(4): 55–66.

REGAN, C. T. * 1902a. On the classification of the fishes of the suborder Plectognathi. Ann. Mag. Natur. Hist. 7(2): 284–303.

    * 1902b. A revision of the fishes of the family Stromateidae. Ann. Mag. Natur. Hist. 7(10): 115–131; 194–207.

    * 1906. A classification of the selachian fishes. Proc. Zool. Soc. London 2: 722-758.

    * 1907. The anatomy, classification, systematic position of the teleostean fishes of the suborder Allotriognathi. Proc. Zool. Soc. London 3: 634–643.

    * 1908a. A synopsis of the sharks of the family Scyliorhinidae. Ann. Mag. Natur. Hist. 8(1): 453–465.

* 1908b. A synopsis of the sharks of the family Squalidae. Ann. Mag. Natur. Hist. 8(2): 39–56.

* 1909a. On the anatomy and classification of the scombroid fishes. Ann. Mag. Natur. Hist. 8(3): 66–75.

* 1909b. The classification of teleostean fishes. Ann. Mag. Natur. Hist. 8(3): 75–86.

* 1910. The origin and evolution of the teleostean fishes of the order Heterosomata. Ann. Mag. Natur. Hist. 8(6): 484–496.

* 1911a. Anatomy and classification of the teleostean fishes of the orders Berycomorphi and Xenoberyces. Ann. Mag. Natur. Hist. 8(7): 1–9.

* 1911b. The anatomy and classification of the teleostean fishes of the order Iniomi. Ann. Mag. Natur. Hist. 8(7): 120–133.

* 1911c. The osteology and classification of the gobioid fishes. Ann. Mag. Natur. Hist. 8(8): 729–732.

* 1912a. Osteology of the teleostean fishes of the order Pediculati. Ann. Mag. Natur. Hist. 8 (9): 277–289.

* 1912b. A synopsis of the myxinoids of the genus *Heptatretus* or *Bdellostoma*. Ann. Mag. Natur. Hist. 8(9): 534–536.

* 1912c. The classification of the blennioid fishes. Ann. Mag. Natur. Hist. 8(10): 265–280.

* 1912d. The osteology and classification of the teleostean fishes of the order Apodes. Ann. Mag. Natur. Hist. 8(10): 377–387.

* 1912e. The anatomy and classification of the teleostean fishes of the order Discocephali. Ann. Mag. Natur. Hist. 8(10): 634–637.

* 1912f. The Caristiidae, a family of berycomorphous fishes. Ann. Mag. Natur. Hist. 8(10): 637–638.

* 1913a. Osteology and classification of the teleostean fishes of the order Scleroparei. Ann. Mag. Natur. Hist. 8(11): 169–184.

* 1913b. The classification of the percoid fishes. Ann. Mag. Natur. Hist. 8(12): 111–145.

* 1914. Systematic arrangement of the fishes of the family Salmonidae. Ann. Mag. Natur. Hist. 8(13): 405–408.

1916. The British fishes of the subfamily Clupeinae and related species in other seas. Ann. Mag. Natur. Hist. 8(18): 1–19.

* 1923a. The fishes of the family Icosteidae. Ann. Mag. Natur. Hist. 9(11): 610–612.

* 1923b. The classification of the stomiatoid fishes. Ann. Mag. Natur. Hist. 9(11): 612–614.

1925. New ceratioid fishes from the N. Atlantic, the Caribbean Sea, and the Gulf of Panama, collected by the "Dana". Ann. Mag. Natur. Hist. Ser. 9, 15(89): 561–567.

1926. The pediculate fishes of the suborder Ceratioidea. Dan. "Dana" Exped. 1920–22, Oceanogr. Rep. 1(2): 1–45, xiii pl.

* 1929. Fishes. In Encyclopaedia Britannica 14(9): 324–325.

REGAN, C. T., AND E. TREWAVAS. * 1930. The fishes of the family Stomiatidae and Malacosteidae. Dan. "Dana" Exped. 1920–22, Oceanogr. Rep. 6: 1–143.

1932. Deep-sea angler fishes (Ceratioidea). Dana-Rep. 2: 1–113.

REID, J. L. JR., G. I. RODEN, AND J. G. WYLLIE. 1958. Studies of the California current system. Calif. Coop. Oceanic. Fish. Invest. Progr. Rep. 1 July–1 Jan. 1958, p. 27–56.

RICH, W. H. 1925. Growth and degree of maturity of chinook salmon in the ocean. Bull. U.S. Bur. Fish. 41: 15–90.

RICHARDSON, J. * 1836. Fauna Boreali-Americana; or the zoology of the northern parts of British America containing descriptions of the objects of natural history collected on the late northern land expeditions under the command of Sir John Franklin, R.N. London. 4 vol., Pt. 3, Fishes: 327 p.

RICKER, W. E. 1962. Comparison of ocean growth and mortality of sockeye salmon during their last two years. J. Fish. Res. Bd. Canada 19(4): 531–560.

1963. Big effect from small causes; two examples from fish population dynamics. J. Fish. Res. Bd. Canada 20(2): 257–264.

1964. Ocean growth and mortality of pink and chum salmon. J. Fish. Res. Bd. Canada 21(5): 905–931.

RICKETTS, E., AND J. CALVIN. 1956. Between Pacific tides. Stanford Univ. Press. 502 p.

RIPLEY, W. E. 1946a. The soupfin shark and the fishery. Calif. Div. Fish Game Fish. Bull. 64: 7–37.

1946b. Recovery of a tagged soupfin shark. Calif. Fish Game 32(2): 101–102.

RISSO, A. 1810. Ichthyologie de Nice. F. Schoell, Paris. Reprinted 1966. A. Asher Amsterdam. 388 p.

ROBINSON, D. G., W. E. BARRACLOUGH, AND J. D. FULTON. MS 1968a. Data record: number, size composition, weight and food of larval and juvenile fish caught with a two-boat surface trawl in the Strait of Georgia, May 1–4, 1967. Fish. Res. Board Can. MS. Rep. Ser. 964: 1–105.

MS 1968b. Data record : number, size composition, weight and food of larval and juvenile fish caught with a two-boat surface trawl in the Strait of Georgia, June 5–9, 1967. Fish. Res. Board Can. MS. Rep. Ser. 972: 1–109.

ROBINSON, J. B. 1960. The age and growth of striped bass (*Roccus saxatilis*) in California. Calif. Fish Game 46(3): 279–290.

ROEDEL, P. M. 1938a. Notes on the ribbon-fish, *Trachypterus rex-salmonorum*. Calif. Fish Game 24 (4): 422–423.

1938b. Record-size mackerel in Santa Monica Bay. Calif. Fish Game 24(4): 423.

1941. A sturgeon in southern California waters. Calif. Fish Game 27(3): 191.

1948a. Pacific mackerel in the Gulf of California. Copeia 1948(3): 224.

1948b. Common marine fishes of California. Calif. Fish Game Fish. Bull. 68: 150 p.

1951. The brown shark, *Apristurus brunneus*, in California. Calif. Fish Game 37(1): 61–63.

1952. A racial study of the Pacific mackerel, *Pneumatophorus diego*. Calif. Dep. Fish Game Fish Bull. 84: 53 p.

1953a. The jack mackerel, *Trachurus symmetricus*: a review of the California fishery and of current biological knowledge. Calif. Fish Game 39(1): 45–68.

1953b. Common ocean fishes of the California coast. Calif. Dep. Fish Game Fish Bull. 91: 184 p.

ROEDEL, P. M., AND J. E. FITCH. 1952. The status of the carangid fishes *Trachurus* and *Decapterus* on the Pacific coast of Canada and the United States. Copeia 1952(1): 4–6.

ROEDEL, P. M., AND W. E. RIPLEY. 1950. California sharks and rays. Calif. Div. Fish Game Fish Bull. 75: 88 p.

ROFEN, R. R. 1966a. Family Paralepididae, p. 205–461. *In* Fishes of the western North Atlantic. Mem. Sears Found. Mar. Res. I(5). 647 p.

1966b. Family Anotopteridae, p. 498–510. *In* Fishes of the western North Atlantic. Mem. Sears Found. Mar. Res. I(5): 647 p.

ROSENBLATT, R. H. 1964. A new gunnel, *Pholis clemensi*, from the coast of western North America. J. Fish. Res. Bd. Canada 21(5): 933–939.

ROSENBLATT, R. H. AND L.-C. CHEN. 1972. The identity of *Sebastes babcocki* and *Sebastes rubrivinctus*. Calif. Fish Game 58(1): 32–36.

ROSENBLATT, R. H., AND D. WILKIE. 1963. A redescription of the rare cottid fish, *Artedius meanyi*, new to the fauna of British Columbia. J. Fish. Res. Bd. Canada 20(6): 1505–1511.

ROULE, L., ET L. BERTIN. 1929. Les poissons Apodes appartenant au sous-ordre des Nemichthyiformes. Dan. "Dana" Exped. 1920–1922, I(4): 1–113.

ROUNSEFELL, G. A. 1930. Contribution to the biology of the Pacific herring, *Clupea pallasii*, and the condition of the fishery in Alaska. Bull. U.S. Bur. Fish. 45: 227–320.

1957. Fecundity of North American Salmonidae. U.S. Fish Wildl. Serv. Fish. Bull. 122, Vol. 57: 449–468.

ROUNSEFELL, G. A., AND E. H. DAHLGREN. 1934. Occurrence of mackerel in Alaska. Copeia 1934 (1): 42.

1935. Races of herring, *Clupea pallasii*, in southeastern Alaska. Bull. U.S. Bur. Fish. 48(17): 119–141.

ROYCE, W. F. 1963. First record of white shark (*Carcharodon carcharias*) from southeastern Alaska. Copeia 1963(1): 179.

SAMSON, V. J. 1940. Notes on the occurrence of albacore (*Germo alalunga*) in the North Pacific. Copeia 1940(4): 271.

SANDERCOCK, F. K., AND N. J. WILIMOVSKY. 1968. Revision of the cottid genus *Enophrys*. Copeia 1968(4): 832–853.

SATHYANESAN, A. G. 1966. Egg laying of the chimaeroid fish *Hydrolagus colliei*. Copeia 1966(1): 132–134.

SCAGEL, R. F. 1949a. General description of scouting operations and fishing experiments. Fish. Res. Board Can. Gen. Ser. Circ. (Nanaimo) 17: 2–4.

1949b. Temperature conditions in relation to albacore occurrence and catches. Fish. Res. Board Can. Gen. Ser. Circ. (Nanaimo) 17: 5–7.

1949c. Feeding of albacore. Fish. Res. Board Can. Gen. Ser. Circ. (Nanaimo) 17: 17–18.

SCATTERGOOD, L. W. 1949. Notes on the kokanee (*Oncorhynchus kennerlyi*). Copeia 1949(4): 297–298.

SCATTERGOOD, L. W., C. J. SINDERMAN, AND B. E. SCUD. 1959. Spawning of North American herring. Trans. Amer. Fish. Soc. 88(1): 164–168.

SCHAEFER, M. B. 1936. Contribution to the life history of the surf smelt *Hypomesus pretiosus* in Puget Sound. Wash. Dep. Fish. Biol. Rep. 35B: 1–45.

——— 1937. Notes on the spawning of the Pacific herring *Clupea pallasii*. Copeia 1937(1): 57.

SCHAEFER, M. B., AND J. C. MARR. 1948. Spawning of the yellowfin tuna (*Neothunnus macropterus*) and skipjack (*Katsuwonus pelamis*) in the Pacific Ocean off Central America with descriptions of juveniles. U.S. Fish Wildl. Serv. Fish. Bull. 44, Vol. 51: 187–196.

SCHAEFER, M. B., AND J. W. REINTJES. 1950. Additional records confirming the trans-Pacific distribution of the Pacific saury, *Cololabis saira* (Brevoort). Pac. Sci. 4(2): 164.

SCHEFFER, V. B. 1940. Two recent records of *Zaprora silenus* from the Aleutian Islands. Copeia 1940(3): 203.

SCHMIDT, J. 1921. Contributions to the knowledge of the sunfishes (*Mola* and *Ranzania*). Medd. Komm. Havunders. Ser. Fisk. 4(6): 1–16.

SCHMIDT, P. J. * 1904. Pisces marium orientalium Rossici (Text in Russian). St. Petersburg. 466 p.

——— * 1930. [On the Pacific halibut.] Dokl. Akad. Nauk SSSR, Ser. A, 8: 203–208.

——— 1934. On the zoogeographical distribution of the chief marine food fishes in the western part of the North Pacific. Proc. Pac. Sci. Congr. V: 3795–3799.

——— 1936. On the systematics and distribution of the genus *Agonus* Bloch and Schneider. Copeia 1936 (1): 58–59.

——— 1942. A fish with feather-like gill-leaflets. Copeia 1942(2): 98–100.

SCHOTT, J. W. 1966. A Greenland halibut, *Reinhardtius hippoglossoides* (Walbaum) recorded in southern California. Calif. Fish Game 52(1): 55.

SCHREIBER, M. R. 1962. Observations on the food habits of juvenile white sturgeon. Calif. Fish Game 48(1): 79–80.

SCHROEDER, W. C. * 1940. Some deep sea fishes from the North Atlantic. Copeia 1936(1): 58–59.

SCHULTZ, L. P. 1929. New records for the quill-fish, *Ptilichthys goodei* Bean. Copeia 1929(171): 40–41.

——— 1930. Miscellaneous observations on fishes of Washington. Copeia 1930(4): 137–140.

——— 1933. The age and growth of *Atherinops affinis oregonia* Jordan and Snyder and of other subspecies of baysmelt along the Pacific coast of the United States. Univ. Wash. Pub. Biol. 2(3): 45–102.

——— 1934a. A new ceratioid fish from the Gulf of Alaska. Copeia 1934(2): 66–68.

——— 1934b. *Zaprora silenus* Jordan from Alaska. Copeia 1934(2): 98.

——— * 1936. Keys to the fishes of Washington, Oregon and closely adjoining regions. Univ. Wash. Pub. Zool. 2(4): 103–228.

——— 1937a. Redescription of the capelin *Mallotus catervarius* (Pennant) of the North Pacific. Proc. U.S. Nat. Mus. 85 (3029): 13–20.

——— 1937b. Notes on *Raja kincaidii* Garman from the Pacific coast. Copeia 1937(4): 235–236.

——— 1938. Review of the fishes of the genera *Polyipnus* and *Argyropelecus* (family Sternoptychidae), with descriptions of three new species. Proc. U.S. Nat. Mus. 86 (3047): 135–155.

——— * 1939. A revision of the toadfishes referred to *Porichthys* and related genera. Proc. U.S. Nat. Mus. 86: 473–496.

——— 1940. The Pacific saury, *Cololabis saira* Brevoort from the North Pacific Ocean. Copeia 1940 (4): 270.

——— 1944. A revision of the American clingfishes, family Gobiesocidae, with descriptions of new genera and forms. Proc. U.S. Nat. Mus. 96 (3187): 47–77.

——— 1961. Revision of the marine silver hatchetfishes (family Sternoptychidae). Proc. U.S. Nat. Mus. 112 (3449): 587–649.

——— 1964. Family Sternoptychidae, p. 241–273. *In* Fishes of the western North Atlantic. Mem. Sears Found. Mar. Res. I(4): 599 p.

SCHULTZ, L. P., AND W. M. CHAPMAN. 1934. A new osmerid fish *Spirinchus dilatus*, from Puget Sound. Ann. Mag. Natur. Hist. 10(13): 67–78.

SCHULTZ, L. P., AND A. C. DeLACY. 1932. The eggs and nesting habits of the crested blenny, *Anoplarchus*. Copeia 1932(3): 143–147.

——— 1936. Fishes of the American Northwest. A catalogue of the fishes of Washington and Oregon, with distributional records and a bibliography. J. Pan-Pac. Res. Inst. 11 (1 and 4).

SCHULTZ, L. P., J. L. HART, AND F. J. GUNDERSON. 1932. New records of marine west coast fishes. Copeia 1932(2): 65–68.

SCHULTZ, L. P., AND A. W. HARVEY. 1945. The flaccid fish *Zaprora silenus*, from off Newport, Oregon. Copeia 1945(4): 237.

SCHULTZ, L. P., AND C. L. HUBBS. 1961. Early nomenclatural history of the nominal cyprinid genus *Oregonichthys* and of the blennioid *Pholis schultzi*, fishes of western North America. Copeia 1961 (4): 477–478.

706

SCHULTZ, L. P., AND R. T. SMITH. 1936. Is *Inopsetta ischyra* (Jordan and Gilbert) from Puget Sound, Washington, a hybrid flatfish? Copeia 1936(4): 199–203.

SCHULTZ, L. P., AND A. D. WELANDER. 1935. A review of the cods of the northeastern Pacific with comparative notes on related species. Copeia 1935(3): 127–139.

SCHUMACHER, R. E., AND J. G. HALE. 1962. Third generation pink salmon, *Oncorhynchus gorbuscha* (Walbaum), in Lake Superior. Trans. Amer. Fish. Soc. 91(4): 421–422.

SCOFIELD, E. C. 1934a. Early life-history of the California sardine (*Sardina caerulea*) with special reference to the distribution of eggs and larvae. Calif. Div. Fish Game Fish Bull. 41: 48 p.

   1934b. The striped bass of California. Calif. Div. Fish Game Fish Bull. 29: 82 p.

SCOFIELD, N. B., AND H. C. BRYANT. 1926. The striped bass in California. Calif. Fish Game 12(2): 55–74.

SCOTT, W. B., A. C. KOHLER, AND R. E. ZURBRIGG. 1970. The manefish, *Caristius groenlandicus* Jensen (Percomorphi: Caristiidae), in Atlantic waters off Canada. J. Fish. Res. Bd. Canada 27(1): 174–179.

SEER, H. H. 1937. The anatomy of the Pacific coast lamprey *E. tridentatus*. Proc. S. Dak. Acad. Sci. 17: 44–47.

SEMAKULA, S. N. MS 1963. The age and growth of the white sturgeon (*Acipenser transmontanus* Richardson) of the Fraser River, British Columbia, Canada. M.Sc. Thesis. Dep. Zool. Univ. British Columbia. 115 p.

SEMAKULA, S. N., AND P. A. LARKIN. 1968. Age, growth, food and yield of the white sturgeon (*Acipenser transmontanus*) of the Fraser River, British Columbia. J. Fish. Res. Bd. Canada 25(12): 2589–2602.

SETTE, O. E. 1923. The occurrence of *Trachypterus rex-salmonorum* at Monterey, and notes on its post-larval growth. Copeia 1923(122): 93–96.

SHAPOVALOV, L. 1936. Food of striped bass. Calif. Fish Game 22(4): 261–271.

SHAPOVALOV, L., AND A. C. TAFT. 1954. The life histories of steelhead rainbow trout (*Salmo gairdneri gairdneri*) and silver salmon (*Oncorhynchus kisutch*). Calif. Dep. Fish Game Fish Bull. 98: 373 p.

SHEPARD, M. P., AND F. C. WITHLER. 1958. Spawning stock size and resultant production for Skeena sockeye. J. Fish. Res. Bd. Canada 15(5): 1007–1025.

SHIMADA, B. M. 1948. Records of lantern fish in Puget Sound. Copeia 1948(3): 227.

SHIPPEN, H. H., AND M. S. ALTON. 1967. Predation upon Pacific hake, *Merluccius productus*, by Pacific dogfish, *Squalus acanthias*. Calif. Fish Game 53(3): 218–219.

SHMIDT, P. Y. 1950. Fishes of the Sea of Okhotsk. Acad. Sci. U.S.S.R. Trans. Pac. Comm., Vol. VI, 1950. (Transl. from Russian by Israel Program for Sci. Transl., Jerusalem, 1965.)

SILLIMAN, R. P. 1941. Fluctuations in the diet of the chinook and silver salmons (*Oncorhynchus tschawytscha* and *O. kisutch*) off Washington, as related to the troll catch of salmon. Copeia 1941(1): 80–87.

   1943. Studies on the Pacific pilchard or sardine (*Sardinops caerulea*). 6. Thermal and diurnal changes in the vertical distribution of eggs and larvae. U.S. Fish Wildl. Serv. Spec. Sci. Rep. 22: 17 p.

   1945. Determination of mortality rates from length frequencies of the pilchard or sardine *Sardinops caerulea*. Copeia 1945(4): 191–196.

SKOGSBERG, T. 1939. The fishes of the family Sciaenidae (croakers) of California. Calif. Dep. Fish Game Fish Bull. 54: 62 p.

SLIPP, J. W., AND A. C. DELACY. 1952. On the distribution and habits of the wattled eel-pout *Lycodes palearis*. Copeia 1952(3): 201–203.

SMITH, J. L. B. * 1951. Trigger action in *Quinquarius capensis* Cuvier 1829, with a description of the adult form. Ann. Mag. Natur. Hist. 12(4): 873–881.

   * 1953. The genus *Tetragonurus* Risso 1810. Ann. Mag. Natur. Hist. 12(6): 53–66.

   * 1954. The sea fishes of southern Africa. Revised ed., Cape Town. 564 p.

SMITH, R. T. 1936. Report on the Puget Sound otter trawl investigations. Wash. Dep. Fish. Biol. Rep. 36B: 1–61.

SMITH, S. B. 1960. A note on two stocks of steelhead trout (*Salmo gairdneri*) in Capilano River, British Columbia. J. Fish. Res. Bd. Canada 17(5): 739–741.

SMITH, W. E., AND R. W. SAALFIELD. 1955. Studies on Columbia River smelt, *Thaleichthys pacificus* (Richardson). Wash. Dep. Fish. Fish. Res. Pap. 1(3): 3–26.

SMOKER, W., AND W. C. PEARCY. 1970. Growth and reproduction of the lanternfish *Stenobrachius leucopsarus*. J. Fish. Res. Bd. Canada 27(7): 1265–1275.

SMOKER, W. A. 1953. Stream flow and silver salmon production in western Washington. Wash. Dep. Fish. Fish. Res. Pap. 1(1): 5–12.

SNOW, C. D. 1959. Occurrence of deep-pitted sea-poacher in Oregon. Fish. Comm. Ore. Res. Briefs 7(1): 78.

707

SOLLER, M., Y. SHCHORI, R. MAOV, G. WOHLFARTH, AND M. LAHMAN. 1965. Carp growth in brackish water. Bamidgeh 17(1): 16–23.

SOUTHWARD, G. M. 1967. Growth of Pacific halibut. Int. Pac. Halibut Comm. Tech. Rep. 43: 40 p.

SPARROW, R. A. H. 1968. A first report of chum salmon fry feeding in fresh water of British Columbia. J. Fish. Res. Bd. Canada 25(3): 599–602.

SPRINGER, V. G., AND J. A. F. GARRICK. 1964. A survey of vertebral numbers in sharks. Proc. U.S. Nat. Mus. 116 (3496): 73–96.

SRIBHIBHADH, A. MS 1959. Racial variations in the populations of the crested blenny, *Anoplarchus purpurescens purpurescens* Gill, in the Puget Sound area. M.Sc. Thesis. Univ. Wash. 86 p.

STARKS, E. C. 1911. Results of an ichthyological survey about the San Juan Islands, Washington. Ann. Carnegie Mus. 7: 162–213.

    1919. The fishes of the croaker family (Sciaenidae) of California. Calif. Fish Game 5(1): 13–20.

STEINDACHNER, F. 1891. Über einige seltene und naue Fischarten aus den Canarishen Archipel. Ichthyologische beitrage. XV. Sitzungber. Akad. Wien, 1891. I Abth. 343–374.

    * 1901. Fische aus dem stillen Ocean. (Ergebnisse Einer Reise nach dem Pacific "Schauinsland" 1896–97). Denkschr. Akad. Wiss. Math.-Nat. Cl. 70: 483–521.

STEPHEN, A. C. 1928. The recent immigration of Ray's bream into Scottish waters. Scot. Natur. 1969: 28.

STEVENSON, J. C. 1947. Preliminary survey of larval herring on the west coast of Vancouver Island, 1947. Fish. Res. Board Can. Pac. Progr. Rep. 73: 65–67.

    1949. The extent of herring spawning in British Columbia in 1949. Fish. Res. Board Can. Pac. Progr. Rep. 80: 57–59.

    1955. The movement of herring in British Columbia waters as determined by tagging. With a description of tagging and tag recovery methods. Rapp. Proces.-Verbaux. Réunions Cons. Perma. Int. Explor. Mer 140(2): 33–34. (Abstracts)

    1962. Distribution and survival of herring larvae (*Clupea pallasi* Valenciennes) in British Columbia waters. J. Fish. Res. Bd. Canada 19(5): 735–810.

STRACHAN, A. R. 1965. New southern record for the silvergray rockfish, *Sebastodes brevispinis* (Bean). Calif. Fish Game 51(3): 220–221.

STRAIGHT, L. 1970a. Fish, game tips. The *Vancouver Sun,* January 15, 1970, p. 28.

    1970b. (Untitled). The *Vancouver Sun,* October 23, 1970, p. 28.

STRASSBURG, D. W., AND J. C. MARR. 1961. Banded colour phases of two pelagic fishes, *Coryphaena hippurus* and *Katsuwonus pelamis*. Copeia 1961(2): 226–228.

SUNDE, L. A., AND C. C. LINDSEY. * 1958. Revised key to the rockfishes (Scorpaenidae) of British Columbia. Inst. Fish. Univ. British Columbia Mus. Contrib. 1: 6 p.

SVETOVIDOV, A. N. 1948. Fishes. Fauna of the U.S.S.R. Zool. Inst. Acad. Sci. USSR, NS 34: 304 p. English translation published 1962 for NSF Jerusalem.

    1952. Fishes. Herrings (Clupeidae). Fauna, U.S.S.R., 2, Part 2(48): 1–331.

SWAIN, L. A. 1947. Vitamin A in dogfish liver. Fish Res. Board Can. Pac. Progr. Rep. 73: 57.

SWAIN, L. A., AND W. E. BARRACLOUGH. 1946a. Vitamin A in brill livers. Fish. Res. Board Can. Pac. Progr. Rep. 69: 74–76.

    1946b. Vitamin A in brill livers. II. Fish. Res. Board Can. Pac. Progr. Rep. 70: 12–14.

TAFT, A. C. 1937. A red salmon (*Oncorhynchus nerka*) taken in the Klamath River. Calif. Fish Game 23(2): 178.

TANAKA, S. 1935. Fishes of Japan. Kazamashobo. Tokyo.

TARANETZ, A. Y. 1933. New data on the ichthyology of the Bering Sea. Vestn. D. V. Filiata Acad. Nauk SSSR. (1/3): 67–78.

TARP, F. H. 1952. A revision of the family Embiotocidae (The surfperches). Calif. Dep. Fish Game Fish Bull. 88: 99 p.

TAYLOR, F. H. C. MS 1940. Preliminary studies in the life history of the Pacific anchovy *Engraulis mordax* Girard. B.A. Thesis. Dep. Zool. Univ. British Columbia.

    1946. Lemon sole spawning grounds in Baynes Sound. Fish. Res. Board Can. Pac. Progr. Rep. 68: 48–50.

    1964. Life history and present status of British Columbia herring stocks. Fish. Res. Board Can. Bull. 143: 81 p.

    1967a. Midwater trawl catches from Queen Charlotte Sound and the open ocean adjacent to the Queen Charlotte Islands. Fish. Res. Board Can. Tech. Rep. 11: 1–44.

    1967b. Unusual fishes taken by midwater trawl off the Queen Charlotte Islands, British Columbia. J. Fish. Res. Bd. Canada 24(10): 2101–2115.

1968. The relationship of midwater trawl catches to sound scattering layers off the coast of northern British Columbia. J. Fish. Res. Bd. Canada 25(3): 457–472.

TAYLOR, F. H. C., A. S. HOURSTON, AND D. N. OUTRAM. 1957. The status of the major herring stocks in British Columbia in 1956–57. Brit. Columbia Fish. Dep. Rep. 1956: 45–77.

TAYLOR, G. T. 1959. The occurrence of lesser lancet fish (*Anotopterus pharao* Zugmayer) in the northeast Pacific. Fish. Res. Board Can. Pac. Progr. Rep. 113: 10–12.

TAYLOR, G. T., AND R. J. LeBRASSEUR. 1957. Distribution, age and food of steelhead trout *Salmo gairdneri* caught in the northeast Pacific Ocean, 1956. Fish. Res. Board Can. Pac. Progr. Rep. 109: 9–11.

TCHERNAVIN, V. V. 1953. Summary of the feeding mechanism of a deep sea fish, *Chauliodus sloani*. Brit. Mus. (Natur. Hist.): 101 p.

TEMMINCK, C. J., AND H. SCHLEGEL. * 1842. Pisces. *In* Siebold's Fauna Japonica. Leyden.

TEMPLEMAN, W. 1948. The life history of the capelin (*Mallotus villosus* O. F. Müller) in Newfoundland waters. Res. Bull. Dep. Natur. Res. Nfld. 17: 1–151.

TESTER, A. L. 1935. The herring fishery of British Columbia – past and present. Bull. Biol. Board Can. 47: 37 p.

  1937a. Populations of herring (*Clupea pallasii*) in the coastal waters of British Columbia. J. Fish. Res. Bd. Canada 3(2): 108–144.

  1937b. The length and age composition of the herring (*Clupea pallasii*) in the coastal waters of British Columbia. J. Fish. Res. Bd. Canada 3(2): 145–168.

  1941. "Bellyburn" in Nanoose Bay herring. Fish. Res. Board Can. Pac. Progr. Rep. 50: 14–15.

  1942a. Herring mortality along the south-east coast of Vancouver Island. Fish. Res. Board Can. Pac. Progr. Rep. 52: 11–15.

  1942b. A high mortality among herring eggs. Fish. Res. Board Can. Pac. Progr. Rep. 53: 16–19.

  1945. Catch statistics of the British Columbia herring fishery to 1943–44. Fish. Res. Board Can. Bull. 67: 47 p.

  1955. Estimation of recruitment and natural mortality rate from age-composition and catch data in British Columbia herring populations. J. Fish. Res. Bd. Canada 12(5): 649–681.

THOMAS, J. L. 1967. The diet of juvenile and adult striped bass *Roccus saxatilis* in the Sacramento–San Joaquin River System. Calif. Fish Game 53(1): 49–62.

THOMPSON, J. A. * 1958. Biological effects of the Ripple Rock explosion. Fish. Res. Board Can. Pac. Progr. Rep. 111: 3–8.

  1962. On the fecundity of Pacific cod (*Gadus macrocephalus* Tilesius) from Hecate Strait, British Columbia. J. Fish. Res. Bd. Canada 19(3): 497–500.

  1963. On the demersal quality of the fertilized eggs of Pacific cod, *Gadus macrocephalus* Tilesius. J. Fish. Res. Bd. Canada 20(4): 1087–1088.

THOMPSON, W. F. * 1915a. A preliminary report on the life-history of the halibut. Rep. Brit. Columbia Commer. Fish 1914: 76–99.

  * 1915b. A new fish of the genus *Sebastodes* from British Columbia. Rep. Brit. Columbia Commer. Fish 1914: 120–122.

  1916. A second occurrence of *Erilepis* in American waters. Copeia 1916(30): 1–2.

  1917a. Further notes on *Erilepis*, the giant bass-like fish of the North Pacific. Copeia 1917 (40): 9–13.

  1917b. A contribution to the life-history of the Pacific herring : its bearing on the condition and future of the fishery. Rep. Brit. Columbia Commer. Fish 1916: 39–87.

  1925. The California sardine and the study of the available supply. Calif. Fish Game Comm. Fish Bull. 11: 3–66.

THOMPSON, W. F., F. H. BELL, L. P. SCHULTZ, H. A. DUNLOP, AND R. VAN CLEVE. 1936. The spawning of the silver smelt, *Hypomesus pretiosus*. Ecology 17: 148–168.

THOMPSON, W. F., AND N. L. FREEMAN. 1930. History of the Pacific halibut fishery. Rep. Int. Fish. Comm. 5: 61 p.

THOMPSON, W. F., AND W. C. HERRINGTON. 1930. Life history of the Pacific halibut. 1. Marking experiments. Rep. Int. Fish. Comm. 2: 137 p.

THOMPSON, W. F., AND R. VAN CLEVE. 1936. Life history of the Pacific halibut. 2. Distribution and early life history. Rep. Int. Fish. Comm. 9: 184 p., 71 figs.

THOMPSON, W. F., JR. 1941. A note on the spawning of the black cod (*Anaplopoma fimbria*). Copeia 1941(4): 270.

TIBBY, R. B. 1937. The relationship between surface water temperatures and the distribution of spawn of the California sardine, *Sardinops caerulea*. Calif. Fish Game 23(2): 132–137.

TONONAKA, G. K. 1957. The occurrence of the squaretail, *Tetragonurus cuvieri*, on the high-seas south of the Aleutian Islands. Copeia 1957(1): 53–54.

TOWNSEND, L. D. 1935. Notes on *Citharichthys sordidus* and *C. stigmaeus* with an extension of range. Copeia 1935(4): 193.

—— 1936. Variations in the meristic characters of the flounders from the northeastern Pacific. Rep. Int. Fish. Comm. 11: 24 p.

TSUYUKI, H., E. ROBERTS, R. H. LOWES, W. HADAWAY, AND S. J. WESTRHEIM. 1968. Contribution of protein electrophoresis to rockfish (Scorpaenidae) systematics. J. Fish. Res. Bd. Canada 25(11): 2477–2501.

TSUYUKI, H., AND S. J. WESTRHEIM. 1970. Analyses of the *Sebastes aleutianus- -melanostomus* complex, and description of a new scorpaenid species, *Sebastes caenaematicus,* in the northeast Pacific Ocean. J. Fish. Res. Bd. Canada 27(12): 2233–2254.

TUCKER, D. W. 1953. The fishes of the genus *Benthodesmus* (Family Trichiuridae). Proc. Zool. Soc. London 123(1): 171–187.

—— * 1955. Studies on the trichiuroid fishes. (2) *Benthodesmus tenuis* (Günther) collected by the Expédition Océanographique Bele dans les eaux côtières de l'Atlantique sud (1948–1949), with additional notes on the genus *Benthodesmus.* Bull. Inst. Roy. Sci. Natur. Belgique 31(64): 1–26.

TULLY, J. P. 1942. Surface non-tidal currents in the approaches to Juan de Fuca Strait. J. Fish. Res. Bd. Canada 5(4): 398–409.

—— 1964. Oceanographic regions and assessment of temperature structure in the seasonal zone of the North Pacific Ocean. J. Fish. Res. Bd. Canada 21(5): 941–970.

TURNER, C. E., AND H. T. BILTON. 1968. Another pink salmon in its third year. J. Fish. Res. Bd. Canada 25(9): 1993–1996.

TURNER, C. L. 1952. An accessory respiratory device in embryos of the embiotocid fish *Cymatogaster aggregata,* during gestation. Copeia 1952(3): 146–147.

VAN CLEVE, R., AND W. F. THOMPSON. 1938. A record of the pomfret and barracuda from Alaska. Copeia 1938(1): 45–46.

VERNICK, S. H. 1963. A second record of the tubenose poacher, *Pallasina barbata aix,* from Oregon. Copeia 1963(1): 188.

VLADYKOV, V. D., AND W. I. FOLLETT. 1958. Redescription of *Lampetra ayresii* (Günther) of western North America, a species of lamprey (Petromyzontidae) distinct from *Lampetra fluviatilis* (Linnaeus) of Europe. J. Fish. Res. Bd. Canada 15(1): 47–77.

VRAT, V. 1949. Reproductive behavior and development of eggs of the three-spined stickleback (*Gasterosteus aculeatus*) of California. Copeia 1949(4): 252–260.

WAGNER, E. J., AND C. E. BOND. 1961. The percoid fish *Pseudopentaceros richardsoni* from Oregon waters. Fish. Comm. Oreg. Res. Briefs 8(1): 71–73.

WAILES, G. H. 1936. Food of *Clupea pallasii* in southern British Columbia waters. J. Fish. Res. Bd. Canada 1(6): 477–486.

WALDRON, K. D. 1962. A synopsis of biological data on skipjack *Katsuwonus pelamis* (Linnaeus) 1758 (Pacific Ocean). FAO World Sci. Meeting. Biology of Tunas and related species. Sp. Synop. 22: 73 p.

WALES, J. H. 1929. A note on the breeding of the viviparous perch *Damalichthys.* Copeia, 1929 (172): 57–58.

—— 1952. Life history of the blue rockfish, *Sebastodes mystinus.* Calif. Fish Game 38(4): 485–498.

WALFORD, L. A. * 1931. Handbook of common commercial and game fishes of California. Calif. Div. Fish Game Fish Bull. 28: 138 p.

—— 1932. Life history of the California barracuda. Calif. Div. Fish Game Fish Bull. 37: 120 p.

—— * 1935. The sharks and rays of California. Calif. Div. Fish Game Fish Bull. 45: 66 p.

—— * 1937. Marine game fishes of the Pacific Coast from Alaska to the Equator. Univ. Calif. Press, Berkeley. 205 p.

WALFORD, L. A., AND K. H. MOSHER. 1943a. Studies on the Pacific pilchard or sardine (*Sardinops caerulea*). 2. Determination of the age of juveniles by scales and otoliths. U.S. Fish Wildl. Serv. Spec. Sci. Rep. Fish. 20: 19 p.

—— 1943b. Studies on Pacific pilchard or sardine (*Sardinops caerulea*). 3. Determination of age of adults by scales, and effect of environment on first year's growth as it bears on age determination. U.S. Fish Wildl. Serv. Spec. Sci. Rep. Fish. 21: 29 p.

WALFORD, L. A., AND G. S. MYERS. 1944. A new species of carangid fish from the northeastern Pacific. Copeia 1944(1): 44–47.

WALKER, B. W. 1953. New records of Pacific sardine and Pacific mackerel in the Gulf of California. Calif. Fish Game 39(2): 263-264.

WALKER, E. T. 1953. Records of uncommon fishes from Puget Sound. Copeia 1953(4): 239.

WATANABE, M. 1958. Studies on the cottid fishes of Japan. Tokyo.

710

1960. Fauna Japonica, Cottidae. Tokyo News Service, Ltd., Tokyo, Japan. 218 p. 40 pl.

WATANABE, M., AND J. L. HART. 1938. Sex ratio among pilchards on the Pacific coast of North America. Bull. Jap. Soc. Sci. Fish. 6(5): 237–239.

WEISEL, G. F. * 1948. Observations on the mudsucker, *Gillichthys mirabilis*. Calif. Fish Game 34(2): 81.

WELANDER, A. D. 1940. Notes on the dissemination of shad, *Alosa sapidissima* (Wilson), along the Pacific coast of North America. Copeia 1940(4): 221–223.

1941. Record of *Arctozenus coruscans* (Jordan and Gilbert) from Puget Sound. Copeia 1941 (1): 117–118.

WELANDER, A. D., AND D. L. ALVERSON. 1954. New and little known fishes of the eastern Pacific. Wash. Dep. Fish. Fish. Res. Pap. 1(2): 37–44.

WELANDER, A. D., D. L. ALVERSON, AND P. BERGMAN. 1957. Rare fishes from the eastern North Pacific Ocean. Wash. Dep. Fish. Fish. Res. Pap. 2(1): 60–66.

WELANDER, A. D., R. C. JOHNSON, AND R. A. HAJNY. 1957. Occurrence of the boar fish, *Pseudopentaceros richardsoni*, and the zeid *Allocyttus verrucosus*, in the North Pacific. Copeia 1957(3): 244–246.

WELLINGS, S. R., L. E. ASHLEY, AND G. E. McARN. 1969. Microsporidial infections of English sole, *Parophrys vetulus*. J. Fish. Res. Bd. Canada 26(8): 2215-2218.

WENDLER, H. O. 1953. Length-weight relationships of the lingcod. Wash. Dep. Fish. Fish. Res. Pap. 1(1): 25–32.

WESTRHEIM, S. J. 1955. Migrations of starry flounder (*Platichthys stellatus*) tagged in the Columbia River. Fish. Comm. of Oreg. Res. Briefs 6(1): 33–37.

MS 1958. On the biology of the Pacific Ocean perch (*Sebastodes alutus*) (Gilbert). M.S. Thesis. Univ. Wash. 106 p.

1964. Rockfish (*Sebastodes brevispinis*) in British Columbia waters. J. Fish. Res. Bd. Canada 21(4): 855–856.

1965. Northern range extensions for four species of rockfish (*Sebastodes goodei, S. helvomaculatus, S. rubrivinctus* and *S. zacentrus* in the northern Pacific Ocean. J. Fish. Res. Bd. Canada 22(1): 231–235.

1966a. Northern range extension records for two rockfish species (*Sebastodes caurinus* and *S. elongatus*). J. Fish. Res. Bd. Canada 23(9): 1455–1456.

1966b. Northern range extensions for three species of rockfish (*Sebastodes flavidus, S. paucispinis, and S. pinniger*) in the North Pacific Ocean. J. Fish. Res. Bd. Canada 23(9): 1469–1471.

1968. First records of three rockfish species (*Sebastodes aurora, S. ciliatus*, and *Sebastolobus altivelis*) from waters off British Columbia. J. Fish. Res. Bd. Canada 25(11): 2509–2513.

1970. Survey of rockfishes, especially Pacific ocean perch, in the northeast Pacific Ocean, 1963–66. J. Fish. Res. Bd. Canada 27(10): 1781–1809.

WESTRHEIM, S. J., D. DAVENPORT, W. R. HARLING, M. S. SMITH, AND R. M. WOWCHUK. 1969. *G. B. Reed* Groundfish Cruise 69–1, February 11–27, 1969. Fish. Res. Board Can. Tech. Rep. 113: 23 p.

WESTRHEIM, S. J., W. R. HARLING, AND D. DAVENPORT. MS 1968. Preliminary report on maturity, spawning and larval identification of rockfishes (*Sebastodes*) collected off British Columbia in 1967. Fish. Res. Board Can. Nanaimo Biol. Sta. MS Rep. 23 p.

WESTRHEIM, S. J., W. R. HARLING, D. DAVENPORT, AND M. S. SMITH. 1968. Preliminary report on maturity, spawning season and larval identification of rockfishes (*Sebastodes*) collected off British Columbia in 1968. Fish Res. Board Can. MS Rep. Ser. 1005: 28 p.

WESTRHEIM, S. J., AND A. R. MORGAN. 1963. Results from tagging a spawning stock of dover sole, *Microstomus pacificus*. Pac. Mar. Fish. Comm. Bull. 6: 13–21.

WESTRHEIM, S. J., AND F. T. PLETCHER. 1966. First record of the twoline eelpout *Bothrocara brunneum*, Greenland halibut, *Reinhardtius hippoglossoides*, and shortbelly rockfish, *Sebastodes jordani* in British Columbia waters. J. Fish. Res. Bd. Canada 23(2): 309–312.

WESTRHEIM, S. J., AND H. TSUYUKI. 1967. *Sebastodes reedi*, a new scorpaenid fish in the northeast Pacific Ocean. J. Fish. Res. Bd. Canada 24(9): 1945–1954.

1972. Synonymy of *Sebastes caenaematicus* with *Sebastes borealis*, and range extension record. J. Fish. Res. Bd. Canada 29(5): 606–607.

WHEELER, G. C. 1931. A bibliography of the sardines. Calif. Div. Fish Game Fish Bull. 36: 1–133.

WHITEAVES, J. F. * 1886. Catalogue of Canadian Pinnipedia, Cetacea, fishes and marine Invertebrata. Ottawa. 42 p.

* 1887. On some Invertebrata dredged or otherwise collected by Dr. G. M. Dawson, in 1885, in the northern part of the Strait of Georgia. Trans. Roy. Soc. Can. 4: 135.

WHITLEY, G. P. 1931. New names for Australian fishes. Aust. Zool. 6(4): 310–334.

1948. A list of the fishes of Western Australia. West. Aust. Fish. Dep. Fish Bull. 2: 35 p.

WICKETT, W. P. 1958. Review of certain environmental factors affecting the production of pink and chum salmon. J. Fish. Res. Bd. Canada 15(5): 1103–1126.

1964. An unusually late-spawning British Columbia chum salmon. J. Fish. Res. Bd. Canada 21(3): 657.

1967. Ekman transport and zooplankton concentrations in the north Pacific Ocean. J. Fish. Res. Bd. Canada 24(3): 581–594.

WIEBE, J. P. 1968a. The effects of temperature and daylength on the reproduction physiology of the viviparous seaperch Cymatogaster aggregata Gibbons. Can. J. Zool. 46(6): 1207–1219.

1968b. The reproductive cycle of the viviparous seaperch, Cymatogaster aggregata Gibbons. Can. J. Zool. 46(6): 1221–1234.

WILBY, G. V. * 1934 Ichthyological treasures from the "Albatross" expeditions in Canadian waters. Can. Field-Natur. 48(8): 121–126.

1936a. On the gobiesocid genus Rimicola. Copeia 1936(2): 116.

1936b. A second record of the cottoid fish Asemichthys taylori Gilbert. Copeia 1936(2): 117.

* 1937. The lingcod, Ophiodon elongatus Girard. Bull. Biol. Board Can. 54: 24 p.

* 1946. Fishes collected by the Wm. J. Stewart in British Columbia waters during 1934 and 1935. Can. J. Res. D 24: 134–155.

WILIMOVSKY, N. J. 1954. List of the fishes of Alaska. Stanford Ichthyol. Bull. 4(5): 279–294.

1956. A new name, Lumpenus sagitta, to replace Lumpenus gracilis (Ayres), for a northern blennioid fish (family Stichaeidae). Stanford Ichthyol. Bull. 7(2): 23–24.

* 1958. Provisional keys to the fishes of Alaska. Fish. Res. Lab., U.S. Fish Wildl. Serv., Juneau, Alaska. 113 p.

1964. Inshore fish fauna of the Aleutian archipelago. Proc. Alaska Sci. Conf. 14: 172–190.

WILIMOVSKY, N. J., A. PEDEN, AND J. PEPPAR. 1967. Systematics of six demersal fishes of the North Pacific Ocean. Fish. Res. Board Can. Tech. Rep. 34: 95 p.

WILKIE, D. W., 1963. Occurrence of the longfin sculpin Jordania zonope Starks 1895, in British Columbia. Copeia 1963(3): 588–590.

MS 1966. Colour pigments in the penpoint gunnel Apodichthys flavidus and their ecological significance. M.Sc. Thesis. Dep. Zool. Univ. British Columbia.

WILLIAMSON, H. C. 1927. Pacific salmon migration: report on the tagging operations in 1925. Contrib. Can. Biol. Fish., N.S. 3(9): 267–306.

1929. Pacific salmon migration: report on the tagging operations in 1926, with additional returns from the operations of 1925. Contrib. Can. Biol. Fish., N.S. (4)29: 455–470.

1930. Notes on the occurrence of various animals on the fishing grounds on the coast of British Columbia. Can. Field-Natur. 44(7): 153–306.

WILLIAMSON, H. C., AND W. A. CLEMENS. 1932. Pacific salmon migration. The tagging operations at Quatsino and Kyuquot in 1927, with additional returns from the operations of 1925 and 1926. Bull. Biol. Board Can. 26: 16 p.

WILSON, D. C., AND R. E. MILLEMANN. 1969. Relationships of female age and size to embryo number and size in the shiner perch, Cymatogaster aggregata. J. Fish. Res. Bd. Canada 26(9): 2339–2344.

WINTERS, G. H. 1970. Record size and age of Atlantic capelin, Mallotus villosus. J. Fish. Res. Bd. Canada 27(2): 393–394.

WISNER, R. I. 1959. Distribution and differentiation of the North Pacific myctophid fish, Tarletonbeania taylori. Copeia 1959(1): 1–7.

WITHLER, F. C. MS 1945. An investigation of the distribution of age groups and sexes of sockeye salmon (Oncorhynchus nerka) throughout the fishing season at the Skeena River. B.A. Thesis. Dep. Zool. Univ. British Columbia.

1955. Coho salmon fingerling attacked by young lamprey. Fish. Res. Board Can. Pac. Progr. Rep. 104: 15.

WITHLER, I. L. 1966. Variability in life history characteristics of steelhead trout (Salmo gairdneri) along the Pacific Coast of North America. J. Fish Res. Bd. Canada 23(3): 365–392.

WOODS, L. P. * 1942. Rare fishes from the coast of Texas. Copeia 1942(3): 191–192.

YARBERRY, E. L. 1965. Osteology of the zoarcid fish, Melanostigma pammelas. Copeia 1965(4): 442–462.

YOSHIDA, H. O. 1965. New Pacific records of juvenile albacore Thunnus alalunga (Bonnaterre) from stomach contents. Pac. Sci. 19(4): 442–450.

YUSA, T. 1957. Eggs and larvae of flatfishes in the coastal waters of Hokkaido. I. Embryonic development of the starry flounder, Platichthys stellatus (Pallas). Bull. Hokkaido Reg. Fish. Res. Lab. 15: 1–14.

ZUGMAYER, E. * 1911. Résultats des campagnes scientifiques du Prince de Monaco: poissons provenant des campagnes du Yacht Princesse Alice (1901–1911). Nos. 35–36.

Numerical Methods in
Laminar and Turbulent Flow